THE MEAT WE EAT

Tenth Edition

THE MEAT WE EAT

John R. Romans

Associate Professor of Animal Science
University of Illinois

and

P. Thomas Ziegler

Professor Emeritus of Animal Husbandry
The Pennsylvania State University

THE INTERSTATE
Printers & Publishers, Inc.

Danville, Illinois

*This edition is dedicated
to our former, present, and
future students and co-workers.*

Contents

PART ONE

PART TWO

Preface / Tenth Edition

To speculate as to which United States industry has changed the most in the years since the last edition of *The Meat We Eat* was published would be unwise in times like these when change is normal and *status quo* is odd. However, for an industry which had been characterized by its nature of steadfastness and rather slow change in the past, the meat industry may have made the biggest turnaround. Because of such forces as consumerism, ecology, energy, pollution, atherosclerosis, nitrosamines, isolated soy protein, leanness, muscling, sanitation, safety, and new processes and equipment to increase efficiency and save labor, to name a few, this industry has had to make rapid and somewhat massive changes.

It is the purpose of this revision of a very widely used, practical meat text to bring it up to date in all broad areas of meat science and technology, while at the same time, retaining the straightforward, practical approach to the meat we eat that has been so well understood in the past. Thus, every detail is not always spelled out, but rather a general approach is sometimes used. It is hoped that the book is organized in such a way that the reader can easily find information he is seeking and can acquire an idea as to where to go for more information if he needs it.

The first debt of gratitude goes to P. Thomas Ziegler for allowing a cooperator to share in his vast knowledge of the subject and for providing the opportunity to build on a solid foundation. Sincere appreciation is due the many friends in industry, government, and education who provided illustrations and materials for this revision. Special mention must be made of the National Live Stock and Meat Board and Ken Franklin; the USDA Agricultural Marketing Service, Livestock Division, and Charlie Murphy, Ned Tyler, and John Pierce; Greg Pietrasozek and *The National Provisioner;* Bud Booth and *Meat Processing* magazine; and other colleagues in the American Meat Science Association and in the meat industry who provided helpful information. Specific mention is made of these contributors throughout the book.

Special thanks go to my colleagues here at the University of Illinois—Jack Everly, John Behrens, and Gary Beaumont, in Ag Communications, and Harold Witt and Roger Courson, in Vo-Ag Services, who helped tremendously in securing many of the pictures used in the text. The meat fabrication work was done largely by Jasper Lewis, whose long service to the university in terms of time and genuine effort constitutes a major educational contribution. Extension colleague Dick Carlisle participated significantly in the pork chapters. Former graduate student-teacher Ray Hankes and present graduate students Doug Parrett and Steve Moore all generously shouldered extra duties and relinquished their personal time to provide their adviser the time and conditions to complete this revision. The friendly and efficient counsel of colleague Glenn Schmidt, whose coming on the university staff allowed this author time for writing in addition to teaching, has been sincerely appreciated. The department leadership provided by Gene Becker, head, stimulated excellence in this task. Lastly, the efficient, accurate typing of Mary Buecker made this revision much more pleasant than it might have been.

From a personal viewpoint, a warm "thanks for the inspirational nudging toward completion" to wife Kay and our Heidi, Hal, Scott, and Sandra.

JOHN R. ROMANS

Urbana/Champaign, Illinois
1974

Preface / Ninth Edition

A comprehensive treatment of this subject in all its ramifications would require volumes. A presentation of the basic facts concerning the meat we eat is the primary aim of this text. In it I have attempted to discuss rather briefly many of the practical and scientific phases of the nation's third largest industry, and sincerely hope that the discussion may be found helpful, useful, and interesting to the farmer, the student, and the housewife. Every attempt has been made at brevity, for experience with present day students leads me to believe that "weeded facts" rather than "cultivated words" are desired.

I wish to express my appreciation and gratitude to all contributors and agencies that so graciously furnished illustrations, charts, and other information. Their names may be found throughout the book. It is my pleasure to make particular mention of the National Live Stock and Meat Board, Chicago, Illinois; The Agricultural Marketing Service of the United States Department of Agriculture; W. H. Tomhave, former Head of the Animal Husbandry Department of The Pennsylvania State University and the one most instrumental in giving me my basic education in meats.

Special appreciation is also expressed to F. L. Bentley, Professor of Animal Husbandry; Dr. R. C. Miller, Professor of Agricultural and Biological Chemistry; Dr. W. T. S. Thorp, Professor of Animal Pathology; Dr. J. F. Shigley, Professor of Veterinary Medicine; P. H. Margolf, Professor of Poultry Husbandry; F. P. Ferguson, Associate Professor of Agricultural Journalism, The Pennsylvania State University, University Park, Pennsylvania; Genevra Carolyn Driscoll, M.D., Philadelphia, Pennsylvania; Miss Dorothy Bowmaster, State College, Pennsylvania.

A final word of thanks is due certain persons in the United States Department of Agriculture and friends engaged in college teaching and extension work for their suggestions and encouragement.

P. Thomas Ziegler

Classification of Our Common Meat Animals

Phyla—*Chordata* (internal skeleton and dorsal nervous system)
  Subphyla—*Vertebrates* (segmented spinal column)
    Class—*Mammalia* (udder secretes milk)
      Subclass—*Placentates* (fetus nourished in uterus)
        Order—*Ungulata* (hoofed animals)
          Suborder—*Artiodactyles* (even toed)
            Section—*Pecora* (true ruminants)
              Family—*Bovidae* (hollow horned)
                Genus—*Bos* (cattle)
                  Group—*Taurine* (of or like a bull)
                    Species—*B. taurus* (cattle)
                              B. indicus (humped cattle)
                Genus—*Ovis* (sheep)
                  Group—*O. Aries* (domestic)
                Genus—*Capra* (goats)
                  Group—*C. hirius* (domestic)
            Section—*Suina* (pointed molars)
              Family—*Suidae* (true swine)
                Genus—*Sus—Sus scrofa* (wild Boar)
                  Group—*S. domesticus* (domesticated swine)
          Suborder—*Perissodactyles* (uneven toed)
            Family—*Equidae* (horse family)
              Genus—*Equus* (horse family)
                Group—*E. caballus* (horse)
                      E. asinus (ass)
                      E. zebra (zebra)

Suggested Supplementary
Reading Materials

BOOKS

American Meat Institute Committee on Textbooks, *By-Products of the Meat Packing Industry*, Rev. ed., Institute of Meat Packing. Chicago: University of Chicago. 1950.

Ashbrook, F. G., *Butchering, Processing and Preservation of Meat*. New York: D. Van Nostrand Co., Inc. 1955.

Bailey, J. W., *Encyclopedia of Labeling Meat and Poultry Products*. St. Louis: Meat Plant Magazine. 1974.

Briskey, E. J., R. G. Cassens, and J. C. Trautman, *The Physiology and Biochemistry of Muscle as a Food*. Madison, Milwaukee, and London: The University of Wisconsin Press. 1966.

Briskey, E. J., R. G. Cassens, and B. B. Marsh, *The Physiology and Biochemistry of Muscle as a Food, 2*. Madison, Milwaukee, and London: The University of Wisconsin Press. 1970.

Bull, Sleeter, *Meat for the Table*. New York: McGraw-Hill Book Co., Inc. 1951.

Cleland, R. G., *The Cattle on a Thousand Hills*. San Marina, California: Huntingdon Library. 1951.

Copley, M. J., *The Freezing Preservation of Foods: Volume 3, Commercial Food Freezing Operations—Fresh Foods*. Westport, Connecticut: AVI Publishing Co. 1968.

Danilov, M. M., *Handbook of Food Products, Meat and Meat Products*. Springfield, Virginia: U. S. Department of Commerce, Clearinghouse for Federal Scientific and Technical Information. 1969. (Translated from Russian)

Gillies, M. T., *Shortenings, Margarines, and Food Oils.* Park Ridge, New Jersey: Noyes Data Corporation. 1974.

Greig, W. S., *Economics of Food Processing.* Westport, Connecticut: AVI Publishing Co. 1971.

Gustavson, K. H., *The Chemistry of the Tanning Process.* New York: Academic Press, Inc. 1956.

Gutcho, M., *Textured Foods and Allied Products.* Park Ridge, New Jersey: Noyes Data Corporation. 1973.

Guthrie, R. K., *Food Sanitation.* Westport, Connecticut: AVI Publishing Co. 1972.

Harris, R. S., and H. Von Loesecke, *Nutritional Evaluation of Food Processing.* Westport, Connecticut: AVI Publishing Co. 1971.

Karmas, E., *Fresh Meat Processing.* Park Ridge, New Jersey: Noyes Data Corporation. 1970.

Karmas E., *Meat Product Manufacture.* Park Ridge, New Jersey: Noyes Data Corporation. 1970.

Karmas, E., *Sausage Processing.* Park Ridge, New Jersey: Noyes Data Corporation. 1972.

Kramer, A., *Food and the Consumer.* Westport, Connecticut: AVI Publishing Co. 1973.

Kramlich, W. E., A. M. Pearson, and F. W. Tauber, *Processed Meats.* Westport, Connecticut: AVI Publishing Co. 1973.

Lawrie, R. A., *Meat Science.* New York: Pergamon Press, Inc. 1966.

Lawrie, R. A., *Proteins as Human Food.* Westport, Connecticut: AVI Publishing Co. 1970.

Levie, A., *The Meat Handbook: Third Edition.* Westport, Connecticut: AVI Publishing Co. 1970.

The National Canners Association Staff, *Laboratory Manual for Food Canners and Processors: Volume 1, Microbiology and Processing.* Westport, Connecticut: AVI Publishing Co. 1968.

The National Canners Association Staff, *Laboratory Manual for Food Canners and Processors: Volume 2, Analysis, Sanitation and Statistics.* Westport, Connecticut: AVI Publishing Co. 1968.

Nickerson, J. T. R., and A. J. Sinskey, *Microbiology of Foods and Food Processing.* New York: American Elsevier Publishing Co., Inc. 1972.

Potter, N. N., *Food Science: Second Edition.* Westport, Connecticut: AVI Publishing Co. 1973.

Price, J. F., and B. S. Schweigert, *The Science of Meat and Meat Products: Second Edition.* San Francisco: W. H. Freeman and Co., Publishers. 1971.

Rietz, C. A., *A Guide to the Selection, Combination and Cooking of Foods: Volume I, Selection and Combination of Foods.* Westport, Connecticut: AVI Publishing Co. 1965.

Rietz, C. A., and J. J. Wanderstock, *A Guide to the Selection, Combination and Cooking of Foods: Volume II, Formulation and Cooking.* Westport, Connecticut: AVI Publishing Co. 1965.

Rogers, J. L., *Production of Precooked Frozen Foods.* Westport, Connecticut: AVI Publishing Co. 1969.

Sacharow, M. A., and R. C. Griffin, Jr., *Food Packaging.* Westport, Connecticut: AVI Publishing Co. 1970.

Swift, L. F., *The Yankee of the Yards.* Chicago and New York: A. W. Shaw Company. 1927.

Tressler, D. K., *The Freezing Preservation of Foods: Volume 4, Freezing of Precooked and Prepared Foods.* Westport, Connecticut: AVI Publishing Co. 1968.

Van Arsdel, W. B., *The Freezing Preservation of Foods: Volume 2, Factors Affecting Quality in Frozen Foods.* Westport, Connecticut: AVI Publishing Co. 1968.

Woolrich, W. R., and E. R. Hallowell, *Cold and Freezer Storage Manual.* Westport, Connecticut: AVI Publishing Co. 1970.

Woolrich, W. R., and D. K. Tressler, *The Freezing Preservation of Foods: Volume 1, Refrigeration and Refrigeration Equipment.* Westport, Connecticut: AVI Publishing Co. 1968.

TRADE JOURNALS

Journal	Address
Food Engineering	Box 2035 Radnor, Pennsylvania 19089
Food Processing	Putman Publishing Co. 111 East Delaware Place Chicago, Illinois 60611
Food Science and Technology Abstracts	Commonwealth Agricultural Bureaux Central Sales Branch Farnham House Farnham Royal, Bucks, England

Journal	Address
Food Science Marketing	EIP, Inc. Headquarters 2132 Fordem Avenue Box 1648 Madison, Wisconsin 53701
Food Technology	Suite 2120 221 North LaSalle Street Chicago, Illinois 60601
Journal of Animal Science	425 Illinois Building 113 North Neil Street Champaign, Illinois 61820
Journal of Food Science	Suite 2120 221 North LaSalle Street Chicago, Illinois 60601
Journal of Nutrition	American Institute of Nutrition 9650 Rockville Pike Bethesda, Maryland 20014
Meat Plant Magazine (formerly Freezer Provisioning)	10225 Bach Boulevard St. Louis, Missouri 63132
Meat Processing	The Davies Publishing Co. 645 North Michigan Avenue Chicago, Illinois 60611
The National Provisioner	15 West Huron Street Chicago, Illinois 60610
Quick Frozen Foods	Harcourt Brace Jovanovich Publications 757 Third Avenue New York, New York 10017
Render	Suite 404 900 Wilshire Boulevard Los Angeles, California 90017
Supermarket News	Fairchild Publications, Inc. 7 East 12th Street New York, New York 10003

MISCELLANEOUS

American Meat Institute Foundation (circulars and bulletins), P.O. Box 3556, Washington, D.C. 20007.

National Live Stock and Meat Board (literature, charts, etc.), 36 South Wabash Avenue, Chicago, Illinois 60603.

Proceedings of Reciprocal Meat Conference, National Live Stock and Meat Board, Chicago, Illinois.

Proceedings of the Meat Industry Research Conference, A. M. I. F., P.O. Box 3556, Washington, D.C. 20007.

PART ONE

PART ONE

CHAPTER 1

Introduction

Physiologists long ago assured us that we are unsuited to the hay guzzling habits of ruminants which have four stomachs to our one. It is the function of these animals (cattle, sheep, and goats) to utilize grasses and grains and convert them into a more suitable and concentrated food for man as well as materials for shoes and clothing. Swine possess but one stomach and cannot utilize roughage to the same degree as ruminants, but they are very efficient in converting grain into pork. These conversion abilities have made flocks and herds of prime economic importance in the development of civilization.

MAN AND MEAT

A liberal meat supply has always been associated with a happy and virile people and invariably has been the main food available to settlers of new and undeveloped territories. Statistics show that per capita meat consumption decreases with density of population. Some European nations (Table 1.1), for example, consumed approximately 50 pounds less meat per person per year than the peoples of the Americas during the decade 1961-1971, while Asiatic nations consumed some 100 pounds less during the same time period. Inhabitants consume more of the food that is abundant in their area because it is easier to get and invariably cheaper. Argentina and Uruguay are cattle countries and their people continue to be the world's heaviest consumers of beef. Australia and New Zealand are the world's most densely populated sheep countries and their people consume 30 times more lamb and mutton than do the people of the United States. The United States in turn consumes two times more pork per person than does New Zealand because the hog population in the United States is considerably larger. A well-balanced agriculture provides its people with a variety of food and consequently a better balanced diet. This type of agriculture also results in a more varied source of income.

Table 1.1—Per Capita Consumption of Red Meat[1] and Fish[2] in Specified Countries

Continent and Country	Total Meat		Beef and Veal		Pork		Mutton, Lamb, and Goat Meat		Horse Meat		Fish
	Average 1961-65	1971	Average 1961-65	1971	Average 1961-65	1971	Average 1961-65	1971	Average 1961-65	1971	1972
					(lbs.)						
North America											
Canada	142	164	85	93	53	67	4	4	-	-	12
Costa Rica	34	34	26	25	8	9	-	-	-	-	-
Dominican Republic	22	21	16	14	6	7	-	-	-	-	-
El Salvador	26	19	17	12	9	7	-	-	-	-	-
Guatemala	22	21	18	17	4	4	-	-	-	-	-
Honduras	22	21	14	14	8	7	-	-	-	-	-
Mexico	37	39	24	24	11	13	2	2	-	-	4
Nicaragua	41	50	29	33	12	17	-	-	-	-	-
Panama	54	65	46	54	8	11	-	-	-	-	-
United States	167	192	99	116	63	73	5	3	-	-	12
South America											
Argentina	199	173	170	137	17	22	12	14	-	-	5
Brazil	53	54	39	39	13	14	1	1	-	-	6
Chile	61	70	41	49	11	12	9	9	-	-	-
Colombia	56	59	49	51	7	8	Note 3	Note 3	-	-	-
Paraguay	104	71	104	71	-	-	-	-	-	-	-
Peru	36	30	19	14	9	8	8	8	-	-	19
Uruguay	241	156	182	89	20	13	39	54	-	-	-
Venezuela	51	53	40	43	10	9	1	1	-	-	-

(Continued)

Table 1.1 (Continued)

Continent and Country	Total Meat		Beef and Veal		Pork		Mutton, Lamb, and Goat Meat		Horse Meat		Fish
	Average 1961-65	1971	Average 1961-65	1971	Average 1961-65	1971	Average 1961-65	1971	Average 1961-65	1971	1972
					(lbs.)						
Europe											
Western											
European Community											
Belgium and Luxembourg	113	140	53	63	52	68	1	2	7	7	–
France	128	140	63	65	55	64	5	7	5	4	18
Germany, West	121	146	48	55	71	90	1	1	1	–	9
Italy	57	75	35	45	18	26	2	2	2	2	14
Netherlands	96	109	44	41	49	64	Note 3	1	3	3	–
EC (average)	102	122	48	55	49	62	2	3	3	2	8
Austria	121	136	43	50	76	85	Note 3	Note 3	2	1	–
Denmark	128	127	37	45	89	80	1	1	1	1	–
Finland	78	95	43	45	32	48	1	Note 3	2	2	–
Greece	57	87	19	34	11	16	27	37	–	–	–
Ireland	110	137	31	45	55	67	24	25	–	–	–
Norway	79	85	33	33	34	41	10	10	2	1	–
Portugal	36	48	14	22	18	23	3	3	1	–	–
Spain	47	64	16	23	21	31	9	9	3	1	30
Sweden	101	104	43	38	54	64	1	2	3	1	–
Switzerland	112	134	53	59	55	72	2	2	2	2	–
United Kingdom	141	143	57	54	59	66	25	23	–	–	19

(Continued)

Table 1.1 (Continued)

Continent and Country	Total Meat		Beef and Veal		Pork		Mutton, Lamb, and Goat Meat		Horse Meat		Fish
	Average 1961-65	1971	Average 1961-65	1971	Average 1961-65	1971	Average 1961-65	1971	Average 1961-65	1971	1972
					(lbs.)						
Eastern											
Bulgaria	69	70	20	24	32	26	17	20	—	—	—
Czechoslovakia	101	118	39	42	60	75	1	1	1	—	—
Hungary	85	110	22	20	60	89	2	1	1	—	—
Poland	80	90	27	34	50	53	2	2	1	1	—
Yugoslavia	61	77	20	26	35	45	6	6	—	—	11
USSR	68	89	32	49	26	30	10	10	—	—	23
Africa											
South Africa, Republic of	77	83	55	51	6	9	16	23	—	—	—
Asia											
China, Taiwan	42	60	1	1	41	59	Note 3	Note 3	—	—	8
Iran	18	18	4	4	Note 3	Note 3	14	14	—	—	—
Israel	31	41	28	37	—	—	3	4	—	—	—
Japan	13	27	4	7	7	16	3	3	—	—	71
Philippines	24	27	6	5	18	22	Note 3	Note 3	1	1	44
Turkey	33	32	11	11	Note 3	Note 3	22	21	—	—	—

(Continued)

Table 1.1 (Continued)

Continent and Country	Total Meat		Beef and Veal		Pork		Mutton, Lamb, and Goat Meat		Horse Meat		Fish
	Average 1961–65	1971	Average 1961–65	1971	Average 1961–65	1971	Average 1961–65	1971	Average 1961–65	1971	1972
					(lbs.)						
Oceania											
Australia	209	212	98	90	23	30	88	92	--	--	--
New Zealand	218	217	98	105	33	24	87	88	--	--	--

1. U.S. Dept. of Agriculture, Foreign Agricultural Service, FIM February 1973, carcass weight.

2. U.S. Dept. of Agriculture, Foreign Agricultural Service, Foreign Agriculture, December 3, 1973, edible weight.

3. Less than 0.5 pound.

Our Eating Habits

The peoples of the world as a whole are always hungry. Many are hungry because of a lack of food, others because of a lack of means to buy it. Under such conditions, likes and dislikes become secondary.

Those of us who dwell in a land of plenty, blessed by the elements but developed through personal initiative under a system of free enterprise, have built for ourselves a rather selective standard of living. We are what we make ourselves, whether morally, spiritually, financially, or physically. These are voluntary, not decreed, acquirements.

Broadly speaking, our eating habits are governed in a large measure by spendable income, concern for our personal well-being, and the doctor. Statistics show that 30% of the family food dollar goes for meat purchases. This will vary with income. Income also governs the consumer's selection of meat cuts. The old expression, "no money, no meat," still holds. In most cases, those in the middle income group are the heavy meat and potato consumers, particularly if their occupations require considerable physical exertion. Youths top the hamburger, hot dog, and pop consuming group. Fortunately, they are also heavy milk and ice cream consumers.

Too few of us realize until too late that appetite is a poor governor for the operation of the intricate human engine. Opening the food throttle can result in many ailments and discomforts. Obesity and heart failure are blood relatives. The old saw that everybody loves a fat man is a hoax. Physical well-being can mean different things to different people.

Some of us are food faddists; we make food a religion. Others follow trends such as the order of the Slim Look or the Olympian. Then we have the Society of Suffering Distaffs who, by diet tricks or pills, take off 10 pounds in 20 days and recover it in 10. They are the Lost and Found. Let's be sensible and make *well-being* and *being well* a little more congruent.

Historically, more than half of the U.S. farmers' cash income has been derived from animal agriculture. In 1972, income from livestock and livestock products accounted for 58.6% of the total farm income, while in 1973, the figure fell to 54.2%,[1] reflecting a greater increase in crop prices versus livestock prices, rather than an absolute decrease in livestock product values in 1973 during rapidly rising prices.

The U.S. meat industry is the nation's largest food industry, but meat packing ranks fortieth out of 40 U.S. industries in return per dollar of sales at 0.8 cent per dollar. Yet, meat remains the consumers' number one food cost.

---

1. USDA Statistical Reporting Service.

Table 1.2—Sales, Raw Material Costs, Expenses, and Net Earnings of the Meat Packing Industry, 1965 and 1972[1]

	1965	1972
	— — — (% of total sales) — — —	
Total sales	100.0	100.0
Cost of livestock and other materials	75.6	79.1
Gross margin	24.4	20.9
Operating Expenses		
Wages and salaries	10.5	8.5
Employee benefits	1.8	1.9
Interest	.2	.3
Depreciation	.8	.7
Rents	.3	.3
Taxes, other than social security		
& income	.3	.2
Supplies and containers	3.4	2.9
All other expenses	5.7	4.6
Total operating expenses	23.0	19.4
Income taxes	.6	.7
Net earnings	.8	.8

1. *Financial Facts About the Meat Industry*, American Meat Institute, 1972.

A breakdown showing where the meat packers' sales dollar goes appears in Table 1.2.

Finally, our food habits may be dictated. As babies we had no choice, no teeth, no cavities. For old age, and sometimes before, there are doctor's orders and store teeth. Our intense desire to enjoy "living it up" to the exclusion of its after-effects brings too many of us to an end which we did not want to foresee.

The Present Trend

The overall trend of the consumer continues to be for leaner meats. Unfortunately, the consumer is now bombarded from many sides with various admonitions concerning the composition of his diet, especially regarding the fat content. In the early fifties, it was discovered that the cholesterol level in the human circulatory system may be raised by the ingestion of certain fats. Cholesterol is found as fat in the human blood stream and may be deposited on the inside walls of arteries and veins, thereby hindering the free movement of blood to and from the heart.

Yet, after 20 years of research costing several billion dollars, scientists are still divided on the diet-heart question. Some insist that diet manipulations to control levels of cholesterol and saturated fats are essential to control coronary heart disease. Animal fats are generally more highly saturated, thus, these scientists condemn animal fat in the diet. Other scientists, by now the larger of the two opposing groups, cite evidence that factors other than diet, such as lack of exercise, high blood pressure, cigarette smoking, obesity, and heredity, have an equal or higher relationship to heart disease. Furthermore, cholesterol is manufactured by the human body itself and is essential in normal body functions. Fat does serve as a rich source of energy, so therefore many of us rather sedentary American folks should not over-consume fat, for if we do, the extra energy will cause obesity. Other roles of fat in the human body are to serve as carriers of vitamins A, D, E, and K, to protect body tissues and vital organs, and to regulate body temperature. Thus fat is essential and by no means a nutrient to be avoided when consumed at proper levels.

The consumer demand for leaner meat has made certain demands on the producer, packer, and retailer. The producer must select and breed for meat quality animals that are more heavily muscled and that will reach a market weight at an earlier age without the extended feeding period. Progeny testing is essential in order to find the strains that produce more edible meat of acceptable quality. The packer must compensate these efforts by paying a premium for animals of superior meat type and quality and, in the meantime, do some fat trimming on the overdone carcasses and cuts. The retailer should in turn give the matter of trim further consideration.

With modern breeding and progeny testing, producers must provide meat animals that grow fast, economically, and efficiently in terms of feed consumed and animals that will produce carcasses yielding a high per cent of edible human food. The consumer has recognized that fat in excess of .30 inch over the outside of a chop, steak, or roast is simply waste. However, this same consumer desires a tender, juicy, and flavorful meat cut. Marbling (fat within the muscle) is becoming less important to overall palatability as we continue to market younger animals. In fact, recent research has shown little relationship between marbling and tenderness in such animals. However, a certain minimum level of marbling is necessary to give meat its characteristic aroma, flavor, and juiciness. This minimum level is an amount of fat that would by no means cause a health hazard in the diet of any so-called "normal" consumer.

There should be no doubt in our minds that eating in moderation

Table 1.3—What the Average American Eats Annually, 1973[1]

	1960	1973		1960	1973
	- - (lbs.) - -			- - (lbs.) - -	
Meats			**Fruits**		
Total red			Fresh	93.4	77.7
(carcass wt.)	160.9	177.9	Apples	18.3	16.7
Beef (carcass wt.)	85.1	110.9	Citrus	33.7	27.6
Pork (carcass wt.			Other	41.4	33.4
excluding lard)	64.9	61.5	Canned	22.6	21.4
Veal (carcass wt.)	6.1	1.8	Dried	3.1	2.5
Lamb and mutton			Juices (canned)	13.0	15.9
(carcass wt.)	4.8	2.8	Frozen		
Fish (ready to cook)	10.3	12.1	(incl. juices)	9.1	11.5
Poultry			**Beverages**		
Chickens (ready to			Coffee	15.8	13.6
cook)	28.0	42.1	Tea	.59	.78
Turkeys (ready to			Cocoa	3.6	4.2
cook)	6.1	9.1			
Eggs (dozens)	29.5	24.3	**Vegetables**		
			Fresh	105.9	96.5
Fats			Canned	43.4	52.5
Lard	7.6	3.1	Frozen	7.0	10.6
Margarine	9.4	11.4	Potatoes	109.4	118.2
Other (shortening)	12.6	16.7	Sweet potatoes	7.1	4.8
			Dry beans	7.3	6.3
Dairy Products			Sugar	97.6	103.2
Fluid milk and cream	322.0	255.0			
Butter	7.5	4.6			
Cheese	8.3	13.8			
Ice cream	18.3	17.7			
Grains					
Wheat cereals	2.8	2.9			
Wheat flour	118.0	109.0			
Rice	6.1	7.0			
Corn meal and flour	6.6	7.4			
Corn syrup	10.1	18.2			
Corn sugar	3.7	4.8			

1. U.S. Dept. of Agriculture, Economic Research Service, National Food Situation, NSF 146, November 1973.

of those foods that furnish us a balanced diet is the answer to most of our overweight ills and that does not mean the exclusion of animal fats.

Although the authors confess to being moderately heavy meat eaters, it is not to be concluded from what is to follow that meat is "something with wings." A mixed diet that includes sufficient leafy vegetables, a liberal amount of raw vegetables, fresh fruit, milk, a savory serving of one of over a hundred possible tasty meat dishes, and as little of those complicated sweets that end up a meal as possible is the sensible one. But even a sensible meal can be made destructive by over-eating. Over-work and over-distension of the digestive tract can be likened to an over-inflated tire run at high speed—it may result in a blowout. A quotation from *Exchange* is worth repeating at this point: "Some business men make more of a feature of their eating than of their business. Their business is merely an interval between meals. These men who hate to let business interfere with eating usually come to the day when their eating puts them out of business."

A Natural Food

The term *natural* takes on an added meaning to most consumers in the present day since much has been made of *organic* or *natural* foods in the popular press. Yet, there is no official definition for *organic* or *natural* foods. The heading to this section does not imply any meaning other than the following: Lean muscle is composed of approximately 20% protein, 9% fat, 70% moisture, and 1% ash. An edible portion of meat with a fat covering of about ¼ inch would be composed of 17% protein, 20% fat, 62% moisture, and 1% ash. The lean and fat tissues are very similar to human body tissue and, because of this, they are highly digestible and can be easily and rapidly assimilated by the human digestive tract. Milk is the only other food of economic importance that can outstrip meat in this respect. A chemical analysis may show that a food is rich in certain food elements, but these elements may not be very digestible, or the body may not be able to absorb and utilize them as efficiently as it would the same elements in another food. This is known as the biological value of a food nutrient.

Meat proteins have a high biological value, followed closely by animal fats. Some products made from soybeans, which are now widely used as meat extenders, lack the complete array of essential amino acids in the proper proportions alone, and thus blend well with meat proteins to raise the biological value of the final product. The concentrated nature of meat with its low fiber content and its ability to be readily and almost wholly absorbed, leaving but little residue in the intestines, makes it a number one food for man.

A Virile and Protective Food

Experience is a great teacher. It has taught the soldier, the laborer, and the trainer of athletes that meat has something besides "fill-in value." Before scientists revealed its rather broad vitamin content and the high biological value of its proteins and fats, its merits were expounded by the expression, "it sticks to the ribs." The body requirement for certain amino acids, of which at least 10 are considered essential to life, are all found in meat. Its proteins have, by individual analyses for the amino acids, been found to be biologically complete.

The human requirements for energy secured through the medium of carbohydrates and fat can be supplied in large measure by the fat in meat since fat has 2.25 times the energy value of carbohydrates.

With the exception of calcium, meat contains all the necessary minerals for human body metabolism. Add to this list of nutritive elements the daily discoveries, through extensive research, that meat is also rich in many of the vitamins so necessary to a normal, healthy body, and the completeness of meat as a food is rather evident. The meat diet of the hardy Eskimo attests to this fact.

The height and weight of humans are governed in large part by the available food supply. The human life span rises with a balanced diet and improved medical knowledge and facilities. Some nations have a rather low red-meat consumption but have a relatively high consumption of seafood. The importance of food overshadows every material need of our people. It is responsible for the world's number one business and is its prime political sedative.

A Palatable Food

Brushing aside for the moment all that has been said, and forgetting high-sounding names, over-zealous scientists, and doctors' admonitions, let us revert to plain hungry mortals seated behind the festive board. Instinctively we look for the platter of meat which to most of us is not only the king but the whole royal family of appetite appeal. It transcends all other foods in aroma, causing a watering of the mouth and a conscious glow in the most bulbous organ of the gastro-intestinal tract. It is a psychological stimulus that causes a flow of saliva and gastric juice, preparing the food chamber for the royal guest. And it does not beguile us; it satisfies. It accomplishes this by supplying what it advertises to our nostrils before we consume it. As we crunch its juicy fibers between permanent or removable ivories, we receive our first pleasant realization of a previous longing sensation. As we swallow the tasty mass, we begin to radiate satisfaction in our eyes, in our speech, and in our actions. We become more amiable, more clear-minded, and more reasonable—certainly a most honorable tribute to any food product.

CHAPTER 2

Preparations for Slaughtering—
Safety and Sanitation

As indicated in the 1962 edition of this text, the practice of raising, slaughtering, and processing the farm pork supply has been more or less traditional in rural America. Speculation was made at that time regarding the possible continuance or increase of this tradition and the inclusion of other types of meat animals. Since 1962, vast changes have occurred in (1) the agricultural and general economy and (2) consumer consciousness regarding the wholesomeness of the food supply such that the opportunity for young people to practice "on the farm—do it yourself" slaughter and processing of meat animals is becoming less prevalent.

The Wholesome Meat Act of 1967 (to be discussed in detail in the following chapter) made all state inspection systems at least equal to the Federal inspection system. This, in reality, eliminated many small locker operators from business who in the past processed farm slaughtered meats or oftentimes went to the farms to slaughter livestock and subsequently brought resulting carcasses into their locker plants for processing. Although Federal law now permits this practice if the product is strictly utilized for the producer and his family and not for sale, absolutely no product for sale can be processed in exactly the same facility unless the facility and all equipment are completely sterilized before processing the product for sale. Furthermore, the two types of product *cannot* be mixed. As a practical matter, it is very difficult for an operator to maintain two completely separate operations. Furthermore, some states, among them Illinois, have regulations that supersede Federal regulations such that a Class II locker (one processing farm slaughtered carcasses not for sale) *cannot* engage in any endeavors other than *strictly custom* work. Thus, before proceeding with any slaughter activity on his own, a person should contact local and state authorities so that he will be assured he is not violating existing laws designed to protect the health and welfare of American citizens, himself included.

The passage of the Wholesome Meat Act strengthened the entire meat industry in the United States, but in so doing probably eliminated some locker operators who catered to the farm slaughtered custom business. Thus, opportunities for new people to engage in farm slaughter are becoming more limited, although interest has increased due to recent price inflations.

Nevertheless, whatever a particular situation may be regarding meat animal slaughter, i.e., on the farm or in an approved locker or meat packing plant, two big S's are of prime importance—*Safety* and *Sanitation*.

SAFETY

A publication entitled *Meat Industry Safety Guidelines* produced by the National Safety Council[1] should be required reading for anyone who is responsible for meat plant safety. Each person working in a meat plant or with meat processing in any form or aspect should be responsible for safety, but of course, within any organization, large or small, certain key people must assume major responsibility for implementing a safety policy.

According to the National Safety Council, meat packing ranks third out of 41 industries in the frequency rate of disabling injuries, showing 21 such injuries per million man hours. Underground mining (other than coal) ranked higher at 28.05, and underground coal mining was highest at 36.64. A disabling injury is defined as one in which the injured employee is unable to perform the normal functions of a regularly established job on his next regular shift. By comparison, the communications industry had the lowest frequency (1.26 per million hours) followed closely by the automobile (1.67) and aircraft manufacturing (2.26) industries. All industries averaged 6.91 disabling injuries per million man hours. The severity rate, i.e., number of days lost per million hours of exposure, is a second meaningful measurement of safety. In this case, meat packing stands just one place better than the average for all industries. Meat packing lost 686 days per million man hours with an average of 33 days lost per case. All industries averaged 689 days lost and 100 days per case. Therefore, although the accident frequency in the meat industry is very high, the severity rate is lower than many other industries. Nevertheless, it is obvious that safety is a major problem in the meat packing industry. To reemphasize, this applies to all slaughtering and cutting situations, not just the very large commercial situations.

---

1. Chicago, Illinois 60611.

Without giving here a detailed discussion of an entire safety program, which is contained in the National Safety Council publication, we will instead lay out a basic framework for the prevention of accidents. Since knife accidents are the most prominent cause of disabling injuries in the meat industry, a more complete discussion of knife use and safety is included.

Prevention of accidents and injuries is achieved through:

1. Control of conditions—the working environment.
2. Control of the actions of people—behavior.

There are gray areas between environmental and personal causes of accidents.

The Sharpening of Knives

A dull knife is inefficient and ineffective except for cutting oneself. Those of us who marvel at the speed and dexterity of the men working in the slaughter rooms of large or small packing houses must remember that these men work with sharp tools and must be expert to hold their jobs.

Grinding

The manufacturers of knives usually do not market them sharpened for immediate use. Although many knives do not need further grinding

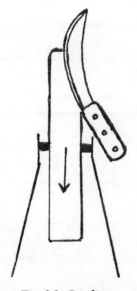

Fig. 2.1—Grinding.

on a coarse stone, all of them need honing. When it is necessary to grind a knife to get extra thinness to the cutting edge before honing, either a sand stone or an emery stone may be used. In either case the stone should be water or oil cooled to avoid heating the knife.

The blade need not be ground back more than ¼ of an inch from the edge, forming what is termed a *bevel*. This bevel should be the same on both sides of a skinning knife so the operator may use it with either hand in siding (removing the hide from the side of a carcass). If the bevel is only on one side of the knife, the bevel side must be next to the hide when skinning. It is advisable to grind the knife by running the stone with the edge of the knife, rather than at a right angle against the edge.

This method is safer and one is less likely to scar the blade any further back than the actual bevel itself, and since the smooth finish of a knife is less likely to rust than the ground surface, this is rather important in maintaining the neat appearance of the blade. A sand stone of medium fine grade is preferable to an emery stone for grinding knives.

Honing

Honing is done on a fine carborundum stone on which water or oil is used to maintain a scum-free abrasive surface. The stone should be set in a block of wood or else placed on a damp cloth to keep it from sliding.

The operator grasps the handle of the knife with his right hand, takes a position slightly to the left of the stone and places the heel of the knife blade on the end of the stone nearest to him. The blade of the knife should be tilted up enough to make the bevel lie flat with the stone. The finger tips of the left hand are placed on the flat of the blade near the back edge to exert pressure on the blade. With a sweeping motion toward

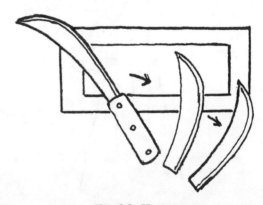

Fig. 2.2—Honing.

the right of the stone, the knife is drawn completely across and inward against the cutting edge of the blade.

The knife is then turned over in the palm of the hand by a twist of the thumb and index finger and drawn across the stone toward the operator. Honing against the edge of the knife avoids the formation of a wire edge. To finish the sharpening process, the knife should be tested for sharpness and smoothness of edge by running the edge of the blade lightly over the flat of the thumbnail. If the knife slides easily, it lacks the proper sharpness. A sharp edge will pull on the nail and a rough or wire edge will rasp the nail. Another method is to move the ball of the thumb lightly over the edge, but this is not recommended for amateurs.

Steeling

There are steels of various types on the market which are adapted to certain uses. The carborundum and ribbed steels are primarily for kitchen use where knives need not be razor sharp. The mirror smooth steel for a razor sharp edge is the one best suited to slaughter house and retail meat dealer needs. Steels range in length from 8 to 14 inches, the 10- and 12-inch lengths being the most popular. With the proper wrist and elbow action, about 7 inches of the steel is all that is used except when a steak knife is being sharpened.

The steel is held firmly in the palm of the hand with the thumb in

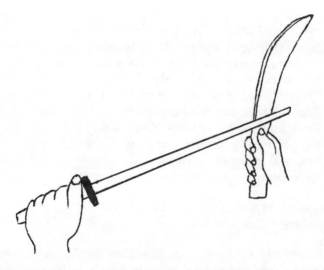

Fig. 2.3—Steeling a knife. Proper way to grip steel. Note how thumb is in line with fingers and thus protected.

line with the fingers rather than using a "surrounding grip" (see Figure 2.3) in a position almost diagonal to the body but with a slight upward tilt. This is important as it permits the free movement of the knife across the steel without drawing it too close to the hand holding the steel. The heel of the blade is placed against either the near or far side of the tip of the steel at a 20- to 25-degree angle and the blade is brought down across the steel toward the left hand with a quick swinging motion of the right wrist and forearm. The entire blade should pass lightly over the steel. Then the knife is brought in position on the opposite side of the steel and the same motion is repeated. Once the single stroke, just explained, is mastered, the double stroke will come easily. This consists of placing the knife on the steel for the backward stroke in addition to the downward stroke. About a dozen strokes of the knife should be sufficient to put an edge on a knife that is not very dull.

Knife Safety

According to the National Safety Council, knife safety can best be obtained by applying the following four control measures:

1. *Utilization of protective equipment.* This equipment consists of metal mesh gloves, properly engineered arm guards, and abdominal protectors.
2. *Proper selection, shaping, and guarding of knives.* This means choosing the right knife for each job, proper sharpening (as discussed above) and utilization of knife guards to prevent the user's hand from sliding over the handle onto the blade.
3. *Safe handling of knives when not being used.* This dictates that the knife be disposed of in a knife scabbard worn on the worker's belt rather than in table slots which have been proven unsafe. The scabbard must be composed of a material that can be routinely cleaned and sterilized, thus metal scabbards are preferred.
4. *Knife safety habit training.* This training falls upon the responsible person or persons to organize the work, engineer the facilities, and maintain a consistency of environment conducive to knife safety.

Other Aspects of Safety (From the National Safety Council)

Buildings and equipment considerations involve such items as electrical hazards, fired and unfired pressure vessels, railings, stairways, floor surfaces, aisles, guarding of power transmission equipment, lifts and noists, chains, cables, many other items of equipment (water hoses, steak tenderizing machines, frozen meat slicers, meat grinders, stuffers, patty forming machines), and the occurrence of fumes and gases.

Materials handling involves lifting, use of hand trucks and power trucks, operation of elevators, and maintenance of storage areas.

Housekeeping is not an occasional push broom effort, but an orderly arrangement of operations, tools, equipment, storage, facilities, and supplies.

Maintenance operations include personnel protection, use of ladders and portable tools, refrigeration maintenance, and welding precautions.

Principles of fire protection involves evaluating factors causing fires and correct use of fire extinguishers.

Use of cleaning compounds is an exceedingly complex area involving only the utilization of chemicals authorized by the USDA Animal and Plant Health Inspection Service (APHIS) and then being absolutely sure of proper uses and amounts to avoid alkali hazards, acid hazards, and germicide hazards.

First aid and medical procedures include knowledge of general rules and emergency procedures and vision and hearing conservation.

For a complete discussion of the above items, refer to the National Safety Council's *Meat Industry Safety Guidelines*.

SANITATION

Sanitation regulations are spelled out in detail in two publications by USDA-APHIS: (1) *The Meat and Poultry Inspection Manual* and (2) *Meat and Poultry Inspection Regulations*. Yet, if one has only a fundamental knowledge of the rich nutritional composition of meat on which certain microorganisms can thrive as do humans, and of the microorganisms themselves which do thrive on meat under certain conditions, a sanitation program and sanitation rules and habits become very necessary and meaningful. Thus one does not generate a sanitation program merely to satisfy a state or Federal meat inspector, but rather to improve the efficiency, service, and, yes, profitability of his meat operation. Ultimately, of course, consumer satisfaction is the goal of a meat operation, and foremost among consumer concerns is wholesomeness of the products that are consumed.

Later, in Chapter 17, where meat preservation is considered, a somewhat detailed discussion of meat microbiology is included. However, our purpose here is to draw the reader's attention to the importance of sanitation before we get into the detail of slaughter and processing, because rightfully the consideration of sanitation must be made *first*.

Back in 1957, C. F. Niven, Jr., spoke of "A Perspective of the Sanitation Problems in the Meat Industry."[2] He concluded: "Thus, the sanitarian has an important and responsible position in the meat industry with regard to aid in the production of safe and wholesome meat foods of good keeping qualities. He has many challenges before him. His problems may be varied and vexing. Even in the most modern plant, he must have at hand the most effective methods of cleaning such diverse materials as wood, fabrics, corrosive metals, brick, concrete, ceramics, and plastics. Often such diverse materials are found on one piece of equipment.

"The food sanitarian must work at a psychological disadvantage. Rarely is it his lot to have a chance to demonstrate to management that he can make money for the company. His recommendations frequently result in increased costs that infringe upon the already narrow profit margins. In many instances he may encounter difficulty in convincing management of the problems involved and of the necessity for recommended precautions against hazards that may not be readily apparent unless a disastrous food spoilage episode is experienced. Then he may have to shoulder part of the blame. His solace must necessarily come from the day by day experiences that all is well in spite of the many challenges before him."

More recently, Union Carbide Films Packaging Division[3] and Dr. Joe Rakosky of Central Soya, Chemurgy Division[4] have published small brochures describing the need for sanitation in plain, easy to understand terms. Union Carbide says to keep it *clean, cold,* and *covered* to maintain product quality. Dr. Rakowsky of Central Soya indicates that the three greatest offenders causing food poisoning or disease are *filth, fingers,* and *flies.*

To summarize sanitation needs, we can expand on the following:

1. *Clean* refers to equipment, buildings, people, wrapping materials, ingredients, and *anything* that comes in contact with the meat food. What looks *clean* may very well not be since bacteria, yeasts, and molds (microorganisms) can only be seen through a microscope. It would take 25,000 of them laid end to end to make one inch. Thus, to *clean* equipment means using water at 180° F or water at a lower temperature in combination with APHIS-approved disinfectants. Or for workers to be *clean,* means wash-

---

2. American Meat Institute Foundation, Circ. No. 39, November 1957.
3. *The 3 C's of Plant Sanitation,* Union Carbide Films Packaging Division, Chicago, Illinois 60638.
4. *Sanitation Simplified,* Central Soya, Chemurgy Division, Chicago, Illinois 60639.

ing with approved soaps and warm water *many* times during the day, especially after breaks. In some plants now, workers completely change clothes when going in to work with meat. They even wear masks as surgical doctors and nurses wear in the hospital operating room. So it is logical that employees should not use tobacco, pick their noses, or scratch their heads while working with meat food. Furthermore, the *water supply* must be potable, i.e., pure and non-contaminated. That is a basic requirement, and is discussed first in the APHIS regulations. Thus, when we speak of being *clean* we have eliminated *filth* sometimes caused by *fingers* and *flies*.

2. *Cold* means *without question* holding meat at a temperature below 40° F, but better yet, down very near to the point where meat begins to freeze, at 28° F. Most microorganisms that cause food borne intoxication and infection grow best at temperatures between 40° F and 140° F, so it is important that meat be kept at either below 40° F or above 140° F, and when it is cooking, it should pass through this range from 40° F to 140° F as quickly as possible and practical. The old saying "life begins at 40" really refers to food microorganisms. The closer to 28° F you hold the meat during storage, transport, or display, the longer the "shelf-life," i.e., maintaining top quality. Thus, federal regulations require that processing rooms and equipment used in rooms where temperatures may exceed 50° F must be completely cleaned and sanitized every four hours. This is an example of a very useful regulation that processors can and must abide by in their scheme of operation.

3. *Covered* means excluding air borne microorganisms and vermin by the use of screens or other suitable barriers between processing areas. It means proper covering of meats, carcasses, wholesale cuts, or primal cuts during transport. It means the proper wrapping of retail cuts for display or for preservation by freezing. It also means workers not coughing, sneezing, or spitting tobacco juices in the presence of meat food.

Thus, sanitation is basic and important, and just good common sense can go a long way toward establishing and maintaining satisfactory sanitation in any meat processing situation.

CHAPTER 3

Federal and State
Meat Inspection

The wholesomeness of each American's poultry and meat supply is protected by the U.S. Department of Agriculture. Federal meat inspection dates back to June 30, 1906, with the passage of the Meat Inspection Act. Previous to that time, a limited form of Federal inspection had been started in 1891, but this was only a voluntary inspection of cattle and hogs intended for export. The Meat Inspection Act of 1906 has been continually evaluated and improved over the years but the most sweeping change was the passage of the Wholesome Meat Act on December 15, 1967. The major thrust of this 1967 law, which still ties to the original 1906 act, was to make all of the various state inspection systems at least equal to the Federal inspection system. Previous to this time, Federal meat inspection applied *only* to meat and meat products in interstate or foreign commerce. Many states had their own inspection systems for meat and meat products moving within their own state borders, but others did not. Thus, consumers in the various states may have had varying levels of protection.

The 1967 law gave the states three years, until December 15, 1970, to inaugurate an inspection system equal to the Federal system. If any state could not or would not develop its own system, the Federal inspection system would take over in that state after December, 1970. As of August 4, 1973, the following ten states did *not* have state inspection within their borders but rather *all* plants, *intra*state and *inter*state, are Federally inspected: Kentucky, Minnesota, Missouri, Montana, Nebraska, Nevada, North Dakota, Oregon, Pennsylvania, and Washington. The USDA also does all the poultry inspection in nine other states: Arkansas, Colorado, Georgia, Idaho, Maine, Michigan, South Dakota, Utah, and West Virginia.

ADMINISTRATION OF THE ACT

Meat inspection was first administered by the Bureau of Animal Industry which later became a part of the USDA's Agricultural Research Service. Later meat inspection came under the USDA's Consumer and Marketing Service (C & MS). On April 2, 1972, the Secretary of Agriculture established the Animal and Plant Health Inspection Service (APHIS) and assigned to this new agency the meat and poultry inspection functions heretofore carried out by the C & MS. APHIS is responsible for the following programs:

Agricultural Quarantine Inspection
Animal Health
Meat and Poultry Inspection
Plant Protection
Veterinary Biologies

Meat and Poultry Inspection—A Capsule Summary[1]

The U.S. Department of Agriculture helps consumers and industry through a comprehensive meat and poultry inspection program.

—Inspects for wholesomeness all meat and poultry products produced by plants selling across state lines or to other countries.

—Inspects all meat and poultry products produced by plants in states which do not have certified, equal-to-Federal inspection programs of their own.

—Reviews state programs that have been certified equal, to see that satisfactory inspection is maintained.

—Reviews foreign inspection systems and packing plants which export meat and poultry to this country, then reinspects imported products at U.S. ports of entry.

—Checks plant facilities and equipment, sanitation, slaughter and processing methods, containers, and labeling.

Inspection is marked by expanding Federal and state cooperation.

—Most states now conduct their own inspection programs, based on Federal guidelines, for plants that sell within the state boundaries.

—State and Federal inspection programs are sharing data, facilities, and manpower resources to fulfill respective consumer protection responsibilities more efficiently.

---

1. USDA, APHIS, MPI, September 4, 1973.

—Federal Government shares the cost of state inspection programs and offers technical, laboratory, and training aid.

Inspection occurs at various points in the marketing process. One product may be inspected numerous times.

—Before slaughter.

—After slaughter.

—During processing, packaging, and labeling.

Federal inspection program is growing. At the beginning of 1973,[2]

—Over 8,800 food inspectors and veterinarians and about 900 management, laboratory, and other support personnel worked in the USDA meat and poultry inspection programs.

—4,030 meat plants, 751 poultry plants, and 982 combination meat and poultry plants were under Federal inspection.

Under the watchful eyes of USDA inspectors, wholesome meat and poultry reach our nation's homes. In 1972,

—USDA inspected more than 3,260 million birds and 123 million meat animals and, during later processing, more than 19 billion pounds of processed poultry products and more than 52 billion pounds of processed meat products.

—Federal inspectors condemned more than 81 million head of poultry, 125 million pounds of poultry parts, 31 million pounds of processed poultry products. They also condemned more than 304,000 meat animals, 6 million parts of meat animals, and 42 million pounds of processed meat products.

—As a "second line of defense" against unfit products in marketing channels, USDA compliance officers detained over 15 million pounds of "suspect" meat and poultry in some 640 detentions. The aim is to prevent fraudulent or illegal practices once the product has left the processing plant. Compliance officers check for uninspected meat or poultry, counterfeit inspection stamps and inaccurate labels, and comtamination or spoilage of products after leaving the plant.

Imported meat and poultry products must meet same standards as those produced in the United States.

—A foreign country's inspection laws, regulations, procedures, ad-

---

2. All figures in this fact sheet are based on calendar year.

ministration, and operations must first meet U.S. standards; USDA then approves the overall program. Individual plants within that country then apply to their own government for certification to export to the United States.

—Each certified plant is subject to continuous inspection by inspectors of the foreign country's government. During 1972, more than 7,770 such inspectors were working in plants exporting meat and poultry products to the United States.

—Certified plants are visited two to four times a year by a U.S. foreign review officer to see that they are operating according to approved procedures.

—Imported meat and poultry products are reinspected as they arrive in this country. They must bear prominent marking as to their country of origin.

—At the end of 1972, 1,042 foreign plants were authorized to export meat and meat products to the United States. More than 1.7 billion pounds of their products were passed for entry into this country during 1972, while more than 29 million pounds were refused entry and/or condemned.

An epidemiology unit in USDA's Animal and Plant Health Inspection Service traces causes of food-borne hazards involving meat and poultry.

—Works with local, state, and Federal public health agencies to control food poisoning outbreaks by speeding identification of products responsible for human health hazards.

—Has found the major cause to be improper handling of products at institution, restaurant, or home level during preparation for serving. Some examples of improper handling:

● Inadequate cooking.
● Storage at warm, "median" temperatures which allow bacteria and other organisms to multiply rapidly.
● Failure to keep raw and cooked products separate during preparation.
● Contamination by human carriers of bacteria.
● Poor sanitation practices.

—Has found that perfringens, salmonella, staphylococcus, and trichina poisonings result from improper handling.

Monitoring program checks against meat and poultry containing drug, pesticide, and chemical residues.

—Monitors both domestic and imported meat and poultry production for possible residues.

—Sample animals, flocks, and herds suspected of illegal residues.

—Alerts drug and pesticide enforcement agencies when violations are found.

—Condemned nearly 4 million pounds of meat and poultry containing illegal residues in 1972.

Additives—ingredients aimed at improving physical qualities such as flavor, color, and shelf-life of a product—must be approved by USDA before use in inspected meat and poultry products. USDA sees that additives used:

—Are approved by Food and Drug Administration and are limited to specified amounts.

—Meet a specific, justifiable need in the product.

—Do not promote deception as to product freshness, quality, weight, or size. Paprika, for example, is not permitted in fresh meat, since its red color can make raw meat look leaner and fresher than it is.

—Are truthfully and properly listed on the product label.

Labels help consumers know what they're paying for.

—Labels on all inspected products must be approved by USDA.

—Labels must contain accurate product name; list of ingredients, in order from greatest to smallest amount; name and place of business of packer, manufacturer, or person for whom product is prepared; net weight; mark of Federal inspection.

—In 1972, 162,000 different label designs for meat and poultry products were reviewed and approved. Some 19,800 other labels which did not give accurate statement of package contents were rejected.

To be labeled with a particular name, a Federally-inspected meat or poultry product must be approved as meeting specific product requirements. Standards are set by USDA so consumers will get what they expect when they shop.

—"Beef with Gravy" must contain at least 50% beef (cooked basis), while the minimum meat content for "Gravy with Beef" is 35% beef (cooked basis).

—"Ham Salad" must contain at least 35% ham (cooked basis).

—"Hot dogs" and "bologna" are limited to 30% fat.

—"Chicken Soup" must have at least 2% chicken meat (cooked, deboned basis).

—"Turkey Pot Pie" must contain at least 14% turkey meat (cooked, deboned basis).

Consumers participate in setting standards.

—When new or revised standards and labeling rules are being considered, USDA makes this information available to news outlets. Consumers seeing such items may let USDA know their views.

SEVEN BASIC REQUIREMENTS[3]

There are seven basic requirements that must be adequate in all Federal plants and thus also in all state plants which are judged on an equal basis.

When it has been determined that a plant is endangering public health (EPH), it must be surveyed for corrective action after five working days. When a plant is deficient in one or more of the seven basic items but is not in an EPH category, it must be resurveyed no later than before the end of the succeeding quarter.

The seven basic requirements that must be met include the following:

I. Ante- and Post-mortem Inspection

Ante- and/or post mortem inspection procedures must be accompanied in a manner that will detect and remove any unwholesome carcass, part, or organ from human food channels.

II. Reinspection (Processing)

Inspection and control of processed products must assure that only sound, wholesome products are distributed into human food channels. This includes acceptable procedures for destroying trichinae in products containing pork muscle, only wholesome ingredients, acceptable chemicals in approved quantities, adequate protection during processing and storing, and control of restricted products.

III. Sanitation

Operational sanitation must permit production of wholesome prod-

---

3. USDA, APHIS, MPI Directive 910.1.

Table 3.1—Meat and Poultry Plants Under Federal Inspection Grants, December 31, 1973[1]

State or Territory	Slaughter Only			Process Only			Slaughter & Process			Total Plants		
	Meat Only	Poul. Only	Meat & Poul.	Meat Only	Poul. Only	Meat & Poul.	Meat Only	Poul. Only	Meat & Poul.	Meat Only	Poul. Only	Meat & Poul.
Ala.	0	21	0	15	4	8	6	0	0	21	25	8
Alas	0	0	0	0	0	0	0	0	0	0	0	0
Ariz.	0	0	0	7	1	3	6	12	2	13	1	3
Ark.	0	19	0	9	7	11	3	11	3	12	38	13
Calif.	6	0	0	152	10	73	50	5	2	208	27	70
Colo.	4	1	0	51	11	11	16	0	0	71	17	13
Conn.	3	0	0	46	3	11	4	0	0	53	3	11
Del.	0	6	0	4	2	3	0	0	0	4	8	3
D.C.	0	0	0	29	6	3	0	0	0	29	6	3
Fla.	5	4	0	29	1	20	1	0	0	35	5	20
Ga.	2	24	0	26	9	24	6	4	1	34	37	25
Guam	0	0	0	3	0	1	0	0	0	3	0	1
Hawaii	0	0	0	2	0	1	1	0	0	3	2	1
Ida.	11	5	0	0	1	1	5	1	0	16	0	1
Ill.	3	4	0	164	16	63	10	2	0	192	23	63
Ind.	8	1	0	38	7	17	17	6	1	52	17	18
Iowa	5	2	0	31	2	15	11	6	2	74	9	17
Kan.	9	0	0	20	2	14	35	1	3	144	5	17
Ky.	0	3	0	160	8	33	18	2	3	16	10	36
La.	0	0	0	10	1	6	6	0	1	12	4	7
Me.	0	0	0	7	4	6	5	5	0	29	9	6
Md.	3	10	0	26	6	14	0	1	1	29	17	15

(Continued)

Table 3.1 (Continued)

State or Territory	Slaughter Only			Process Only			Slaughter & Process			Total Plants		
	Meat Only	Poul. Only	Meat & Poul.	Meat Only	Poul. Only	Meat & Poul.	Meat Only	Poul. Only	Meat & Poul.	Meat Only	Poul. Only	Meat & Poul.
Mass.	0	1	0	115	9	35	3	2	0	118	12	35
Mich.	2	0	0	36	13	10	9	0	1	47	13	11
Minn.	4	4	0	39	9	73	46	11	19	89	24	92
Miss.	2	18	0	7	0	6	5	0	1	14	18	7
Mo.	21	11	0	123	19	44	97	13	8	241	43	52
Mont.	2	0	0	11	0	32	22	6	8	35	0	40
Neb.	19	0	0	37	5	31	56	6	13	112	11	44
Nev.	1	0	0	5	2	11	3	0	2	9	2	13
N.H.	0	0	0	11	1	5	1	1	0	12	2	5
N.J.	9	5	0	91	13	45	2	1	0	102	19	45
N.M.	5	0	0	5	1	5	9	0	1	19	1	6
N.Y.	15	7	0	243	13	80	14	0	2	272	20	82
N.C.	3	18	0	43	2	17	3	4	0	49	24	17
N.D.	2	0	0	11	0	7	28	0	7	41	0	14
Ohio	4	5	0	65	8	29	33	3	2	102	16	31
Okla.	3	3	0	7	1	5	9	0	0	19	4	5
Ore.	1	2	0	60	2	13	49	5	1	110	9	14
Pa.	163	13	0	316	50	80	157	13	8	636	76	88
P.R.	18	1	1	57	0	16	0	0	0	75	1	17
R.I.	2	0	0	21	4	4	2	1	0	25	5	4
S.C.	2	4	0	6	2	4	1	1	1	9	7	5
S.D.	1	2	0	2	1	0	8	1	0	11	4	0

(Continued)

Table 3.1 (Continued)

State or Territory	Slaughter Only			Process Only			Slaughter & Process			Total Plants		
	Meat Only	Poul. Only	Meat & Poul.	Meat Only	Poul. Only	Meat & Poul.	Meat Only	Poul. Only	Meat & Poul.	Meat Only	Poul. Only	Meat & Poul.
Tenn.	1	8	0	45	2	25	15	6	1	61	10	26
Tex.	8	20	0	108	8	41	52	8	14	168	36	55
Utah	0	2	0	6	3	2	8	2	0	14	7	2
Vt.	0	0	0	10	1	0	2	1	0	12	2	0
Va.	3	10	0	45	8	18	6	3	2	54	21	20
V.I.	1	0	0	0	0	1	1	0	0	2	0	1
Wash.	2	1	0	75	1	28	36	6	2	113	8	30
W. Va.	0	2	0	9	1	4	1	0	1	10	3	5
Wis.	2	5	0	41	8	23	17	6	2	60	19	25
Wyo.	0	0	0	1	0	2	1	0	0	2	0	2
Total	355	248	1	2,426	288	1,034	926	144	115	3,707	680	1,150

1. The National Provisioner, March 2, 1974.

Table 3.2—Number of Animals, Ante-Mortem and Post-Mortem Inspection of Animals, Fiscal Year 1972[1]

Species	Ante-Mortem Inspection				Post-Mortem Inspection		
	Passed	Suspected[2]	Condemned[3]	Total	Passed	Condemned[3]	Total
Cattle	31,711,955	131,888	9,489	31,853,332	31,754,114	89,261	31,843,375
Calves	2,593,072	1,125	11,473	2,605,670	2,576,750	17,052	2,593,802
Sheep	10,072,171	3,087	9,496	10,084,754	10,031,936	43,264	10,075,200
Goats	225,635	9	533	226,177	224,342	1,296	225,638
Swine	83,108,614	20,466	81,986	83,211,066	82,968,190	158,206	83,126,396
Horses[4]	68,198	119	99	68,416	67,717	600	68,317
Other equines[4]	4,657	72	12	4,741	4,702	27	4,729
Total	127,784,302	156,766	113,088[5]	128,054,156	127,627,751	309,706	127,937,457

1. Federal Meat and Poultry Inspection Statistical Summary for 1972, USDA, APHIS.

2. "Suspected" is used to designate animals suspected of being affected with diseases or conditions that may cause condemnation in whole or part on post-mortem inspection.

3. For causes and additional condemnation, see tables 3.3 to 3.6, inclusive.

4. Horses and mules are slaughtered and their meat handled and prepared in establishments separate and apart from those in which cattle, calves, sheep, goats, and swine are slaughtered and their meat handled and prepared.

5. Includes 3,611 previously suspected animals that died in pens.

Table 3.3.—Number of Carcasses Condemned for Various Diseases and Conditions on Post-Mortem Inspection, Fiscal Year 1972[1]

	Number of Carcasses Condemned						
Cause of Condemnation	Cattle	Calves & Lambs	Sheep & Lambs	Goats	Swine	Horses	Other Equines
Degenerative and Dropsical Conditions							
Anasarca	1,212	15	51	147	47	3	1
Emaciation	5,188	1,216	9,492	434	781	108	
Miscellaneous	1,069	25	129		506	3	
Infectious Diseases							
Actinomycosis, Actinobacil	685	142			10		
Anaplasmosis	160	5					
Caseous Lymphadenitis			8,637	286			
Coccidioidal Granuloma	11						
Hog Cholera					3		
Leptospirosis	2						
Listerellosis	2				3		
Mucosal Diseases	5						
Necrobacillosis and Necrosis	114	6			5		
Swine Erysipelas					3,317		
Tuberculosis Nonreactor	27	3			5,777		
Tuberculosis Reactor with Lesions	32	4					
Miscellaneous	56		13		35		
Inflammatory Diseases							
Enteritis, Gastritis, Peritonitis	3,980	1,462	342	8	9,438	16	1

(Continued)

Table 3.3 (Continued)

Cause of Condemnation	Cattle	Calves & Lambs	Sheep & Lambs	Goats	Swine	Horses	Other Equines
Eosinophilic Myositis	4,438	7	28		27		
Mastitis, Mammitis	897	1	5		59		
Metritis	1,926	15	143	3	1,233		
Nephritis, Pyelitis	2,981	182	796	2	3,183	2	
Pericarditis	4,443	55	167		1,308	1	1
Pneumonia	12,167	3,585	7,625	150	20,276	143	1
Miscellaneous	321	163	260		419	2	
Neoplasms							
Carcinoma	2,353	5	13	6	251	4	1
Epithelioma	14,835						
Malignant Lymphoma	5,423	76	30	2	1,667	11	1
Sarcoma	202	1	9		204	133	5
Miscellaneous	509	11	23	1	507	59	4
Parasitic Conditions							
Cysticercosis	241		190		6		
Sarcosporidiosis	215		4,621		19		
Stephanuriasis			105		3,401		
Miscellaneous	94	75		1	144		
Pigmentary Conditions							
Melanosis, Non-Malignant	61	12	22	3	404		
Miscellaneous	141	7	4	8	68		

(Continued)

Table 3.3 (Continued)

Cause of Condemnation	Number of Carcasses Condemned						
	Cattle	Calves & Lambs	Sheep & Lambs	Goats	Swine	Horses	Other Equines
Septic Conditions							
Abscess, Pyemia	8,992	541	1,803	146	36,690	22	2
Septicemia	6,149	1,848	870	28	9,676	28	2
Toxemia	3,428	121	300	1	2,563	3	
Miscellaneous	216	45	11	1	176	1	
Other							
Arthritis, Polyarthritis	1,478	2,814	1,407	12	24,399	2	
Asphyxia	41	158	1,121		3,328		
Bone Conditions	22	11			159		
Contamination	394	107	387	1	6,397	6	
Icterus	495	2,891	1,616	29	14,959		
Immaturity		284	1		4		
Injuries, Bruises	2,778	1,103	599	24	4,305	52	4
Sexual Odor					737		
Skin Conditions	4	2			102		
Uremia	1,227	39	2,143	2	1,272	1	
Miscellaneous General	247	15	301	1	341		4
Total	89,261	17,052	43,264	1,296	158,206	600	27

1. Federal Meat and Poultry Inspection Statistical Summary for 1972, USDA, APHIS.

Table 3.4—Foreign Meat and Meat Food Products Passed for Entry, Fiscal Year 1972[1]

	Fresh Meats and Edible Organs									
Country of Origin	Beef				Veal			Mutton and Lamb		
	Manu-facturing	Carcasses and Cuts	Head Meat & Tongue	Edible Organs	Manu-facturing	Carcasses and Cuts	Edible Organs	Manu-facturing	Carcasses and Cuts	Edible Organs
	------------------------------- (lbs.) -------------------------------									
Argentina										
Australia	357,623,400	94,410,842	89,580	117,791	3,507,831	1,495,578	42,413	34,949,618	8,604,377	
Austria										
Belgium										
Brazil										
Bulgaria										
Canada	44,243,729	12,700,694	822,662	71,042	1,318,511	3,097,042	187,943	5,093	230,210	1,110
Colombia										
Costa Rica	23,827,447	18,307,217				25,772				
Czechoslovakia										
Denmark										
Dominican Republic	4,830,465	5,103,861								
El Salvador	555,240	403,458								
England and Wales										
France										
Germany	17,652,492	11,348,662		1,593						
Guatemala	743,760	1,239,497		14,522						
Haiti			4,282							
Honduras	18,965,267	10,556,986	85,394	36,877			19,200			
Hungary										
Iceland									516	

(Continued)

Table 3.4 (Continued)

Fresh Meats and Edible Organs

(lbs.)

Country of Origin	Beef				Veal			Mutton and Lamb		
	Manufacturing	Carcasses and Cuts	Head Meat & Tongue	Edible Organs	Manufacturing	Carcasses and Cuts	Edible Organs	Manufacturing	Carcasses and Cuts	Edible Organs
Ireland	25,611,622	12,696,108								
Italy										
Japan										
Mexico	47,463,830	2,563,044			2,827,037	3,420				
Netherlands										
New Zealand	186,103,143	29,503,071	4,725	130,400	4,106,361	3,254,616	475,060	197,431	16,436,823	
Nicaragua	34,168,188	17,257,272	191,569	43,244		5,687				
Northern Ireland	1,089,209	476,173								
Panama	1,382,932	1,165,069								
Paraguay										
Poland										
Romania										
Scotland										
Spain										
Sweden										
Switzerland										
Yugoslavia										
Total	764,260,724	217,731,954	1,198,212	415,469	11,759,740	7,882,115	724,616	35,152,142	25,271,926	1,110

(Continued)

Table 3.4 (Continued)

Country of Origin	Fresh Meats and Edible Organs—Pork			Cured Meats			Cooked Beef		Miscellaneous	Horse Meat
	Manufacturing	Carcasses and Cuts	Edible Organs	Beef	Pork	Sausage (Trichina Treated)	Restricted	Other		
					(lbs.)					
Argentina							24,829,876	17,852,873	4,457,980	13,417,589
Australia		19,333						2,568,884	707,404	
Austria				55,499		12,405				
Belgium				39,595	3,104	53,633			238	
Brazil				415,042					182,968	
Bulgaria							11,725,039	3,422,355		
Canada	12,885,838	46,758,231	360,891	88,620	3,946,757	1,985,065		6,703	7,998,523	3,002,870
Colombia										
Costa Rica							104,134		124,215	
Czechoslovakia										
Denmark				9,072	74,782	8,929,129			10,289	
Dominican Republic										
El Salvador								447		
England and Wales										
France					7,324	1,937			3,707	
Germany				122,225	106,042	583,691			10,163	
Guatemala					41,516	24		8,390	813,215	
Haiti									77,995	
Honduras				59,150		8,782			295,791	
Hungary										
Iceland									546	

(Continued)

Table 3.4 (Continued)

Country of Origin	Fresh Meats and Edible Organs—Pork			Cured Meats			Cooked Beef		Miscellaneous	Horse Meat
	Manufacturing	Carcasses and Cuts	Edible Organs	Beef	Pork	Sausage (Trichina Treated)	Restricted	Other		
						(lbs.)				
Ireland										
Italy				38,386	48,181			75,333		
Japan										
Mexico									27,000	4,049,063
Netherlands		35,566		743,469	61,361	22,925		194,637	338,336	
New Zealand						630			1,231,096	
Nicaragua										
Northern Ireland										
Panama				121,322	394,951				108,415	
Poland									2,640	
Romania										
Scotland										
Spain									960	
Sweden										
Switzerland				9,744	10,961	5,937				
Yugoslavia										
Total	12,885,838	46,813,130	360,891	1,702,124	4,694,889	11,604,158	36,659,049	24,129,622	16,391,481	20,469,522

(Continued)

Table 3.4 (Continued)

| Country of Origin | Corned Beef | Other Beef | Canned Meats — Canned Hams (lbs.) | | | Picnics | Other Pork | Luncheon Meat/Chopped Ham | Other | Country Total |
			Under 3 Lbs.	3 to 6 Lbs.	Over 6 Lbs.					
Argentina	31,680,196	9,587,569							40,852	101,922,434
Australia	62,340		15,360						74,053	504,328,399
Austria										12,405
Belgium									2,831	59,716
Brazil	27,329,910	2,281,227	115,233	169,423	189,336	94,248	144,000	294,480	135,182	45,491,723
Bulgaria										722,064
Canada		594			779,794	44,208	98,664	546	19,183	140,939,179
Colombia									357	104,491
Costa Rica										42,284,651
Czechoslovakia				102,120	923,746	99,000	21,600	64,400	5,400	1,216,266
Denmark	23,775		6,097,559	4,471,196	68,825,521	23,588,695	6,280,960	15,210,396	2,476,400	135,997,774
Dominican Republic										9,934,773
El Salvador										958,698
England and Wales									295,634	295,634
France			13,801	22,936					186,767	199,735
Germany					385,295		21,178		64,812	1,207,918
Guatemala										29,988,117
Haiti										2,088,838

(Continued)

Table 3.4 (Continued)

Canned Meats (lbs.)

Country of Origin	Corned Beef	Other Beef	Canned Hams — Under 3 Lbs.	Canned Hams — 3 to 6 Lbs.	Canned Hams — Over 6 Lbs.	Picnics	Other Pork	Luncheon Meat/Chopped Ham	Other	Country Total
Honduras									512,710	30,531,375
Hungary				38,700	3,376,068	1,567,713	145,058	69,948		5,197,487
Iceland									256	1,318
Ireland									30,127	38,461,371
Italy		103,261							48,984	190,631
Japan		6,030								6,030
Mexico										56,993,394
Netherlands			3,765,431	2,312,937	48,474,789	9,157,231	463,218	1,500,086	234,223	65,992,201
New Zealand	38,393									241,562,661
Nicaragua										52,891,369
Northern Ireland									144,450	1,715,519
Panama		2,375,728								2,548,001
Paraguay	5,215,904	2,640								8,216,320
Poland			322,082	4,467,907	18,835,118	4,529,809	567,088	6,789,590	44,898	35,561,772
Romania				9,558	657,468	291,324	252,660	73,017		1,284,027
Scotland									1,080	1,080
Spain									74,461	74,461
Sweden							1,050		47,572	48,662
Switzerland									63,402	91,004
Yugoslavia		36	88,788	294,927	6,808,393	2,530,198	732,393	5,399	10,836	10,470,970
Total	64,350,518	14,357,085	10,418,254	11,889,704	149,255,528	41,902,426	8,727,869	24,007,862	4,514,470	1,569,532,428

1. Federal Meat and Poultry Inspection Statistical Summary for 1972, USDA, APHIS.

ucts, and must also permit product handling and processing without undue exposure to contaminants. Facilities and equipment must be properly cleaned at regular intervals. All personnel must practice good personal hygiene, and management must provide necessary equipment and materials to encourage such hygiene. Particular emphasis should be placed on product and product zones. Reviewers should consider the significance of individual instances in arriving at a judgment of overall sanitation of the plant.

IV. Potable Water

When water is used in areas where edible products are slaughtered, eviscerated, dressed, processed, handled, or stored, it must be potable.

To determine potability, the plant must have a local authority certification on an analysis of samples taken from within the facility; the certification must be on an annual basis if the supply is from a municipal source, and if the supply is from a private well, cistern, spring, etc., the certification must be on a semiannual basis. Additional testing and certification are required when there is reason to believe that water is being contaminated—cross connection of potable and nonpotable lines, back siphonage, surface drainage or ineffective drainage, floods, etc. Outdated certification is not sufficient evidence to judge a supply as nonpotable if there is no history of potability problems. However, it should be cited as a deficiency needing correction.

V. Sewage and Waste Disposal Control

Sewage and waste disposal systems must effectively remove sewage and waste materials—manure, paunch contents, trash, garbage, and paper. Such systems must also prevent undue accumulation or development of odors, and must not serve as harbors for rodents or insects. Deficiencies not resulting in a direct threat to the overall sanitation of the plant may not adversely affect the item rating. Systems must be approved by local or state health authorities for official plants.

VI. Pest Control

The plant's pest control program must be capable of preventing or eliminating product contamination. Plant management must make reasonable efforts to prevent entry of rodents, insects, or animals into areas where products are handled, processed, or stored—including effective closures to outside openings (doors, screens, windows), use of exterminating procedures, sprays, baits, etc. In evaluating the system's effectiveness, management's efforts to eliminate or correct faulty facilities and other such control factors should be considered.

VII. Condemned and Inedible Material Control

Condemned and inedible products or materials must be controlled so as to prevent their diversion into human food channels. Condemned materials should be maintained under inspection control until effectively denatured or rendered incapable for use as human food. Inedible materials should be maintained under plant and inspection control until effectively denatured or rendered incapable for use as human food, or until packaged and identified as food not fit for human consumption. Unmarked containers or other deficiencies that do not affect the plant production of wholesome products may not affect the item rating, but should be cited for correction.

If any of the following conditions exist, the plant must be designated as endangering public health (EPH) and corrective action must be taken immediately.

1. Use of nonpotable water in edible products departments.
2. Improper sanitation that results in bacterial growth and development in or on product, foreign matter entering product, or failure to control vermin and insects.
3. Presence of carcasses or parts showing sufficient evidence to identify a systemic diseased condition or containing evidence of bearing a disease transmissible to man.
4. Use of unsound meat/poultry in processing meat/poultry food products.
5. Presence of harmful chemicals and preservatives in excess of permitted tolerances.
6. Failure to properly treat or destroy trichinae.

EXPLANATION OF THE SEVEN BASIC REQUIREMENTS (GLOSSARY OF TERMS)

I. Ante- and Post-mortem Inspection

Ante-mortem Inspection Facilities: Lighting in Inspection Areas— Including Suspect Pen. A minimum of 10 foot-candles in area where and when routine inspection is performed, measured 3 feet above the floor, either natural or artificial, or a combination of both. A minimum of 20 foot-candles over the entire suspect pen and restraining facilities, measured 3 feet above the floor.[4]

---

4. Not applicable to poultry.

Suspect Pen—Squeeze Chute.[5] A separate, paved, drained pen, under weathertight roof; identified pen may not be necessary for very small operations.

Handling Equipment for Examination of Suspects.[6] Facilities such as chutes, squeeze gates, boxes, nose tongs, or any other effective device for restraining animals requiring close examination must be provided. Also, suitable and conveniently located facilities and equipment with sufficient supplies, such as thermometer, suspect and condemned tags, suspect cards, hog ringer and rings, etc., shall be available.

Ante-mortem Inspection Procedures.

1. *Meat.* The inspector shall observe the animals at rest in the pen and from each side when animals are being slowly moved around.
2. *Poultry.* An ante-mortem inspection of each class of poultry shall be made on the day of slaughter to the extent necessary to detect disease and/or other conditions.

Ante-mortem Handling and Control of Suspects and Animals to Be Condemned. Suspect animals should be restrained and identified and held for a detailed examination by a veterinarian. Animals to be condemned should be tagged "U.S. Condemned" and killed immediately by an establishment employee, or may be released to proper authorities for treatment under official supervision.

Control over Inspected Animals and Poultry. There must be a method of animal identity set up and in operation whereby the inspector can and does check that all animals being slaughtered have had ante-mortem inspection on the day of slaughter.

Control over Dead Animals.

1. *Meat.* Dead meat animals must be immediately tagged "U.S. Condemned" and tanked or effectively denatured under the supervision of a program employee.
2. *Poultry.* Dead poultry must be placed in containers marked "U.S. Condemned" and effectively denatured under the supervision of a program employee.

Dispositions. Animals showing signs of disease must be separated and final disposition made by a veterinarian. A company employee designated by management shall be available for moving, sorting, restraining, and identifying the animals. After a detailed examination of an ani-

---

5. Not applicable to poultry.
6. Not applicable to poultry.

mal, the veterinarian may release it without restriction or hold it for further examination and disposition by the post-mortem inspector.

Post-mortem Facilities and Inspection; Lighting at Inspection Points.

1. *Meat.* All areas of the head when on an inspection rack and head wash area at level of head hook, bottom of viscera truck pan, top of viscera conveyor, and at the level of carcass shoulders must be illuminated to a minimum of 50 foot-candles.
2. *Poultry.* A minimum of 50 foot-candles at the lowest inspection point and final post-mortem areas.

Head Inspection (Meat).

1. *Cattle.* Before any incision is made, the head must be examined on all surfaces for pathological conditions and contamination, inspectors must properly incise and examine the mandibular, atlantal (if present), suprapharyngeal, and parotid lymph nodes (2 each). The external and internal muscles of mastication must be inspected by incising them in such a manner as to split the muscles in a plane parallel to the lower jawbone. The tongue shall be observed and palpated along its entire length. (Checked for bruises, hair sores, and other abnormalities.)
2. *Calves.* Visual inspection is made to determine if heads are free of hair, hide, horns, and contamination. Incisions for node inspection may be confined to the suprapharyngeal lymph nodes unless there is reason to believe that other nodes should be examined.
3. *Swine.* Both mandibular lymph nodes shall be sliced and examined for abnormalities.

Viscera Inspection—Lungs, Heart, Liver, Spleen (Meat and Poultry).

1. *Cattle.*
    a. *Lungs.* Inspection includes the incision and examination of the tissue of the right and left bronchial and anterior, middle, and posterior mediastinal lymph nodes, palpation of the parietal or curved surface, and observation of the ventral surface.
    b. *Heart.* The inner and outer surfaces of the heart must be examined, and the muscles of the left ventricle and interventricular septum must be incised and examined.
    c. *Liver.* Inspection includes the opening of the bile duct and incision of the portal lymph nodes.
    d. *Spleen.* The spleen, along with the mesenteric lymph nodes and abdominal viscera should be observed and the rumino-

reticular junction palpated. Mesenteric lymph nodes should be incised if necessary.

2. *Calves.* Lungs, heart, and liver must be observed and palpated, and the viscera, including paunch and intestines, must be carefully observed.

3. *Swine.* Lung inspection includes observation of the parietal and ventral surfaces and palpation of the parietal surface, bronchial, and mediastinal lymph nodes. Both sides of the liver must be observed and the parietal surfaces and portal lymph nodes palpated and incisions made if necessary. The heart, spleen, and mesenteric lymph nodes incised if necessary.

4. *Sheep and Goats.* Observation and palpation of the lungs and related lymph nodes, heart, spleen, and liver shall be made. The main bile duct must be opened (by an establishment employee) and examined for parasites. The viscera must be carefully observed.

Rail or Carcass Inspection (Meat and Poultry).

1. *Cattle.* All surfaces must be observed for pathology and cleanliness. The superficial inguinal (super-mammary), internal iliac, lumbar and renal lymph nodes, exposed kidney and pillars, and flat portion of the diaphragm are to be palpated and observed. Incisions are to be made if necessary.

2. *Swine.* All parts of the carcass must be observed. Remnants of the liver and lungs, bruises, wounds, and other abnormalities shall be removed by an establishment employee before rail inspection. These parts must be very carefully observed in order to detect parasitic infestations, particularly kidney worms. The kidneys shall be palpated and observed for evidence of pathology.

3. *Calves.* There should be a visual inspection and observation of the carcass. The exposed kidneys and iliac nodes should be palpated when necessary. The back of "hide-on" calves shall be palpated to detect grubs and dirt.

4. *Sheep and Goats.* There should be an observation of the internal and external surfaces of the entire carcass. The prefemoral, superficial inguinal, popliteal, iliac lymph nodes, and diaphragm, kidneys, spleen (if present), and prescapular lymph nodes should be palpated.

5. *Poultry.* The inspector must observe all external and internal surfaces of the cavity of each carcass, including a careful examination of the air sacs, kidneys, and sex organs. He must observe and palpate the legs, heart, liver, and spleen. The spleen is to be

crushed on adult birds. The inspector shall signal the trimmer of action to be taken with regard to removing defective parts and recording condemnations.

Dispositions.

1. *Meat.* Contaminated or diseased heads shall be condemned or retained. When heads show pathological conditions, corresponding carcasses as well as the head must be tagged for examination by a veterinarian. He may permit the food inspector to dispose of viscera with localized lesions (abscessed livers, contaminated viscera, etc.). Carcasses which are contaminated, bruised, or have other abnormal conditions shall be retained for trimming or examination by a veterinarian before being passed for final washing.
2. *Poultry.* Correct disposition of carcasses and parts must be made in accordance with the regulations. Questionable birds must be retained for final post-mortem inspection by a veterinarian.

Final Inspection Procedures and Dispositions.

1. *Meat.* All organs, body cavities, and surfaces of the carcasses shall be checked and examined. The lymph nodes shall be exposed and incised if necessary (TB, malignancies, etc.). Disposition of carcasses and parts must be made in a professional manner on the basis of scientific training and reason and according to meat inspection law and regulations. If necessary, samples shall be sent to the laboratory for final pathological diagnosis to aid with dispositions.
2. *Poultry.* All carcasses and viscera retained for final inspection must be thoroughly examined by a veterinarian. Sufficient checks must be made on all condemned as well as edible product to assure that proper dispositions are being made by the post-mortem line inspectors. Final disposition of carcasses and parts shall be made in a professional manner on the basis of scientific training, knowledge, and reason. Samples may be sent to a laboratory for final pathological diagnosis to aid with dispositions.

Chilling and Moisture Control (Poultry). Immediately after slaughter, evisceration, and washing, carcasses shall be chilled by an approved method that will preclude adulteration. An internal temperature of 40° F or less must be achieved for product according to time specification for each class.

1. *Giblets and Parts.* Giblets shall be chilled within two hours after

their separation from the viscera, except when cooled within the carcass. Parts must be chilled in ice only (slush ice and water are not acceptable).

2. *Temperature.* All poultry products shall be cooled immediately after processing to an internal temperature of 40° F or less, unless further processed immediately at the establishment. All poultry must conform with time and temperature requirements.

3. *Moisture Pickup.* Chilling of carcasses and parts must be in compliance with approved moisture procedures.

Control of Restricted Products, Animal Food Products, and Condemned and Inedible Materials.

1. All *restricted* products must be under direct control or lock or seal at all times until rendered acceptable for human consumption.

2. *Animal food products* must be under the inspector's control until packed and identified or denatured. Like products cannot be saved for human consumption and animal food simultaneously.

3. *Condemned* carcasses or parts must be under the inspector's control until tanked or properly denatured.

4. *Inedible* material must be handled in a prompt, efficient manner, making use of properly marked inedible containers, under the inspector's supervision or control, until tanked or properly denatured, or identified as food other than for humans.

II. Reinspection (Processing)

Facilities—Sufficient Lighting in All Areas.

1. *Meat.* All inspection areas (boning tables, overgrinders, bacon presses, slicers, choppers, etc.) shall have 50 foot-candles of lighting. All other areas must contain at least 20 foot-candles, except dry storage, where lighting sufficient for purpose is acceptable, and 10 foot-candles at front shank level of carcass in coolers. All lights shall have protective coverings in processing rooms and areas where product is exposed.

2. *Poultry.* There shall be 30 foot-candles in operating areas, 50 foot-candles at inspection stations, and 10 foot-candles in storage areas and coolers.

Management Controls—Products Received from Acceptable Source.

1. *Meat.* Carcasses, cuts, and manufacturing meats must bear legible marks of inspection where slaughtered and/or last processed.

2. *Poultry.* Carcasses must be properly labeled with inspection legends.

3. *Nonmeat.* Supplies must be properly identified and labeled as required by the Federal Food and Drug Administration.

Use and Handling—Storage of Raw Meat.

1. *Meat.* Raw meat, emulsions, and the finished, perishable product shall be stored at a room temperature of 50° F or lower, accessible to inspection, and handled in a manner to avoid contamination.
2. *Poultry.* Raw poultry meat, emulsions, and the finished perishable products shall be held at an internal temperature of 40° F or less and handled in a manner to avoid contamination.

Formulation Control and Identification. All ingredients, emulsions, mixtures, liquids, etc., must be identified through all phases of processing. All formulas and formulating procedures are readily available for review by operating personnel and inspectors. The quantity of meat and nonmeat materials is controlled to produce a product in compliance with published standards and label declarations. Controls must be such that the inspector can evaluate adequacy of the formulation.

Processing Controls—e.g., Curing and Smoking.

1. *Curing and Pumping.* Restricted ingredients (nitrates, nitrites, phosphates, ascorbates, corn syrup) are used according to specific standards. All formulas for pickle and curing solutions are readily available for review by plant management and inspector. All pumping and curing procedures are available, and product is uniformly pumped and cured.
2. *Smoking.* Uniform procedures are used to shrink product into compliance with applicable regulations. All pork products shall be heated to a temperature not lower than 137° F, and the method and control used shall be known to insure such results. When poultry rolls are heat-processed in any manner, cured and smoked poultry rolls shall reach an internal temperature of 155° F prior to being removed from the cooking media, and all other poultry rolls shall reach an internal temperature of at least 160° F prior to being removed.

Trichinae Control. Pork products that are not customarily cooked in the home or elsewhere before being consumed must be subject to an approved treatment for destruction of trichinae. The treatment shall consist of heating, refrigerating, or curing according to section 318.10 of the regulations (see page 66 following).

Inspection Responsibilities—Knowledge of Regulations and Proce-

dures. Inspection knowledge of regulations and procedures should be adequate to carry out inspection responsibilities of assignment.

Knowledge of Management Controls. The inspector must be knowledgeable of management's practices in all areas of his assignment. The inspector must be knowledgeable of procedures and controls used by management in the manufacture and formulation of all finished products.

Application and Use of Inspection Procedures. The inspector must have the ability to apply procedural requirements to all phases of processes being conducted in his area of assignment to the extent that products are in compliance.

Control of Inedible, Condemned, and Restricted Products.

1. *Inedible* materials should be placed in marked containers under the plant and inspector's control until effectively denatured or rendered incapable for use as human food or until packaged and identified as food not for human consumption.
2. *Condemned* material should be under the inspector's control until properly denatured.
3. *Restricted* products should be under the inspector's supervision or control until rendered capable for use as human food.

Adequacy of Corrective Action. The inspector should take immediate action to correct deficiencies in all phases of the operation within his purview.

Security of Brands, Certificates, and Seals. All brands and devices used for marking articles with the inspection legend, self-locking seals, official certificates, or other accountable items shall be kept under adequate security such as lock or seal, and an up-to-date inventory shall be maintained of such security items (does not include printed labels).

Sampling and Interpretation of Laboratory Results.

1. Inspectors should make use of the laboratories to check on various products even though the primary control is vested in the establishment by the inspector.
2. Samples must be properly identified from the time they are taken until they reach the laboratory.
3. Information on forms which accompany the sample must be fully explanatory and include the name of the product as it will appear on the label, list of ingredients in the order of their percentages at the start of preparation, and establishment from which the product originated.

4. All procedures in sampling shall be so carried out as to provide the laboratory with as nearly representative a sample as is possible under practical operating conditions.
5. Ground samples must be prepared without delay in a manner that will assure a true representative sample for analysis. Interpretation of laboratory results will be made in accordance with published standards, or criteria specified in the *Meat and Poultry Inspection Manual*.

III. Sanitation

Preoperative and Operational Sanitation Throughout Establishments—Floors, Walls, Ceilings. Floors shall be free of an accumulation of fats, blood, and other foreign material. Walls must be free of dirt, mold, blood, scaling paint, and other contaminants. Ceilings and overhead must be free of dust, scaling paint, scaling plaster, mold, rust, condensation, leaks, etc.

—Equipment. All equipment must be in good condition and free from contaminants, i.e., rust, dust, dried blood, scrap meat, grease, etc. The following equipment must be sanitized after use on each carcass.

1. *Cattle.* Brisket saw, weasand rods, front shank tie-down chains, and dehorning equipment.
2. *Calves.* Brisket saw or cleaver.
3. *Swine.* Knife or other tools used to partly sever the head, and brisket splitting device, saw or cleaver, if carcass-splitting occurs before viscera inspection is completed.

—Personnel, Clothing, and Personal Equipment.

1. Establishment employees shall wear clean and washable or disposable outer clothing. Street clothing should be properly covered. The wearing of sleeveless garments that would permit the exposure of the underarm should not be permitted. Suitable head coverings applicable to both sexes shall be worn to adequately cover the hair. Program employees must appear neat and clean and demonstrate good working and sanitary practices expected of food inspection employees.
2. All personnel will wash their hands as often as necessary to prevent product contamination, and always after returning from toilet rooms. The use of tobacco in any form, spitting, and smoking are not permitted in rooms where edible product is handled. Any practice which may be considered insanitary is prohibited.
3. Personnel equipment (knives, scabbards, steels, tool boxes, gloves, etc.) must be kept in a sanitary condition at all times.

—*Employee Welfare Facilities, e.g., Lunchroom, Locker, and Toilet Facilities.* Dressing rooms equipped with lockers or suitable alternate devices, toilet rooms (showers in meat slaughter plant), urinals, and other than hand-operated wash basins with soap and towels are required. Toilet rooms and toilet room vestibules, which shall be separated from adjoining dressing rooms, shall have solid, self-closing doors. These areas shall be free of odor, properly maintained, and kept clean at all times. Small establishments can refer to guidelines in *Federal Facilities Requirements for Existing Small Meat Plants.*

—*Coolers, Rails, Hooks, Drains, and Equipment.*

1. Equipment in coolers shall be free of corrosion, rust, dust, dry blood, scrap meat, and accumulation of fat. Also, overhead pipes, beams, and light fixtures as well as ceilings and walls must be free of contaminants. Walls and ceilings should be free of mold and condensation.
2. Rails must be clean, free of flaking paint, excessive oils and grease, rust, etc. Hooks must be clean and in good repair.
3. Equipment must be clean, in good repair, and free of debris.
4. All drains and gutters shall be properly installed with approved traps and vents.

—*Inedible and Condemned Rooms.*

1. *Meat.* The area and equipment of inedible or condemned products handling shall be adequate for the quantity of product. It shall be separate from the edible products department and properly maintained. An acceptable area for truck sanitizing shall be available.
2. *Poultry.* Refuse facilities shall be entirely separate from other rooms in the establishment. They shall be properly constructed and vented, drained as required, and kept in good repair. Acceptable water connections for cleanup shall be provided.

—*Offal Rooms and Coolers—Facilities and Equipment.* Coolers shall be free of condensation, and floors, walls, and ceilings shall be free of the accumulation of dry blood, fat, scrap meat, mold, dirt and dust, and nuisances. Chutes, tables, pans, etc., must be constructed of rust resistant materials and maintained in a clean and acceptable manner.

—*Offal Rooms and Coolers—Condensation.* Condensation should be controlled to the extent that product is not contaminated.

—*Product Handling.*

1. The product shall be handled in a clean and acceptable manner.

Cooked, ready-to-eat products shall be handled in accordance with part 8.54 of the *Meat and Poultry Inspection Manual*. Raw meat, emulsions, and finished perishable products shall be stored at a room temperature of 50° F or lower (poultry, 40° F) and be accessible to inspection.

2. Finished frozen products shall be maintained at a frozen state, reasonably free of overhead frost, and be accessible to inspection.
3. Inventory of nonmeat material, where applicable—approved by the Federal Food and Drug Administration—properly identified. Product received only at specified area until reviewed by inspector. Nonmeat approval stickers are to be applied as applicable.
4. A suitable compartment or refrigerated area for holding return product pending disposition shall be equipped for sealing in order to maintain security.
5. Well-arranged and adequate facilities for handling inedible and condemned material must be provided. Layout must be such that will allow positive control of condemned materials.
6. Unpackaged custom products shall be held separately from inspected products (separate rail, racks, etc.)
7. A thorough cleanup and the sanitizing of equipment are required after slaughter or processing of custom exempt product prior to resuming handling of inspected product.
8. Viscera separation and product handling shall be conducted in a sanitary manner. Community baths are forbidden for all products. Paunches must be emptied without contaminating outer surfaces. Accumulation of offal is not permitted. Pork hearts must be opened completely and all blood clots removed. Pork stomachs, chitterlings, and/or ruffle fat must be clean and free of ingesta or any other contaminants.

Carcass Cleanliness and Prevention of Contamination (Sanitary Dressing Procedures).

—*Head Handling: Cattle.* Head and corresponding carcass shall be identified by duplicating numbered tags or by other acceptable means, and removed in a manner to avoid soilage with rumen and contents. Horns and all pieces of hide shall be removed before washing the outer surfaces of the head.

—*Head Handling: Sheep and Goats.* Heads must be gushed and washed in a cabinet if they are being saved for edible purposes.

—*Carcass Preparation: Swine.* The carcass shall be free of hair and scurf after passing through the scalding and dehairing equipment, and the hind feet should be clean of hair and scurf before being gambrelled. If hogs are dipped in rosin, the nostrils and mouth shall be closed with rubber bands or other acceptable means prior to dipping. No shaving is permitted after the head is dropped.

—*Carcass Preparation: Calves.* Calves may be showered before stunning to aid in washing the hide, and must be washed clean before any incisions (except stick wounds) are made.

—*Carcass Skinning: Cattle.* The area of the skinning bed shall be acceptably clean before the carcass is lowered; the head skin shall be manipulated so that the neck is protected; the front and hind feet are removed before any other incision; the carcass shall be removed from the skinning bed in a manner to prevent contamination; lactating udders must be removed in a way to prevent soilage of carcass with udder contents; the supramammary lymph nodes shall be left attached to the carcass until inspection is completed; the dropping of bung should be made part of rumping operations; the rectum must be tied and the bladder tied or removed to prevent contamination.

—*Carcass Skinning: Calves.* The establishment has the responsibility for skinning and handling calf carcasses in a sanitary manner. When skinning operations start, the entire carcass should be skinned.

NOTE: In cases where the establishment handles "hide-on" carcasses, the operation shall be conducted in a sanitary manner. Hair-to-carcass contact is not permitted. Calf carcasses skinned after chilling must be examined closely to detect injection lesions, foreign bodies, parasites, bruises, or other pathology. All abnormal tissue must be removed.

—*Carcass Skinning: Sheep and Goats.* All operations in removing the pelt shall be done in a manner to prevent contamination of the carcass.

—*Carcass Evisceration.* This shall be done without contaminating carcasses or organs. The rectum must be tied to prevent soilage. Viscera shall be presented in an orderly manner to facilitate inspection.

—*Carcass Washing.* All carcasses must be thoroughly and properly washed.

—*Slaughter, Scalding, and Picking: Poultry*

1. *Procedures.* A continuous intake of water must be sufficient to maintain acceptably clean scalding water and provide a mini-

mum overflow of one quart of water per bird per minute. There shall be a complete removal of hair and feathers with a final wash of potable water.

2. *Product Washing.* The product shall be effectively washed inside and out to remove excess blood, loose tissue particles, or any foreign material. Contamination of any tissue, other than the external skin surface, shall be removed by trimming. All product must be clean before being chilled.

3. Carcasses shall be protected against possible contamination from floor cleanup or any fixed objects.

IV. Potable Water

Potable. Potable water supply must be tested and certified adequate and be amply distributed to all parts of the plant for cleanup, etc.

Vacuum Breakers. Vacuum breakers of an acceptable type shall be provided on waterlines connected to various equipment, where necessary, to prevent contamination of waterlines by back-siphonage.

Ice Shall Be from Acceptable Source. Ice shall be made from potable water, certified by appropriate local or state health agency, and handled and stored in a manner to avoid contamination. Block ice shall be washed immediately before crushing.

Nonpotable Water. Use of nonpotable water shall be limited to prescribed areas with adequate identification of such lines.

V. Sewage and Waste Disposal Control

System Approval. The disposal system must be approved by local or state health authorities for official plants (not required for exempt plants, since it is a condition of a grant of inspection). If there is no local or state agency with jurisdiction or if the system is hooked directly into municipal lines, documentation should be provided.

Onsite Handling. Onsite handling must be acceptable—no accumulation, rodent harborage, nuisance, nor sanitary problems being created.

VI. Pest Control

No Evidence of Insects or Rodents in or Around Premises. Necessary measures must be taken to control and eliminate insect and rodent pests in and around the plant.

Approved Insecticides and Rodenticides to Be Used. Only approved insecticides and rodenticides may be used and must be applied in an approved manner.

VII. Condemned and Inedible Material Control

Adequate Measures Must Be Taken for Denaturing, Identifying, or Sealing Restricted or Condemned and Inedible Material—Dead on Arrival Livestock and Poultry.

1. *Livestock carcasses* must be immediately tagged "U.S. Condemned" and, if not tanked on the premises, denatured by injection or freely slashing and denaturing.
2. *Poultry carcasses* must be placed in containers marked "U.S. Condemned" and effectively denatured.

—*Condemned.* Animals condemned on ante-mortem shall be tagged "U.S. Condemned," withheld from slaughter, and destroyed to prevent their use for food purposes. Carcasses and/or parts condemned upon post-mortem must be under control of the inspector until tanked or properly denatured and disposed of.

—*Inedible.* Inedible material is to be handled in a prompt and efficient manner under the inspector's supervision or control, making use of properly marked inedible containers until tanked or otherwise properly denatured and disposed of, or packaged and identified as food other than for humans.

Miscellaneous (Federal Plants Only)

Safety: Facilities and Equipment. Adequate facilities and equipment shall be provided or so constructed as to prevent and minimize safety hazards.

Safety: Practices and Procedures. The inspector shall take proper safety precautions during the performance of his duties, including the use of required safety devices such as helmets, knife guards, etc. He shall be alert to recognize hazards to himself and employees.

THE MARKS OF FEDERAL AND STATE INSPECTION

Each establishment under Federal or state inspection is granted an official number which appears on the inspection stamp and identifies the product wherever found.

This is the stamp put on meat carcasses. It is only stamped on the major cuts of the carcass, so it may not appear on the roast or steak you buy.

You will find this mark on every prepackaged processed meat product — soups to spreads — that has been federally inspected.

This is the mark used on federally inspected fresh or frozen poultry or processed poultry products.

Fig. 3.1–Examples of Federal inspection stamps.

Fig. 3.2—An example of *one* state's inspection stamp.

THE COST OF MEAT INSPECTION

Meat is a highly perishable food that takes 25 to 30 cents of our food dollar. Unlike any other food, meat is very much like the human body. Animals are subject to many of the same diseases as man. For our protection, we must have rigid standards of inspection of the health of each animal and its products and the sanitary conditions under which it is processed. Who should pay for this inspection? Some say the meat packer (processor); others say Uncle Sam. If it is the packer, the added cost will be reflected in the price of the product and we pay by proxy.

Back in 1947, Congress included a provision in the USDA appropriation bill to pass along the cost of Federal inspection to packers and processors. Federally inspected plants were required to pay for the service on the basis of a set charge of $89.60 per inspector-week with the Meat Inspection Division designating the time for inspection. Inspection plants were required to post a payment bond equivalent to 10 times the total weekly fee which they were to be charged. In addition to the set charge, there was a per-man-hour overtime charge of $2.58 for Monday through Friday and $1.64 for holidays.

This shift of the cost of meat inspection from the government to the packer was in effect until the passage of the Kem bill (S2256), when the cost reverted again to the USDA, effective July 1, 1948. In 1973, the meat packing industry reimbursed the government for overtime or special services only, at a base time rate of $10.24 per hour. Politically or otherwise, a one-year trial was sufficient.

Probably the main reason why shifting the cost of inspection to the packer did not succeed was the fact that those who did not have Federal inspection were able to undersell those who had to bear the cost of inspection.

Even with the inflated prices of this decade (the seventies), the cost of meat inspection for each consumer remains amazingly low, somewhere between 2 and 3 cents per month.

Our Federal tax dollars support the Federal inspection system.

Federal monies also currently support 50% of each state's inspection system, except in those 10 states which have no state system and are thus supported 100% by Federal monies. There is presently a bill in Congress which would raise the Federal support of the state systems to 80%. Many processors feel this support is necessary in order to retain state inspection systems. The alternative, which looks desirable to some state legislatures and governors interested in balancing their states' budgets, is to forego state inspection, turn it over to the Federal, and thus save all of the state cost, be it the 50% now required, or the 20% proposed.

VIOLATION OF WHOLESOME MEAT ACT

Violation involving intent to defraud or any distribution or attempted distribution of an article that is adulterated shall make the person or persons representing a firm or corporation subject to imprisonment for not more than three years, or a fine of not more than $10,000, or both.

THE MEAT INSPECTOR

APHIS personnel are divided into several classifications: (1) professional inspectors, administrators, laboratory scientists, etc., trained in veterinary science, chemistry, microbiology, meat science, and related disciplines who have passed required civil service examinations and (2) non-professional or lay inspectors who are required to pass a civil service examination and are designated as Grade 1 and Grade 2.

EXEMPTIONS

The requirements of the Wholesome Meat Act and the regulations for inspection do not apply to the following.

1. The slaughtering by any individual of livestock of his own raising, and the preparation by him, and transportation in commerce of the carcasses, parts thereof, meat and meat food products of such livestock exclusively for use by him and members of his household and his nonpaying guests and employees.
2. The custom slaughter by any person of cattle, sheep, swine, or goats delivered by the owner thereof for such slaughter, and the preparation by such slaughterer, and transportation in commerce of the carcasses, parts thereof, meat and meat food products of such livestock, exclusively for use, in the household of

such owner, by him and members of his household and his nonpaying guests and employees, nor to the custom preparation by any person of carcasses, parts thereof, meat or meat food products derived from the slaughter by any individual of cattle, sheep, swine, or goats of his own raising or from game animals, delivered by the owner thereof for such custom preparation, and transportation in commerce of such custom prepared articles, exclusively for use in the household of such owner, by him and members of his household and his nonpaying guests and employees.

However, if custom operations are conducted in an official establishment, all of the provisions of the act shall apply to such establishment, including the following.

a. If the custom operator prepares or handles any products for sale, they are kept separate and apart from the custom prepared products at all times while the latter are in his custody.

b. The custom prepared products are plainly marked "Not for Sale" immediately after being prepared, and are kept so identified until delivered to the owner.

c. If exempted custom slaughtering or other preparation of products is conducted in an official establishment, all facilities and equipment in the official establishment used for such custom operations shall be thoroughly cleaned and sanitized before they are used for preparing any products for sale.

d. The exempted custom prepared products shall be prepared and handled in accordance with the provisions of the act and shall not be adulterated.

3. Operations of types traditionally and usually conducted at retail stores and retail-type establishments in any state or organized territory, for sale in normal retail quantities, or service of such articles to consumers at such establishments. Operations of types traditionally and usually conducted at retail stores and restaurants are the following.

a. Cutting up, slicing, and trimming carcasses, halves, quarters, or wholesale cuts into retail cuts such as steaks, chops, and roasts, and freezing such cuts.

b. Grinding and freezing products made from meat.

c. Curing, cooking, smoking, or other preparation of products, except slaughtering, rendering, or refining of livestock fat or the retort-processing of canned products.

d. Breaking bulk shipments of products.

e. Wrapping or rewrapping products.

f. Any quantity or product purchased by a consumer from a particular retail supplier shall be deemed to be a normal retail quantity if the quantity so purchased does not in the aggregate exceed one-half carcass. The following amounts of product will be accepted as representing one-half carcass of the species identified.

	One-half Carcass (lbs.)
Cattle	300
Calves	37.5
Sheep	27.5
Swine	100
Goats	25

g. A retail store is any place of business where the sales of a product are made to consumers only; at least 75% in terms of dollar value, of total sales of a product represents sales to household consumers, and the total dollar value of sales of product to consumers other than household consumers does not exceed $18,000 per year; only Federally or state inspected and passed product is handled or used in the preparation of any product.

THE KOSHER STAMP

The Humane Slaughter Act of 1960 does not apply to *ritual* slaughter methods such as Kosher killing where the live animal is suspended (unstunned) and bled by an incision across the throat (cut throat) made by a specially trained rabbi or shohet. The knife has a 14-inch blade and is razor sharp. The throat of the animal must be washed free of any grit or foreign material so it will not nick the knife. The shohet makes no inspection of the carcass prior to placing the Kosher stamp in script or block letters on the carcass. The stamp carries no implication of the

Fig. 3.3—Kosher stamp.

health or grade of the animal; only that it is proper, according to the law, and clean.

The law referred to is found in Leviticus 17:14, which states, "You shall not eat the blood of any creature, for the life of every creature is its blood; whoever eats it shall be cut off."

The explanation given by those of the Jewish faith as to why they consume forequarter meat primarily is because it contains less blood than the hindquarter and is more easily veined.

ANIMAL DISEASES AND OTHER LOSS FACTORS

Anyone doing a limited amount of slaughtering, whether it be for home use or for subsequent sale, should be able to recognize unhealthy or unthrifty animals and know something about the effect of the more common ailments on the quality and value of carcasses. Whenever there is any doubt concerning the health of an animal, a veterinarian should be consulted.

Pregnancy

Animals should not be slaughtered in the advanced stages of pregnancy. The physiological condition of the female is disturbed and the flesh is not normal.

Accidental Death

A healthy animal that is killed through accident, suffocates from bloat, or dies from a heart puncture caused by a nail or wire, is fit for food providing someone is there to cut the throat and bleed the animal. In case of a poor bleed, the meat can be soaked overnight in a weak salt solution which will draw out the remainder of the blood.

If a kerosene drench is given to an animal suffering from bloat, and the animal suffocates 10 to 15 minutes later, time and trouble can be saved by burying or tanking the animal, unless the consumer relishes a kerosene taste in meat.

Trichina

The microscopic parasite *Trichinella spiralis*, or trichina, is not a common parasite in this country and is easily controlled. The encapsulated larvae are found in the muscles of rats, dogs, cats, swine, and humans. Man acquires the parasite by eating the improperly prepared meat of infected swine. The swine receive their infection by eating infected rats or uncooked or partially cooked viscera or flesh of infected animals, generally through the medium of garbage.

The encysted larvae are liberated in the stomach of the host and pass on to the small intestine where they reach sexual maturity in a few days. After mating, the female penetrates the lining of the intestine and gives birth to young larvae which are carried by the blood stream to the striated muscles where they attain maturity after several weeks. Encapsulation then takes place and if the cycle is not repeated, the larvae in the cysts eventually die.

Due to the widespread improvement of sanitary conditions in our large hog-producing areas and state and Federal legislation requiring all garbage to be cooked before being fed to swine, the likelihood of any trichina infection is very small. Yet, the incidence in the United States is greater than in many other countries (Table 3.5), and remains a problem for complete consumer acceptance of pork in this country.

A trichinoscope (microscope), which can detect one trichina/gram, has been used in Germany since 1866 to determine the presence of trichina in pork muscle. A digestion system developed in the United States can detect one trichina/45-50 grams of diaphragm. Thus, in comparing prevalence in the United States with other countries to be an equal basis, all infections of less than one trichina per gram are dis-

Table 3.5—Comparative Prevalence Rates for Trichinosis in Swine[1]

Countries	Prevalence	Rate per Million Swine
United States	0.031^2	310
Denmark	0.0	0
Poland	0.012	120
Federal Republic of Germany	0.00005	0.5
Romania	0.026	260
USSR		
Moscow area	0.0033	33
Byelorussia	0.01	100
Lithuania	0.00033	3.3
Chile	0.20	2,000
Mexico	0.30	3,000

1. Dr. William J. Zimmerman, Livestock Conservation, Inc., Annual Meeting Report, 1972.

2. Adjusted for equivalency to microscopic method as used in other countries. Actual prevalence = 0.125%.

regarded (Table 3.5). Most recently, breakthroughs in antibody methodology have allowed the development of a rather quick (15 minutes) and sensitive (many times more sensitive than the trichinoscope) blood test, which may provide an avenue for the elimination of trichinae from U.S. pork.

Wildlife has received increased attention in the United States with at least 40 species having been reported as natural hosts. Bears are gaining significance as sources of human infection—7.8% of reported human cases during the past five years were attributed to ingestion of bear meat.

The following processing treatments to destroy trichinae are prescribed by USDA, APHIS.

1. Heating to a temperature not lower than 137° F.
2. a. Freezing at temperature indicated.

Temperature	6" Thick or Less	More Than 6" but Less Than 27" Thick
(°F)	(days)	(days)
5	20	30
−10	10	20
−20	6	12

   b. Internal product temperature at center of meat pieces.

Temperature	Hours
(° F)	
0	96
−5	72
−10	56
−15	43
−20	30
−25	17

3. Curing. Five methods for curing sausages and three methods for curing hams and shoulders are spelled out in *Meat and Poultry Regulations* (USDA, APHIS).

Generally, the combined effects of time and temperature, i.e., a lower temperature requiring a longer time and vice versa, are utilized to destroy any trichinae.

Swine (Porcine) Stress Syndrome (PSS)

"Some pigs are unable to withstand the stress of management procedures that involve handling and crowding, transportation or sudden environmental change. When these pigs are subjected to such stressful situations, they show a reaction that often results in death.

"The term Porcine Stress Syndrome (PSS) was coined in the late 1960's by Dr. Topel of Iowa State University to describe the signs and symptoms that characterize these animals. The following sequence of events is typical, if a pig suffering from PSS is subjected to stress. The pig may be difficult to move and shows signs of trembling or muscle tremors. These initial symptoms are followed by irregular blotching of the skin, labored breathing and increased body temperature. The terminal stage of the syndrome is total collapse and a shock-like death of the animal. The monetary loss due to PSS is real in view of the increasing number of reported sudden or unknown deaths in animals subjected to stress.

"A recent survey revealed that an estimated one-third of U.S. hog producers have encountered the *Porcine Stress Syndrome* (PSS) problem. The PSS condition is usually associated with unexplained swine death following stress and with low quality or *Pale, Soft and Exudative* (PSE) pork. Dark, firm and dry (DFD) pork may also result from the PSS condition. The PSE condition has been observed in 18% of the hams processed by a major U.S.A. pork packer during a 12-month study. Findings indicate an increase in these conditions in the past few years. A recent survey has revealed that the PSS-PSE incidence is relatively high among modern large-scale operations utilizing partial or total confinement systems. These observations suggest threats to the production of a quality pork product that will maintain consumer acceptance."[7]

Jowl Abscesses

Packers and other interested members of Livestock Conservation, Inc. (LCI) became aware of a high incidence of jowl abscesses in slaughter hogs which had been increasing at a straight-line rate from 1948 to 1965. A national survey conducted by LCI in 1963 indicated an annual product loss at the processing level of $12,000,000.

At the time of the serious questioning in 1962, there was no generally accepted control. In fact, there was little agreement or recognition of what was actually causing the problem. The LCI Swine Abscess Committee coordinated the findings of four state research groups and one

---

7. Pork Quality Symposium, University of Wisconsin, 1972.

USDA group and prepared and distributed a leaflet containing suggested control measures. The *Group E Streptococcus* was found to be the principle cause of jowl abscesses.

"Parts condemned for abscesses" in Federally-inspected hogs for the fiscal year ended June, 1972, were at the lowest rate in 22 years, only slightly more than half of the rate of the 1965 peak.

Swine Dysentery

According to a 1972 LCI national swine dysentery survey, 8.4 per cent of the nation's swine herds experienced the swine dysentery problem in 1972. And, the herd incidence rate of producers marketing 500 or more swine annually was twice that of those marketing a lesser volume.

The survey also indicated that the herd frequency of swine dysentery problems was almost 2½ times higher for farms involving the purchase of feeder pigs than those not reporting such involvement.

Death losses were found to be an estimated 5.9 pigs per 1,000 marketed, the bulk of these occurring prior to 150 pounds of weight. On the basis of 1972 slaughter volumes and live values, the death loss alone would be in excess of $20,000,000 annually. To this could be added a projected loss of efficiency in added feed costs of another $90,000,000 based on 1972 costs. Currently, these losses would be materially higher.

Brucellosis

"The incidence of brucellosis has decreased over the past years; this disease is still an economic drain to the livestock industry. The cost to the producer from abortions and delayed breeding is sizable, but many times unrecognized. Packers are affected because brucellosis reduces the supply of slaughter animals which increases their operating costs.

"The other area of concern is the health hazard from brucellosis, primarily to producers and workers in packinghouses. I'm sure that anyone who has had undulant fever can tell you it's not pleasant. In many cases it is a long drawn-out recovery. There are several packers who have had a large number of employees infected with brucellosis at one time. This has been costly and troublesome to them in terms of hiring and training substitute employees, down time and additional expenditures."[8]

"In 1972, a total of 200 cases of brucellosis in humans were reported

---

8. Donald C. Utterback, LCI, Annual Meeting Report, 1973.

as compared with 190 cases reported in 1971. Thirty-five states reported cases in 1972 compared with 35 in 1971 and 34 in 1970. Five states (California, Georgia, Iowa, Oklahoma, Virginia) reported 53 per cent of the years total cases.

"Brucellosis remains a disease that affects young and middle-aged adults, primarily males. Males between the ages of 20 and 60 years accounted for 116 (75 per cent) of the 156 cases where age and sex were reported; 127 of the 156 patients (82 per cent) were males.

"One-hundred-seven (69 per cent) of the 156 reports recorded swine as the most probable source of infection, 24 (15 per cent) mentioned cattle, and 10 (6 per cent) mentioned cattle and swine.

"In 1972, 108 of the 156 case reports received (69 per cent) were on individuals working in packing plants. Swine were the source of infection in 89 of these 108 cases (82 per cent). Most of these people worked in the 'kill area,' although others worked in cooler rooms and in finished-product preparation areas. Several infections occurred in personnel such as maintenance men and mechanics who did not actually handle raw meat.

"A review of brucellosis cases in the meat processing plant workers from 1965 to 1971 points up the current trend in the epidemiology of brucellosis. Ninety-six per cent of the 770 cases reported during this period occurred in men, and 68 per cent of all patients were between 20 and 39 years of age. The single most probable source of infection was swine in 64 per cent of the 770 cases, and *Brucella suis* was identified in 67 per cent of the isolates from blood and other clinical specimens taken from these patients during this period."[9]

Tuberculosis

"Various types of tubercle bacilli exist, and they most commonly infect a single species of animal. These bacilli are capable, however, of causing disease in a wide range of hosts—including man and his domestic animals. But you are concerned primarily with three types: human, bovine, and avian.

"The human type tubercle bacilli are usually associated with the familiar lung disease in man. They can also cause disease in other parts of the body and in other animals, including cattle, hogs, dogs, cats, canaries, and monkeys.

"The bovine bacilli are usually associated with tuberculosis in cattle. Many other species including man may also become afflicted—if they

---

9. Richard L. Parker, LCI, Annual Meeting Report, 1973.

come in contact with infected cattle or drink unpasteurized milk from infected cattle.

"The avian bacilli infect chickens primarily but they may cause the disease in varying degrees in a wide variety of birds and mammals.

"Hogs are susceptible to infection by all three types of tubercle bacilli. Odds are against hogs becoming infected with human or bovine types in the United States, however. This is due primarily to an extensive campaign to eradicate bovine tuberculosis. The prevalence of this disease has been reduced to less than 0.1 per cent among U. S. cattle. Laws requiring the cooking of all garbage before it can be fed to hogs have also played a part.

"Avian tuberculosis, on the other hand, is still a major cause of condemnation of pork at slaughter houses."[10]

In February, 1972, new meat inspection regulations went into effect pertaining to tuberculosis.

1. *Carcasses Passed Without Restriction*
   a. To be passed without restriction, a cattle carcass must be found to be free of TB lesions during post-mortem inspection and not identified as a tuberculin test reactor.
   b. A swine carcass may be passed without restriction as long as the lesions are localized and limited to one primary site Primary sites are cervical, mesenteric and mediastinal lymph nodes.

2. *Carcasses Passed for Cooking*
   a. A cattle carcass with a localized lesion of tuberculosis in any location must be passed for cooking.
   b. A swine carcass with a localized lesion of tuberculosis in any two primary sites must be passed for cooking. Primary sites include cervical, mesenteric, and mediastinal lymph nodes. Therefore, a lesion in the head and intestinal tract would result in that carcass being passed for cooking.
   c. Tuberculin test reactors must be passed for cooking even if they are free of tuberculosis lesions or when such lesions are localized.

3. *Condemnations*
   Causes for condemnation are basically the same as the present regulations with one exception. Lesions of TB in the hepatic lymph node which drains the liver indicate the condition is generalized and the carcass must be condemned.

---

10. *Avian Tuberculosis in Hogs,* USDA, APHIS PA-775, 1972.

An LCI survey conducted from March 1972, through February 1973, indicated:

1. That 11.5 carcasses were condemned per 100,000 total slaughter (1 per 8,695 hogs).
2. That 84.3 carcasses were "Passed for Cooking" per 100,000 total slaughter (1 per 1,186 hogs) resulting in a $6,581,588 estimated total loss for all TB infected swine. The loss due to "Passed for Cooking" is estimated to be ¾ of the market value of the animal. "Passed for Cooking" requires holding the product at 170° F for 30 minutes.

Cattle Grubs

"Two kinds of cattle grubs are found in the United States.

"The common cattle grub[11] occurs in all 48 adjacent States. The northern cattle grub[12] is abundant in Canada and the Northern United States, and occurs as far south as an imaginary line through southern California and the northern parts of Arizona, Oklahoma, Tennessee, and South Carolina.

"Except for an infestation first reported in Chile in 1959, cattle grubs are confined to the Northern Hemisphere.

Life Cycle

"The adult insects (heel flies) lay their eggs on the heels, legs, and other body parts of cattle. The eggs hatch into larvae (grubs) in 3 or 4 days.

"Soon after hatching, the young grubs burrow into the skin and slowly work their way through the animal's body until they reach the gullet (common cattle grub) or spinal canal (northern cattle grub). The grubs remain in the gullet or spinal canal several months before starting another migration, this time to the muscles in the animal's back.

"When the grubs reach the animal's back, they settle just beneath the hide and cut breathing holes through it. At this time, you may notice swellings, often called warbles or wolves, forming beneath the hide. The grubs remain in the animal's back for about 6 weeks. During this period, they gradually enlarge their breathing holes.

"When full grown, the spiny grubs work their way out through the breathing holes and drop to the ground, where they change to pupae.

---

11. *Hypoderma lineatum.*
12. *H. bovis.*

Three to 10 weeks later, the time depending upon the temperature, the adult heel flies emerge from the pupal cases and are ready for mating and egg laying. The entire life cycle takes about a year, 8 to 11 months of which are spent as grubs in the bodies of cattle.

Losses

"Cattle grubs probably cause greater losses than any other pest of cattle. Besides damaging meat and hides by their burrowing, they lower beef cattle gains and milk production of dairy cattle throughout the year. Beef cattle producers and dairymen often fail to notice the hidden toll these insects take, but profit losses are estimated in the millions of dollars each year.

"The losses begin when heel flies lay their eggs on the cattle. The heel flies cause no pain to cattle, but they frighten the animals and make them difficult to manage. When attacked, cattle run about wildly with their tails in the air, and are often injured in this wild stampeding.

"Cattle find some relief from heel flies by standing for hours in deep shade or water. Failure to graze during this period causes reduced milk production and subnormal weight gains.

"At slaughter, some of the meat must be trimmed from expensive cuts and discarded. Tissues underlying the warbles are yellowish and gelatinlike. The butcher calls this "licked beef," a material that must be removed from the carcass. Besides the actual loss of meat, the carcass is downgraded, and brings a lower price. Trim loss on heavily infested carcasses may range from $5 to $7.

"The usefulness of a grubby, perforated hide for leather is reduced, and its sale value is greatly lowered.

Control

"Six systemic insecticides, famphur, fenthion, ronnel, coumaphos, trichlorfon, and crufomate,[13] give excellent control of grubs in beef cattle. Control in dairy cattle is more difficult because these systemics can only be used on nonlactating dairy animals within a specified time before freshening.

"The insecticides are called systemics because they are distributed inside the body of the animal. The circulatory system carries the insecticide to the site where the grubs occur."[14]

---

13. Trade names are used solely for the purpose of providing specific information. Mention of trade names does not constitute a guarantee or warranty of the products named.

14. *How to Control Cattle Grubs*, U.S. Dept. of Agriculture, Leaflet No. 527, 1972.

Shipping Losses

The growers of our nation's meat supply face innumerable problems in raising the animals for market. The fight against birth losses, disease, predatory animals, the elements—heat, cold, and drought—nutrient and vitamin deficiencies, and against the dishonest side of man himself is a continuous one. The finished animals go to market but it has been estimated that they represent only 60% of the pigs, 85% of the cattle, and 80% of the sheep that were born. A heavy toll is lost in this first battle of production.

The National Livestock Loss Prevention Board, organized in 1934 and reorganized in 1952 under the name of Livestock Conservation, Inc.,[15] for the purpose of studying the causes of livestock losses on the farm and on the way to market, has unearthed shocking figures to prove that man is his own worst enemy. He fails to fight disease and parasites as he should, he is negligent in removing hazards on the premises, and he forgets that the hide or skin is not an armour plate to protect a product that he worked long and hard to produce. Those who do the right things find that losses may be caused by those who handle their product and over whom they have no control. The loss in shipping starts on the farm. The precautions to be taken to prevent these losses are as follows:

1. Keep fences, feed racks, and barns in good repair and free from protruding nails and boards.
2. Keep feed lots and barnyards clean and free from trash, machinery, and other obstacles and provide good footing in the barns.
3. Do not crowd animals through narrow gates or runways.
4. Dehorn the cattle.
5. Use a canvas slapper instead of a stick, cane, or whip to herd livestock.
6. Have the truck standards on the outside and see that no sharp objects protrude in the truck.
7. Cover the truck floor with sand to provide a good footing; wet the sand in warm weather, but cover dry sand with bedding in winter.
8. Have cleated floors in loading chutes and see that no nails or sharp objects protrude from the sides.
9. Never get in a hurry when loading.
10. Separate mixed loads with partitions to prevent stock from moving about or trampling each other. A partition is good for both full and partial loads.

15. Livestock Conservation, Inc., Omaha, Nebraska 68107.

Table 3.6—Suggested Loadings for Livestock

Hogs and Calves

Single–Deck Trucks

Floor Length	100 Lbs.	150 Lbs.	175 Lbs.	200 Lbs.	225 Lbs.	250 Lbs.	300 Lbs.	350 Lbs.	400 Lbs.
8 ft.	27	21	19	18	16	14	13	11	9
10 "	33	26	24	22	20	18	16	14	12
12 "	40	31	28	26	24	22	19	17	14
15 "	50	39	36	33	30	27	24	21	17
18 "	60	47	43	40	36	33	28	25	21
20 "	67	52	48	44	40	35	32	28	24
24 "	80	62	57	52	48	44	38	34	28
28 "	93	72	67	61	56	51	44	39	33
30 "	100	77	72	66	60	55	47	42	35
32 "	107	83	76	70	64	58	51	44	38
36 "	120	94	86	79	72	66	57	50	42
42 "	140	109	100	92	84	77	63	55	49

Hogs and Calves

Divide Equally for Double–Deck Trucks

Floor Length	100 Lbs.	150 Lbs.	175 Lbs.	200 Lbs.	225 Lbs.	250 Lbs.	300 Lbs.	350 Lbs.	400 Lbs.
8 ft.	43	33	31	29	27	24	21	18	16
10 "	53	41	38	36	33	30	26	23	20
12 "	63	50	46	43	40	36	31	28	24
15 "	79	62	56	54	50	45	39	34	30
18 "	95	75	70	65	60	55	46	41	36
20 "	105	83	77	72	67	61	52	46	40
24 "	127	100	93	87	80	73	62	55	48
28 "	148	116	109	101	93	86	73	64	56
30 "	158	125	116	108	100	91	78	68	60
32 "	169	133	130	115	107	97	83	73	64
36 "	190	150	140	130	120	110	94	82	72
42 "	220	172	164	151	142	128	109	96	80

(Continued)

Table 3.6 (Continued)

Cattle

Floor Length	450 Lbs.	600 Lbs.	800 Lbs.	1,000 Lbs.	1,200 Lbs.	1,400 Lbs.
8 ft.	8	7	5	4	4	3
10 "	10	8	7	6	5	4
12 "	13	10	8	7	6	5
15 "	16	13	10	9	8	7
18 "	20	16	13	11	9	8
20 "	22	18	14	12	10	9
24 "	27	22	17	15	13	11
28 "	31	25	20	17	15	13
30 "	34	27	22	19	16	14
32 "	36	29	23	20	17	15
36 "	41	33	26	22	19	17
42 "	48	39	31	28	22	20

Sheep

Suggested Load per Deck

Floor Length	60 Lbs.	80 Lbs.	100 Lbs.	120 Lbs.
8 ft.	28	23	20	18
10 "	35	29	26	23
12 "	43	35	31	28
15 "	54	45	40	36
18 "	65	54	48	43
20 "	73	60	54	48
24 "	88	73	65	58
28 "	103	85	76	68
30 "	110	92	81	73
32 "	118	98	87	78
36 "	133	110	98	88
42 "	145	128	115	103

11. Cover front end of slatted trucks with canvas or heavy building paper in winter.
12. Caution driver to avoid sudden stops and starts, make frequent inspection for "downers," and see that animals are not piling up.

The annual loss in handling all classes of livestock that go to slaughter during the year is estimated to amount to over $50,000,000.

CHAPTER 4

Hog Slaughter

GOVERNMENT LIVE HOG GRADE STANDARDS

A more complete discussion of market hog and pork carcass grades appears in Chapter 11, where pictures representing typical live and carcass grades are found.

A system for classifying and grading market hogs was formulated by the United States Department of Agriculture in 1918 for use in the livestock market reporting service. Revisions were made consistent with changes in production and marketing conditions in 1930, 1940, 1949, 1952, 1955, and the most recent in 1968.[1] At that time, the minimum backfat thickness requirement for barrows and gilts for the U.S. No. 1 grade was eliminated, and a new U.S. No. 1 grade was established to properly identify the superior pork carcasses being produced. The former No. 1, No. 2, and No. 3 grades were renamed No. 2, No. 3, and No. 4 respectively. The former Medium and Cull grades were combined and renamed U.S. Utility. Also, the maximum adjustment to actual fat measurements due to superior or inferior muscling was increased from one-half to one full grade.

To assure that the U.S. grades for swine and pork are of maximum benefit to the industry, the grades for slaughter hogs are correlated directly with the grades for pork carcasses. Similarly, the grades for feeder pigs are also correlated with the grades for slaughter hogs. Thus, a U.S. No. 1 feeder pig, for example, can develop into a U.S. No. 1 slaughter hog, which in turn should produce a U.S. No. 1 carcass.

Since sex condition has exerted little if any effect on secondary physical characteristics, barrows and gilts are treated as a single class, and the grade standards are equally applicable to both. The standards have not been made applicable to stags and boars, but a separate measurement standard has been made for sows. The 1968 updating did not

---

1. Marketing Bulletin No. 51, USDA, C & MS, August 1970.

Table 4.1—Market Classes and Grades of Slaughter Hogs[1]

Barrows and Gilts	Sows
U.S. Nos. 1 & 2 180–200 lbs. 200–220 lbs. 220–240 lbs.	U.S. Nos. 1, 2, & 3 270–330 lbs. 330–400 lbs.
U.S. Nos. 2 & 3 180–200 lbs. 200–220 lbs. 220–240 lbs.	U.S. Nos. 2 & 3 400–550 lbs.
U.S. Nos. 3 & 4 240–270 lbs. 270–300 lbs.	
U.S. Nos. 1, 2, & 3 180–200 lbs. 200–220 lbs. 220–240 lbs.	

1. As utilized by the Livestock Division, Agricultural Marketing Service, U.S. Dept. of Agriculture.

apply to sows; thus, U.S. grades for sows remain U.S. No. 1, U.S. No. 2, U.S. No 3, Medium, and Cull.

CHANGE OF GOAL

Hog type has changed several times in the past 50 years. These changes in type were made to increase size, strength of bone, length of body, arch and strength of back, and depth of body-structural characters that increased prolificacy, fecundity, and ability to make rapid and economical gains. This resulted in a change from the small-boned, roly-poly, scruffy type hog to the medium and large type hog. The development of hogs with large bones, long legs, long bodies, great arch of back, and considerable scale went to the point where the ordinary height hog fence was too low and entrances to standard hog houses too small. Poundage was the goal. Lard, during wartime, was as important a product as lean meat. It had no competition.

Hog size was getting out of hand, so type was given another workout, with the result that a medium size edition became popular. Lard was still the shortening. Today the picture has changed. Vegetable shortenings have made heavy inroads on the sale of lard. It was not the fault of lard as a fat but the failure of lard as a shortening when it had to compete against certain qualities that scientific research had given to vegetable shortenings.

In the meantime, the meat packer discovered that a staff of scientists in a properly equipped laboratory is as important to his business as the advertising department. He began to catch up on his home work and make better grades—but he had had a late start. To date, he has produced a new and modern lard that is now the equal, and in some respects the superior, of any vegetable shortening.

The increasing consumer demand for lean pork made another hurdle that had to be taken in stride with the result that a genuine meat type hog has the pole position in this race for fewer calories. The development of the meat type hog in the United States dates from 1934 when the Danish Landrace hog was first introduced. Since then many cross-bred and in-bred lines have made their appearance. Breed associations co-operating with state experiment stations went to work. The "probe" for determining back fat thickness became a popular tool.

To develop this meat type hog, testing stations were set up in different sections of the heavy hog-producing areas where breeders could have litter tests made by adhering to a designed program. In the All-Breed Swine Certification Program, if the two pigs submitted from each litter entered meet the specifications, the sire and dam acquire merit points toward a Lean Meat Certification. The litter mates entered have to meet the following requirements: (1) they must weigh 220 pounds or more in 180 days, (2) the carcass must measure 29.5 inches or more (1st rib to aitchbone) at 220 lbs., (3) the loin eye must have an area of 4.5 square inches or more at 220 lbs., and (4) the carcass must display not more than 1.50 inches of average backfat at 220 lbs. Respective breed registries have established more rigid standards and given recognition to superior performance.

With more widespread cooperation of hog breeders, the consumer hog will arrive. Whether the consumer will stay pleased is another matter. If the pork cuts are lean and tasteless, *No*; if they are lean, tender, juicy, and flavorful, *Yes*. For most, they must have juiciness and flavor; the cook can make them tender.

Priced on Merit

With corn plentiful and low in price, and hogs scarce and high in price, showing a wide corn-hog ratio,[2] it is more profitable to market

---

2. By corn-hog ratio is meant the number of bushels of corn required to equal

the corn as pork. So the feeder shovels in the corn and produces heavy, lardy hogs. As long as the buyer uses the double talk of wanting a meat type hog and yet pays the same price for both, where is the feeder's gain? That is why hogs must be priced on a Merit Basis.

"Double talk" by the livestock buyer has decreased significantly in recent years with the increase in carcass weight and grade selling of livestock of all species. In this system, the producer is paid on the basis of the weight of the carcass and the grade of the carcass. Thus, estimation of carcass merit by the buyer and seller is not the basis for selling, but rather actual carcass value is used. About 37% of all slaughtering plants now buy some animals on a carcass weight and grade basis. Carcass purchases of hogs have increased from 2.6% of total marketings in 1963 to 5.2% in 1972, a slower rate than the increase in carcass sales of cattle and lambs.

Slaughter Pigs

Roasting pigs range in weight from 30 to 60 pounds liveweight and include barrows, gilts, and boars. Since they possess rather similar qualities, they are not graded according to sex. Roasting pigs are not split at the breast nor between the hams. This permits stuffing with a sauerkraut or bread filling without leakage in roasting.

Age and Sex

Barrows and gilts from five to seven months of age produce the highest quality pork. Sows find a ready market and are well suited to packing house needs where a great deal of the meat is incorporated with beef in the manufacture of various sausages. Young sows make desirable pork for farm home consumption where the larger cuts are well suited for large families.

A Good Slaughter Weight

The great demand by the consumer trade for 14- to 17-pound hams and chops averaging six to the pound has made it necessary for hogs to be marketed at weights ranging from 200 to 240 pounds. These weights are more profitable to the grower since it has been demonstrated that growth-weight-gains are cheaper than fat-weight-gains. However, in

---

in value one hundred pounds of live hog. A normal ratio is considered to be 11.4 (the value of 11.4 bushels of corn will be the same as 100 pounds of live market hog) and a ratio above this means cheap corn and high priced hogs with profit to the feeder, whereas a ratio below 11.4 means high priced corn and a low price for hogs or a loss to the feeder.

cases of a food emergency, it is considered desirable to feed them to heavier weights, thereby increasing the poundage of available pork with considerably fewer numbers. The most desirable weight hog for the average farm family is probably 250 to 300 pounds. These heavier weights usually carry more finish and are therefore a juicier, more highly flavored product. The size of the farm family is generally such that the larger hogs can be used more efficiently.

PORK OPERATIONS

Immobilization

The Federal Human Slaughter Act went into effect on July 1, 1960. The act applies to those packers who transact business with Federal agencies. Many states have enacted laws similar to the Federal law. Ritual slaughter methods, such as Kosher killing, are exempt from the act.

The Federal act recognizes three methods of immobilization: (1) the mechanical, (2) the chemical, and (3) the electrical. To comply with the law, the use of any one of the three methods must produce complete unconsciousness with a minimum of excitement and discomfort. The mechanical stunners are the penetrating type and the concussion type. In the former, the captive bolt enters the skull, while in the concussion type, the force is delivered through a mushroom head on the end of the bolt. Blank cartridges with different powder loads for different sized animals are triggered off by contact to propel the bolt into the head. The least costly is the captive bolt pistol which resembles a pistol. The stunning can be administered to the forehead or in back of the poll.

The chemical method employs carbon dioxide gas, which, because it is heavier than air, can be held in a pit with a minimum loss of gas. The hogs ride in individual compartments down an incline into the chamber which holds a concentration of 65% to 75% carbon dioxide. The time of exposure to render the hog unconscious depends upon the size of the animal and the production rate. As the hogs emerge, they may be stuck in the prone position or shackled and stuck on the rail.

In the electrical method, the hogs move along by conveyor to a squeeze box which halts them until the electric probe can be applied to the head for from one to four seconds, depending upon the weight of the hog. A five- to seven-second interval between stunning and sticking is advisable, since a longer time interval may result in blood spattering, i.e., capillary rupture in the muscle causing unsightly blood spots in the meat. The prone bleed is favored to reduce the time lapse.

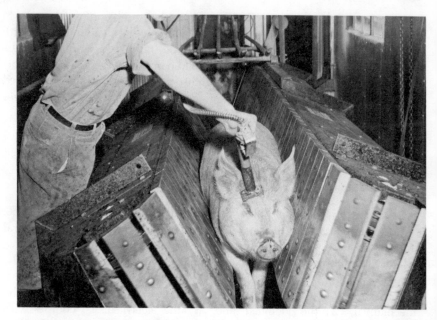

Fig. 4.1—A commercial electric stunner. Hogs are driven into a squeeze whose moving sides propel the subject to the stunner. (Courtesy, Cincinnati Butchers' Supply Co., Cincinnati, Ohio)

The advantages of any of the above methods, aside from the humane factor, are the elimination of excitement, fewer internal ham bruises, safer and better working conditions, more economical operation, and an improved product.

The first state humane slaughter law in the nation that requires the positioning of beef, calves, and sheep for ritual slaughter was passed in Pennsylvania in September 1965, and became effective September 14, 1966. Nothing in the act shall be construed to apply to the farmer while slaughtering his own livestock.

Farmers still go for the rifle. The bullet is aimed at a point in the center of the forehead about one inch higher than the eye or right behind the ear, if the shooting occurs from the side. Extreme caution must be exercised when using live firearms. Furthermore, hog heads become contaminated and unfit for human consumption due to the lead slug entering the head.

Sticking

Hogs may be shackled and hoisted mechanically to a sticking rail after being stunned. Normally, the sticking is done with the hog lying

Fig. 4.2–An inexpensive electric stunner suitable for use in smaller slaughter plants. (University of Illinois photo)

on its side or being held on its back. A proper stick means a fast bleed. A 6-inch sticking knife, sharpened on both sides of the tip, is large enough for the ordinary hog. For large hogs (400 to 600 pounds), the 7-inch blade is desirable. If the hog is suspended, the operator should steady it by placing the flat of his hand on the hog's shoulder (never by grasping a leg) and inserting the knife several inches in front of the breast. With the point of the knife directed toward the tail (this is very important), the operator should give an upward thrust, dipping the point until it strikes the backbone, and then withdraw the knife. Care must be exercised in keeping the knife midway between the shoulders to avoid a shoulder stick. No twisting or cross cutting of the knife is necessary.

The blood yield: 500-lb. hog—12½ lbs.; 390-lb. hog—8½ lbs.; 200-lb. hog—5¼ lbs.; 100-lb. hog—4¾ lbs. Dried blood (10% moisture) yield: 5 lbs. per 1,000 lbs. of live weight.

Aids in Scalding

Sufficient water of the right temperature (150°F ± 5°), the removal of the hog from the water when the hair slips readily, and plenty of elbow grease are necessary for a good, quick job. There are alkalies, however, that can be added to the water to loosen the scurf and make

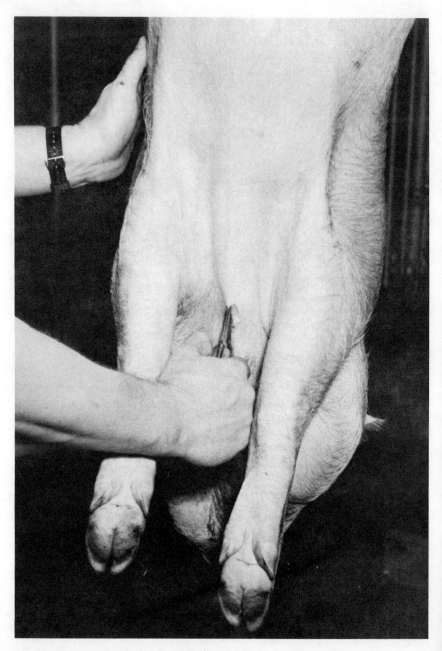

Fig. 4.3—Sticking a hog (suspended).

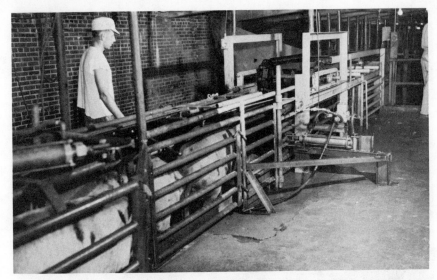

Fig. 4.4—Hogs passing through a lane toward the CO_2 chamber. Hesitant hogs are urged forward by the light application of an electric prod. (Courtesy, G. A. Hormel & Co.)

Fig. 4.5—Hogs emerging from the CO_2 chamber in an immobile and unconscious form after being in the chamber 45 seconds. The attendant is positioning the hogs on the conveyor so the heads are over the bleeding trough. (Courtesy, G. A. Hormel & Co.)

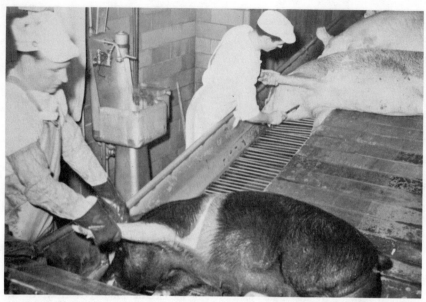

Fig. 4.6—All hogs on the sticking conveyor face in the same direction, backs toward the overhead belt conveyor and head over the bleeding trough. The sticker is about to stick a hog as it is in this position. (Courtesy, G. A. Hormel & Co.)

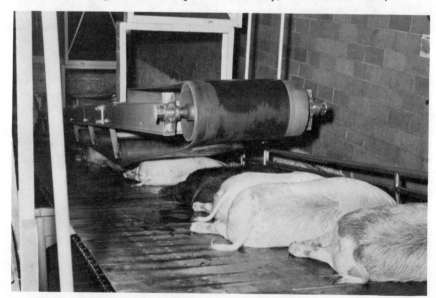

Fig. 4.7—Bled hogs emerging from the double conveyor. The overhead belt conveyor with movable weight rollers that press the belt against the hog is for the purpose of pinning the hog in place during the entire bleeding process. (Courtesy, G. A. Hormel & Co.)

Fig. 4.8–Hogs sliding into a scalding tub and from there into the dehairing machine. (Courtesy, G. A. Hormel & Co.)

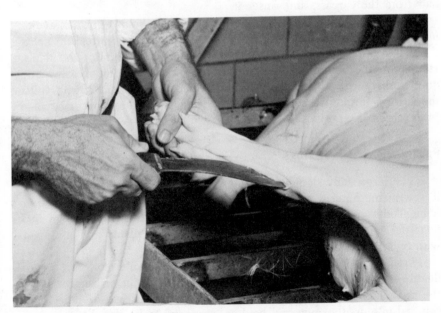

Fig. 4.9–Loosening the tendons. The small and large tendons on the back of the hocks are used for supporting the carcass on the gambrel stick.

the skin whiter, but they do not make the hair come off any easier. A shovelful of wood ashes, a handful of borax, a teaspoonful of lye, or a half pound of lime added to a barrel of scalding water will aid materially.

A bell type scraper that is fairly sharp is an important factor in the effective removal of scurf. The round working surface permits rapid dehairing, and plenty of pressure can be applied to remove the bristles and dirt.

Scalding, Scraping, and Eviscerating

A safe scalding temperature is 135° to 160° F, the lower temperature requiring more time. Water up to 180° F can be used but is not recommended since the operator must withdraw the hog as soon as the hair slips easily. Over-scalding causes the skin to contract around the base of the bristles, holding them tight, and is referred to as "setting the hair." If the hog is scalded in a barrel, the operator inserts a hook in the side of the mouth (for light hogs) or between the lower jaw bones and scalds the rear half of the hog. After this half is scraped and the hind feet are shaved clean, he opens the tendons and inserts the gambrel. Using the gambrel for manipulating the hog, he immerses the front half and scalds and scrapes it. Then he hoists the carcass, shaves the remainder of the hair from the carcass, and rinses it.

The operator makes a cut down the belly from hams to breast, avoiding cutting the intestines by guarding the point of the knife, and splits the pelvic bone by following the white tissue that separates the hams. He loosens the bung and pulls out the intestinal tract, removes the bile duct from the liver, cuts the diaphragm and removes the pluck, spilts the carcass through the center of the backbone and removes the face from each side, and loosens the leaf fat while the carcass is still warm.

Packer Slaughter of Hogs

The large daily slaughter of hogs by packers has made it necessary to devise mechanical equipment to handle large numbers of hogs per hour. Today, a single dehairing machine will handle from 150 to 500 hogs per hour, depending upon its length. Large plants are equipped with twin machines that will handle up to 1,000 hogs per hour.

Prior to slaughter, all hogs are subjected to an ante-mortem (before death) inspection, either at the scale or at some point on their way to the resting pen. The animals that show signs of disease or illness are shunted into another pen and held as "suspects" to be slaughtered separately. Hogs are given a shower in the resting pen before they are

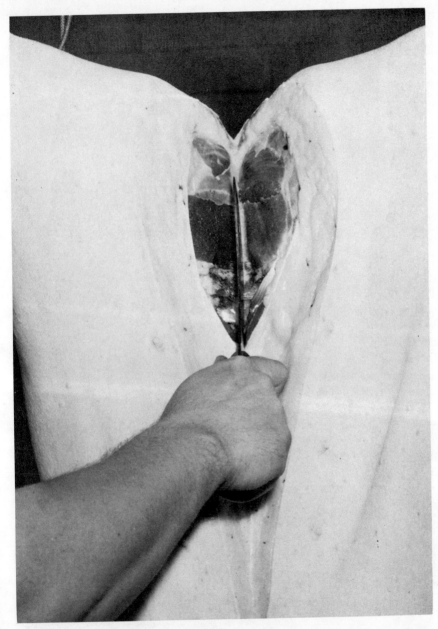

Fig. 4.10—Splitting the pelvis. The cut is made midway between the two hams, following the white tissue that separates the hams. This tissue leads to the fusion point of the pelvis which is cartilagenous in nature. Take a good grip on the knife in the position illustrated and give a sharp thrust toward the backbone. The hand will prevent the knife blade from cutting the bung gut.

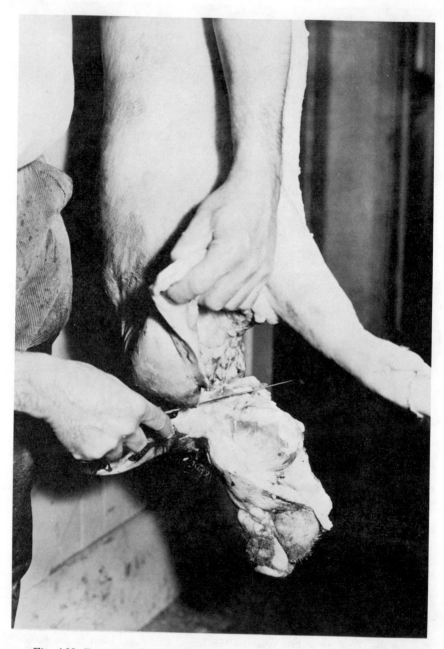

Fig. 4.11—Removing the face. The jowl remains on the carcass and the head is removed behind the ear at the atlas joint.

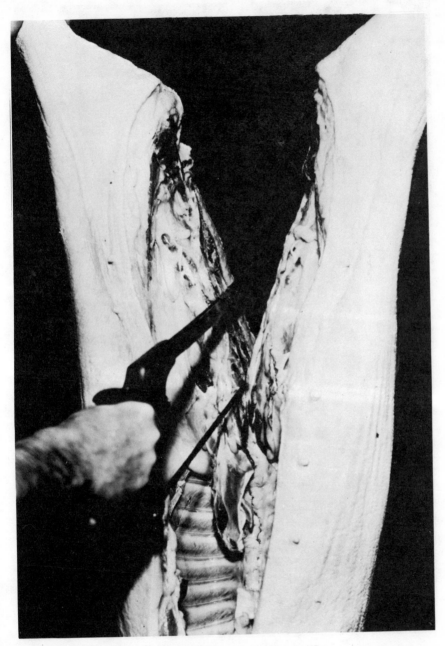

Fig. 4.12—Halving the carcass with a hand saw.

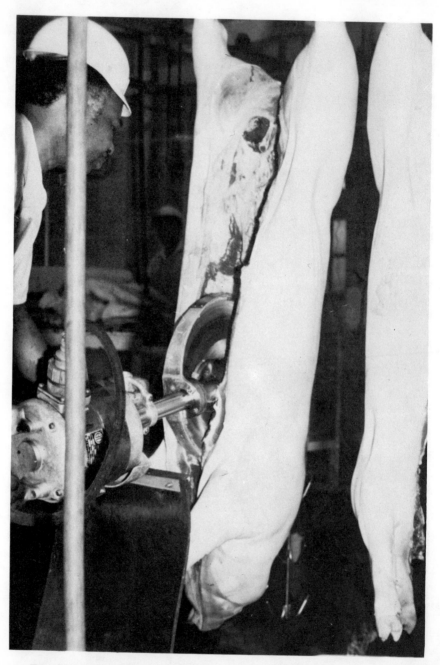

Fig. 4.13—Halving the carcass with an electric disc saw, such as packers use. (University of Illinois photo)

Fig. 4.14—Loosening the leaf fat. Insert the thumb under the leaf fat at the end of the sternum (X) and pull it up and away from the side, leaving it to hang attached to the base of the ham. Packers remove the leaf fat and use bell scrapers to free the inside of the bellies of any adhering leaf fat.

driven to the dispatching room. After immobilization and bleeding, the hogs are automatically released into the scalding vat.

Vats are usually 3 to 3½ feet deep and 5 to 5½ feet wide. If mechanical dunkers or immersers are used to keep the hogs under water, the depth is 4½ to 5½ feet. One pail of slaked lime per hour for each 20 feet of tub length is added by some packers to aid scalding. Some use a mixture of sal soda, lime, and soft soap. A plant that is slaughtering 400 hogs per hour would use a scalding vat 56 feet in length and water at 139° F, requiring the hogs to be immersed 4½ minutes. The hogs are propelled mechanically through the length of the scalding vat toward the elevator (moving incline) which moves them into the dehairing machine. These machines[3] are constructed of heavy V-shaped bars, a heavy steel frame, and two shafts to which belt scrapers with metal tips are attached. The lower shaft runs from 55 to 60 rpm and the upper shaft around 100 rpm. Both shafts run in the same direction. A hot water spray, 140° F, is played on the hogs as they pass through the dehairer toward the discharge end.

During the hard hair season (September, October, November), the water temperature should be 139° to 140° F and the immersion period 4 to 4½ minutes, while in the easy hair season (February, March), a temperature of 136° F for 4 minutes is preferable. Proper scalding will eliminate singeing (except of the head) and will produce a skin that has good leather qualities.

As the hogs are discharged from the machine, several attendants open the tendons on the hind legs, insert gambrel sticks, and place the hogs on rollers on the overhead tracks. A conveyor now moves the hogs slowly along a prescribed course where attendants do specified tasks, such as singeing, washing, shaving, eviscerating, removing the head, splitting or halving the carcass with an electric saw, loosening the leaf fat from the sides of the carcass, exposing the kidneys for inspection, and facing the hams (removing the skin and fat from over the inside face or cushion of the ham).

Each carcass and its viscera are given a post-mortem (after death) inspection, and if it is found to be free from disease, the carcass is stamped "U. S. Inspected and Passed" and sent to the chill room. If the inspector finds the carcass diseased, the carcass and all the internal organs (viscera) are shunted into a government retaining room for further inspection. If the carcass is found to be diseased as suspected, it

---

3. Two types of automatic dehairers are popular. In the one type (vertical) the hog carcasses are suspended as they move through the dehairer (Albright-Nell), and in the other (horizontal) the hogs are not suspended but move through lying down (Boss).

is stamped "U. S. Condemned" and sent to the tank room along with the viscera, where it is cooked under steam pressure in sealed tanks until all the disease germs are destroyed.

Skinning a Hog

This method of slaughtering a hog fits in well where there is a scarcity of labor. It is a one-man job and does not require hot water or scalding equipment. A hog trough or skinning rack to hold the hog on its back, a skinning knife, and a hoist or block and tackle are the only pieces of equipment necessary, other than the sticking knife and stunning instrument. The hog can be held on its back by the use of the regular beef skinning rack. The skin is opened in exactly the same pattern as the beef hide. (See Chapter 5.)

The skin is opened down the back of the front legs, down the back of the back legs, and down the middle of the belly. The legs are skinned out, then the belly and the sides. The knife should very carefully be kept tight against the skin at all times, because the fat is soft and easily cut. Deep gashes made by uncontrolled strokes of the knife do considerable damage to hams and bacons that are to be cured.

The tongue should be removed, the tendons on the hind legs loosened, and the gambrel inserted. The hog is hoisted, and with the loosening of the tail, the skin can be pulled off the back. After the face is skinned out, the carcass is washed and ready to be eviscerated.

The skin represents from 5% to 7% of the weight of the live hog. For other than home consumption, skinning has not previously been economical because of this fact, and also because it was a slower process. For home use, pork skin or rind is not necessary either in the curing or subsequent keeping of the cured meat. Curing tests conducted at The Pennsylvania State University have shown that skinned pork cuts take the cure faster and keep as well as unskinned cuts. The advantages are that the task can be done by one man; there is no messing around with hot water, no rinding of pork fat for rendering; the pork cures more rapidly and thoroughly and keeps as well as if it had a skin covering.

Recently a number of commercial hog skinning operations have begun in the United States. One of the leaders has been the Jimmy Dean Meat Company which skins hogs for the production of its whole-hog pork sausage (see Figure 4.15). This technique is almost certain to increase since a majority of hams and bellies are now merchandised skinless. Furthermore, the hide is more valuable when removed intact before curing, as portions are used for human burn treatments.

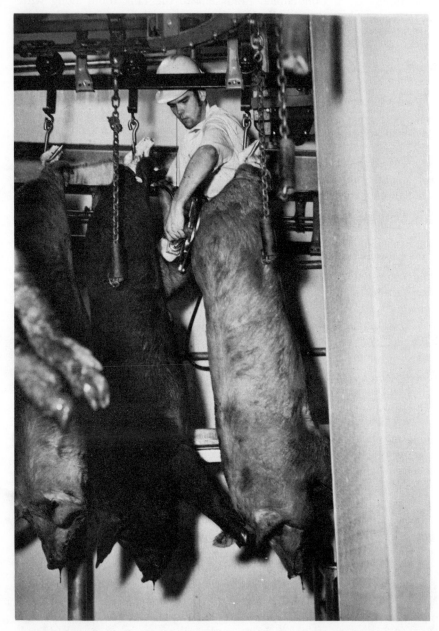

Fig. 4.15—Power clippers are used to cut hind feet and tail in this skinning operation. (Courtesy, *The National Provisioner* and the Jimmy Dean Meat Co.)

Fig. 4.16—The beginning of skinning operation is the folding over of skin on the ham region. (Courtesy, *The National Provisioner* and the Jimmy Dean Meat Co.)

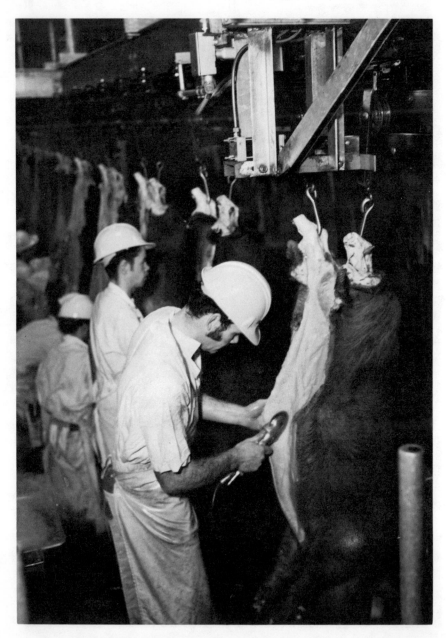

Fig. 4.17—Employee continues by folding skin down to chest area. (Courtesy, *The National Provisioner* and the Jimmy Dean Meat Co.)

Fig. 4.18–Carcass at right of photo shows folded-over skin and anchoring loop. Next carcass is in the process of being skinned, and the process has been completed on the remaining carcasses. (Courtesy, *The National Provisioner* and the Jimmy Dean Meat Co.)

Fig. 4.19—Carcass at left indicates extent to which head area is skinned out. Operator loops chain around skinned-out lower portion. Carcass is anchored by hook in jaw cavity. (Courtesy, *The National Provisioner* and the Jimmy Dean Meat Co.)

Fig. 4.20—Skin take-off, at this instant, is at the point of bung area. Note the skinned hide at the operator's right. (Courtesy, *The National Provisioner* and the Jimmy Dean Meat Co.)

Depilating Hog Carcasses

A patented process of removing hair, stubble, and roots from hog carcasses after they have been scalded and passed through the dehairing machine was conceived by F. M. Tobin, of Rochester, New York, and developed by the Albright-Nell Company of Chicago, Illinois. The process consists of mechanically dipping each carcass, after it is dehaired, into a hot solution (250° to 300° F) of rosin and cottonseed oil for a period of six to eight seconds. In some plants the nostrils of the hogs are plugged with cotton, the mouth is closed by means of a clamp, and the bung is plugged with a six-inch-long dampened wooden plug to keep out the depilating compound. The compound forms a seal-like coating over the entire carcass; the heat turns the moisture in the skin and on its surface into steam which penetrates to the roots of the hairs and loosens them.

Fan cooling the dipped carcass has been found by some to be preferable to showering with water since the introduction of water into the dip causes foaming. When the rosin coating has plasticized, it is stripped from the hog by pull-rolling it down the carcass. With it are removed the sebaceous material loosened from the skin by the steam and also the remaining hair, stubble, and roots not taken off by the dehairing machine. If the temperature of the dip is kept at 250° F, the skins are suitable for leather. The rosin dip is reclaimed by screening out the hair and refortifying with more plasticizer when the adhesive becomes too brittle.

The method employed by the originator of the system was to add water to the rosin and water mixture until it bubbled. The temperature was held to 240° to 250° F. The water and adhesive formed an emulsion which was plastic when cool. It could be scraped off easily, would not burn or yellow the skins, and did not give off fumes.

In recent years, shortages of trees, wood, and thus rosin have caused many packers to discontinue its use.

Styles of Dressing and Yield

Three styles of dressing pork (excluding Wiltshires) are common in the United States. They are (1) shipper's style—unsplit carcass with head on and leaf fat in, (2) packer's style—two sides with jowls attached but head removed and leaf fat out, and (3) farmer's style—carcass split on either side of the backbone, making two sides and backbone.

The dressed yield of hogs is affected by fill (although hogs have but one stomach) and by the degree of fatness or finish. The hogs that grade as U. S. No. 1 are reported to give a warm dressed yield, head on,

Fig. 4.21—Depilating hogs. Dipped hog carcasses travel a short distance so that the adhesive will become plastic. The first operator starts stripping from the hind feet downward. Further stripping or "peeling off" is done by one or two more operators.

of 74% to 76% or 68% to 70% packer style (head off, leaf out, ham facings off). U. S. No. 2 carcasses range approximately 2% higher, and U. S. No. 3 hogs range from 72% to 76% (packer style). The Utility grade hog will yield the same or lower than the U. S. No. 1 hog, depending upon its conformation.

In estimating the cost of the carcass, divide the dressing percentage into the price per hundred pounds live weight. This figure, however, does not include the true cost of the carcass, since labor in handling and slaughtering and overhead have not been included.

Chilling the Hog Carcass

The carcass is split through the center of the backbone with a saw or a cleaver, dividing it into two sides. The head is removed but the jowl is left attached to the carcass. The leaf fat should be pulled loose

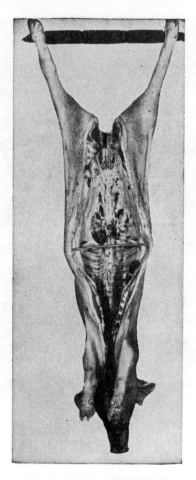

Fig. 4.22—Shipper's style.

from the inside of the carcass and left attached at the ham. This hastens the chilling of the side and lessens the danger of souring. After the blood is washed from the neck, the carcass is moved into the chill room where the tempertaure is held around 34° F. Where large numbers of warm carcasses are handled, the chill room is generally precooled to a temperature several degrees below freezing to compensate for the heat from the carcasses which raises the cooler temperature considerably.

The cooler shrink on a 24-hour chill will average between 2% and 3%, depending upon the humidity of the cooler. The inside temperature of the ham should reach 38° F for thorough chilling.

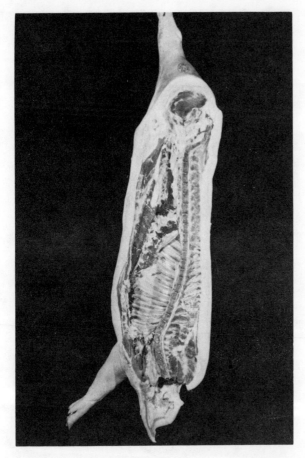

Fig. 4.23—Packer's style.

WILTSHIRE SIDE

A Wiltshire is an English style side of pork that must conform to rather rigid specifications in order to satisfy the English market. It consists of the entire side, or half, of a hog carcass minus the head, feet, aitchbone, backbone, tenderloin, and skirt. The sparerib and neck rib are left in the carcass.

The ideal side weighs approximately 60 pounds; minimum 40 pounds, maximum 80 pounds. The ideal length from the fore part of the first rib to the fore end of the aitchbone knob is 29 inches; minimum 26 inches, maximum 32 inches. Wiltshires are cured and then packed, either in

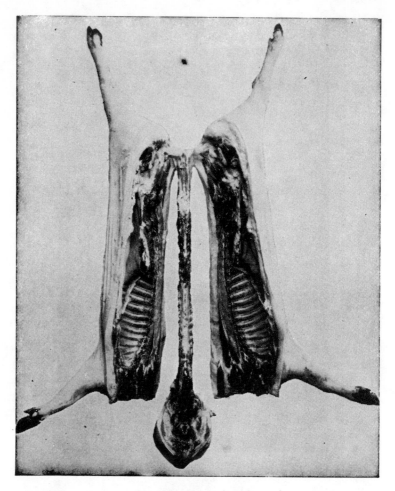

Fig. 4.24—Farmer's style.

bales or in boxes, for export. They are smoked after they reach their destination.

CANADIAN HOG MARKETING

In 1940, Canada instituted the plan of marketing hogs on the rail instead of on foot. This system of marketing, based on rail grading, has standardized the Canadian hog market and operates as follows: Ownership of the hog is established by tattooing an indelible brand on the shoulder of each animal. The hog is dressed and weighed. A government grader marks the grade on the grading tag with the tattooed identification number. Part of the tag is sent to the accounting office for the estimate of payment, the other part of the tag is attached to the carcass. The farmer receives a statement with his check showing the grade, the price per grade, insurance, Dominion premium, and other charges. The government pays the farmer bonuses for grades A and B1 hogs.

FACTS ABOUT HOGS AND PORK

Aged boars are practically inedible because of sex odor, and should be sold to a packer who processes them for their by-products. Young boars should be castrated several months before being slaughtered.

Cracklings is the term applied to the pressed, rendered pork fat remaining after the lard has been extracted.

The record receipts of hogs on the Chicago market in a single day was 122,749 head on December 15, 1924. Prior to World War II, the United States consumed 85% of its pork production.

The lowest cash price for prime steam lard per 100 pounds on the Chicago market since 1896 was $3.57½ (June 1932) as against the record price of $40.00 (October 1946).

The greatest amount of lard exported in any one year was 1,039,-000,000 pounds in 1924.

It requires the slaughter of 145 female hogs to produce one pound of fresh ovaries from which corpus luteum and ovarian extracts are prepared. These extracts are prepared in either powder, tablet, or liquid form, and are of great therapeutic value in treating menstrual disorders in women.

One source of pharmaceutical pepsin is the lining of the pig's stomach at the pyloric end.

Pigskin has been replaced by cattle hides as a covering for footballs. Its most common use is in leather for gloves, pocketbooks, handbags, brief cases, toilet cases, tobacco pouches, book bindings, and leggings.

The greases secured from inedible hog fat are "A" white grease (less than 2% free fatty acid), "B" white grease (less than 3.5% free fatty acid), and brown grease.

Lard oil is made from "A" white grease and is used for making a high grade lubricant used on delicate running machine parts. The oil from "B" white grease is sometimes called "extra neatsfoot oil" and is used in giving added viscosity to mineral oils. The oils made from the brown grease are used in compounding cutting oils, heavy lubricating oils, special leather oils, illuminating oils, and stearic acid and combined with paraffin in candle making.

Processing Hog Hair

The hair is cooked in wooden vats in either (1) plain water, (2) water with acetic acid added (100 to 1), or (3) water with detergent (76% solid caustic soda). The cooking loosens the cuticle and scurf and requires from four to six hours. The hair passes from the cookers into high speed cylinders studded with 3½-inch steel pins into which hot water and steam are fed. These washers and pickers remove the cuticle

Table 4.2—Commercial Hog Slaughter, Number of Head (in Thousands), Ranked by States, 1972[1,2,3]

Rank	State	Number	Rank	State	Number
1	Iowa	20,932.0	24	New York	878.5
2	Illinois	6,283.0	25	Washington	722.0
3	Minnesota	5,097.0	26	Delaware & Maryland	510.7
4	Pennsylvania	4,047.0	27	Florida	497.0
5	Ohio	4,040.0	28	South Carolina	438.5
6	Michigan	3,885.0	29	Arkansas	429.0
7	Indiana	3,620.0	30	New Jersey	401.5
8	Wisconsin	3,308.0	31	Montana	354.7
9	Virginia	3,099.0	32	Louisiana	204.2
10	Tennessee	2,894.0	33	Oregon	196.8
11	Nebraska	2,576.0	34	Arizona	180.2
12	South Dakota	2,438.0	35	Idaho	123.3
13	Kansas	2,180.0	36	New Mexico	115.9
14	Texas	1,957.0	37	Utah	90.1
15	Georgia	1,943.0	38	New England[4]	73.4
16	Missouri	1,891.0	39	West Virginia	70.8
17	Kentucky	1,843.0	40	Hawaii	53.5
18	North Carolina	1,797.0	41	North Dakota	31.6
19	California	1,503.0	42	Wyoming	20.5
20	Mississippi	1,237.0	43	Nevada	4.4
21	Colorado	999.5			
22	Alabama	903.5			
23	Oklahoma	900.5	Total		84,760.6

1. Livestock and Meat Statistics, USDA Stat. Bul. No. 522.

2. Includes slaughter under Federal inspection and other commercial slaughter. Excludes farm slaughter.

3. Commercial slaughter not estimated in Alaska.

4. New England includes Maine, New Hampshire, Vermont, Massachusetts, Rhode Island, and Connecticut.

and scurf, and the picked hair passes by conveyor to the feed apron of a drying machine where blasts of hot air dry and fluff it. A suction tube draws the dried and fluffed hair into a winnowing machine which removes the dust and fine hair. A cut away intake in the suction tube permits the toenails to drop through. The finished hair is baled in burlap bags. The yield of finished hair on the basis of a 10% moisture content is 35% in summer and 75% in winter.

CHAPTER 5

Cattle Slaughter

MARKET CLASSES AND GRADES OF SLAUGHTER CATTLE

A more complete discussion of beef carcass grading, including live and carcass pictures, appears in Chapter 11.

Beef steers (15 to 24 months old) furnish the bulk of the high-grade beef sold on the market. Open (not bred) and spayed (ovaries removed) beef heifers furnish a high-grade meat that is even finer in

Table 5.1—Market Classes and Grades of Slaughter Cattle[1,2]

Steers	Heifers	Cows (All Wts.)	Bulls (Yearlings Excluded)
Prime	Prime	Commercial	Good
990–1,100 lbs.	700–900 lbs.	Utility	Commercial
1,100–1,300 "	900–1,100 "	Cutter	Utility
Choice	Choice	Canner	Cutter
900–1,100 "	700–900 "		
1,100–1,300 "	900–1,100 "		
Good	Good		
900–1,100 "	500–700 "		
Standard	700–900 "		
All wts.	Standard		
Utility	All wts.		
All wts.	Utility		
	All wts.		

1. As utilized by the Livestock Division, Agricultural Marketing Service, U.S. Dept. of Agriculture.

2. Recently, use of USDA Yield Grades has supplemented the quality designations, i.e., Choice, Yield Grade 2-3; Prime, Yield Grade 2-3; Choice, Yield Grade 3-4, etc.

texture than steer beef, but heifers run slightly lower in dressed yield due mainly to a greater amount of internal fat. Buyers discount prices offered for open heifers as insurance against pregnancy, which lowers dressing percentage. Tests have shown very small differences in the yield of various cuts between steer and heifer carcasses of the same grade.

Most high-grade beef steers and heifers are grain fattened. Grass-fed cattle generally fall into the lower grades and great numbers are bought by Corn Belt farmers for further feeding until they will grade U.S. Choice.

Slaughter Cattle

All of the market classes and grades of cattle bought for immediate slaughter come under this general classification.

The trend toward direct purchases by packers of cattle continues with 72.2% of cattle procured at country points, while 10 years earlier the figure was 43.1%. Now, 13.2% are purchased at terminal markets, and 14.6% are purchased at auctions. For steers and heifers, which are mostly fed cattle that represent the primary output of the specialized beef enterprise, packer sources last year were country, 81.1%, terminals, 11.1%, and auctions, 7.0%. For cows and bulls, which represent important by-products from beef-breeding herds and the dairy enterprise, sources were country, 34.4%, terminals, 18.4%, and auctions, 47.2%. Cattle pur-

Table 5.2—Slaughter Steers at Six Markets[1,2] 1971-72

Quality	Number	Average Weight	Percent of Total
Prime	70,312	1,164	7
Choice	722,455	1,120	71
Good	213,462	1,103	20
Standard	31,809	1,167	2
All grades	1,038,038	1,121	100

1. Six markets are Kansas City, National Stock Yards, Omaha, Sioux City, Sioux Falls, and So. St. Joseph.

2. Ed Kimbrell, USDA, CMS, National Beef Seminar II, Knights of AK-SAR-BEN, Omaha, Nebraska.

chases on a carcass grade and weight basis accounted for 22.6% of the total.

Prime Cattle

As noted in Table 5.2, only a small percentage (7%) of slaughter steers marketed in terminals are fed to the prime grade. Even a smaller percent of direct purchases are prime. Normally, prime cattle have excess waste fat as a result of long feeding. Today, feeders cannot afford to feed cattle beyond the choice grade into the prime grade, where gains are slow and very expensive. Furthermore, consumers abhor fat as do all segments of the beef industry—the packer, provisioner, and retailer. The prime cattle that do come to market now end up largely in the hotel and restaurant trade.

Carcass yield is easily confused with *USDA Yield Grade,* but the two terms signify distinctly different aspects of animal value. *USDA Yield Grade* refers to the percent of the carcass that is available for sale as retail product, while *carcass yield* refers only to the weight of the entire carcass, (muscle, fat, and bone) expressed as a percent of the animal's live weight. The second term, *carcass yield,* is more clearly designated *dressing percent.* Hot dressing percent (hot carcass weight/live weight × 100) is a function largely of fill and fat; thus, the fatter prime cattle will dress from 63% to 66%. The highest reported dressing percent to date is 76¾% made by a spayed Angus heifer shown at the Smithfield *Fat* Stock Show in England.

Choice Cattle

Animals to grade as choice should have most of the characteristics of the prime grade in moderation. They should dress from 59% to 61%.

Good Cattle

Cattle of this grade not only carry less finish than choice animals but also lack the uniform beef conformation of that grade. They are more uneven in their top, are slightly higher off the ground, and do not show the uniform depth of body nor the fullness of muscling characteristic of the choice grade. They should dress from 54% to 60%. Dairy-bred steers which have been fed a concentrated ration for a period of time may qualify for this grade.

Standard Cattle

These are young, soft-boned cattle that are generally lightweight,

Table 5.3—Commercial Cattle Slaughter, Number of Head (in Thousands), Ranked by States, 1972[1,2,3]

Rank	State	Number	Rank	State	Number
1	Nebraska	4,699.0	24	Oregon	294.1
2	Iowa	4,662.0	25	Mississippi	277.5
3	Texas	3,516.0	26	Georgia	265.9
4	California	2,761.0	27	Utah	265.5
5	Kansas	2,495.0	28	New Jersey	239.8
6	Colorado	2,461.0	29	Montana	210.2
7	Minnesota	1,493.0	30	North Dakota	206.3
8	Illinois	1,450.0	31	Kentucky	196.1
9	Wisconsin	1,108.0	32	Louisiana	175.7
10	Ohio	1,064.0	33	Arkansas	156.5
11	Missouri	931.5	34	New England[4]	152.7
12	Pennsylvania	640.5	35	North Carolina	151.8
13	Michigan	627.5	36	Virginia	131.9
14	Washington	613.0	37	Delaware & Maryland	102.1
15	Oklahoma	607.5	38	Alabama	92.4
16	South Dakota	550.0	39	South Carolina	71.0
17	Arizona	541.5	40	Hawaii	63.8
18	Tennessee	515.5	41	West Virginia	55.3
19	Indiana	439.0	42	Nevada	25.7
20	Idaho	416.0	43	Wyoming	20.7
21	New Mexico	388.0			
22	Florida	368.0			
23	New York	340.4		Total	35,842.4

1. Livestock and Meat Statistics, USDA Stat. Bul. No. 522.

2. Includes slaughter under Federal inspection and other commercial slaughter. Excludes farm slaughter.

3. Commercial slaughter not estimated in Alaska.

4. New England includes Maine, New Hampshire, Vermont, Massachusetts, Rhode Island, and Connecticut.

unfinished cattle of either sex, deficient in conformation. The yield is from 52% to 58%. Young dairy-bred steers often grade standard.

Commercial Cattle

Cattle showing advanced maturity and consisting in the main of breeding cows make up this grade. The yield is from 52% to 56%.

Utility Cattle

These cattle are rangy, angular, and thinly fleshed and vary considerably with age. They may dress in the low fifties.

Cutter and Canner Cattle

These grades are represented mainly by old cattle having the characteristics of the dairy breeds which lack the inherent meat qualities of beef animals.

BEEF OPERATIONS

Cattle should be kept off feed at least 24 hours previous to slaughter. Results of a test conducted at the Pennsylvania Agricultural Experiment Station to determine the effects of fasting beef animals for periods ranging from 24 hours to 48 hours on the yield and appearance of the carcasses were definitely in favor of the longer fast period. The fasted animals bled out more thoroughly, were easier to dress, and the carcasses were brighter in appearance than those from cattle allowed feed up to the time of slaughter. Undue rough handling or excitement causes the blood to be forced to the outermost capillaries from which it will be unable to drain as thoroughly as it would under normal heart action. This results in a fiery carcass (pink tinge to the fat), which has lower keeping qualities due to the retained blood.

Stunning

One of a number of compression guns can be used. They are made

Fig. 5.1— A power actuated stunner. It uses .22 caliber rim fire power loads in five graded strengths for effective stunning of all weights of cattle, calves, hogs, and sheep. This packing house tool meets all legislative and humanitarian requirements and delivers effective stunning blows to pates or backs of heads. Automatic penetrator rod retraction, lever type trigger, sleeve style bolt, and lightweight and compact design are among the features of the stunner, made for easy portability and comfortable, one-hand operation. (Courtesy, Remington Arms Co., Bridgeport, Connecticut)

with long or short handles and are of the penetrating or non-penetrating type. They operate on the forehead or behind the poll. Several different types of stunners and the location of stunning are shown in figures 5.1, 5.2, and 5.3.

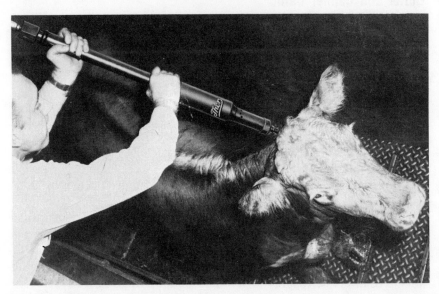

Fig. 5.2—A compression stunner for cattle. In this case, the stunner (penetrating type) is aimed at the medulla oblongata. (Courtesy, Thor Power Tool Co., Aurora, Illinois)

Sticking

Standard Method

Make an incision over the point of the brisket toward the jaw. Insert the knife in front of the brisket at a 45° angle and sever the carotid arteries and jugular vein. See figures 5.4 and 5.5.

Kosher Method

Hoist the animal without stunning it and cut across the throat. The sticking is done by the rabbi or shohet.

Heading

Open the hide from the horn to the nostril and skin out the front of the face. Continue the opening from the stick down through the center of the jaw and skin out of the side of the face. Turn the head and skin the

Fig. 5.3—X marks the spot—to stun.

opposite side. Grasp the jaw in one hand, bend the head back on its poll, and remove the head by cutting through the Adam's apple and the atlas joint.

Shanking or Legging

Place the skinning rack under the withers and roll the animal on the rack. Open the hide on the rear of the fore shank and the rear of the hind shank, continuing the cut to the mid-line to be made on the belly from the neck to the bung. Sever the tendon by cutting across the shank and snipping off the dew claws. Skin out the shanks and remove them at the break or smooth joint below the knee and hock. The break or smooth joint is at the enlargement, about an inch below the knee joint, just where it tapers down to the cannon bone. On the hock it is about an inch from where the

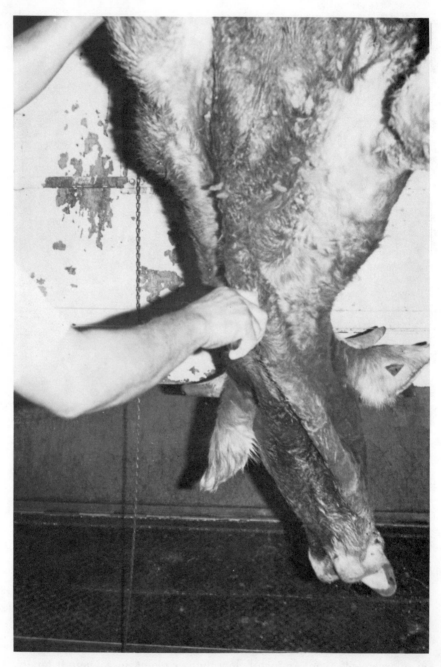

Fig. 5.4—Sticking. Knife is inserted in front of brisket at a 45-degree angle . . . (Courtesy, University of Illinois)

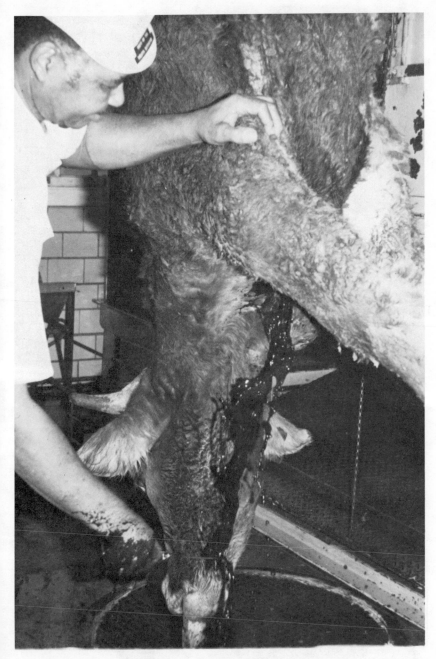

Fig. 5.5– . . . severing carotid arteries and jugular vein. (Courtesy, University of Illinois)

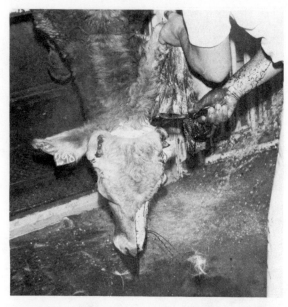

Fig. 5.6—Heading. Skinning out one side of face. (Courtesy, University of Illinois)

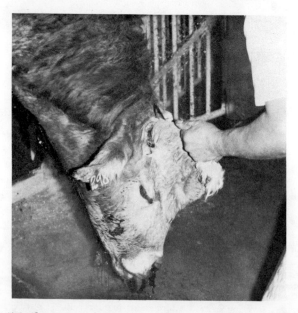

Fig. 5.7—Skinning out front of face. (Courtesy, University of Illinois)

Fig. 5.8–Skinning out third side of face. (Courtesy, University of Illinois)

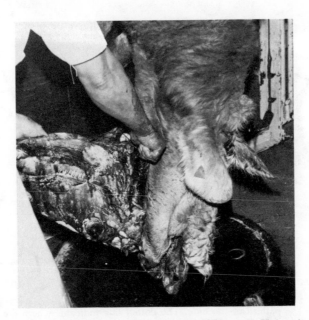

Fig. 5.9–Removal of head after severing atlas joint. (Courtesy, University of Illinois)

taper takes place. A decided groove is evident when the knife rests at the proper spot. Cut around to either side and then grasp the shank near the foot and give a sharp thrust downward and outward from the stifle joint. Occasionally the break joint will have ossified in aged animals, in which case it will be necessary to use a saw.

Siding

Grasp the hide firmly with an upward pull and with long, smooth strokes of the skinning knife, remove the hide down over the sides. The bevel of the knife must be flat to the hide to avoid making cuts or scores. This is one of the most difficult tasks in the skinning operation and requires considerable experience before satisfactory progress can be made. Attempt to avoid scoring or cutting the hide, as this lowers its value for leather.

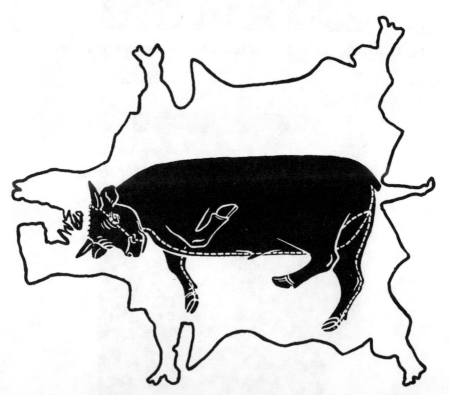

Fig. 5.10—The pattern of the hide. The dotted line indicates where the opening is made in the hide. (Courtesy, USDA)

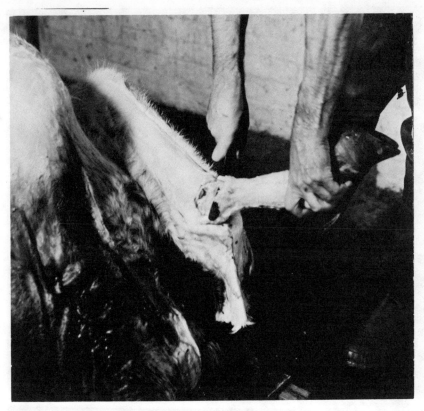

Fig. 5.11—Removing the fore shank.

Opening

Cut through the center of the brisket with a knife and then saw through the sternum. At this point, "rod the weasand," i.e., separate the esophagus from the trachea and tie a knot in the esophagus to prevent spillage of rumen contents when carcass is raised (Figure 5.15). Insert the handle of the knife in the abdominal cavity with the blade leaning backward and open the belly cavity. In case of a male, the pizzle must be removed first. It is well to pull the small intestines out of the abdominal cavity before separating the rounds at the aitchbone. Each top round muscle is covered with a tough membrane, and where the two join over the high point of the pelvis they form a decidedly heavy, white-appearing membrane. Follow the membrane and avoid cutting into the muscle. The knife is then readily forced between the soft cartilage that joins the pelvic bone at this point. In old animals, the pelvis will have to be sawed.

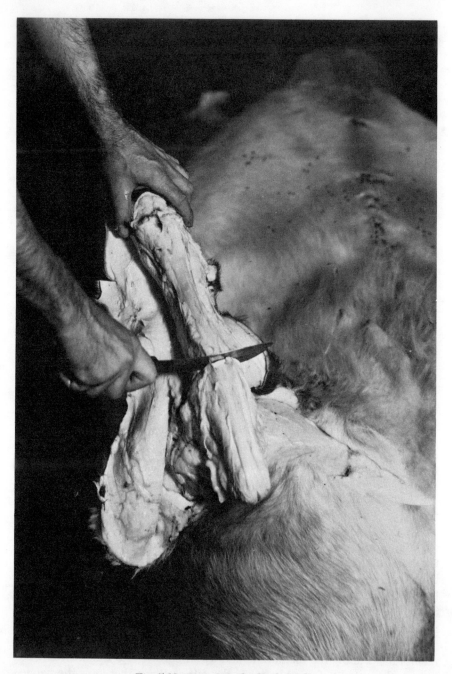

Fig. 5.12—Removing the hind shank.

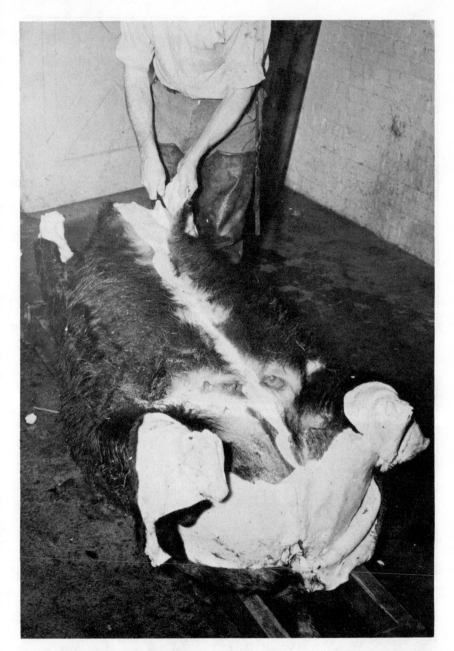

Fig. 5.13—Siding can be started at the fore or rear end. This beef is held on its back by means of a skinning rack.

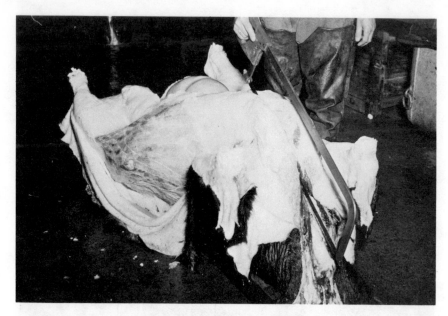

Fig. 5.14–Splitting the brisket.

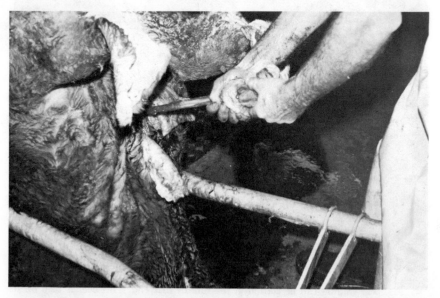

Fig. 5.15–"Rodding the weasand." Esophagus (weasand) has been separated from the trachea and is here tied in a knot to prevent rumen spillage on carcass. (Courtesy, University of Illinois)

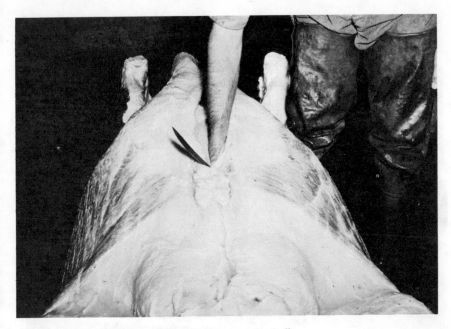

Fig. 5.16—Opening the belly.

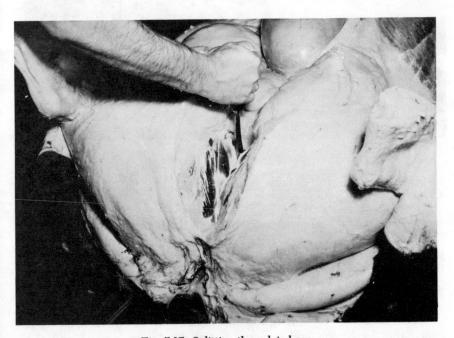

Fig. 5.17—Splitting the pelvic bone.

Rumping

The beef tree is inserted in the hocks and the carcass raised to a convenient height for tailing and removing the hide from the round and rump. Skin around the base and split the hide the entire length of the tail. Sever the tail two joints from the body and skin entirely around its base. By placing a cloth over the skinned base stub, the tail can easily be pulled out the remainder of the way. Cut around the bung, tie it with a heavy cord, and let it drop inside the carcass.

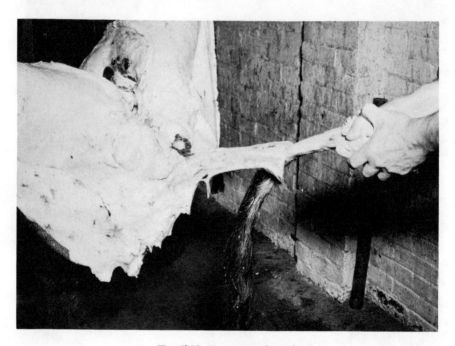

Fig. 5.18—Removing the tail.

Eviscerating

Loosen the fat and membrane that hold the bung gut and bladder to backbone. A few well-placed cuts of the knife will allow the paunch and intestines to drop into the gut cart. Loosen the liver with the hands and then sever it from the backbone with a knife. Remove the gall bladder by cutting across the top of the bile duct at the center of the liver and peeling it rather than cutting it out.

The membrane separating the abdominal from the thoracic cavity is called the diaphragm and consists of the diaphragm muscle and the

Fig. 5.19—Pulling the hide from the outside round. The knife is not used in this region because it is easier and swifter to pull or pound off the hide. The above heifer carcass is identified by the lean area of the *gracilis* muscle and the presence of the dug or udder. (See Chapter 11.)

membrane joining the muscle. Cut out only the membrane, as the diaphragm muscle is good edible meat and is known as the *skirt*. The organs that lie in the thoracic cavity are called the *pluck* and consist of the heart, lungs, gullet, and windpipe.

Backing

That part of the hide attached to the outside round is either pulled or pounded off. The backing operation consists of running the knife around the back between the hide and the carcass and letting the hide drop of its own weight. The hide may also be removed by cutting in from either side as a completion of the siding operation.

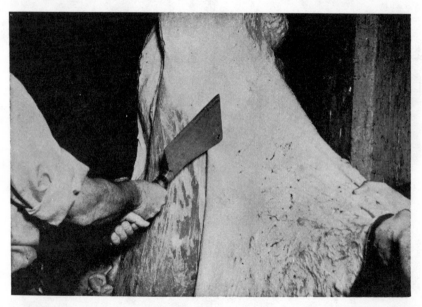

Fig. 5.20—Pounding the hide from the round and hip loin to avoid breaking the fell.

Halving

Splitting the beef into sides by sawing or chopping through the exact center of the backbone is begun before the forequarters of the carcass are off the floor. A beef-splitting saw or large cleaver is used. Standing on the belly side of the carcass, saw through the caudal vertebrae to the sacrum and then take up a position on the opposite side of the carcass and saw through the sacrum and the lumbar vertebrae. Special care should be taken to split each superior spinus process of each

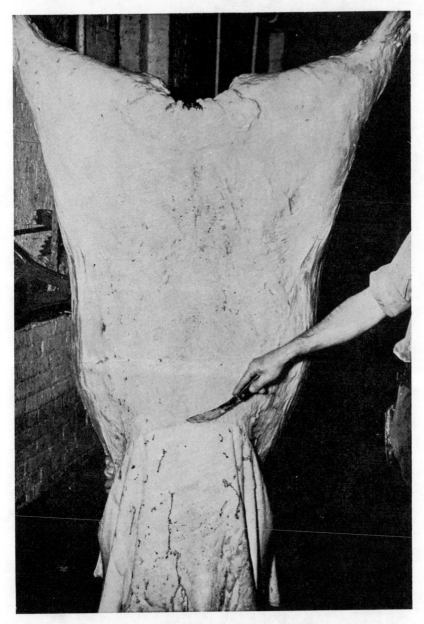

Fig. 5.21—Dropping the hide over the shoulders and neck.

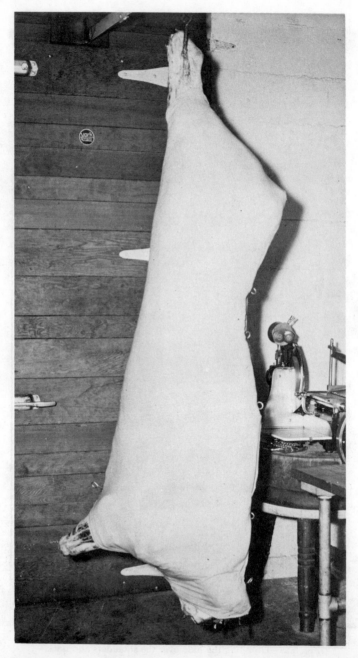

Fig. 5.22—Shrouding or clothing. This gives a smooth, dense appearance to the fat.

vertebra since this has an important bearing on the weights of wholesale and retail loin, rib, and chuck cuts. Since the feather bones in the dorsal region (rib area) of the backbone are quite long and narrow, it is desirable to first saw through the main body of the backbone. This is done by pointing the saw toward the neck and sawing at an angle to the backbone. Sawing through each individual dorsal vertebra at a 45-degree angle assures the operator of a 50-50 split of the feather bones since the spine (if the saw is in the center) steers the saw blade and holds it steady.

After the splitting is completed to the point where the hide is still attached, the carcass is hoisted and the hide removed from the shoulders and neck. The splitting of the forequarters is completed and the vein removed from the inside of the neck.

Washing and Shrouding (Clothing)

All blood should be washed off both the inside and the outside of the carcass, and the shoulders should be pumped by working the shanks up and down. Cold or lukewarm water is used to wash the carcass. Shrouds made from unbleached duck cloth are immersed in warm water and pinned over the outside of the sides of warm beef before they are moved into the cooler. The shrouds absorb the blood, smooth the external fat covering, and cause the fat to appear white and dense. The shrouds, or cloths, are removed after the carcass has chilled. A practice that has been utilized is to wet the clothing in a 14° to 18° salimeter strength salt brine at a temperature of 115° to 125° F. It is claimed that brined cloth has greater adhesiveness and that it helps the cloth to absorb blood and more of the bruise discoloration which may be on a carcass. Thus, the purpose of the shroud is only to improve the appearance of the carcass for the potential buyer. With the advent of increased fabrication of beef carcasses into wholesale and retail cuts in packing plants, some packers have discontinued the use of the shroud in an effort to save unnecessary costs. Cooler shrinkage averages from 2% to 3% in the first 48 hours or from 4% to 6% in the first two weeks. The amount of cooler shrinkage is dependent upon cooler humidity and the finish of the carcass.

Commercial Beef Slaughtering Operations

Slaughter of beef in Federally inspected plants accounts for nearly 90% of the total beef slaughtered in the United States. Approximately 10% of the total is slaughtered in commercial non-Federal (state inspected) plants and only about 0.8% is slaughtered on the farm. Thus the student should be aware of commercial beef slaughter operations.

It is not unusual to find operations in the United States killing some 2,000 cattle in an 8-hour day, or 250 per hour. To accomplish such an endeavor, considerable use is made of mechanized equipment as can be noted in figures 5.23 through 5.27.

Canada Packers, Ltd., were the designers of a system of on-the-rail dressing of beef that has eliminated stooping while working. There are 14 stations in the operation. Driving, knocking, and shackling the beef are performed by one man at station one. Sticking and scalping (heading) are performed at station two. One worker legs, butts, inserts trolley, and removes the shackle at the third station, while a fourth worker legs, butts, and inserts trolley in the second leg at the fourth station. At the fifth station, one worker removes the front foot, performs work on the brisket, dehorns, and removes the head. One worker rims, clears shanks, and works on the chuck and neck at the sixth station. At station seven, work is performed by a single worker on the rump; the bung is dropped, and the tail is pulled. The rosette is cleared, using an air-operated skinning tool, flanking is performed, and the hide is pulled by the machine operated by one man at station eight. The brisket is sawed and the carcass eviscerated at station nine, and completion of the hide pull is

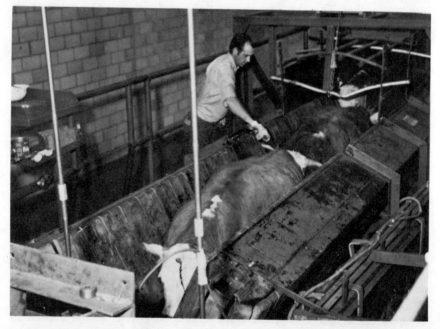

Fig. 5.23—Easily and quickly, employee places stunning instrument on head of restrained animal in commercial operation. (Courtesy, *The National Provisioner*)

Fig. 5.24—Making full use of power tools, employees sever front feet and horns, if any, from bled carcasses. (Courtesy, *The National Provisioner*)

made at station ten. In the pull-off, the hide drops directly into a chute. The splitter and scriber at station eleven operates on an elevating bench, using a foot switch. Trimming is done at station twelve, weighing at station thirteen, and shrouding at station fourteen.

An even newer concept in beef hide pulling, the Anderson Hide Down Puller® (figures 5.29-5.30), has the following advantages, according to the manufacturer:

1. Hide borne contaminants such as loose hair, dirt, manure, etc., etc., either fall to the floor or drop progressively away from the carcass to the lower portions of the hide.
2. Trimming loss to meet strict government regulations is minimized.
3. Cheek and head meat yields are increased.
4. Carcass weight is increased.
5. No. 2 hide tonnage is reduced.
6. Hide stretch and damaged or torn fibers are eliminated.
7. Carcass wash time and labor are decreased.

®Anderson IBEC, Strongsville, Ohio.

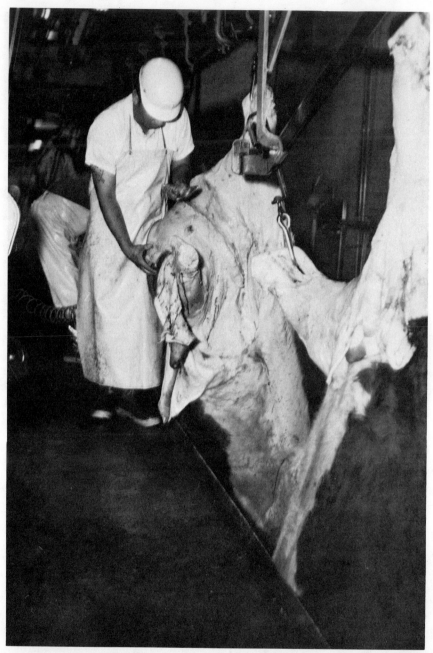

Fig. 5.25—At second transfer station, carcasses are shown being taken up as employee performs butting operation on next carcass. (Courtesy, *The National Provisioner*)

Fig. 5.26—Final step in hide preparation for strip-off includes freeing of small of the back as shown. (Courtesy, *The National Provisioner*)

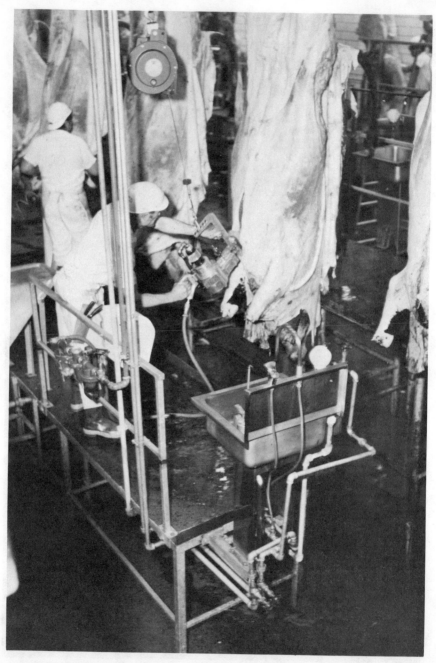

Fig. 5.27—With power tool, employee at hide removal station opens brisket. (Courtesy, *The National Provisioner*)

Fig. 5.28—Can-Pak hide puller.

8. Head skinning is eliminated and head washing time is reduced.
9. Floor space requirement is reduced, resulting in low maintenance.
10. Pulling won't cause carcass to slip or be pulled from the rail.
11. Any size hide is pulled cleanly and completely.
12. Tail is pulled along with the hide.

Fig. 5.29–The Anderson Hide Down Puller. (Courtesy, Anderson IBEC, Strongs-ville, Ohio)

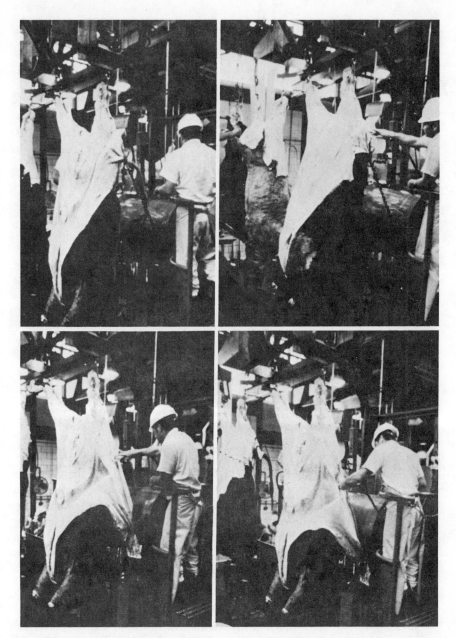

Fig. 5.30—The Hide Down Puller in action. (Top left) Start of pull. Note pattern. (Top right) Pulling over rump and round. (Bottom left) Clearing the tail. (Bottom right) Clearing the fell. (Courtesy, Minden Company c/o Anderson IBEC, Strongsville, Ohio)

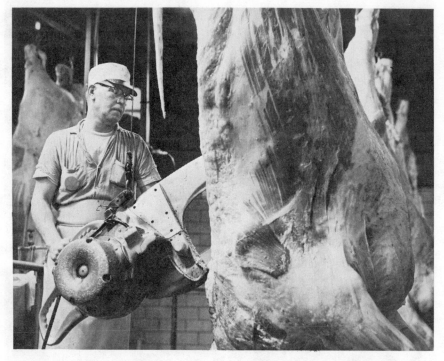

Fig. 5.31—At this station, a cantilever platform moves the butcher downward and forward as he splits the carcass. (Courtesy, Monfort of Colorado, Inc.)

Drift

Cattle will lose from 3% to 4% of their weight if kept off their feed for 24 hours. This is referred to as shrink or drift. It has become a general practice for buyers to demand this shrink, either as a mathematical deduction from full-feed weight or as an actual off-feed practice. If a reputation means anything to a feeder he will never salt or fill his cattle before sale time. A cattle buyer is seldom fooled and then only once by the same man. The carcass yield will betray the perpetrator.

Hide Yield

The weight of the hide varies with the breed of cattle. Herefords carry the heaviest hides, followed by the Aberdeen-Angus, Holsteins, and Brown Swiss. Shorthorns and the dairy breeds carry the lightest weight hides. Hides from the average run of cattle slaughtered by the large packing concerns average 7% of the live weight of the animals. Slaughter records of the purebred steers killed and dressed in the meats laboratory of The Pennsylvania State University show that Hereford hides average 8½%, Angus 7½%, and Shorthorn 6½% of the live weight of the animals.

Hides should be trimmed (ears, lips, and fat off), spread out, hair side down, in a cool place and given a liberal application of ice cream salt or coarse sack or stock salt. It requires from 15 to 18 pounds of the latter to cure a 50- to 70-pound hide or ½ pound of rock salt per pound of hide. For best results, the hide cellar should have a uniform temperature of 50° to 60° F and lower for long time storage. Hides will shrink from 15% to 25% in curing and from 40% to 50% if left to dry. It has been estimated that the hide represents one-third of the value of all other by-products of cattle and that the United States uses one-fifth of the world's supply.

Yield of Edible By-products

The offal fat (internal or killing fat surrounding rumen and intestines) will average around 3% of a beef animal's live weight, ranging from 1% in good cattle up to 6½% in prime cattle. The heart, tongue, and liver are not weighed in with the carcass in determining dressed yield. They are sold separately. The kidney is considered a part of the carcass and is never removed in slaughtering. The liver will average about 1% of the live weight, the heart .35%, the tongue .25%, and the liquid blood about 3½% or 7¼ pounds of dried blood with 10% moisture content per 1,000 pounds of live weight.

The first (rumen) and second (reticulum) stomachs of cattle are washed, soaked in lime water, and scraped to remove the inside wall. They are then cooked (and sometimes pickled in vinegar) and sold as tripe. The intestines are soaked, slimed, and scrubbed, and used as sausage casings. Casings made from the small intestines are called rounds, those made from the large intestines are called middles or middies, and the blind gut is called the bung. Cleaned casings are cured in fine salt, tied into bundles or hanks, and packed in tierces for sale to sausage makers.

Care of the Beef Carcass

A thorough chilling during the first 24 hours is essential, otherwise the carcass may sour at the hip joint—a deep-seated joint from which the heat is slow to escape.

A desirable cooler temperature for chilling warm carcasses is 33° F. Since a group of warm carcasses will raise the temperature of a chill room considerably, it is a good practice to lower the temperature of the room to 5° below freezing before the carcasses are moved in.

Traditionally, carcasses of beef have been quartered before they were handled for shipment. The quarters were placed in special crimped paper sacks and covered with a stockinet. Great care had to be taken to keep carcasses away from odors or unclean places. The great difficulty in transporting fresh meat on long distance hauls was the fact that it came into indirect contact with so many odors before it ultimately reached the consumer that it very often lost its identity as far as flavor was concerned. Meat is very susceptible to foreign odors.

In 1966, some of the first pioneering moves were made to change the system of fresh meat distribution. Beef carcasses were fabricated centrally, packaged, and delivered to stores in boxes instead of in the conventional carcass form. In 1972, less than six years later, more than half the beef shipped to supermarkets was centrally prefabricated. That is a composite of all supermarkets. The chain supermarkets received two-thirds of their beef in this form. Thus, freight is being saved, that which used to pay for the shipment of waste fat and bones around the country. Furthermore, meat packaging has improved such that meat is stored and transported in airproof and moistureproof bags, thus maintaining its natural wholesomeness and quality for a much longer period.

FACTS ABOUT BEEF

Since cattle gain approximately 2% to 3% of their live weight at a meal, it would be logical to assume that a sales practice of deducting 2½% of the live weight to arrive at a just sales weight would be fair for all concerned. This should eliminate much quibbling over fill and should permit cattle to have feed and water at normal times or before them at all times.

There are a number of programs under which the United States has supplied livestock and meat products to nations handicapped by a lack of purchasing power. The two most important of these are Title I sales under Public Law 480, which are paid for in foreign currency, and dollar purchases financed under Section 402 of the Mutual Security Act.

In every 1,000-pound steer there is an amount of phosphorus equal to that found in a 100-pound bag of superphosphate.

Meat extract made from whale meat has a weaker flavor than beef extract, requiring 20% to 30% more of it to replace beef extract in a formula.

Kosher killed cattle are not stunned.

One ton of carcass beef requires 106 cubic feet of storage space; if boned it requires 80 cubic feet; if boned, compressed, and quick frozen it requires only 50 cubic feet of space.

The carcass meat formerly carried by 10 ships requires 3.7 ships to handle the meat if boneless, 1.6 ships to handle the meat if dehydrated, and only 1 ship to handle if the meat is compressed and dehydrated.

The hides from more than 100,000 cattle are required every year for leather accessories in the sports field.

Meat rationing was instituted on March 29, 1943, and ended November 23, 1945. Meat and livestock controls were removed October 15, 1946.

According to estimates of a tax expert, 114 hidden tax levies can be traced directly to the various ingredients of a hamburger sandwich and about 164 federal, state, and local taxes are molded into a cake of soap.

CHAPTER 6

Lamb Slaughter

Sheep and lamb production has long played an important part in the U.S. livestock industry. Since earliest records, sheep and lamb numbers have gone through several cyclical phases of increasing and decreasing production. An early estimate of sheep numbers indicates a peak in the United States of about 53 million head in 1884, peaks again near this level in 1909 and 1932, and an all-time high in 1942 of about 56 million head. Since 1942, sheep numbers have generally trended downward, reaching a level of about 16.5 million head on January 1, 1974.

"Sheep and lambs are produced on about 200,000 farms and ranches located in every state. The job of assembling, sorting, transporting, slaughtering, processing, and distributing sheep and lambs and subsequent products is a complex and costly job. In recent years, the job has become more difficult and costly as volume has declined and costs have increased. The relatively small and declining volume of numbers and products handled and the continual pressure on the parts of market operators, slaughterers, processors and distributors to increase per unit and per employee volume has put lamb at a relative disadvantage.

"Somewhat in contrast to the decentralization occurring in hog and cattle marketing and slaughtering, sheep and lamb slaughtering is concentrating in a few, larger more specialized plants. Many large areas of the country are no longer served by either adequate live markets or slaughtering facilities.

"Imports of lamb and mutton have increased during recent years until they now are equivalent to about 25% of combined U.S. lamb and mutton production of about 600 million pounds. This is approximately 20% of the total domestic supply which is about 750 million pounds. This situation has developed primarily because of a decrease in U.S. production and a need on the part of our major suppliers, Australia and New Zealand, for an additional market for their products.

"In recent years, Australia has accounted for more than 80% of the total combined lamb and mutton imports. New Zealand is the second largest source and represents about 17% of the total."[1]

The period between 1925 and 1940 witnessed the almost complete elimination of mutton from the diet of the American public. The Agricultural Marketing Service reports show that lamb constitutes over 94% of the ovine meat supply. The marketing of sheep at an early age has eliminated much of the consumer objection to this type of meat because mutton flavor is minimized or is entirely absent in lamb.

"It is important to note that imports of U.S. lamb and mutton products are primarily mutton. In 1968, total imports were approximately 147 million pounds (carcass weight equivalent) of which about 124 million pounds (carcass weight equivalent) was mutton and 23 million pounds was lamb. In terms of U.S. production, mutton imports represent about three times the domestic production whereas lamb constitutes about 4% to 5% of domestic lamb production.

"The end uses of lamb and mutton are quite different. Therefore, their use should be analyzed separately. Lamb is sold primarily in the form of consumer cuts whereas mutton is used largely in soup stock, sausages and other prepared meats."[2]

Hothouse lambs are rated by epicureans as being the most delectable of the lamb age groups.[3] They are dropped during the months of October, November, December, and January and are marketed between the ages of 6 to 10 weeks. The name hothouse is rather ambiguous, but its name indicates that these lambs have been housed in barns or sheds where they are protected from the cold weather.

Hothouse lambs may be defined as lambs that are dropped out of the regular lambing season and marketed at live weights ranging from 25 to 60 pounds. This makes the hog dressed weight, which is about 70% of the live weight, range between 18 and 42 pounds. The full dressed weight is 48% to 55% of the live weight. New York City prefers lambs weighing 30 to 40 pounds hog dressed (head and pelt on).

Hothouse lambs are followed by the spring lamb crop from our early lamb producing sections in the Southwest. Both of these groups furnish only a limited quantity of our bulk lamb supply. Lambs born during the regular spring lambing season and marketed the following winter are the chief source of lamb carcass meat. It is during the summer months that the supply of yearling mutton is heaviest, and helps to fill in the period when lambs are rather scarce. A yearling for slaughter purposes is a ewe or wether between 15 and 20 months of age. Over 20

---

1. Purdue University, Cooperative Extension Service.
2. Purdue University, Cooperative Extension Service.
3. Dr. Ellis Pierce, Cornell University.

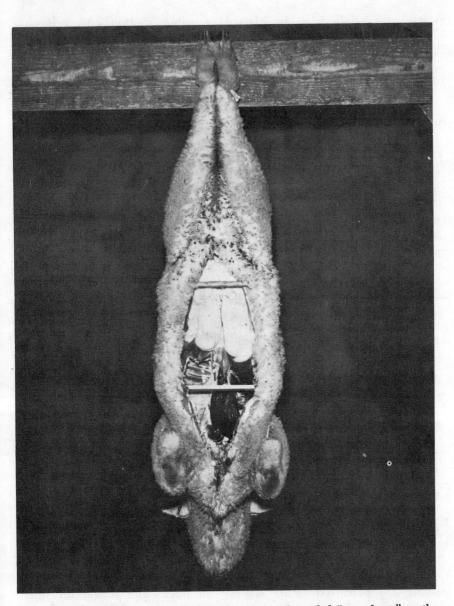

Fig. 6.1—Hothouse lamb (hog dressed). This lamb graded "extra fancy" on the New York City market. It was sired by a purebred Southdown ram and was out of a Hampshire-Dorset-Merino cross-bred ewe. It had an abundance of kidney fat, which is one of the most important factors in judging the finish and determining the grade. Hothouse lambs are dressed "pluck in." The pluck, in this case, consists of the liver, heart, lungs, gullet, and windpipe. This lamb weighed 39 pounds alive and 28 pounds, hog dressed.

months of age, all sheep are classed as mature mutton, and it is no longer possible to remove the foot at the break joint. Yearlings are divided into two main weight groups—those under 100 pounds and those over 100 pounds. Rams are classified as yearlings and two-year-olds and over, all weights. The top grade for rams is choice.

GRADE DESCRIPTION

A more complete discussion on lamb carcass grading with live and carcass pictures appears in Chapter 11.

Table 6.1—Market Classes and Grades of Slaughter Sheep and Lambs[1,2,3]

Lambs (110 Lbs. and Down)	Lambs (Shorn)	Ewes (Shorn)
Prime	Prime	Good
Choice	Choice	Utility
Good	Good	Cull
Utility	Utility	
Cull	Cull	

1. As utilized by the Livestock Division, Agricultural Service, U.S. Dept. of Agriculture.

2. USDA Yield Grades 1-5 exist for lambs, but are not normally utilized in reporting market classes and grades.

3. At times, length of pelt is attached to the market quotations of classes and grades using the following grade classifications: 1 = 1/2 in. to 1 in. wool length; 2 = 1/4 in. to 1/2 in.; 3 = 1/8 in. to 1/4 in.; 4 = 1/8 in.; fall clips = 1 in. to 1 1/2 in.; wool pelts = 1 1/2 in.

During the late spring and early summer, heavy lambs, those weighing over 100 pounds which produce carcasses weighing more than 50 pounds, are penalized rather severely in price. The reason for this lower price has been that lambs coming to market at that time were usually older yearlings carrying more waste fat which remained in and on the carcass after slaughter. Recently, modern lamb management, breeding, feeding, selection, and testing practices have fostered the production of young, fast growing, muscular and efficient lambs with lean carcasses. Thus, such heavy lean lambs should *not be* discounted at the market place but instead be given a premium. Modern management must be fostered or the U.S. lamb industry will continue to spiral downward into oblivion.

Currently, 74.3% of the slaughter sheep and lambs are procured direct at country points, 13.7% at terminal markets, and 12.0% at auction markets. In 1963, direct purchases accounted for only 56% of the slaughter sheep and lambs. Now, 8.4% are purchased on carcass grade and weight.

Prime

Currently, 12% of the lamb carcasses graded qualify for U.S. Prime. Furthermore, 73% of all lamb carcasses are quality graded. Thus, only a small percent ($73\% \times 12\% = 8.7\%$) of the total lamb population is graded U.S. Prime. Lambs to grade prime must have the wide, deep, smooth, compact conformation characteristic of animals of the meat type. Shoulders should be thick and neat, back broad and thick, and the legs exceptionally plump. The finish must be sufficient to cover the backbone so that the backbone is not noticeable to the touch. This finish must be firm and evenly distributed.

Choice

Eighty-seven percent of lambs graded qualify for the U.S. Choice grade. Thus, it is almost "all-inclusive." Lambs of this grade are slightly deficient to prime lambs in conformation and differ primarily in a more moderate amount of finish. Choice lambs have sufficient quality to satisfy consumer requirements.

Good

Less than 1% of lambs graded qualify for U.S. Good. This grade includes lambs that are somewhat deficient in meatiness and finish and includes a number of the better animals of the fine wool breed. It represents a grade that produces carcasses that are in demand because of their lack of trimming fat.

Utility

Approximately ¼ of 1% of lambs graded, grade Utility. Lambs that are narrow and somewhat rangy, with long legs, high twist, and unsymmetrical conformation come in this grade. The backs of these lambs will show a decided prominence of bone, have rough, prominent shoulders, bare ribs and loins, and show inferior breeding.

Cull

Representatives of the Cull grade are practically non-existent. Thin, unsymmetrical, gaunt, leggy, rangy, narrow, long necked, and low quality lambs make up this grade.

DRESSING LAMB

A 24-hour fast previous to slaughter is probably of greater importance with sheep than with other forms of livestock. It not only facilitates the eviscerating process but adds materially to the bright appearance of the carcass. Some claims are made, although not proven, that the removal of the pelt is made easier by a fasting period.

Handling

Never lift a sheep by grasping the fleece as this causes a surface bruise on the carcass. Instead, place one hand under the jaw and the other at the dock and lead the lamb. Grasp a sheep by the leg when catching it.

Tools and Equipment

A 5-inch scimitar boning knife or a thin, well-ground skinning knife is best adapted for the job of pelting a sheep.

A trough-like skinning rack on legs about 18 inches high for holding a sheep on its back is very handy. The trough is 6 inches wide at the bottom with sloping sides 6 inches high. These racks are also used for veal and are called lamb or veal racks. In the absence of a rack, use a table or a platform.

Stunning and Sticking

A sharp blow on top of the poll will stun sheep that do not have horns. The use of the captive bolt with the mushroom head or the use of an electric stunner (see figures 6.2 and 6.3) is recommended.

Hoist or place the stunned sheep on a table, or on a sheep and veal rack. Grasp the jaw with the left hand, insert the knife behind the jaw, blade-edge outward, and draw the knife out through the pelt (Figure 6.4).

Pelting

With the sheep lying on its back in the rack, grasp a foreleg or

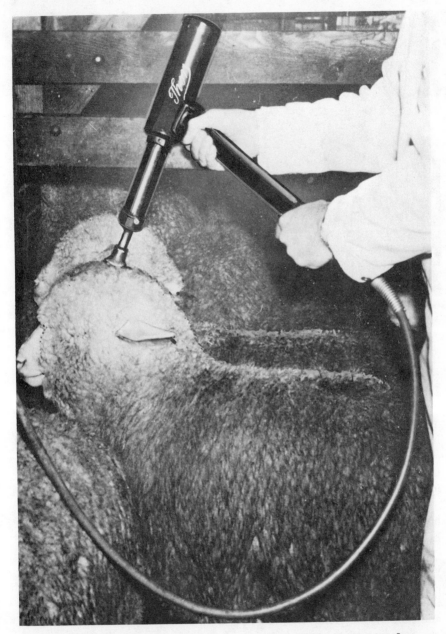

Fig. 6.2—A compression stunner. This particular model uses compressed air—no cartridges. Its high velocity blow is effective in painlessly stunning cattle, hogs, and sheep. It is furnished with penetrating or non-penetrating head. The above illustrates the mushroom or non-penetrating type head used for veal and lamb. (Courtesy, Thor Power Tool Co., Aurora, Illinois)

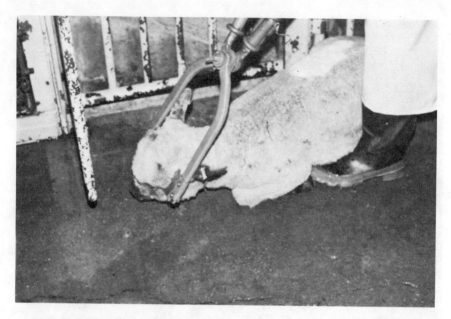

Fig. 6.3—An inexpensive electric stunner. (Courtesy, University of Illinois)

secure foreleg to scabbard chain with a bent shroud pin and open the pelt down the front of the leg to the jaw. Do the same on the other foreleg, having the two cuts meet in a point in front of the brisket. Skin out the forelegs at this time (Figure 6.5). The front foot is removed at the "break joint" in lambs. The break joint is recognized by a swelling in the cannon bone at its lower extremity just above the hoof (wrist or spool joint). In yearling mutton, and mutton older than 15 months, the break joint is ossified and the front foot is removed at the spool joint. A comparison of a spool and break joint is shown in Figure 6.6.

Grasp a hind leg and open it down the back of the leg from the hoof to the bung. The knife should be held fairly flat to the carcass in making the opening in order not to cut the fell or expose the muscle.

Skin out the hind shank (Figure 6.7) and remove the foot at the joint just above the hoof, two full joints from the pastern or mutton joint (Figure 6.8). Loosen the tendon over the back of the hock and then proceed to skin out the opposite hind leg. Figure 6.9 shows forelegs and hind shanks being skinned out.

Standing to the rear left side of the sheep, grasp the cut edge of the pelt at the bung and pull, at the same time using the fist of the right hand to fist the pelt loose. Loosen it around the flank, cod, or udder area, and then step to the right front side of the sheep and grasp and

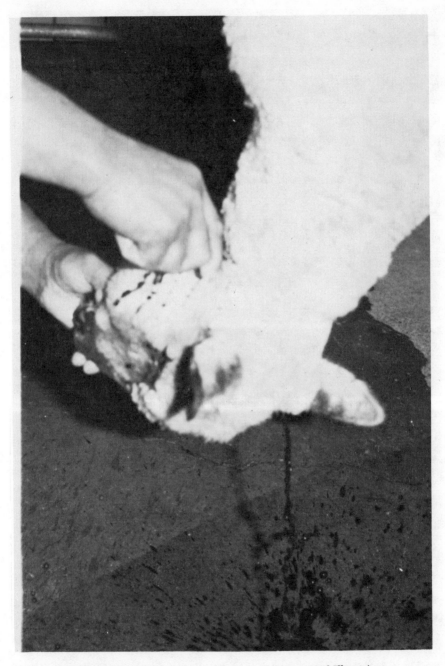

Fig. 6.4—Bleeding the lamb. (Courtesy, University of Illinois)

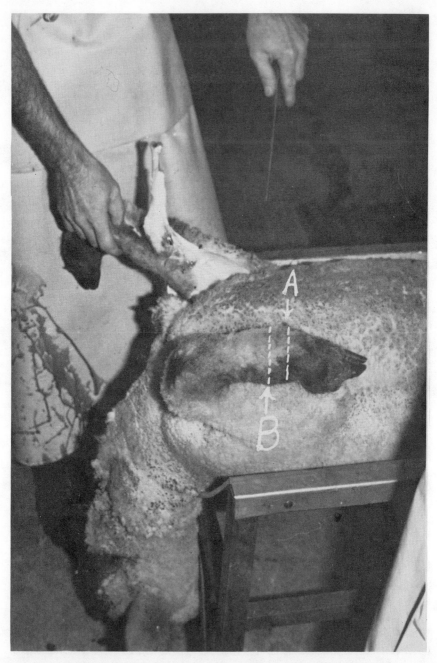

Fig. 6.5—Skinning out a foreleg. (A) Location of spool or mutton joint. (B) Location of lamb or break joint. (Courtesy, University of Illinois)

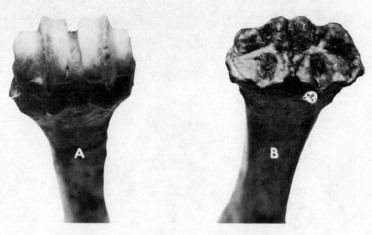

Fig. 6.6—(A) A spool or mutton joint. (B) A lamb or break joint.

pull the V-shaped piece of pelt over the brisket. The pelt may then be fisted over the belly by turning and pushing the fist against the pelt, not against the carcass.

A strong cord may be used to tie the tendons of both hind legs together, or an S-hook may be inserted through the tendons of both legs to engage in an overhead trolley or rack. In order to prevent back and groin injuries to the workers, a mechanical hoist should be used to hoist the lamb to the overhead trolly or rack. If a mechanical hoist is not available, the job should be done by two men.

Open the pelt down the center of the belly and fist it loose around the side and up the leg, being careful to avoid breaking the fell—a thin, colorless, connective tissue membrane that separates the pelt from the carcass and that should always be left intact on the carcass. It is safer to fist up the leg than to pull the pelt down the leg. Unless the skin is started right, pulling the pelt down the leg may tear the protective fell and expose the muscle. Sever the bung and pull the pelt from the tail.

The pelt is then fisted over the shoulder and pulled off the back and neck. It is necessary to maintain clean hands when fisting to avoid contaminating the lamb carcass.

Sever the head at the atlas joint. Skin out the head and remove the tongue.

Eviscerating

Make an opening at the cod, insert the first and second fingers to

Fig. 6.7—Opening the pelt on the back of the hind leg.

Fig. 6.8—Disjointing the foot on the hind leg. The dotted line across marks the break joint. If the foot were removed at this joint, the anchorage of the tendons (A) would be weakened and the legs would have to be tied together at the hocks instead of the tendons.

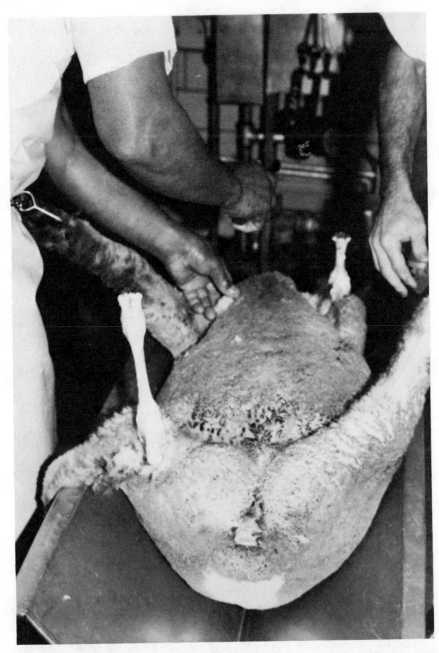

Fig. 6.9–Technique used to skin out forelegs and hind shanks. Butchers hold legs taut with shroud pin hook while skinning. Note break joint on foreleg, spool joint on hind leg. (Courtesy, University of Illinois)

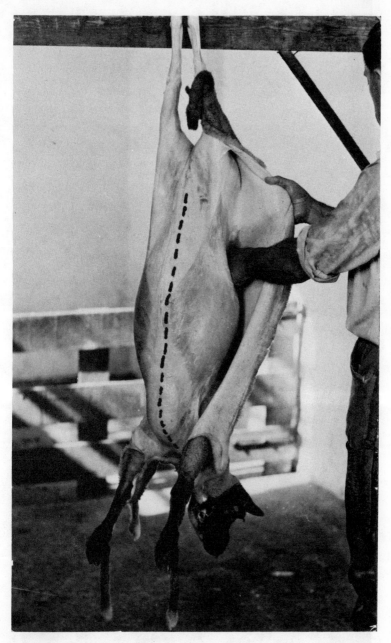

Fig. 6.10—Fisting. Practically the entire pelt is removed from the carca:s by forcing the fist between the pelt and the carcass. The dotted line shows where the carcass is to be opened for evisceration. The pelvis of a sheep is rarely split.

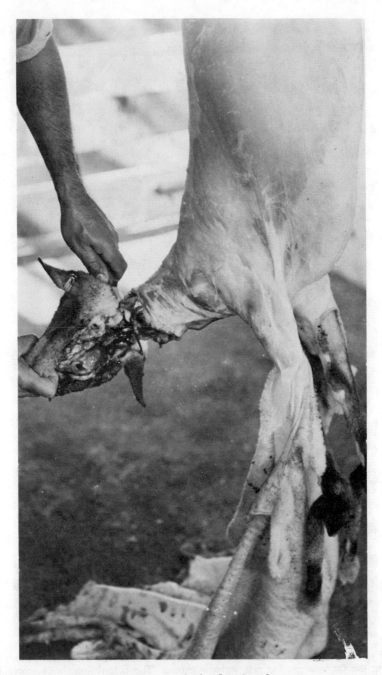

Fig. 6.11—Removing the head at the atlas joint.

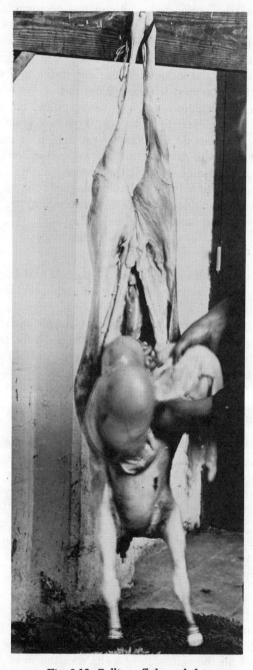

Fig. 6.12—Pulling off the web fat.

guard the point of the knife, and continue the opening to the breast. Remove the caul or web fat. Taking a position to the rear of the carcass, cut around and loosen the bung. Assume the original position, insert the thumb and finger and grasp the loose bung. Use the knife to sever the ureters that lead to the kidneys. These are strong and will tear out the kidneys and the kidney fat if they are not cut.

The stomach and intestines are now easily pulled out and the bile duct removed from the liver. Split the chest with a knife or saw and remove the pluck. Packers do not remove the spleen or smelts.

Wash the inside and outside of the carcass and especially wash the blood out of the neck and chest cavity with tepid water. Trim all scrag ends off the neck and skewer the foreshank up against the arm. This latter operation plumps the shoulder and keeps the foreshank out of the way in a crowded commercial lamb cooler.

The Intestinal Tract

The liver from a lamb weighs about 1¼ pounds and is equal to veal liver in tenderness. It does not have any mutton taste but is slightly dryer than veal liver.

The small intestines are stripped and cleaned and if free from nodules are used for weiner casings. Violin strings, tennis racket strings, and surgical ligatures are also made from the small intestines.

The endocrine glands are used for manufacturing gland products such as thyroxin, adrenalin, insulin, pituitary extract, and ovarian extract.

Commercial Lamb Slaughter

Currently more than 94% of the sheep and lambs slaughtered in the U.S. are slaughtered in Federally inspected plants, 3.8% in other commercial plants (state inspected) and 2.1% on the farm. Thus, the majority of sheep and lamb slaughter takes place in large, highly mechanized slaughter plants, each capable of handling 200,000 to 700,000 per year. With automated equipment, including a continuously or intermittently moving rail, rate of slaughter generally ranges from 250 to 350 animals per hour. A glimpse of such a mechanized operation is provided in figures 6.13 through 6.16.

Pelts

The pelt is rubbed with fine salt to preserve it until the time it is sold. In packing houses, a depilatory paste made of lime and sodium sulphide is spread on the skin side of pelts and the next day the wool can be pulled. The skins are sold to tanners. Wool is the chief by-product

Table 6.2—Commercial Sheep and Lamb Slaughter, Number of Head (in Thousands), Ranked by States, 1972[1,2,3]

Rank	State	Number	Rank	State	Number
1	Colorado	1,889.0	24	Idaho	12.4
2	California	1,742.0	25	Kansas	4.7
3	Texas	1,505.0	26	Louisiana	3.7
4	Nebraska	903.5	27	Wisconsin	3.6
5	New Jersey	649.5	28	Nevada	3.4
6	Utah	517.0	29	Wyoming	3.0
7	Iowa	465.0	30	West Virginia	2.6
8	Illinois	430.5	31	Montana	2.4
9	South Dakota	427.5	31	Oklahoma	2.4
10	Michigan	405.0	33	Virginia	1.7
11	Minnesota	231.3	34	Arizona	1.2
12	Kentucky	225.4	35	North Carolina	0.9
13	Washington	198.4	35	North Dakota	0.9
14	Pennsylvania	134.5	37	Florida	0.7
15	New Mexico	123.7	38	Arkansas	0.2
16	Oregon	94.5	38	Mississippi	0.2
17	Tennessee	85.4	40	Alabama	0.1
18	Ohio	66.0	41	South Carolina	0.1
19	New York	65.2	42	Georgia	- -
20	Delaware & Maryland	48.7	43	Hawaii	- -
21	Indiana	19.5			
22	Missouri	17.1			
23	New England[4]	13.1	Total		10,301.0

1. *Livestock* and *Meat* *Statistics*, USDA Stat. Bul. No. 522.

2. Includes slaughter under Federal inspection and other commercial slaughter. Excludes farm slaughter.

3. Commercial slaughter not estimated in Alaska.

4. New England includes Maine, New Hampshire, Vermont, Massachusetts, Rhode Island, and Connecticut.

of sheep slaughter and ranges from two to eight pounds of pulled wool per head.

The value of a sheep skin for tanning decreases as the value of the wool for spinning and weaving purposes increases.

A common depilatory used on the farm is made by slaking burnt limestone and spreading the fresh paste about ⅛ inch thick over the skin side of the moist pelt. In several days the wool can be pulled.

Fig. 6.13—Lambs are suspended by all four limbs to position for initial legging.
(Courtesy, John Morrell & Co.)

Fig. 6.14—Pelt is pulled by hand as lambs move at approximately 200 per hour
(Courtesy, John Morrell & Co.)

Fig. 6.15—Federal inspector (in white) examines each carcass following evisceration. (Courtesy, John Morrell & Co.)

Fig. 6.16—Partial view of some 2,000 to 3,000 lamb carcasses in cooler containing the day's kill. They are crowded but adequately spaced for chilling. (Courtesy, John Morrell & Co.)

Yield

Yearlings in prime condition, with the proper 24-hour shrink will dress from 55% to 61%.

Fat show lambs average about 2% to 3% lower.

Choice lambs should average 52%, whereas the run of mutton type slaughter lambs in good condition will average 48% as against 40% for the fine wool breeds.

Aging Lamb and Mutton

Lamb and mutton rank with beef in keeping qualities, dependent upon the temperature of the refrigerator and the amount of fat covering the carcass. The higher grades can be aged for several weeks and choice yearling carcasses are best if aged three or four weeks. However, most packers move lamb out of their coolers and into the marketing sequence as soon as possible after killing, i.e., 24 hours or less after slaughter.

Mutton Flavor

The peculiar mutton flavor characteristic of some yearlings and many aged sheep has been ascribed to:

1. Slow dressing—the flesh absorbing the gases formed in the intestinal tract.
2. Improper dressing—the fleece being allowed to come in contact with the dressed carcass and soiling it with dung.
3. Age—the absorption of the wool oil by the fat.

To offset the absorption of gases, it is a practice in some countries to force water or air into the intestinal tract through the rectum.

The author made a series of interesting tests consisting of the following:

1. A lamb was bled and left hanging with the fleece on for several hours until it was well bloated before it was eviscerated. After aging for seven days under refrigeration, some rib chops were taken from the carcass and broiled. Result—no mutton flavor.
2. A lamb carcass was rubbed with the wool side of the pelt. Result—no mutton flavor.
3. A lamb chop from a carcass previously tested for mutton flavor (which was absent) was suspended in a jar that was then filled with gas drawn from the rumen of another carcass. The chop remained in the gas-filled jar for 12 hours. Result—no mutton flavor.
4. A similar chop was rubbed with extracted wool oil. Result—an objectionable flavor but different from the characteristic mutton flavor.
5. A rib chop from each of 10 aged Merino ewes was broiled. No mutton flavor (likewise no fat).
6. The fat from three fat yearling show wethers was fried. Result—no mutton flavor; in fact, it tasted somewhat similar to bacon fat.
7. The same writer was served two lamb chops in a restaurant. Result—mutton flavor and no way to tell what caused it.

FACTS ABOUT LAMB

Lamb is the most easily digested of our commercial meats and therefore finds wide use in the diet of convalescents.

There is less religious prejudice against lamb and mutton than any other meat except fish.

The flesh of goats is called "chevon."

The fat surrounding the paunch and intestines of sheep is called the "web" or "caul" fat.

About 30% of a good lamb or mutton carcass is in the leg.

Fewer lamb and mutton carcasses are condemned by the meat inspectors than any other class of livestock.

New Zealanders consume more lamb and mutton than any other people.

The size and keeping quality of a lamb carcass make it a very suitable source of farm meat.

A common practice in some markets is to drape the web fat over the front of the hind legs.

"Hog dressed" means to dress with head and pelt on but feet and viscera removed. The object of this method of dressing is to hold down shrinkage and thus aid in maintaining pink color of baby lamb.

Hot-house lambs are dressed "pluck-in," packed in barrels or bundles, and shipped by express or truck to large metropolitan centers where a demand for this specialized product exists.

Hot-house lambs are now sold on a per cent basis. Before World War II, they were sold by the carcass and not by the pound. Choice to fancy grades averaged between $8 nd $10 per head, the higher prices being realized on 30- to 40-pound carcasses for the Christmas market.

The condition in hot-house lamb is based on the amount and covering of kidney fat. A short, thick, compact lamb with kidneys entirely covered with white fat will grade as extra fancy, which is the top grade in this class.

The record receipt of sheep in one day on the Chicago market was 71,792 on Oct. 16, 1911.

The United States imports about five million pounds of sheep casings annually and eleven million pounds of other natural casings.

The record year (1943) for sheep and lamb slaughter (inspected, non-inspected and farm) was a total of 27,070,000 head.

The dressed yield for sheep and lambs in the United States (inspected, non-inspected, and farm) averages 49.5%.

California and Arizona spring lambs reach the eastern market during April, May, and June.

About 3.75 pounds of grease wool is required to make one pound of woolen cloth.

Pulled wools constitute about one-seventh of all the wool produced in the United States.

Sheep skins from which the wool has been pulled from long wooled sheep supply the best wearing leather, Merino the poorest.

Goat skins are more valuable than sheep skins because they are larger and wear better.

A great deal of sheep skin is used for bookbinding, hat sweat bands, shoe linings, gloves, and chamois skins.

A "hoggett," a "haggerel," a "lamb hog," or "tup hog" (if castrated— a "wether hog") are terms applied to a male lamb from weaning time until shorn.

"Haggis" is a Scottish food made from hearts, lungs and livers of sheep or calves, highly seasoned, mixed with oatmeal, and broiled in a sheep stomach.

The small intestines from 11 sheep are needed to supply the gut strings for a tennis racket.

CHAPTER 7

Veal and Calf Slaughter

Considerable confusion is evident in circles outside the livestock industry as to the distinction that exists between a vealer and a calf. The United States Department of Agriculture defines a vealer as an immature bovine animal usually not over 3 months of age that has subsisted largely on milk or milk replacers, thus making the color of its lean light, grayish pink. Such veal has the characteristic trimness of middle associated with limited paunch development. A calf is defined as an immature bovine animal between 3 and 8 months of age which for a considerable period of time has subsisted in part or entirely on feeds other than milk and has thus developed a heavier middle. Grayish red is the typical color of calf carcass lean.

Since it is rather difficult to determine the age of a vealer or calf, no set age can be given as a definite dividing line. Weight and conformation are used more as a basis for determining their classification, with weight being the determining price factor among vealers and calves of equal conformation, finish, and quality.

VEALERS

There is no sex classification made for vealers since they are not old enough for sex conditions to have had any influence on their physical characteristics. They are sold on the market for slaughter purposes only. The greatest supply of vealers comes from dairy farms during the spring and fall months. The large market centers for veal are New York City, Buffalo, Chicago, Detroit, Milwaukee, and South St. Paul.

MARKET WEIGHTS AND GRADES OF VEALERS

Prime Grade

Vealers of this grade are usually crossbred or high grade animals

Table 7.1—Market Weights and Grades of Vealers

Lightweight (110 Lbs. and Down)	Mediumweight (110 to 180 Lbs.)	Heavyweight (180 Lbs. and Up)
Choice	Prime	Prime
Good	Choice	Choice
Standard	Good	Good
Utility	Standard	Standard
	Utility	

of beef type or exceptional individuals of the dairy breeds. They are smooth, deep, thick, and compact, and the udder or scrotum shows a marked fullness, indicating good condition. Vealers of this grade range from 4 to 8 weeks of age, weigh between 140 and 190 pounds, and dress from 62% to 67%. They are rather scarce on the market.

Choice Grade

Representatives of this grade are quite similar to prime veal in every respect except finish. They are more plentiful on the market than prime veal and are usually slightly younger. They range in weight from 110 to 140 pounds and dress around 60%. Some beef breeding is represented in this grade, although animals of dairy breeding predominate.

Good Grade

Vealers of this grade must possess a moderately high degree of the qualities of the higher grades, but they carry less finish and show more bone and less uniformity. They range between 3 to 6 weeks of age, usually weigh from 110 to 120 pounds, and dress from 55% to 60%. They show mostly dairy breeding.

Standard Grade

Vealers of this grade are largely of dairy type or scrub breeding. They lack finish, are rather leggy and hippy, rough in the shoulder, and light in the round. The market supply is greatest during April, May, and June. They are relatively young, weigh from 90 to 110 pounds, and dress from 50% to 55%.

Utility Grade

This grade is deficient in every respect, the vealers being thin, rangy, and angular. They include a rather wide range of weights (90 to 180 pounds) and individuals may be very fine boned and small, or large boned and coarse. The breeding is very plain and the dressed yield averages 50%.

Immature Veal

The practice on many dairy farms which do not have purebred stock is to allow the calf to suckle the dam for several days to remove the colostrum milk. The calf is then sold to a dealer for slaughter or it may be sold to a farmer or dealer who keeps some cows for the purpose of vealing calves. The carcasses of these immature vealers are usually designated as *bob veal*. To discourage the sale of immature veal, most states have legislation regulating the legal age at which veal can be slaughtered.

Vealing calves refers to the feeding of young calves either by hand or by letting them suckle strange cows and supplementing the milk ration with a grain gruel. The most recent calf feeding practice is to use milk replacements. When such feeding has produced calves of the desired weight they are sent to slaughter.

MARKET CLASSES OF SLAUGHTER CALVES

Sex conditions have caused some changes in the physical characteristics of calves over 3 months of age that are not evident in vealers, and hence the market classifies calves as to sex. Size and weight are important in the selection of calves, either for slaughter purposes or for further feeding. The choice and good grades are individuals that show varying degrees of beef breeding, usually being high grade or crossbred calves, and are only offered occasionally at any market for slaughter purposes. They are generally resold as stocker or feeder calves to be grown out and fattened as yearlings or as two-year-olds.

Table 7.2—Market Classes of Slaughter Calves (Steers, Heifers, and Bulls)

Lightweight (200 Lbs. and Down)	Mediumweight (200 to 300 Lbs.)	Heavyweight (300 Lbs. and Up)
Choice	Choice	Choice
Good	Good	Good
Standard	Standard	Standard
Utility	Utility	Utility

The standard and utility grades are deficient in conformation, finish, and quality and show dairy or scrub breeding. They are numerous throughout the year, especially in the autumn.

METHODS OF DRESSING VEAL

Veal is dressed with either "skin off" or "skin on" (hog dressed). Most markets require the "hog style" carcass because it prevents the outer surface of the carcass from becoming dark and dry. Where carcasses have the skin off, the practice is to remove the skin just before shipment and cover the carcass with muslin or a gelatin dip to keep it from becoming soiled in handling and to preserve the fresh appearance and bloom. Calf carcasses are dressed generally with skin off and split into sides, in the same manner as beef.

Handling, Stunning, and Sticking

Vealers and calves should be kept off feed for 18 hours before slaughter. They should be handled with care to avoid bruises and undue excitement.

Any of the mechanical stunners can be used but the mushroom type head is preferable. Electric stunning works well on calves.

Fig. 7.1—Fisting the skin from the sides.

Two methods of sticking are common. The one is to "kosher stick," or cut the throat just back of the jaw. The other is to stick in front of the brisket as in the sticking of beef. Since calves struggle for a longer period ofter sticking than other classes of livestock, it is well to hoist them before sticking. This keeps them clean and makes it easier to skin out the head and foreshanks.

Dressing

Skin off.—The method of opening the skin is the same as in beef. Since a calf skin is thinner and softer and more readily scored or cut than is a beef hide, the better plan is to pull or pound it off the sides and back of the carcass.

Skin on (hog dressed).—The skin is opened from the hoof to the knee on the foreshank and to the hock on the hind shank. Skin out the foreshanks and hind shanks and remove them at the break joint. Skin out the head and remove it at the atlas joint. Split the skin and carcass over the median line of the belly from the back end of the brisket to the cod or udder. Cut around the bung and let it drop into the abdominal cavity. Remove the entrails from the abdominal cavity but leave the liver in the carcass. The gall bladder must be removed from the liver.

Cut the diaphragm and remove the pluck. Care must be exercised in this operation in order to keep from mutilating the thymus gland or sweetbreads. The sweetbread and liver are considered part of a veal carcass and are weighed with the carcass. They are removed in calf carcasses.

The caul or stomach fat is draped over the legs (rounds) of the veal carcass if the veal is dressed, skin off.

Commercial Veal and Calf Slaughter

Public markets (terminals and auctions) continue as the predominant source of slaughter veal and calves accounting for 68.4% of the purchases, while 31.6% are purchased direct. Only 6.7% of total purchases are on a carcass weight and grade basis.

Seventy-six percent of the veal and calves slaughtered in the United States are slaughtered in Federally inspected plants, 20% in other (state inspected) plants, and 4% on the farm. A modern veal and calf processing plant, utilizing a continuous, mechanically powered rail system is depicted in figures 7.3 through 7.5.

FACTS ABOUT VEAL

There is no age limit set by law on veal slaughtered in Pennsylvania.

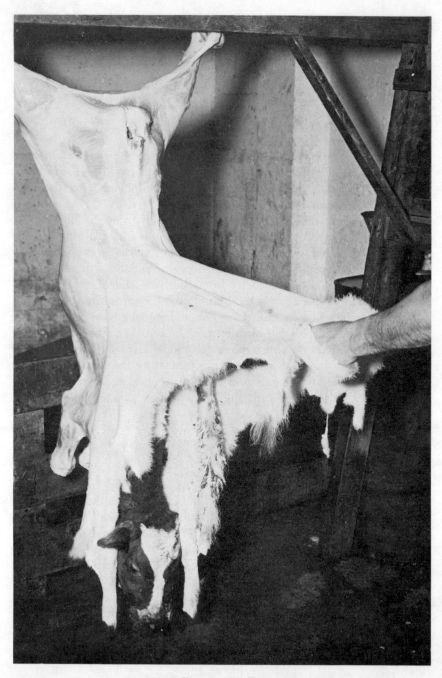

Fig. 7.2–Pulling the skin from the back.

Table 7.3—Commercial Veal and Calf Slaughter, Number of Head (in Thousands), Ranked by States, 1972[1,2,3]

Rank	State	Number	Rank	State	Number
1	New York	643.0	24	Oregon	7.8
2	New Jersey	275.1	25	Minnesota	7.5
3	Pennsylvania	258.3	26	Oklahoma	4.3
4	Wisconsin	233.0	27	Nebraska	4.2
5	New England[4]	215.1	28	Alabama	4.0
6	Louisiana	171.6	29	Arkansas	2.8
7	Iowa	163.5	30	Tennessee	2.7
8	Texas	160.5	31	Arizona	2.5
9	California	119.5	32	Utah	2.0
10	South Carolina	116.1	33	West Virginia	1.8
11	Tennessee	108.4	34	Nevada	1.2
12	Michigan	95.0	35	Idaho	0.5
13	Florida	92.7	36	Kansas	0.4
14	Virginia	81.8	37	Wyoming	0.2
15	Illinois	81.1	38	Colorado	0.1
16	Ohio	45.4	38	North Dakota	0.1
17	Mississippi	44.8	38	South Dakota	0.1
18	Indiana	40.1	41	Hawaii	--
19	Georgia	18.9	41	Montana	--
20	Delaware & Maryland	15.0	41	New Mexico	--
20	Missouri	15.0			
22	North Carolina	8.9			
23	Washington	8.1	Total		3,052.9

1. *Livestock* and *Meat* *Statistics*, USDA Stat. Bul. No. 522.

2. Includes slaughter under Federal inspection and other commercial slaughter. Excludes farm slaughter.

3. Commercial slaughter not estimated in Alaska.

4. New England includes Maine, New Hampshire, Vermont, Massachusetts, Rhode Island, and Connecticut.

"Bob" or immature veal, although not unwholesome, is an uneconomical buy because of (1) the high moisture content, (2) the large proportion of bone to lean, and (3) the low quality.

The skins from stillborn calves are called "slunk skins" and have a short fine hair. Cattlemen have them tanned and made into jackets and vests.

The skins from immature or "bob veal" are called "deacon skins" and generally weigh under 9 pounds.

Fig. 7.3—A general view of a well illuminated, compact, veal and calf dressing department. Note hearts and livers on rack in right foreground. (Courtesy, *Meat Processing*)

Fig. 7.4—The Federal inspector checks heads along the modern viscera table. (Courtesy, *Meat Processing*)

Fig. 7.5—Two views of an eviscerator at work. (Courtesy, *Meat Processing*)

The most desirable calf skins weigh from 9 to 15 pounds. Those weighing between 15 and 25 pounds are called "kip skins."

Veal consumption in the United States is greatest among the foreign population.

A large percentage of gelatin comes from the bones of veal.

The largest percentage of veal is slaughtered in packing plants located in large dairy centers.

Each state has its own regulations concerning the age at which veal can be slaughtered, ranging from the statement that veal must be wholesome (Pennsylvania) to three, four, six, and eight weeks of age.

Veal carcasses are sold either whole or divided into fore and hind saddles. Calf carcasses are also split and sold by the side.

A veal liver of usual size weigh from three to four pounds and sells for two to three times the price of beef liver.

Sweetbreads of veal are sold either by the pair or by weight.

The heads of veal calves find favor with peoples of foreign extraction who cook them and use the head meat and broth with noodles or as gelled meat.

Because of the high moisture and gelatin content of veal, it finds wide use in a beef, pork, and veal mixture for the making of meat loaf.

Live veal prices in the east are generally a dollar per hundredweight higher than top prices for similar grades in Chicago.

About 4% of the calves slaughtered in the United States are slaughtered on farms or for farmers by freezer plants.

CHAPTER 8

Dressing Poultry and Game

POULTRY

Since 1925 there has been a spectacular rise in the production of commercial broilers in the United States. Broiler production started to expand in the Delmarva section of Delaware, Maryland, and Virginia and increased in the United States from 34 million (4% of the total chicken meat supply) in 1934 to 3,089 million at the present time, accounting for over 90% of all chicken meat consumption and almost 22% of the combined poultry and red meat consumption.

A highly commercialized operation for killing, dressing, eviscerating, cutting up, packaging, and transporting chickens has been developed that provides a constant supply of ready-to-cook poultry in supermarkets across the United States. So rapid and constant are the present supply channels that less than 10% of this product is sold frozen, the major portion being sold fresh chilled. Turkeys are still highly seasonal, with 80% being frozen for future consumption, while the corresponding figure for ducks and geese is 40%.

Standards and Grades[1]

The difference between standards of quality and grades is sometimes misunderstood. The standards of quality enumerate the various factors that determine the grade. These factors, such as fat covering, fleshing, exposed flesh, discolorations etc. when evaluated collectively, determine the grade of the bird.

The U.S. Consumer Grades for Poultry are by far the most important, since they are the grades used at the retail level. The U.S. Consumer Grades are: U.S. Grade A, U.S. Grade B, and U.S. Grade C.

---

1. *Poultry Grading Manual,* Agricultural Handbook No. 31, U.S. Dept. of Agriculture.

The U.S. Procurement Grades are designed primarily for institutional use. These grades are: U.S. Procurement Grade I and U.S. Procurement Grade II. The procurement grades place more emphasis on meat yield than on appearance.

Modern breeding, feeding, and management practices have resulted in improved poultry. These factors, together with more efficient marketing and procurement practices, have made it unnecessary to have wholesale poultry grades and live poultry grades. The individual quality standards for live poultry are still used on a limited basis, since they provide a criterion to determine when flocks are ready to market.

Classes of Poultry[2]

"Kind" refers to the different species of poultry, such as chickens, turkeys, ducks, geese, guineas and pigeons. The kinds of poultry are divided into "classes" by groups which are essentially of the same physical characteristics such as fryers or hens. These physical characteristics are associated with age and sex.

The kinds and classes of live, dressed, and ready-to-cook poultry listed here are in general use in all segments of the poultry industry.

The following provisions apply to live poultry, dressed poultry, and individual carcasses of ready-to-cook poultry, in determining the kind of poultry and its class.

Chickens

The following are the various classes of chickens:

1. ROCK CORNISH GAME OR CORNISH GAME HEN. A Rock Cornish game hen or Cornish game hen is a young, immature chicken (usually five to seven weeks of age) weighing not more than 2 pounds (ready-to-cook weight), which was prepared from a Cornish chicken or the progeny of a Cornish chicken crossed with another breed of chicken.
2. BROILER OR FRYER. A broiler or fryer is a young chicken (usually 9 to 12 weeks of age) of either sex, with tender meat, soft, pliable, smooth-textured skin, and flexible breastbone cartilage.
3. ROASTER. A roaster is a young chicken (usually three to five months of age) of either sex, with tender meat, soft, pliable, smooth-textured skin, and breastbone cartilage that may be somewhat less flexible than that of a broiler or fryer.

---

2. *Poultry Grading Manual*, Agricultural Handbook No. 31, U.S. Department of Agriculture.

4. CAPON. A capon is a surgically unsexed male chicken (usually under eight months of age) with tender meat and soft, pliable, smooth-textured skin.

5. STAG. A stag is a male chicken (usually under 10 months of age) with coarse skin, somewhat toughened and darkened flesh, and considerable hardening of the breastbone cartilage. Stags show a condition of fleshing and a degree of maturity intermediate between that of a roaster and a cock or rooster.

6. HEN OR STEWING CHICKEN OR FOWL. A hen or stewing chicken or fowl is a mature female chicken (usually more than 10 months of age) with meat less tender than that of a roaster and nonflexible breastbone tip.

7. COCK OR ROOSTER. A cock or rooster is a mature male chicken with coarse skin, toughened and darkened meat, and hardened breastbone tip.

Turkeys

The following are the various classes of turkeys:

1. FRYER-ROASTER TURKEY. A fryer-roaster turkey is a young, immature turkey (usually under 16 weeks of age) of either sex, with tender meat, soft, pliable, smooth-textured skin, and flexible breastbone cartilage.

2. YOUNG HEN TURKEY. A young hen turkey is a young female turkey (usually five to seven months of age) with tender meat, soft, pliable, smooth-textured skin, and breastbone cartilage that is somewhat less flexible than a fryer-roaster turkey.

3. YOUNG TOM TURKEY. A young tom turkey is a young male turkey (usually five to seven months of age) with tender meat, soft, pliable, smooth-textured skin, and breastbone cartilage that is somewhat less flexible than in a fryer-roaster turkey.

4. YEARLING HEN TURKEY. A yearling hen turkey is a fully matured female turkey (usually under 15 months of age) with reasonably tender meat and reasonably smooth-textured skin.

5. YEARLING TOM TURKEY. A yearling tom turkey is a fully matured male turkey (usually under 15 months of age) with reasonably tender meat and reasonably smooth-textured skin.

6. MATURE TURKEY OR OLD TURKEY (HEN OR TOM). A mature or old turkey is an old turkey (usually in excess of 15 months of age) of either sex, with coarse skin and toughened flesh.

(For labeling purposes, the designation of sex within the class name is optional and the three classes of young turkeys may be grouped and designated as "young turkeys.")

Ducks

The following are the various classes of ducks:

1. BROILER DUCKLING OR FRYER DUCKLING. A broiler duckling or fryer duckling is a young duck (usually under 8 weeks of age) of either sex, with tender meat, a soft bill, and a soft windpipe.
2. ROASTER DUCKLING. A roaster duckling is a young duck (usually under 16 weeks of age) of either sex, with tender meat, a bill that is not completely hardened, and a windpipe that is easily dented.
3. MATURE DUCK OR OLD DUCK. A mature duck or an old duck is a duck (usually over 6 months of age) of either sex, with toughened flesh, hardened bill, and hardened windpipe.

Geese

The following are the various classes of geese:

1. YOUNG GOOSE. A young goose may be of either sex, with tender meat and a windpipe that is easily dented.
2. MATURE GOOSE OR OLD GOOSE. A mature goose or old goose may be of either sex, with toughened flesh and hardened windpipe.

Guineas

The following are the various classes of guineas:

1. YOUNG GUINEA. A young guinea may be of either sex, with tender meat and flexible breastbone cartilage.
2. MATURE GUINEA OR OLD GUINEA. A mature guinea or an old guinea may be of either sex, with toughened flesh and hardened breastbone.

Pigeons

The following are the various classes of pigeons:

1. SQUAB. A squab is a young, immature pigeon of either sex, with extra tender meat.
2. PIGEON. A pigeon is a mature pigeon of either sex, with coarse skin and toughened flesh.

The Grading Service

Poultry grading services of the U.S. Department of Agriculture are permissive, in that individuals, firms, or govermental agenices that desire to utilize them may request them of their own volition. Services are performed on the basis of regulations promulgated by the Secretary of Agriculture. These regulations have been developed in cooperation with the industry, including all affected or related groups, such as health and marketing officials, producers, processors, and consumers.

Grading generally involves the sorting of products according to quality and size, but it also includes the determination of the class and condition of products. For poultry, grading may be for determining class, quality, quantity, or condition, or for any combination of these factors.

Grading for quality can be accomplished by examining each carcass in the lot, or by examining a representative sample of the lot of poultry to be graded. Only ready-to-cook poultry that is first inspected for wholesomeness and then graded on an individual-bird basis may be individually marked with an official grade mark.

Ready-to-cook poultry must have been officially inspected for condition and wholesomeness before it may be graded for quality, whether the grading is done in an approved plant or elsewhere. The U.S. Consumer Grades are applicable only to poultry which has been graded on an individual carcass basis by a grader or by a limited licensed grader working under the supervision of a grader. The U.S. Procurement Grades are generally applied when the poultry has been graded on the basis of an examination of a prescribed sample of the lot.

Standards of Quality for Dressed and Ready-to-Cook Poultry[3]

A *Quality*

CONFORMATION. The carcass or part is free of deformities that detract from its appearance or that affect the normal distribution of flesh. Slight deformities such as slightly curved or dented breastbones and slightly curved backs may be present.

FLESHING. The carcass or part has a well developed covering of flesh. The breast is moderately long and deep and has sufficient flesh to give it a rounded appearance with the flesh carrying well up to the crest of the breastbone along its entire length.

FAT COVERING. The carcass or part, considering the kind, class, and part, has a well developed layer of fat in the skin. The fat is well dis-

---

3. *Poultry Grading Manual*, Agricultural Handbook No. 31, U.S. Dept. of Agriculture.

tributed so that there is a noticeable amount of fat in the skin in the areas between the heavy feather tracts.

DEFEATHERING. The carcass or part has a clean appearance, especially on the breast. The carcass or part is free of pinfeathers, diminutive feathers, and hair which is visible to the inspector or grader.

EXPOSED FLESH. Parts are free of exposed flesh resulting from cuts, tears, and missing skin (other than slight trimming on the edge). The carcass is free of these defects on the breast and legs. Elsewhere the carcass may have exposed flesh due to slight cuts, tears, and areas of missing skin providing the aggregate of the areas of flesh exposed does not exceed the area of a circle of the diameter as specified in Table 8.1.

Table 8.1—Maximum Exposed Flesh Area for A Quality

Carcass Weight		Maximum Aggregate Area Permitted	
Minimum	Maximum	Breast & Legs	Elsewhere
None	1 lb. 8 oz.	None	3/4 in.
Over 1 lb. 8 oz.	6 lbs.	None	1 1/2 in.
Over 6 lbs.	16 lbs.	None	2 in.
Over 16 lbs.	None	None	3 in.

DISJOINTED AND BROKEN BONES AND MISSING PARTS. Parts are free of broken bones. The carcass is free of broken bones and has not more than one disjointed bone. The wing tips may be removed at the joint and, in the case of geese, the parts of the wing beyond the second joint may be removed if removed at the joint and both wings are so treated. The tail may be removed at the base. Cartilage separated from the breastbone is not considered as a disjointed or broken bone.

DISCOLORATIONS OF THE SKIN AND FLESH. The carcass or part is practically free of such defects. Discoloration due to bruising shall be free of clots (discernible clumps of red or dark cells). Evidence of incomplete bleeding, such as more than an occasional slightly reddened feather follicle, is not permitted. Flesh bruises and discolorations of the skin such as "blue back" are not permitted on the breast or legs of the carcass or on these individual parts, and only lightly shaded discolorations are permitted elsewhere. The total areas affected by flesh bruises, skin bruises, and discolorations such as "blue back" singly or in any combination shall not exceed one-half of the total aggregate area of permitted discoloration. The aggregate area of all discolorations for a carcass or a part therefrom

Table 8.2—Maximum Discolorations for A Quality

Carcass Weight		Maximum Aggregate Area Permitted		
Minimum	Maximum	Breast & Legs	Elsewhere	Part
None	1 lb. 8 oz.	1/2 in.	1 in.	1/4 in.
Over 1 lb. 8 oz.	6 lbs.	1 in.	2 in.	1/4 in.
Over 6 lbs.	16 lbs.	1 1/2 in.	2 1/2 in.	1/2 in.
Over 16 lbs.	None	2 in.	3 in.	1/2 in.

shall not exceed the area of a circle of the diameter as specified in Table 8.2.

FREEZING DEFECTS. With respect to consumer packaged poultry, the carcass, part, or specified poultry food product is practically free from defects which result from handling or occur during freezing or storage. The following defects are permitted if they, alone or in combination, detract only very slightly from the appearance of the carcass, part, or specified poultry food product.

1. Slight darkening over the back and drumsticks, provided the frozen bird or part has a generally bright appearance.
2. Occasional pockmarks due to drying of the inner layer of skin (derma); however, none may exceed the area of a circle ⅛ inch in diameter for poultry weighing 6 pounds or less, and ¼ inch in diameter for poultry weighing over 6 pounds.
3. Occasional small areas showing a thin layer of clear or pinkish colored ice.

B Quality

CONFORMATIONS. The carcass or part may have moderate deformities, such as a dented, curved, or crooked breast, or crooked back, or misshapen legs, or wings which do not materially affect the distribution of flesh or the appearance of the carcass or part.

FLESHING. The carcass or part has a moderate covering of flesh considering the kind, class, and part of the bird. The breast has a substantial covering of flesh with the flesh carrying up to the crest of the breastbone sufficiently to prevent a thin appearance.

FAT COVERING. The carcass or part has sufficient fat in the skin to prevent a distinct appearance of the flesh through the skin, especially on the breast and legs.

DEFEATHERING. The carcass or part may have a few nonprotruding pin-feathers or vestigal feathers which are scattered sufficiently so as not to appear numerous. Not more than an occasional protruding pinfeather or diminutive feather shall be in evidence under a careful examination.

EXPOSED FLESH. Parts may have exposed flesh resulting from cuts, tears, and missing skin, provided that not more than a moderate amount of the flesh normally covered by skin is exposed. The carcass may have exposed flesh resulting from cuts, tears, and missing skin, provided that the aggregate of the areas of flesh exposed does not exceed the area of a circle of the diameter as specified in Table 8.3.

Table 8.3—Maximum Exposed Flesh Area for B Quality

Carcass Weight		Maximum Aggregate Area Permitted	
Minimum	Maximum	Breast & Legs	Elsewhere
None	1 lb. 8 oz.	3/4 in.	1 1/2 in.
Over 1 lb. 8 oz.	6 lbs.	1 1/2 in.	3 in.
Over 6 lbs.	16 lbs.	2 in.	4 in.
Over 16 lbs.	None	3 in.	5 in.

Notwithstanding the foregoing, a carcass meeting the requirements of A Quality for fleshing may be trimmed to remove skin and flesh defects, provided that no more than one-third of the flesh is exposed on any part and the meat yield of any part is not appreciably affected.

DISJOINTED AND BROKEN BONES AND MISSING PARTS. Parts may be disjointed but should be free of broken bones. The carcass may have two disjointed bones or one disjointed bone and nonprotruding broken bone. Parts of the wing beyond the second joint may be removed at a joint. The tail may be removed at the base.

DISCOLORATIONS OF THE SKIN AND FLESH. The carcass or part is free of serious defects. Discoloration due to bruising shall be free of clots (discernible clumps of red or dark cells). Evidence of incomplete bleeding shall be no more than very slight. Moderate areas of discoloration due to bruises in the skin or flesh and moderately shaded discoloration of the skin such as "blue back" are permitted, but the total areas affected by such discolorations singly or in any combination may not exceed one-half of the total aggregate area of permitted discoloration. The aggregate area of all discolorations for a carcass or a part therefrom shall not exceed the area of a circle of the diameter as specified in Table 8.4.

Table 8.4—Maximum Discolorations for B Quality

Carcass Weight		Maximum Aggregate Area Permitted		
Minimum	Maximum	Breast & Legs	Elsewhere	Part
None	1 lb. 8 oz.	1 in.	2 in.	1/2 in.
Over 1 lb. 8 oz.	6 lbs.	2 in.	3 in.	1 in.
Over 6 lbs.	16 lbs.	2 1/2 in.	4 in.	1 1/2 in.
Over 16 lbs.	None	3 in.	5 in.	1 1/2 in.

FREEZING DEFECTS. With respect to consumer packaged poultry, the carcass, part, or specified poultry food product may have moderate defects which result from handling or occur during freezing or storage. The skin and flesh shall have a sound appearance but may lack brightness. The carcass or part may have a few pockmarks due to drying of the inner layer of skin (derma). However, no single area of overlapping pockmarks may exceed that of a circle ½ inch in diameter. Moderate areas showing layers of clear pinkish or reddish colored ice are permitted.

C Quality

A part that does not meet the requirements for A or B Quality may be of C Quality if the flesh is substantially intact.

A carcass that does not meet the requirements for A or B Quality may be of C Quality. Both wings may be removed or neatly trimmed. Trimming of the breast and legs is permitted, but not to the extent that the normal meat yield is materially affected.

U.S. Procurement Grades for Ready-to-Cook Poultry[4]

The U.S. Procurement Grades for ready-to-eat poultry are applicable to carcasses of ready-to-cook poultry when they are graded as a lot by a grader on the basis of an examination of each carcass in the lot or each carcass in a representative sample thereof.

U.S. Procurement Grade I

Any lot of ready-to-cook poultry composed of one or more carcasses of the same kind and class may be designated and identified as U.S. Procurement Grade I in the following situations.

4. *Poultry Grading Manual*, Agricultural Handbook No. 31, U.S. Dept. of Agriculture.

1. When 90% or more of the carcasses in such lot meet the requirements of A Quality, with the following exceptions:
   a. Fat covering and conformation may be as described above
      for B Quality.
   b. Trimming of skin and flesh to remove defects is permitted to
      the extent that not more than one-fourth of the flesh is ex-
      posed on any part, and the meat yield of any part is not ap-
      preciably affected.
   c. The wings or parts of wings may be removed if severed at a
      joint, and the tail may be removed at the base.
2. When the balance of the carcasses meet the same requirements,
   except that they may have only a moderate covering of flesh.

U.S. Procurement Grade II

Any lot of ready-to-cook poultry of the same kind and class which
fails to meet the requirements of U.S. Procurement Grade I may be designated and identified as U.S. Procurement Grade II provided that (1)
trimming of flesh from any part does not exceed 10% of the meat and
(2) portions of a carcass weighing not less than one-half of the whole
carcass may be included if the portion approximates in percentage the
meat to bone yield of the whole carcass.

The Inspection Services

Inspection refers to the condition of poultry and its healthfulness and
fitness for food. It is not concerned with the quality or grade of poultry.
The inspection mark on poultry or poultry products means that they have
been examined during processing by a veterinarian or by qualified laymen
under the supervision of a veterinarian. Plants which apply for inspection
service and are approved are known as official plants or establishments.

A complete discussion of meat and poultry inspection and a pictorial
view of a poultry inspection stamp was provided in Chapter 3.

DRESSING POULTRY

Selection of Birds for Dressing

The value of poultry and turkey for meat varies considerably with
the breed. Some are thin-meated, some are deep-sided and rangy, while
others are thcik-meated and particularly full-breasted. The thick-meated,
full-breasted, well finished bird will be a top grade bird on any market
provided it has been properly dressed. To avoid having too many birds

of the lower grades, the thin chickens should be put on a fattening ration for another week. Turkeys should be fed until the skin no longer appears blue. Produce what the market demands and not what is convenient at the time, is good advice to follow.

Handling Previous to Dressing

Birds, like animals, should receive careful handling to avoid bruises, abrasions, and broken limbs. The holding pens should be cool and well ventilated, and the birds should have free acess to water. Water is a heat regulator and helps the birds to eliminate waste products. Birds denied water for too long a time lose weight and dress rather soft. Feed should be withheld for 8 to 10 hours before the chickens are killed, since a bird full of feed will not bleed as well, will be harder to eviscerate, and the full crop is unsightly and wasteful in an undrawn bird. A marked loss in dressing yield has been shown to occur after 12 hours of fasting.[5]

The fowl should be caught by the leg below the thigh and not allowed to strike its breast on a hard surface. One wing should be held when a bird is picked up by the shank to prevent its struggling. Overheated, over-excited birds will bleed poorly, producing a carcass of higher blood content and lower keeping quality.

Tools and Equipment

The old method of chopping off the heads of the fowl with a hatchet or cleaver and tossing the headless birds into a barrel, one on top of the other as rapidly as the beheader could swing the hatchet, was considered the acme of speed. But this practice disappeared into the limbo as science streamlined and mechanized the commercial dressing practices of animals and fowl. In fact, the mechanical processing of fowl was patterned very closely after the methods employed by the meat packing industry in the slaughter of hogs. The commercial poultry processing plant has overhead tracks (much lighter in structure and lower than those used for animals) which take the form of a belt chain to which oval link chains are suspended to hold the shackles for suspending the bird. These belt chains move at a controlled speed in the same manner as those employed for hogs.

Other equipment may consist of such items as an automatic stunner, automatic killer, scalder, picker, hock picker, automatic hock cutter, outside bird washer, eviscerating trough, oil sac cutter, opening cut machine, automatic drawing machine (Figure 8.1), automatic gizzard processing

---

5. NCM-46 Regional Technical Committee, USDA.

system, automatic lung remover, automatic neck breaker, combination washer, automatic head cutter and neck skin cutter, automatic continuous chill system, continuous giblet chiller, automatic giblet wrapper, automatic sizing system, automatic cutup machines (Figure 8.2), and numerous other items of equipment which allow poultry processors to process some 3,000 birds per hour with a single system of machines.

Fig. 8.1—An automatic drawing machine which is a completely self-contained unit mechanically driven from an overhead conveyor, thus eliminating synchronizing problems. Specially designed drawing spoons are washed and sanitized automatically after each drawing operation. Two machines replace four to six operators on eviscerating lines of a 6,000-bird-per-hour operation. (Courtesy, Gainesville Machine Co., Inc., Gainesville, Georgia)

Where only a few birds are dressed, the equipment consists of a scalding tub, a shackle for holding the bird, and probably a bleeding cup. The knives necessary in each case are a sticking knife (a 3-inch blade for chickens and a 4-inch blade for turkeys), pinning knife (a paring knife will do), several sizes of boning knives (3½-inch to 6-inch blades) for eviscerating, a linoleum knife for splitting the back (or a power meat saw, if available), a thermometer for testing water temperature, and bone

Fig. 8.2—The new USDA-approved Gainesville Automatic Poultry Cut-up System consists of two machines, one to cut up the front half of the bird (left) and one to cut up the back half of the bird (right).

The complete systems have been field proven in many plant operations throughout the country since July 1970.

The two machines can make either an eight-piece cut (two wings and two pieces of breast on the front half machine and two drumsticks and two thighs on the back half machine) or a nine-piece cut (two wings and three pieces of breast on the front half machine and two drumsticks and two thighs on the back half machine). The back half machine can be further adjusted to make a strip cut varying from ⅜ inch to as wide as necessary.

This system, which gives a more uniform cut than hand operations, works as fast as the operator can feed birds into it. Some plants are cutting up to 44 birds per minute.

Improved sanitation is achieved because each machine has a built-in continuous water rinse. End of day clean-up can be handled in 20 to 30 minutes by one operator.

The Gainesville Automatic Cut-up System reduces labor costs by requiring fewer workers, and these may be unskilled.

Increased safety reduces downtime due to absenteeism. (Courtesy, Gainesville Machine Co., Inc., Gainesville, Georgia) shears for severing heads, necks, and shanks. Although the blades of the knives used for sticking and braining are narrow-bladed (⅛-inch wide), the handles should be of standard grip.

Bleeding Practices

1. Severing the neck (chopping block method or barrel method).
2. Cutting the throat (kosher method). The cut is made on the outside.
3. Dislocating the neck (simple and sanitary but not recommended except for home use). It is accomplished by placing the thumb on the top of the neck in back of the comb and the fingers under the lower jaw and giving a quick downward pull and a backward jerk of the head by compressing the third and fourth fingers in the opposite direction to the thumb.
4. Cutting the throat inside the bird's mouth. This is the approved and most widely practiced method employed today. The bird is suspended by the legs with shackles, made of heavy wire, which not only hold the feet in the V-shaped vise but also spread the

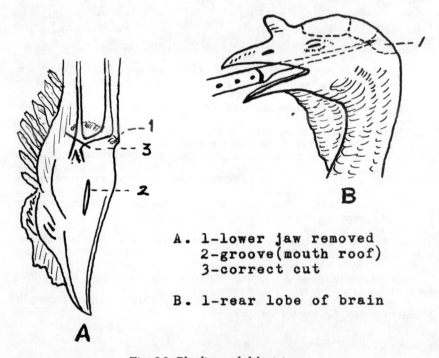

A. 1-lower jaw removed
   2-groove(mouth roof)
   3-correct cut

B. 1-rear lobe of brain

Fig. 8.3—Bleeding and debraining.

legs. The use of a sash cord with a 2-inch square wooden block attached is a simple homemade shackle, but it leaves one leg free. The feet of the fowl should be level with the eyes of the worker for convenience of operation.

5. Grasp the head and hold it firmly in the left hand (if you are right handed), pressing the thumb and forefinger on both sides of the junction of the upper and lower beaks. This forces the mouth open so the point of the sticking knife can be inserted, sharp edge downward, to the base of the skull. Press the point of the knife into the flesh, lift the handle upward, and cut downward and to the right, severing the veins. If a good bleed does not result, try again until there is free bleeding.

Dry-Picking

If the fowl is to be dry-picked, hold the head of the bird in the same position, insert the knife blade (blade edge up) into the cleft in the roof of the mouth and force it through to the rear lobe of the brain (medulla oblongata). The chicken gives a peculiar squawk if properly debrained, whereas the turkey relaxes its wings and the main tail feathers spread out fan shaped. The puncturing of the brain relaxes the feather muscles, causing the feathers to become loose and easily plucked. This condition lasts for two to three minutes when the muscles again begin to tighten up due rigor mortis, making it necessary to have rapid and orderly plucking. "Roughing" the bird before the muscles reset is the process of removing the major part of the plumage in the order in which the parts of the bird bleed out. It consists of twisting out the tail and main wing feathers, plucking the breast, neck, back, thighs, and legs. This is followed by the more tedious task of pinning. The object is to pluck and handle the bird that the outside layer of skin is free from tears, abrasions, or bruise spots and maintains its natural bloom. Dry-picking has been largely replaced by semi-scalding.

Scalding Practices

Hard, or Hot Scalding

Hard, or hot scalding is one of the earliest methods used for the quick removal of the feathers. It is still the common practice employed in home dressing birds of all kinds. The speed at which feathers are loosened is dependent upon the temperature of the water and the period of immersion. The hotter the water, the quicker the feathers are loosened. But the temperature of the water to use also is dependent upon the age and nature of the fowl to be scalded. Young birds with tender skins should not be scalded in water over 150° F, whereas mature birds scald well at 155° to 160° F. Mature fowl can be scalded in water around 185° F, but the immersion period must be short to avoid cooking the skin. When high scalding temperatures are used, it is well to immerse the scalded bird in cold water as soon as the feathers are loosened. This stops further scalding action.

The hot scald works well on birds having a large number of pin feathers. The practice gives good results if the operator is careful not to overscald. The latter causes the skin to tear and discolor and gives the bird a cooked appearance, producing a carcass that lacks bloom and turns brown rapidly. Fat birds will hold their natural color longer because the melted fat forms a film over the skin, excludes the air, and retards dessication. Where a deep yellow color is desired on fat birds of the yellow-skinned variety, it is a practice to dip the dressed fowl into boiling water and then douse it immediately into cold water. The hot water melts the fat and draws it, along with the yellow pigment, to the surface of the skin. The cold water causes the fat to harden and the color to set in the fat. Hot scalding is not practiced on birds destined for the regular market.

Semi-Scalding (Slack Scalding)

This method was developed in the late twenties and is now universally used in all the large poultry packing plants. It lends itself well to mechanization and has the advantage of lower labor costs. The appearance of the birds is improved and they do not turn red or brown but retain a natural bloom. This incidentally throws more birds into the higher grades, resulting in greater financial return.

The temperature of the water should be 125° to 126° F for young, tender skinned birds, 127° to 128° F for roasters and young turkeys, and 130° to 132° F for aged birds. These temperatures do not loosen the feathers as much or as rapidly as the hot scald but neither do they cook or cause the outer skin to peel. Because the skin is not weakened in strength, this type of scalding makes it possible to use the mechanical picker. These picking machines consist of a drum upon whose circumference are mounted innumerable suction tubes made of rubber. As the drum revolves, the semi-scalded birds are held against its outer surface and the feathers are rubbed off.

The period of immersion varies from 20 to 30 seconds for broilers and up to 40 seconds for older birds. The birds should be suspended from shackles, if plucked by hand, and the plucking cannot be done by rubbing as in the hot scald method. The feathers must be pulled out in tufts as in dry-picking. The scalding vats should be equipped with thermostatically controlled steam jets in order to keep the desired water temperature.

Wax Picking

This works very well with the semi-scald method and is usually employed in combination with it. After the birds are roughed on the picking machine, they are dried by passing them through a drying machine. The wax will stick to the dry feathers and stubs more tightly than it will to wet feathers.

The dried birds are then dipped, by hand or automatically into a preparation of melted wax (patented) at a temperature of 125° to 130° F for a period of 30 to 60 seconds. When birds are moving along a processing rail, the bucket containing the heated wax moves up and envelops the bird that is suspended by the head and feet. This specially prepared wax has a melting point of around 120° F and is hardened by passing the bird under a cold water spray or through a cool air blast. The hardened wax is then pulled from the bird with the feathers, pin feathers, hair, and scale encased in it, producing an attractively dressed product. This wax is renovated for reuse by boiling out the water (if water spray was used for cooling) and straining off the feathers.

Chilling and Storing

The immediate removal of body heat by subjecting the birds to a temperature of 32° to 36° F is highly essential. Freezing warm birds before the animal heat has been removed is to be avoided, since "cold shortening" may occur, causing the meat to be less tender as the actin and myosin filaments of the muscle fibers slide and lock together. If artificial refrigeration is not available, the next best thing is to place the birds in tubs of ice water. This plumps the birds and chills them, but it also lowers their keeping quality and is not advocated except in an emergency for holding the birds overnight.

When the birds are thoroughly chilled, their heads should be wrapped with paper, their wings tied against their bodies, and the birds packed in paper-lined boxes or barrels for shipment. Birds processed to this point are designated as blood-and-feather-dressed.

Full-Dressing

Birds that are to be frozen should be full-dressed. The different operations in their proper order are as follows:

1. Remove the head. Peel back the skin on the neck and sever the neck close to the shoulders (use the bone shears).

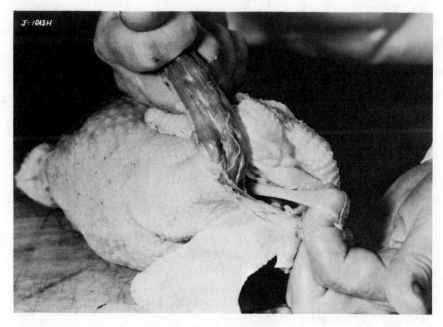

Fig. 8.4—Removing the crop.

2. Remove the crop and windpipe by hooking the short gullet (between crop and gullet) with the index finger and peeling the crop loose from the skin by working it forward.
3. Use the index finger to loosen the lungs from the chest wall by inserting it between the ribs and the lungs.
4. Remove the feet at the hock joint.
5. Make an incision from the rear end of the keel bone to the rectum and cut around the rectum.
6. Draw the intestinal tract, including the heart, lungs, and liver through this opening. Chilled or partially chilled birds are easier to draw than warm ones.
7. Remove the bile sac from the liver.
8. Split along the edge of the fleshy part of the gizzard sufficiently deep to cut the muscle but not the inner lining. The pressure of both thumbs pulling the halves apart will permit peeling without breaking the lining and spilling the contents of the gizzard. Gizzards are easier to peel if they have been partially chilled in ice water.

The bird should be shaped to give it a plump, compact appearance. The wings are compressed against the sides of the carcass and the legs are

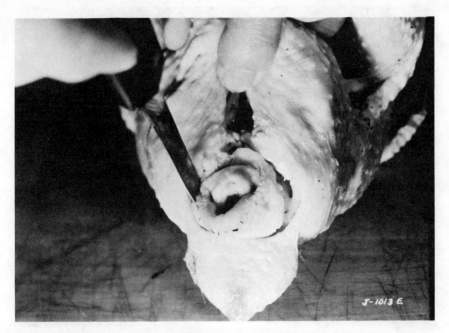

Fig. 8.5—Cutting around the vent with the opening made to the rear of the keel bone.

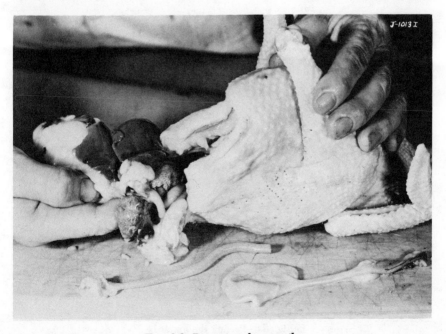

Fig. 8.6—Removing the entrails.

Fig. 8.7—Making the opening cut on the fleshy side of the gizzard.

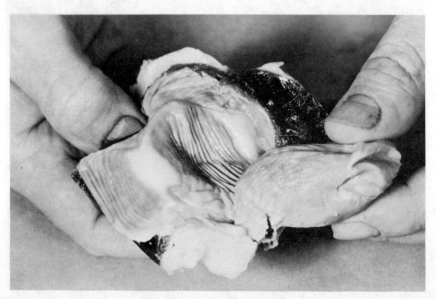

Fig. 8.8—Peeling the gizzard.

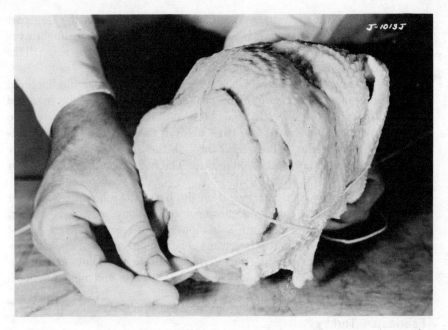

Fig. 8.9—The first step in trussing.

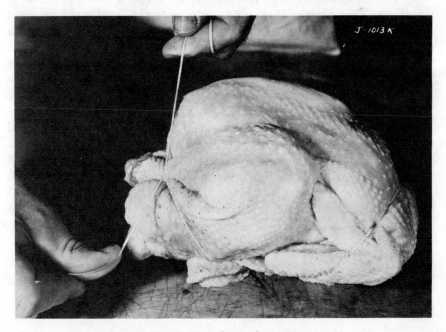

Fig. 8.10—Completing the trussing.

brought together at the vent. A length of cord is drawn over the fore part of the breast and over the wings and crossed over the back, brought over the ends of the drumsticks, and tied tightly at the back of the rump. This style of trussing is employed on a bird for roasting.

Broilers and springers receive a different treatment. Use the linoleum knife to cut along either side of the backbone, beginning at the rear and cutting forward. This leaves the backbone and neck in one piece. Remove the neck with a bone shears. The two halves of the fowl are laid open sufficiently to remove the entrails. Split through the breast with a cleaver, or preferably a power saw, to halve the bird. The halves can be quartered, if desired.

There has been a popular trend on the part of the buying public for cut-up chicken which enables a consumer to buy any part of a chicken. This is popular because they are not compelled to buy parts they do not like in order to get the parts they want. The cuts in order of their monetary value are breasts, thighs (also divided into second joints and drumsticks), wings, backs, necks, and gizzards. The livers and hearts bring a good price.

Fabricated Turkey

The utilization of large tom turkeys for roasting is not practical in most American homes. Their chief outlet is to the hotel and restaurant trade. To widen the market for large toms and keep their price more in line with hen turkeys which better meet the weight requirements of the average family, several variations of turkey processing have been devised by investigators and are presently in use in industry.

The binding of pieces or chunks of meat together to form rolls or loaves has received considerable attention by the poultry industry, especially in the utilization of turkey meat. It is estimated that 25% of all turkey meat produced is used in the production of these convenient items. Cornell University workers[6] have summarized current information on roll manufacture and indicated that the addition of dried egg whites and gluten (vital), or gliadin, all protein materials, aided significantly toward binding meat chunks together into a simulated roast to be easily sliced and served by the consumer.

Half and Quarter Turkey

Halving a bird and roasting one-half with the filling underneath has been well received.

---

6. Vadehra and Baker, *Food Technology,* 24:766, 1970.

Fig. 8.11—Opening the back by splitting along either side of the backbone. The side can be quartered, if desired.

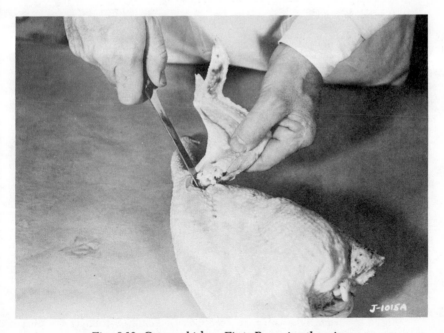

Fig. 8.12—Cut-up chicken. First—Removing the wing.

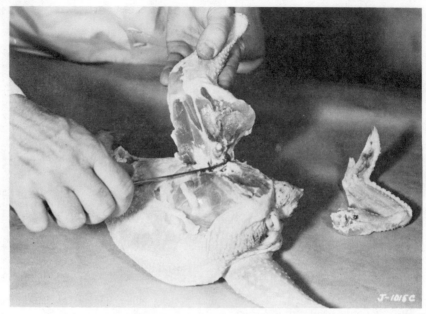

Fig. 8.13—Second—Removing the leg.

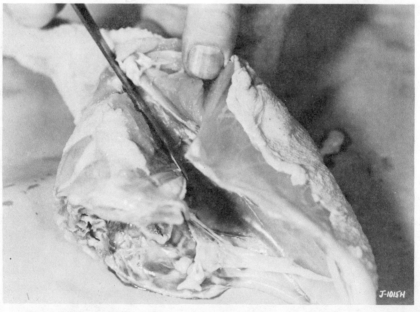

Fig. 8.14—Remove the tail piece (not shown). Fourth—Separating the rib and neck piece from the breast.

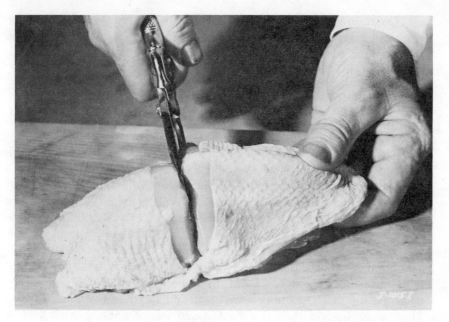

Fig. 8.15—Fifth—Dividing the breast into two sections.

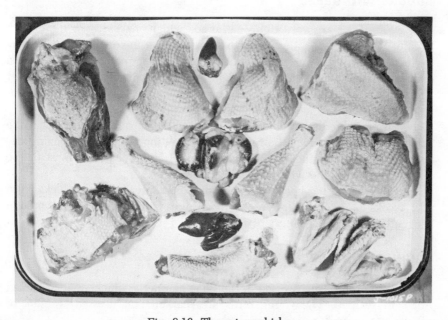

Fig. 8.16—The cut-up chicken.

Quartering a large bird by making the division mid-way between the wing and leg is a practice that works out well for small families. The idea that turkey is something that must be roasted has somewhat retarded the sale of "cut-up" turkey.

Dressing Percent

The overnight fasting shrink varies from 2% in chickens to 3% in turkeys.

The dressing loss, whether blood-and-featherdressed or full-dressed, depends upon the weight and condition of the bird. Chickens under 5 pounds will lose an average of 11% blood-and-feather-dressed as against 25% full-dressed. Chickens over 5 pounds will average 7% and 18% loss respectively. Male turkeys weighing between 13 and 17 pounds will lose an average of 10% blood-and-feather-dressed and those over 20 pounds will lose about 8%. The same birds full-dressed will average a loss of 23% and 24% respectively. Blood-and-feather-dressed female turkeys weighing under 10 pounds average 10% loss, those between 10 and 12 pounds average 9%, and those weighing between 12 and 15 pounds average 7½% loss. These same birds will show a full-dressed loss of approximately 24% to 25% or slightly more than the toms.

DUCKS AND GEESE

Waterfowl are very tight-feathered, which makes them difficult to scald. It is necessary, therefore, to steam them. This is accomplished by churning them in water that is near the boiling point or wrapping a burlap sack around the birds and immersing them in hot water. Water temperatures as low as 160° F can be used, but the scalding time is considerably longer.

Properly bled and debrained waterfowl are easily dry-picked, but the fine down feathers must be removed by scalding or waxing. Waxing destroys the value of the down feathers and is employed after most of the down has been otherwise removed.

Long Island has been a large production center for green ducks (8 to 12 weeks of age); therefore, Long Island Ducklings have become a legend among connoisseurs of food.

GUINEA FOWL AND PHEASANT

Most guineas are dressed in the same manner as chickens—dry-picked or semi-scalded. The young birds are marketed at dressed weights of 2 pounds or under.

Pheasants are probably one of the meatiest birds for their size of any bird used for human consumption. They are marketed blood-and-feather-dressed or full-dressed, generally dry-picked. They weigh from 1 to 2 pounds in the carcass, and the major portion of the meat is on the breast. The bones are quite small in proportion to the amount of edible meat.

RABBITS

Classes of Ready-to-Cook Domestic Rabbit[7]

Fryer or Young Rabbit

A fryer or young rabbit is a young domestic rabbit carcass weighing not less than 1½ pounds and rarely more than 3½ pounds processed from a rabbit usually less than 12 weeks of age. The flesh of a fryer or young rabbit is tender and fine grained and is a bright pearly pink color.

Roaster or Mature Rabbit

A roaster or mature rabbit is a mature or old domestic rabbit carcass of any weight, but usually over 4 pounds, processed from a rabbit usually eight months of age or older. The flesh of a roaster or mature rabbit is more firm and coarse grained, and the muscle fiber is slightly darker in color and less tender, and the fat may be more creamy in color than that of a fryer or young rabbit.

Quality Grades[8]

A carcass found to be unsound, unwholesome, or unfit for food shall not be included in any of the quality designations.

A Quality

Is short, thick, well rounded, and full-fleshed.

Has a broad back, broad hips, and broad, deep-fleshed shoulders, and firm muscle texture.

Has a fair quantity of interior fat in the crotch and over the inner walls of the carcass and a moderate amount of interior fat around the kidneys.

Is free of evidence of incomplete bleeding such as more than an occasional slight coagulation in a vein. Is free from any evidence of reddening of the flesh due to fluid in the connective tissues.

---

7. Poultry Division, Agricultural Marketing Service, U.S. Dept. of Agriculture.
8. Poultry Division, Agricultural Marketing Service, U.S. Dept. of Agriculture.

Is free from all foreign material (including, but not being limited to, hair, dirt, and bone particles) and from crushed bones caused by removing the head or the feet.

Is free from broken bones, flesh bruises, defects, and deformities. Ends of leg bones may be broken due to removal of the feet.

B Quality

Is short, fairly well rounded and fairly well fleshed.

Has a fairly broad back, fairly broad hips, and fairly broad and deep-fleshed shoulders, and fairly firm muscle texture.

Has at least a small amount of interior fat in the crotch and over the inner walls of the carcass with a small amount of interior fat around the kidneys.

Is free of evidence of incomplete bleeding such as more than an occasional slight coagulation in a vein. Is free from any evidence of reddendening of the flesh due to fluid in the connective tissues.

Is free from broken bones and practically free from bruises, defects, and deformities. Ends of leg bones may be broken due to removal of the feet.

C Quality

A carcass that does not meet the requirements of A or B Quality may be of C Quality and such carcass:

May be long, rangy, and fairly well fleshed.

May have thin, narrow back and hips, and soft flabby muscle texture.

May show very little evidence of exterior fat.

May show very slight evidence of reddening of the flesh due to blood in the connective tissues.

Is free from all foreign material (including, but not being limited to, hair, dirt, and bone particles) and from crushed bones caused by removing the head or feet.

May have moderate bruises of the flesh, moderate defects, and moderate deformities. May have not more than one broken bone in addition to broken ends of leg bones due to removal of the feet and may have a small portion of the carcass removed because of serious bruises. Discoloration due to bruising in the flesh shall be free of clots (discernible clumps of dark or red cells).

Inspection

Rabbit inspection is identical in scope and completeness to poultry inspection which is discussed in detail in Chapter 3. The mark of inspection is identical for poultry and rabbit and is illustrated in Chapter 3.

Handling

Rabbits should not be lifted by the ears or legs but by grasping a fold of skin over the shoulders and then supporting the rump with the free hand, holding the back of the rabbit against the body.

Dressing Rabbits

The method of slaughtering rabbits consists of the following:

1. Give a sharp blow on the top of the rabbit's head to stun it.
2. Make an incision at the rear of the hock between the bone and the tendon.
3. Suspend the carcass by hanging it on a hook through the hock.
4. Sever the head at the atlas joint.
5. Remove the free rear leg at the hock joint.
6. Remove the tail and forelegs (knee joint).
7. Cut the skin on the rear of the loose leg to the base of the tail and up the rear of the suspended leg.
8. Pull the edges of the cut skin away from the flesh and down over the carcass. Make no other cuts in the skin.
9. Eviscerate by opening the median line of the belly, leaving the heart, liver, and kidneys in the carcass.
10. Remove the suspended rear leg and rinse the carcass in cold water to remove any hair or blood.
11. Joint the carcass by removing the forelegs and hind legs, cutting the loin in one piece, and separating the shoulders.

Pelts

Rabbit pelts have a fur skin value. The small ones should be stretched on a thin board or wire stretcher 24 inches long and 4 inches wide at the narrow end and 7 inches wide at the base. The skins of 10- and 12-pound rabbits need a board 30 inches long, 4 inches wide at the narrow end, and 9 inches wide at the base. Stretch the warm skin on the board with the fore part over the narrow end, and smooth out the wrinkles. Have both front legs on one side of the shaping board. Remove any surplus fat and make sure that the skin dries flat. Do not dry in the sun or artificial heat, and do not use salt. When dry, the skins can be stored in a tight box, but each layer should be sprinkled with naphtha flakes to keep out moths.

An infectious disease known as tularemia is prevalent in wild rabbits

Fig. 8.17—The procedure followed in skinning a rabbit. (Courtesy, U.S. Fish and Wildlife Service)

and is communicable to man through abrasions in the skin while dressing a rabbit having the disease. It is transmitted from one rabbit to another by the rabbit louse or tick. The disease has not been observed in domestic rabbits and the germ is destroyed by cooking.

VENISON

The preservation of game by legislation restricting the period when such game may be legally shot is making venison more abundant and therefore, a more noticeable addition to the family larder. Its scarcity, however, makes it all the more obvious that better care should be taken of the carcass to prevent the flagrant waste that is often evident in its preservation and utilization.

Precautions at Time of Kill[9]

This may sound silly, but make sure your deer is dead! Many a hunter has leaned his gun against a tree and prepared to field dress his

---

9. Excerpts from *Field Dressing Your Deer*, Illinois Dept. of Conservation.

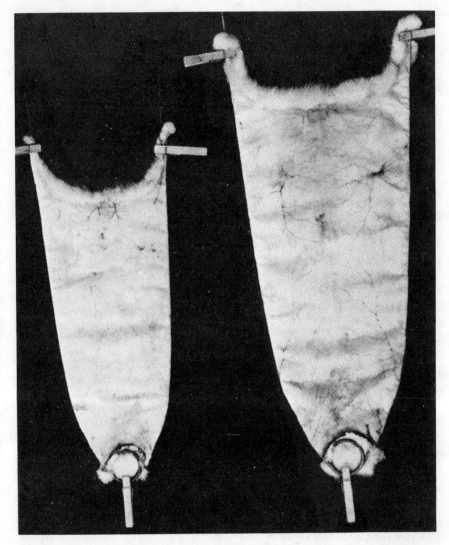

Fig. 8.18–Rabbit skins on wire stretchers. (Courtesy, U.S. Fish and Wildlife Service)

deer only to see it spring up and bound off. Approach the deer with caution from its tail end. Have your gun ready for another shot and nudge the deer with your foot. It may have been wounded and simply dropped from exhaustion. If it's still alive, you will know it. Keep out of reach of the legs until you are certain the deer is dead. Adhere to the state laws regarding tagging and reporting the kill.

Bleeding

It is not necessary to bleed your deer unless it has been shot in the head and often not then. A shotgun slug in the neck or body cavity does a good job of bleeding it for you. But if you want to bleed your deer and it happens to be a cornfed trophy buck, don't ruin the head by slashing the neck. Make a small cut at the base of the neck. Insert the blade of the hunting knife (4½- to 5½-inch blade) several inches in front of the point of the breast with the point of the blade aimed toward the tail. Plunge it up to the hilt, press the blade downward to the back bone, and withdraw it with a slicing motion. Elevate the rear portion of the deer to permit the blood to drain by gravity.

Removing Intestinal Tract

Many hunters think that you should cut the glands from a deer's legs. You can if you want to but it's not necessary. Deer have glands not only on their legs but between their toes and at the corners of their eyes. All glands are inactive after death. Use a knife that is small, sharp, and handy. Don't handicap yourself with a big knife unless you plan on bagging a deer in hand to hoof combat. Those Bowies with the 10- and 12-inch blades may look good swinging from your belt, and they may be just the tools for Green Berets or Commandoes, but when it comes to field dressing a deer, they are nothing except awkward. A clasp knife or a sheath knife with a sharp 4- or 6-inch blade is all you need.

A 6- to 8-foot section of good clothesline is handy. With it you can tie the deer's leg to a tree to give yourself working space. If you do not have a rope, you can spread the deer's hind legs by propping them open by inserting a small branch about 3 feet long between them. With the animal on its back, block it on either side with logs or rocks to keep it in place.

If you have shot a buck, cut the genitals from the body. Carefully cut the hide from the breastbone to the rectum. If you have shot a young deer you may be able to split open the pelvic girdle with your knife. Split the pelvis, where the hind legs are joined, by making the cut with the white membrane that separates the two rounds. This leads to the fusion point on the pelvis which is easily split with a knife, unless the deer is aged, in which case you must saw the bone at a later date. In this case you must cut around the anus. Cut open the body cavity. Tilt the animal sideways and let the blood drain from the body cavity. Having loosened the rectum, remove all of the intestinal tract excepting the kidney and the pluck (heart, lungs, liver, gullet, and windpipe). This constitutes a hog-dressed carcass with pluck in. Flush the blood and any dung out of the carcass with clear brook water. In case the pluck is removed to permit more rapid chilling, do not discard the heart and liver as they make nutritious and palatable dishes. The liver makes a good camp meal.

Tagging and Transporting

Many hunters prefer to tag their whitetail as soon as they find it. Others prefer to tag it after it is dressed. The important thing is to be sure that it is tagged before you load it into your car. There is no easy way to get your deer out of the timber into your car, but one method seems to require the least effort. Tie the front legs of your deer to its head and drag it. Remember, normally, you must check in your deer at the check station specified for your county on the same day it was killed. Check local laws.

Cornfed whitetails are fine eating, but you must take good care of the carcass. Keep it as cool as possible. The hog-dressed deer generally is transported on the outside of the hunter's car to give mute evidence of his good fortune and to serve as refrigeration in transit, as long as it is not resting over the hood, absorbing engine heat. At the journey's end, after being checked in, the deer should be skinned, unless it is to be hung and aged in the cold for a week. Leaving the skin on the carcass during aging holds down shrinkage and avoids discoloration. The aging temperature should be 32° to 38° F.

Disposition of the Carcass

If the hunter is going to process the carcass himself, he must be especially aware that the temperature of the carcass should not exceed 40° F while it is aging.

If the carcass is to be deposited with a locker operator for processing, previous arrangements must be made, since there are strict Federal and state regulations governing the processing of game in meat processing establishments.

—Wild game carcasses shall be dressed prior to entering the processing or refrigerated areas of the licensed establishment.

—Wild game carcasses stored in the refrigerated areas of the licensed establishment shall be contained and handled in a manner that will assure complete separation of wild game from meat and meat products. This may be accomplished by, but not limited to, the following: (1) the use of separate coolers, (2) the enclosing of game in metal cages, and (3) the complete enclosing of game carcasses with plastic or shrouds.

—A written request shall be made by the establishment to the responsible governmental agency for a listing of the days and time of day wild game carcasses may be processed.

—All equipment used which comes in contact with wild game shall be thoroughly cleaned and sanitized prior to its use on animal or poultry carcasses.

Skinning

Open the skin over the rear of the hock and down the back of the leg to the rectum. Skin around the hock and remove the leg at the break joint on the lower part of the hock. Make an opening between the tendon and the hock and insert a hog gambrel. Raise the carcass until the haunches are at shoulder height and proceed to pull the pelt from the rounds. Use the first to remove the pelt from the sides and continue to pull it down the back. Remove the forelegs at the smooth joint (just below the knee joint). Very little knife work is necessary, since the pelt can be pulled and fisted from the carcass. If the head is to be mounted, the skin on the neck (cape) should not be opened on the underside of the neck but should be opened along the crest of the neck (Figure 8.19).

The head is removed at the atlas joint, similar to the practice with all other animals. After the pelt and head have been removed, split the underside of the neck and remove the gullet and windpipe and the remainder of the pluck if this has not been done previously. Use a stiff brush and plenty of clean water to wash the hair and soil from the inside of the carcass. Place the carcass under refrigeration.

Pelts

Care of Hide and Head

Rub the skin side with a liberal amount of fine salt and apply plenty of salt to the head. Let the salt be absorbed for 24 to 48 hours, then fold the pelt, hair side out, and tie securely with strong cord. Tag it according to law and ship it to a taxidermist for mounting and tanning. Use clean table salt to avoid mineral stains, particularly if the pelt is to be made into buckskin. Save time and money by discarding badly torn or scored pelts.

Cutting the Carcass

Split the carcass through the center of the backbone, dividing it into two sides. However, if the neck is to be used as a pot roast or

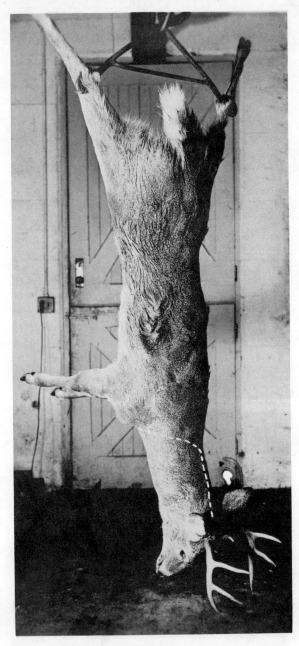

Fig. 8.19–The white dotted line indicates the opening to be made when skinning out the cape for a head that is to be mounted. (Courtesy, The Pennsylvania State University)

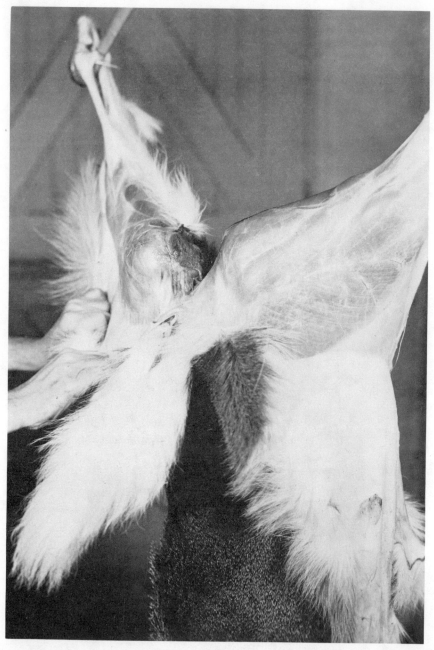

Fig. 8.20—The skin has been opened over the rear of the hock and haunch to the bung and is being pulled from the haunch. (Courtesy, The Pennsylvania State University)

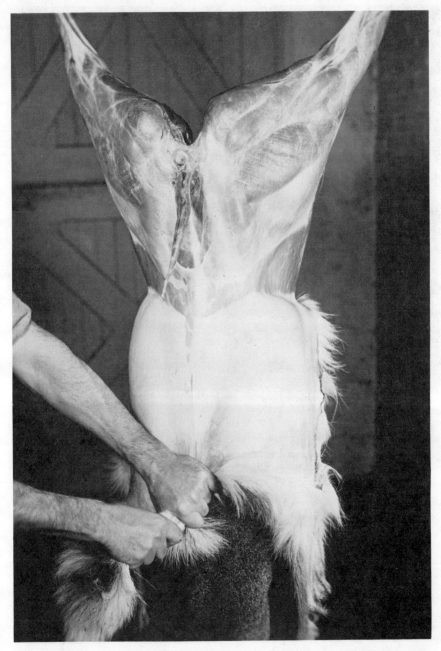

Fig. 8.21—Pulling the pelt from the loin. (Courtesy, The Pennsylvania State University)

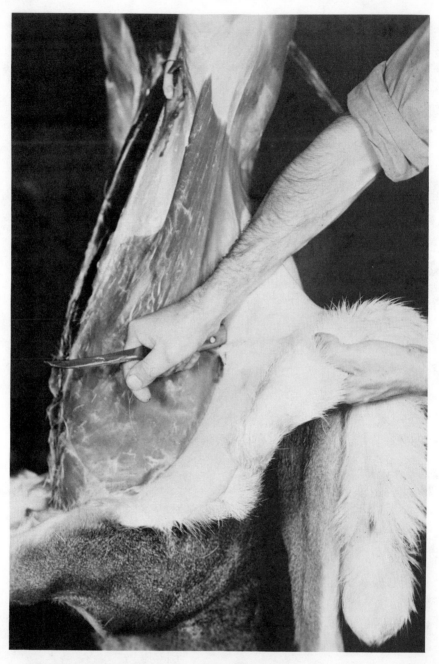

Fig. 8.22—Fisting over the side can be done with the fist, the heel of a knife, or shin bone. (Courtesy, The Pennsylvania State University)

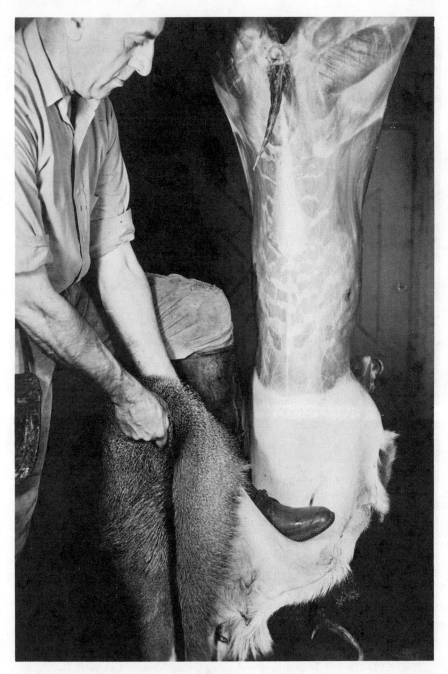

Fig. 8.23—Using body weight to pull the pelt over the back and shoulder. (Courtesy, The Pennsylvania State University)

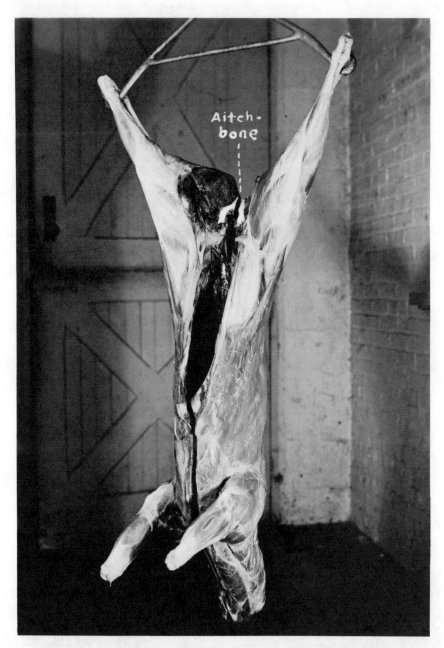

Fig. 8.24—The full-dressed carcass showing the aitchbone. (Courtesy, The Pennsylvania State University)

neck slices, it should be removed before splitting the carcass. Place the side of venison on the table, inside down, and remove the haunch by cutting in front of and close to the hip bone. Move forward to the shoulder and remove it by cutting between the fourth and fifth rib. The back with breast attached must have the breast removed. Cut across the ribs about 3 inches from the backbone on the blade end to the loin end. The ribs are separated from the loin by cutting directly behind the last rib. The leg is placed on the table, aitchbone on top. Cut parallel to the aitchbone and remove the rump. Remove the flank.

Venison round steaks are cut from the leg or round, and the heel is used for stewing or grinding. The rump, which also contains the hip loin, can be cut into hip steak. The shoulder is divided into the top, the arm, and the shank. The shanks and breast are boned and ground into deerburgers or incorporated with pork for summer sausage.

An alternate method of cutting is to make all cuts boneless, including the rib and loin chops. Butterfly chops from these tender cuts are highly desirable. Furthermore, by making boneless cuts, the need for a saw is eliminated, which is a desirable factor in home cutting. The reader may refer to Chapter 14 on lamb cutting and apply many of those principles to cutting a venison carcass.

Mutilated or Bloodshot Areas

If a large area of the carcass is affected by the shot, it can be salvaged by washing it free from hair and soaking it in a weak brine made by dissolving ½ pound of salt in 1 gallon of water. The salt will draw out most of the blood overnight and the meat will be suitable for grinding or stewing. Badly mutilated meat makes good dog food.

Preserving Venison

Venison lends itself well to corning (corned venison), to curing, drying, and smoking (dried venison), to sausage making, when mixed with 50% or more of fat pork trimmings and prepared as summer or smoked sausage, to canning, and to freezing. Probably the most widely used method of preservation is by freezing and storing at –10° F.

Corned Venison

Use boned shoulders and cut into 3- to 4-pound pieces. Place the meat in a stone crock. Dissolve 1½ pounds of salt, ½ pound of cane or brown sugar, 1 ounce of cream of tartar, 1 ounce of baking soda, and 1 ounce of pickling spice in 1 gallon of hot water. Allow the brine to cool

Fig. 8.25—One method of cutting a venison carcass: (1) rear shank (2) heel; (3) round steak; (4) rump and hip loin; (5) loin chop or roast; (6) rib chop or roast; (7) top of shoulder or chuck; (8) neck pot roast; (8A) neck slices; (9) arm roast; (10) foreshank; (11) breast; (12) flank. The letters in white indicate the line where wholesale cuts are made. The above carcass weighed 92 pounds and was in excellent finish. (Courtesy, The Pennsylvania State University)

before pouring it over the meat. Make enough pickle to cover the meat and weight it down with a clean board and a rock. Cure for several weeks.

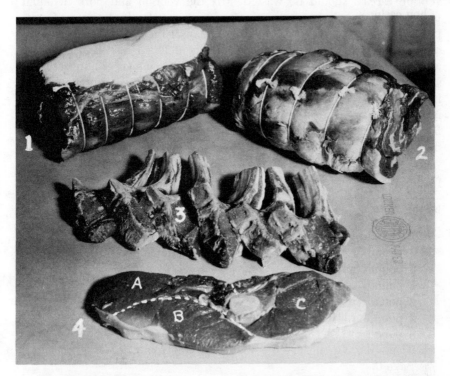

Fig. 8.26—Some cuts of venison. (1) Rolled shoulder of buck with slice of fresh pork fat for self basting; (2) rolled shoulder of fat doe (it has sufficient fat); (3) rib chop; (4) venison round steak indicating A-inside round, B-outside round, and C-round tip. (Courtesy, The Pennsylvania State University)

Dried Venison

Cure the muscles of the round separating them into inside, outside, and round tip. Rub them with a mixture of 3 parts of salt and 1 part of granulated sugar for three consecutive times at 4- to 5-day intervals. Place the rubbed meat on a table or shelf in a cool cellar during the curing process, and at the end of three weeks brush off any remaining salt and hang the meat to smoke for three days. Hang the smoked venison in a dry place for a month or more to dry, after which it can be sliced similar to dried beef.

Sausage

One taste of sausage made from the less tender cuts of venison ground with fat pork trimmings will assure anyone that no part of the venison carcass should be wasted. Mix the venison and pork in equal parts and season the same as sausage (6 ounces of salt, 1 ounce of pepper, and a pinch of sage for 20 pounds of sausage meat). It can be stuffed in hog casings and smoked for 8 to 10 hours at 110° F and held the same as cured pork, or it can be made into patties and canned. In case the sausage is to be frozen or stored, wrap the unseasoned sausage tightly in laminated freezer paper, freeze, and store at –10° F. Thaw and season it just before using. Unseasoned sausage will maintain its fresh taste for five or six months, but seasoned sausage will turn flat and rancid after 60 days.

A good meat loaf consists of 2 pounds of salt pork ground with 20 pounds of venison.

Mince Meat

2 pounds venison (neck)	2 teaspoons nutmeg
1 pound beef suet	1 tablespoon allspice
6 pounds apples	1 tablespoon cinnamon
2 pounds currants	¼ teaspoon ginger
1 pound sultana raisins	1 teaspoon cloves
2 pounds raisins	1 tablespoon salt
½ pound citron	2 oranges
6 cups brown sugar	8 cups cider or grape juice

Bake the venison 40 minutes in a moderate oven (350° F). Cool and chop. Mix it with the chopped suet; pared, cored and chopped apples; currants, raisins, and citron. Add the sugar, spices, juice of two oranges, finely chopped rind of one orange, and the cider or grape juice. Simmer 30 minutes and pack hot into jars. Seal and process 60 minutes for pints and 70 minutes for quarts at 15 pounds pressure or 3 hours in a boiling water bath. This formula makes sufficient mince meat for 10 to 12 nine-inch pies.

CHAPTER 9

Curing and Tanning
Hides and Pelts

CLASSIFICATION OF HIDES

Hides, pelts, and skins are classified according to (1) the species and class from which they come, (2) their weight, (3) nature and extent of branding, and (4) the type of packer producing them.

The general term *hide* refers to beef "skin" weighing more than 30 pounds. Those weighing less than 30 pounds are classified as skins, and are subdivided into calfskins (the lightest) and kipskins (intermediate between calfskins and hides). Hides are designated as steer or cow and may further be classified by weight into extra-light (ex-light), 30 to 48 pounds, light, 48 to 58 pounds, and heavy, 58 pounds and up.

Brands and their locations affect the value of hides, since those branded on the side and butt (rear quarter) cause damaging scar tissue in this most valuable area when they are processed into leather. The terms *Colorado* and/or *Texas* are applied to those hides branded on the side, the *Texas* hides generally being plump and close grained. *Butt-branded* hides are often indicated as such in the market. Unbranded hides are known as *natives*.

Hides are further classified into *major packer, small packer,* and *country* hides. The principal differences exist in the manner of take off and subsequent handling. *Major packer* hides are uniform in pattern, have a minimum of cuts and scores, are free from dung, and have been cured, sorted, and stored under standard conditions. *Small packer* and *country* hides generally are not uniform in take off (pattern), contain more cuts and scores, and because of various systems of handling by different individuals, they are sometimes undersalted, showing hair slips and maggot infestation. Hides are graded 1, 2, or 3, depending on the extent of deterioration, Grade 1 being the highest quality hide.

Hides that come from animals that died previous to slaughter are called *renderer* or *murrain* hides.

Sheep Pelts

As indicated in Table 6.1, sheep pelts are classified by the length of wool they carry as follows: full wool, 1½ inches or more, fall shorn, 1 through 1½ inches, Shearling No. 1, ½ through 1 inch, Shearling No. 2, ¼ through ½ inch, Shearling No. 3, ⅛ through ¼ inch, and Shearling No. 4, ⅛ inch.

Sheep pelts are further classified as to their origin as follows:

River—Missouri River markets area
Southwest—Texas, Oklahoma, Arizona area
Northern—Minnesota and the Dakotas area

Although historically the value of sheep pelts has been largely due to the amount and quality of wool they contained, a relatively new use for shearlings has become economically important. Three years of tests in professional institutions have convinced the Agricultural Research Service scientists of the U.S. Department of Agriculture that glutaraldehyde-tanned shearling bed pads are far superior to any other product.

The specially tanned shearlings, sheepskins with the wool evenly clipped, were found to be effective nursing aids for preventing and healing bedsores. The painful sores develop in patients who cannot move and must lie for long hours in one position.

Shearlings have long been recognized as ideal bed pads, but before the development of glutaraldehyde tanning,[1] the pads were tanned by conventional methods and shrank and hardened after a few launderings. The glutaraldehyde-tanned shearlings, however, can be run through a washer and dryer as many as 54 times and still retain their original shape and resiliency.

Both patients and staff in eight hospitals, a nursing home, and an outpatient clinic highly praised the new washable bed pads. The shearlings were serviceable for as long as 28 months and proved more effective than bed pads made from synthetic fibers.

When in use, the wool of the shearling is placed in direct contact with the patient's skin. This allows for free circulation of air and absorption of perspiration. It also minimizes skin abrasion, thereby aiding in preventing and in healing the bedsores. The pads are resilient and distribute the weight of the patients evenly. The wool is highly flame-

---

1. U.S. Department of Agriculture, *Agricultural Research*, December 1965, p. 8.

retardant—an important safety factor for the bedridden or disabled patient.

ARS chemist William F. Happich and his associates at the Eastern marketing and nutrition laboratory, who developed the glutaraldehyde tanning process for shearlings, conducted the tests in the Philadelphia, Pennsylvania, area in close cooperation with nursing administrators.

Pigskins

As indicated in Chapter 4, most U.S. pork processors have used in the immediate past and are presently using a dehairing technique, thus leaving skin on pork carcasses until they are processed into wholesale or retail cuts. Using such a system, the only fresh skin available of any consequence is that resulting from the fat back and the hams, and this skin has largely been used in gelatin production. Most whole pigskins for tanning have been imported.

However, with the introduction of the mechanical pig skinner (Chapter 4), several processors are gearing up to hog skinning operations. At the 1972 annual meeting of the National Hide Association, it was estimated that 1 million pigskins would be removed mechanically in 1973 in the U.S. The process is currently being used at the Jimmy Dean Packing Company, Plainview, Texas and Osceola, Iowa; Hillshire Farm, New London, Wisconsin; and Shane Packing Company, Chester, Pennsylvania, among others.

Fresh hog skins are being used by the Burn Treatment Skin Bank, Inc., of Phoenix, Arizona as a skin dressing in the treatment of severe burn victims throughout the nation. Because of the cellular structure closely related to that of human skin, pigskin (in the form of a porcine dressing) has become accepted as the most suitable dressing for the treatment of severe burn victims. Applied directly to the burn area, porcine dressing serves as a temporary skin which prevents body fluid loss and protects against infection and pain.

Skins for porcine dressings are selected daily by a representative of the Skin Bank at a particular plant and flown to Phoenix. Upon arrival there, the skins are treated with antibiotics, shaved, cut to a thickness of .015 inch, packaged in a variety of forms in surgically clean conditions, and chill-stored to await shipment to hospitals and burn treatment centers throughout the nation.

In explaining the rapidity of this process, the director of the Skin Bank, Francis Hope, said that within 24 hours from the time the hide is removed from a hog, the porcine skin made from the hide can be a dressing on a burn victim almost anywhere in the United States. It has been estimated by the Skin Bank that these porcine skin dressings save at least one life per day in this country, and it is known that the dressings alleviate much pain and shorten hospitalization for other severe burn victims.

The balance of pigskins not shipped to the Skin Bank are sold to tanners, many of which are used in manufacturing a high quality sueded pigskin upper shoe leather.

HANDLING PELTS

The ultimate destination of most pelts is the tannery. The condition of the pelt and the directness of marketing affect the price received by the farmer. Packers have a decided advantage in that (1) they deal directly with the tannery buyer, (2) their hides have a good take-off with a minimum of cuts and scores and (3) they have large quantities of the different classes and grades with which to attract large buyers.

Since the hide is the most valuable by-product of cattle, the livestock producer should consider the hide as well as the flesh in his livestock management program. Lice, ticks, grubs, fleas, mange, scabies, pox, ringworm, and warts, most of which can be controlled by dipping, sorely lower the value of hides for leather; so do the branding iron, thorn and wire gashes, or horn and nail scores.

A man who deliberately allows large, hard clumps of dung to adhere to the hide; who fails to remove the dewclaws, sinews, lean, fat, lips, ears, and tail bone; who uses dirty salt or insufficient salt and allows the hide alternately to freeze and thaw; who is careless in removing the hide, making deep scores or cuts; a man who binds up the hide with baling wire (leaving a rust stain)—he is the man who makes country hide prices what they are.

A VOLUNTARY HIDE TRIM STANDARD

A hide trim that is designed to encourage economy in shipping hides and improve the quality of leather products was developed at the University of Cincinnati and became effective April 4, 1965. It is designated:

> Commercial Standard CS268-65
> Hide Trim Pattern for Domestic Cattlehides
> (Office of Commodity Standards)
> (U. S. Department of Commerce)

Its use has been accepted and is currently widely used by the industry.
The trim is as follows:

Head.—Ears, ear butts, snouts and lips, fat, and muscle tissue should be removed. The pate should be removed from the pate (crown) side of the head by cutting through the eye hole. The narrow side of the head should be trimmed through the eye in a similar manner. All ragged edges should be removed.

Kosher heads.—These should be removed by cutting across at the top of the kosher cut. (Headless kosher hides are to be put into their respective weight classifications by lowering the testing weights 3 pounds in the case of cow hides and ex-light steer hides and 5 pounds in the case of light and heavy steer hides.)

Shanks.—Foreshanks should be trimmed straight across through the knee at a point which will eliminate the cup. Hind shanks should be trimmed just above the dewclaws.

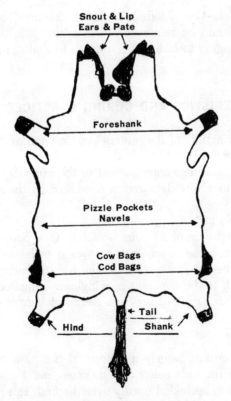

Modern Hide Trim Standard

Fig. 9.1—The shaded portions must be trimmed off in order to conform to the trim standard.

Cow Bags, Teats, Cow Navels, and Cod Bags.—Remove straight with the belly line.

Cow Bags.—Cow hides that have the bags trimmed out due to government regulations are not considered as being off pattern if properly shaped in other respects and are deliverable as No. 1 hides if conforming to other trade standards of that designation.

Pizzle Pocket.—Split through the center, but leave on the hide for identification.

Tails.—Maximum tail length should be no more than 6 inches cured, measured from the root. (Removal of the switch is necessary because it is difficult to cure. The presence of a poorly cured appendage will cause the hide proper to spoil.)

Cheek Brands.—When a hide has a cheek brand and no other, that portion of the head should be trimmed off and the hide placed in a native selection.

Wire in Hides.—Green hides should be examined carefully, and all wire hog-rings should be removed before salting the hides. Their presence can be damaging to hide processing and tanning machinery and to leather.

HIDE CHARACTERISTICS AND CURING PRACTICES

Hides consist mainly of the protein keratin (hair and epidermis) and collagen (body of the hide). Acids destroy collagen and alkalies destroy keratin (the reverse is also true, but not to the same degree). Hides and wooled pelts are therefore dehaired or dewooled by the use of the alkali, lime.

Approximately 62% of a green hide is water. This 62 pounds of water can dissolve a maximum of 23 pounds of salt. One pound of salt is used per pound of hide, some of which is recovered to be reused (the salt is washed before reusing). This refers to the use of crushed rock salt (ice cream salt) which is the common packinghouse practice. In farm practice, ¼ pound of fine sack salt for each pound of hide is sufficient.

Salt Pack Curing

In salt pack curing, largely a process of the past, hides are spread hair side down in the hide cellar or hide room and 1 pound of rock salt per pound of hide is sprinkled evenly over the flesh side. Another hide is spread over the salted hide and given a similar application of salt. This progresses until the day's kill is salted. The hides are allowed to cure for approximately 30 days, after which they are freed of any undissolved salt. They are sorted as to weight; graded on the basis of cuts, scores, grub holes, and slips; and folded and tied individually. The undissolved salt is washed and reused on a fresh pack with some fresh salt. During the curing process, 100 pounds of green hide can lose up to 35 pounds of water and gain up to 6 pounds of salt.

Brining Hides

Realizing that excess water, fat, manure, and head and shank parts of hides do not make leather, packers have adopted or are adopting the brine curing method. The necessary equipment depends on whether hides are to be fleshed and demanured before brining them in vats containing a saturated salt brine, or whether they are to be washed and brined but not fleshed (defatted). Fleshing and demanuring machines are available.

A process that cuts labor costs and is not as expensive is drum brining. In this process, the hides (with head removed, shank removed at the knee, and switch end of tail removed) are placed in large revolving drums and washed in clean water (at 55° to 65° F) for 10 minutes and then drained. The drums are recharged with fresh water to which salt is added (⅛ of a pound for each pound of hide) and run for one hour. Another ⅛ of a pound of salt per pound of hide and 1 pound of chlorinated lime or similar bacteria and mold deterrent are added and the drums rotated for another two hours. At the end of this drumming period, the hides are removed and placed on wooden horses and allowed to drain for several days. They are then graded and bundled for shipment, and if they are palletized, loading is easier, quicker, and less costly.

Brining is an example of the progress made in the preservation and handling of a valuable by-product that has long been neglected and (under old methods) was never a business that had any social standing. Now the clean, defatted, brine-cured hide has a pleasant antiseptic odor and can be merchandised with pride. The costs of curing have been increased, but so has the price offered for the superior product. Costs show that there is no profit in tanning heads and shanks; that curing time is cut from 30 days to hours, releasing considerable storage space; that there is a saving of salt; and that there is a considerable saving in freight charges by removing the non-usable hide components; all of which result in a more reliable product that is easier to handle and store, and one that permits of more accurate inspection.

New equipment developments in hide curing border on the phenomenal. Curing time can be reduced to six hours by means of an ultrasonic wave generated by a unit manufactured by Conceria, Teocchi-G & A, Bergamo, Italy. The unit is attached to existing tanning equipment to accomplish soaking and tanning in approximately 24 hours.

Due to the complex nature of such equipment, a sizable investment is required to set up and operate a hide curing process. Thus the trend has been to collect hides into a central location from several slaughter operators for processing. Since hides are so perishable, the time and distance of travel has been limited. Recently Rohm & Haas Company, Philadelphia, Pennsylvania, has developed a fresh hide preservative for more effective distribution. The firm's product—Hyamine F.H.P. 80% Concentrate—carries approval of the Environmental Protection Agency and retards bacterial action that causes rot and hair slip on those hides transported long distances to central curing facilities.

TANNING

Commercial Tanning

To produce the desired qualities in the various leathers requires many different manipulations which necessarily make tanning a rather complicated process. The several steps in tanning a hide for leather are, briefly, as follows:

Trimming.—Ears, shanks, and tails are removed. The trimmings from calfskins are sold to be manufactured into gelatin.

Splitting.—Beef hides are split lengthwise into two sides.

Soaking.—Dried skins are soaked in fresh water (changed every 24 hours) from 2 to 5 days at a temperature of 52° F.

Washing.—The soaked hides must be washed thoroughly to remove dung, dirt, and blood.

Fleshing.—Adhering fat, flesh, and membranes are removed by a fleshing machine designed for the purpose. The person doing home tanning should use a sharp, flexible bladed knife.

Dehairing.—Hides immersed in a milk lime solution, made by dissolving 8 pounds of hydrated lime in 4 gallons of water, can be dehaired in 3 to 4 days. The addition of sodium or calcium hydrosulfide materially hastens the loosening of hair and wool and is used in commercial tanneries. Sheep pelts are dewooled by making a lime paste and covering the skin side with a layer ¼ inch thick. The pelt so treated is folded along the line of the backbone (limed sides together) and placed in a warm room until the wool slips.

Scudding.—The dehaired skins are placed, grain side up, over a rounded wooden beam and with a specially designed two-handled knife, the beamster (the man who uses the knife) pushes the knife over the skin, forcing out any material remaining in the hair follicles.

Deliming.—The hide is soaked in a sulfuric acid bath (½ pound of sulfuric acid and 9 gallons of water for 50 to 60 pounds of hide) and left to soak for one hour, changing the position frequently. The object is to remove the lime.

Bating.—This is the process of digesting the degradation products and the elastin fibers in the skin. Prior to 1910, practically all bating was accomplished by the use of manures. When hen or pigeon manure was used, the process was called "bating," but the use of dog manure was called "puering." The active principle in these dung bates was found to be protein-digesting enzymes which caused the skin to become soft and pliable. The enzymes of the pancreatic gland and those produced from wood have displaced the objectionable dung bates. Dessicated pancreas mixed with a dry deliming agent (ammonia salt) can be purchased under the trade name of Oropon (Rohm and Haas Company). Hides and skins are bated in revolving drums at a temperature of about 90° F for 1 to 1½ hours, after which they are washed in clear water.

Pickling.—If the bated skins are to be preserved for storage and future tanning, they are placed in a pickle bath (7 pounds of salt, 5 gallons of water, and ¼ pound of concentrated sulfuric acid) for several hours.

Tanning.—The common tanning processes may be grouped into vegetable, chrome, and miscellaneous.

1. Vegetable Tanning—Tannin is a chemical substance found in certain classes of plant life that is capable of combining with animal protein, converting it into leather. The tannin is extracted by leaching the wood or bark in water. Commercial tan-bark is the shredded, spent bark from which tanneries have leached the tannin. In order of rank, the species of plants that furnish the major quantity of tannin for the leather industry are quebracho, American chestnut, mangrove, myrobalans, wattle bark, valonia, spruce, oak, hemlock, gambier, and sumac.

   Hides are immersed in tan liquors of a given strength, being moved daily through a series of rocker vats and then a similar number of layer vats, requiring from 30 to 45 days to tan. Harness leather receives the shorter tan, sole leather the longer tanning period. Especially thick hides may be split into several layers to hasten tannin penetration.

2. Chrome Tanning—Sodium dichromate ($Na_2Cr_2O_7$), a red crystalline compound, is the tanning material used in chrome tanning. When converted into chromic sulfate, it combines with hide protein to produce a leather with a greater resistance to heat and abrasion than vegetable tanned leather. Chrome tanning is rapid,

requiring only a few days. Unlike vegetable tanning, which imparts various shades of tan to the leather, chrome tanning imparts shades from green to blue. Chrome tanning is sometimes combined with aluminum salts to produce a white leather that has some of the desirable characteristics of chrome leather. Vegetable tanned leathers are often chrome retanned to secure a leather that combines the good qualities of both leathers.

Blue stock which is properly prepared through chrome tanning can produce almost any type of leather. While the process has demonstrated versatility, tanners should be cautioned about its high level of pollution. Adequate effluent control requires the manufacturer's ability to interpret and apply analytical data. Knowledge of the function of chemicals can reduce total effluent, but big gains are the result of reuse of wash waters and process liquors containing chemicals, according to Thomas C. Blair, Rohm & Haas Company.

3. Miscellaneous Tannages—A number of "syntans" (synthetic tannins) are on the market. They produce a white leather that lacks the durable qualities of the vegetable and chrome tanned leathers, but which may be combined with the latter processes to produce serviceable leather suitable for special uses. Some common syntans are Leukonal, Tanigan, Tanak, Tanasol, Mertanol, and Arkotan. Other methods of tanning that serve special needs are Calgon, alum, aldehyde, oil, quinone, and tungsten tanning.

   a. Setting out—This is the mechanical extraction of excess water from the hides as they come from the tanning vats. The same thing is accomplished by hand by means of a "hand slicker" (metal scraper).

   b. Splitting—Thick hides that are not to be used for sole leather, but made into upholstery leather, are split by a machine into two or three layers. The wool sides of pickled sheep skins are split into grain layers or skivers which are used for making hat bands, bookbinding, etc. The flesh layers are used for making chamois leather.

   c. Shaving—Light skins need not be split and are run through shaving machines to even the thickness and make them smooth and clean.

   d. Fatliquoring—In order to prevent the cohesion of the leather fibers during the drying process, it is necessary to rub or stuff the damp leather with a fat or oil. This keeps the leather from drying out hard and stiff. Neat's-foot oil and glycerin are recommended for home tanning.

    e. Staking—Flexing the tanned hide or skin over a rounded metal blade set in the end of a block of wood (3 feet high) fastened to the floor is known as "hand staking." This is an important operation because it stretches and flexes the leather fibers and makes them pliable.

    f. Other operations consist of dyeing, drying, buffing (sandpapering to produce a nap), glazing, plating, and finishing. Patent leather, also called japanned or enameled leather, is a chrome tanned leather that has received three separate coatings of a linseed oil varnish. Chamois skin is the flesh side of an oil tanned sheep skin. Cod, whale, seal, or shark oil is used.

Home Tanning

Several simple methods of tanning skins have been devised which make it possible for a novice to make a serviceable product.

Salt Alum Tanning.—The salted sheep skin is soaked in water until soft and then placed on a table or beam where it is trimmed and fleshed. Washing can be done either in a tub or on the table. Any good soap powder will do. The water should be warm (125° F). Rub and rinse repeatedly until clean and then extract the water by hand or by using an ordinary washing machine wringer. The pelt is placed on the table fleece side down and given a thorough rubbing with a mixture of 1 part of powdered alum to 2 parts of common salt (4 ounces of alum and 8 ounces of salt will tan the average sized sheep pelt). The pelt is left in this position overnight, but the next morning it is hung over a rail, skin side up. The following morning the skin is sponged to remove the unabsorbed salt, and 1 to 2 ounces of neat's-foot oil or glycerin is rubbed into the damp, soft skin. As the skin dries, during the next two days, it must be staked several times to keep it from becoming hard. When dry, the skin is buffed, using a coarse grade sandpaper fastened over a block of wood. The wool is carded, using an ordinary wool card, and the pelt is ready for use. It makes a comfortable cover for the hard, cold seats on farm implements.

Alum Tanning.—This method is suitable for fur skins since the aluminum sulfate does not color the hair or skin. Dissolve 1 pound of aluminum sulfate in 1 gallon of water; dissolve 4 ounces of crystallized sodium carbonate (soda ash) and ½ pound of salt in ½ gallon of water and pour this slowly into the alum solution while stirring it vigorously. The prepared skin (soaked, fleshed, and washed) is placed in the solution for 2 to 4 days, depending upon its thickness, and is then rinsed and put through a wringer. The damp skin is now rubbed with glycerin and as it dries, it is staked and finally buffed. Before it is rubbed with oil or glycerin, retanning the skin with 1 pound of Leukanol (a syntan made by Rohm & Haas Company), dissolved in 1 gallon of water, makes the skin tougher and softer without discoloring it.

Vegetable Alum Tanning.—Dissolve ½ pound of aluminum sulfate and ½ pound of salt in a small quantity of water. Dissolve 2 ounces of gambier or Terra Japonica in a little boiling water. Mix the two solutions and add sufficient water to make 1 gallon. Use sufficient flour with the 1 gallon of tanning liquor to make a moderately thin paste. Take a properly prepared pelt (soaked, trimmed, fleshed, and washed) and apply three coatings about ¼ inch thick at two-day intervals to the skin side of the pelt, removing each previous coating before applying the next. When practically dry, rinse the pelt in warm water containing some borax and then rinse in fresh water. Squeeze out the water and slick the skin with a dull knife. Apply a coating of glycerin and hang up to dry. Stake the pelt several times while drying and then buff with coarse sandpaper.

This method produces a yellow skin of good tensile strength.

A LEATHER FUTURE?

At one time, the greatest use for leather in the United States was to manufacture harnesses for the many horses that provided power for work and transportation. With the advent of mechanized power and transportation the need for harness leather decreased rapidly. There remained, however, a brisk demand for leather for shoe manufacture, until gradually synthetic composition soles began to take over, and by 1960, only 35% of the shoes manufactured in the United States had leather soles. Technology was able to produce the composition soles cheaper. Presently it is estimated that 80% to 85% of the shoes sold in the United States have non-leather composition soles. However, probably some 90% have leather uppers, meaning the resilient, pliable wearing qualities of leather have prevailed at that point.

United States hide producers are exploring new frontiers in domestic hide consumption and at the same time eyeing the growing demand for hides for export. To do this, greater use of research and technology is being made. The United States is a prime source of raw materials for countries that manufacture leather as evidenced by the export of 12,500,000 whole hides out of the estimated 37,000,000 produced in a recent year.

New domestic uses for hides are being developed, as evidenced by the previous discussion concerning the medical uses of pigskins and lamb shearlings. One author has recently encountered interest by the automobile industry in returning to leather seats, since plastics are currently in somewhat short supply and their manufacture requires strict attention to environmental constraints.

Is there a leather future? Indications are that the single most valuable by-product will remain so.

CHAPTER 10

Packing House By-Products

The student is reminded that each chapter on slaughter (chapters 4, 5, 6, and 7) contains a discussion on by-products, usually under the heading "Facts About . . ."

Modern conditions make it almost impossible to cut production and distribution expenses for the majority of commodities; hence, one of the most important opportunities for gaining competitive advantage, or even for enabling an industry or individual business to maintain its position in this new competition, is to reduce its manufacturing expense by creating new credits for products previously unmarketable. From the viewpoint of individual business, this manufacture of by-products has turned waste into such a source of revenue that in many cases the by-products have proved more profitable per pound than the main product.

By-products are everything of value produced on the killing floor other than the dressed carcass and are classified as edible and inedible. Livers, hearts, tongues, kidneys, brains, oxtails, sweetbreads, fats, and blood represent the edible by-products, and these, along with parts of the carcasses, can be converted by manufacture into many other edible products. Far the greatest number of manufactured by-products are made from the inedible by-products, and it is in this business that an integration has taken place between packers, subsidiary corporations, and corporations outside of their control.

The greatest financial return is realized from the by-products of cattle, followed by those from sheep and hogs. Although the per-head money return on hog by-products is low, the large number of hogs slaughtered makes the total sum quite large. Values change as science develops new uses and new products through research.

OLEOMARGARINE (MARGARINE)

A widely used product made in part from animal fats is oleomargarine. Oleo means beef fat. Margarine is the generic name for many different brand formulations and is generally taken to mean a vegetable oil product. It was invented in 1869 by a French chemist who thereby won a competition held by Emperor Napoleon III. The inventor called it oleomargarine because he believed it was basically the type of food fat that earlier had been named margarine and because he used oleo fat.

At this writing, many margarine packages carry both names because some state labeling laws require "oleomargarine," regardless of the product's composition.

How Margarine Is Made

Margarine is manufactured from selected ingredients according to strict standards and laboratory controls. It is manufactured in a manner that complies with the quality and health controls of Federal and state pure food laws and the Federal Standard, as well as Federal and state laws specifically concerned with margarine. A typical process follows these general steps:

1. *Milk is prepared.* Usually it is skim milk, which contains the proteins, milk sugar, and lactic acid of whole milk that are the principal sources of the palatable qualities and flavor of both margarine and butter.

   The milk, pasteurized and cooled, is carefully treated with harmless micro-organisms to create the desired flavor. If necessary, diacetyl, a substance normally formed by this milk "ripening," may be added to standardize the flavor.

2. *Highly refined fats and oils are blended.* Their selection and proportionate use depend on the manufacturer's formula for the margarine being made. One, some, or all of the ingredient fats and oils may have been partly hardened by hydrogenation before or after blending. The fats and oils are always stated on the carton and wrapper of the finished product.

3. *The fats and oils blend is then emulsified with the prepared milk.* This phase especially reflects the manufacturer's art and skill. It involves combining the ingredients (which may be accomplished in different ways), mixing and agitating them in a warm liquid state, tempering the mixture, and chilling it. During the mixing process the milk and fat are intimately combined so that the result is an emulsion. Vitamins, salt, emulsifying agents, coloring, and other ingredients are added during the process. Margarines may differ considerably from each other in flavor and in physical

properties, even though they are processed much the same way under the Standard.

All parts of the mixing process are conducted within strict limits of time, temperature, portions, and other controls. Frequent laboratory tests take place. Stainless steel manufacturing equipment is the rule. It is cleaned and scrubbed daily.

4. *Texturating.* The blended mixture is then chilled and kneaded in a specially designed machine to produce the required texture and crystallization.

5. *Packing.* The margarine, direct from this process, is mechanically wrapped and packaged. Most margarine is double packaged, first in parchment or foil or some other protective material, and then in a hard, protective carton of treated paperboard. Some products employ paperboard cartons to which foil has been laminated or which have been overwrapped with some other protective material.

6. *Distribution.* The packaged margarine is immediately placed under refrigeration and ordinarily is kept under refrigeration until sold to the consumer. It should be kept under refrigeration in the home.

Most margarine is colored yellow and packaged in ¼-pound units within a 1-pound carton.

Composition of Margarine

By weight, margarine is—

* 80% refined food fat—the principal ingredient. Most margarines are "vegetable" and contain only refined oils such as soybean, cottonseed, corn, and peanut oils. Some are blends of animal and vegetable oils.
* 17% to 18½% skim milk, pasteurized and "cultured" with harmless bacteria to create the pleasing flavor associated with table spread.
* 1½% to 3% salt. (There are some unsalted margarines.)

In addition:

* Every pound of margarine is fortified to provide substantial amounts of vitamin A. Some margarines also provide vitamin D. All margarines contain some vitamin E, as well as vitamin K, that occur naturally.
* Other ingredients are added in very small amounts to improve the product's usefulness and keeping qualities.
* The food fat portion of every pound offers a relatively high level of linoleic acid—considered to be a vital element in the diet—

Table 10.1—Composition of the Refined Food Fat in Margarine in 1964, 1969, and 1973.[1]

Refined Fats and Oils	1964		1969		1973	
	Million Lbs.	Percent of Total Fat	Million Lbs.	Percent of Total Fat	Million Lbs.	Percent of Total Fat
Soybean oil	1,146	73.0	1,332	76.4	1,490	78.9
Cottonseed oil	101	6.5	75	4.3	62	3.3
Corn oil	148	9.0	173	9.9	213	11.3
Safflower oil[2]	112	8.0	44	2.5	32	1.7
Other veg. oil			21	1.2	4	0.2
All veg. oil	1,507	96.5	1,645	94.3	1,801	95.4
Lard	41	2.6	87	5.0	72	3.8
Beef fat	15	0.9	12	0.7	15	0.8
All animal fats	56	3.5	99	5.7	87	4.6
Total	1,563	100.0	1,744	100.0	1,888	100.0

1. George Kromer, U.S. Dept. of Agriculture, Economic Research Service.

2. Safflower oil and other vegetable oil combined in 1964.

ranging from about 8% to 30%, and 70% to 85% of unsaturated fatty acids.

These are other ingredients that may be found in margarine:

- Vitamin A—for nutrition. Minimum is always 15,000 USP (United States Pharmacopeia) units per pound. All table margarines, and many industrial margarines, have vitamin A.
- Vitamin D—for nutrition. May or may not be included.
- Salt—for flavor and, in part, as a preservative.
- Lecithin (a harmless substance derived from soybeans) may be used to reduce spattering when panfrying. Mono- and di-glycerides may also be used for this purpose and to prevent loss of

moisture. These substances are not used individually or together in an amount to exceed 0.5% of the total weight.

- Among the preservatives, besides salt, that may be added to prevent mold and to protect flavor are sodium benzoate and potassium sorbate, which neither separately nor together should exceed 0.1% of the weight.
- Artificial coloring. Pro-vitamin A is deemed to be artificial coloring.
- Any safe and suitable artificial flavoring substance that imparts to the food a flavor in semblance of butter.
- Butter.
- Citric acid incorporated in the fat or oil ingredient used.
- Isopropyl citrates incorporated in the fat or oil ingredient used, in an amount not to exceed 0.02% by weight of the finished oleomargarine.
- Stearyl citrate incorporated in the fat or oil ingredient in an amount not to exceed 0.15% by weight of the finished oleomargarine.
- Potassium sorbate, in an amount not to exceed 0.1% by weight of the finished oleomargarine.
- Calcium disodium EDTA (calcium disodium ethylenediaminetetraacetate) in an amount not to exceed 75 parts per million by weight of the finished oleomargarine.
- BHA (butylated hydroxyanisole) or BHT (butylated hydroxytoluene), or a combination of these, incorporated in any animal fat ingredient permitted in an amount not to exceed 0.02% by weight of such animal fat content.

Margarine Color

Like that of many foods, color is added in the form of carotene or a vegetable color. Carotene, which is the precursor of vitamin A in nature, may be natural or manufactured. Another coloring is derived from vegetable sources. All colorings used are approved by the U.S. Food and Drug Administration and state food authorities.

Margarine Helps the Farmer

More than a million farmers grow the crops from which margarine's principal ingredients are drawn. These crops are sources of farm income in most states.

For soybean oil, its leading ingredient, margarine has provided an

Table 10.2—Butter and Margarine: Consumption and Retail Prices, Past and Present[1]

Year	Civilian Consumption					Retail Price		Butter–Margarine Ratio
	Total		Per Person			Per Pound		
	Butter	Margarine	Butter	Margarine	Butter and Margarine	Butter	Margarine	
	-(million lbs.)-		- - - - - -(lbs.)- - - - - -			- - - - (¢) - - - -		
Average 1935–1939	2,195	371	17.0	2.9	19.9	36.7	18.1	2.0
Average 1947–1949	1,533	817	10.6	5.6	16.2	79.9	37.7	2.1
Average 1957–1959	1,441	1,532	8.4	8.9	17.3	74.3	29.3	2.5
1964	1,274	1,835	6.7	9.7	16.5	74.4	26.1	2.8
1969	1,123	2,246	5.4	10.8	16.2	84.6	27.8	3.0
1973	965	2,271	4.8	11.3	16.1	91.6	37.4	2.4

1. Robert Miller, U.S. Dept. of Agriculture, Economic Research Service.

expanding market for many years, and is likely to continue to do so—accounting for from 25% to 27% of the domestic use of this oil.

Margarine is a factor in the complex of protein and food fat production. Soybeans and cottonseed are crushed for their protein, which is in demand for feed for livestock and poultry that in turn produce our valued meat and dairy products. Besides the protein, edible soybean and cottonseed oils are produced. These are in large supply, so that today the United States exports these and other fats and oils.

By providing a large total market for soybeans, cottonseed and other oils and fats, margarine is a factor for better prices for all those products and, indirectly, helps make the protein feed available at lower cost than would otherwise be the case. Thus, margarine's farm contribution is twofold—indirectly to the livestock, dairy, and poultry industries and directly to the growers and processors of soybeans, cottonseed, and other products containing fats and oils.

TALLOWS AND GREASES

Classification and Grading

The major classifications are *edible* and *inedible*, which refers to human consumption. Edible fats may be produced, only from edible carcass parts maintained under approved USDA conditions. The beef and pork fats utilized in margarine manufacture are examples of edible fats, as is lard. Nearly all other fats are inedible.

There are many grades for tallow and grease. The system for grading is based on certain chemical and physical characteristics and is rather complex, so will not be fully explained here. Briefly, the criteria used are:

1. Minimum titer refers to the temperature developed as the liquid fat cools to a solid. A higher titer is more desirable. Fats with titers equal to or over 40° C (104° F) are *tallows* and those with titers under 40° C (104° F) are *greases*.
2. Free fatty acid content. A lower percent of free fatty acid is more desirable.
3. MIU (moisture, insolubles, and unsaponifiable). A lower percent of MIU, indicating less "contamination" with useless material, is preferred.
4. F. A. C. (Fat Analysis Committee). Color designation varies in descending desirability from the lightest and whitest to the darkest as follows: Fancy, Fancy (Bleachable), Choice White A,

Table 10.3—World Production of Tallow and Grease by Country,[1] (in Thousands of Metric Tons)

	1971	1972
USA	2,609	2,551
USSR	320	350
Australia	248	268
Canada	200	225
U.K.	147	150
Argentina	131	146
France	130	134
New Zealand	84	86
Other	740	750

1. Jack Crouse, Render, October 1973, p. 10.

Choice White B, Yellow, House (intermediate between Yellow and Brown), and Brown.

Tallow and Grease Production and Utilization

Average tallow and grease production in the United States in two recent years averaged 2,580 metric tons per year which was nearly eight times the production of the USSR, our closest competitor (Table 10.3), and more than equalled the rest of the world's production.

It follows then that a large portion of U.S. tallow and grease production is available for export. As can be seen in Table 10.4, approximately 50% was exported in two recent years.

Use in Animal Feeds

The major domestic use of tallows and grease is in animal feeds (Table 10.4). These fats are usually stabilized with an approved antioxidant to prevent rancidity from developing which would make the feed unpalatable. Fat is the richest food nutrient in terms of energy, and as such has been used successfully in cattle, poultry, and pet feeds.

The pet food business has rapidly expanded in the U.S. with sales

Table 10.4—U.S. Tallow and Grease Production/Utilization 1971-1972[1]

	Millions of Pounds	Percent of Total
Production	4,900	100
U.S. Consumption		
Soap	588	12
Fatty Acids	637	13
Animal Feed	1,127	23
Other	98	2
Exports	2,450	50

1. Jack Crouse, Render, October 1973, p. 11.

reaching almost $1.6 billion in the most recent year reported. This figure is up 12% from the previous year and totaled only $350 million in 1958. About ⅔ of the $1.6 billion was attributed to dog food sales, with the other ⅓ going for cat food. The dry foods continued to show the greatest growth increasing 19%, where they now account for 40% of the total dog food sales.

New research has shown tallow to be effective in increasing efficiency with no detrimental effects on carcass quality when fed to finishing pigs. Baby pigs can also utilize added dietary fat effectively. Other researchers have shown the value of fat in rations for poultry and cattle.

Soap

Prior to 1965, the greatest utilization of tallow and grease had been in soap making.

The two main classes of soap are (1) boiled soap and (2) cold or semiboiled soap. The bulk of our soap supply is boiled soap which appears on the market as hard soap (soda base).

Soft soaps (potash base) are made by the semiboiled method and find wide medical use (green soap). They are more expensive than the soda soaps, but they leave fabrics and polished woodwork surfaces in a less harsh condition.

The glycerin remains in cold or semiboiled soaps, but is a separate and important by-product in the making of boiled soap. It is in the form of a syrupy red liquid which is freed from the fat and settles to the bottom of the kettle during the soap making operation. Glycerin is purified by distillation, and one of its uses is in the medical profession as a vehicle for certain medicines to be applied externally. It also finds wide use in the manufacture of nitroglycerin and other high explosives. One hundred pounds of animal fat will yield sufficient glycerin to make 24½ pounds of nitroglycerin.

Raw materials for the manufacture of soap are (1) animal fats—lard oil and tallow and (2) vegetable oils—coconut, olive, corn, palm, palm kernel, cottonseed, peanut, linseed, rapeseed, and sesame.

Other greases used for making cheap grades of soap for special purposes are extracted from garbage, wool scourings, bone boiling, glue making, and hide trimmings. The garbage grease is changed into fatty acid and distilled, resulting in a very white fat of good odor that is used by practically all large soap manufacturers.

Fats, composed of fatty acids combined with glycerin, will unite with the elements sodium and potash hydroxide to form soap, glycerin, and water. A pure soap (regardless of the fat used) is a neutral soap where there is an exact balance between the fat and the alkali used.

Boiled soaps appear on the market as milled soaps, framed soaps, or in the form of chips, flakes, powder, etc. Toilet soaps are examples of scented milled soaps; chips, flake, and powder soaps are the unpressed milled soaps, and bar laundry soaps are examples of framed soaps.

Floating soaps contain many minute air bubbles that make them lighter than water but with a 15% to 20% higher moisture content than milled soaps. "Cleanser" is a mixture of soap, alkaline salts, and mineral abrasive.

Washing powder is a mixture of pulverized soaps containing a large amount of filler, usually soda ash.

Dry-cleaning soaps are partially saponified lime soaps dispersed in organic solvents, insoluble in water but soluble in gasoline, benzine, naphtha, etc.

Soft soaps contain about 50% water.

Efficiency of soaps for certain purposes is increased by the addition of fillers, either alkaline salts such as soda, ash, sal soda, and trisodium phosphate, or inert fillers such as talc, starch, and clay. The alkaline salts act as water softeners and detergents.

From 1947 until 1964, soap production declined some two billion pounds, due primarily to the increased use of detergent powders and liquids.

Old-fashioned soap—its traditional limitations overcome by research—may become the detergent of choice in this ecology-conscious age.

Scientists from the U.S. Department of Agriculture's Agricultural Research Service have had success in the continuing evaluation and refinement of their completely biodegradable soap-based formulations. These "supersoaps" are at least 60% tallow.

Unlike ordinary soap, the scientists reported, these supersoaps work in hard water and in cool or lukewarm water because they contain a lime-soap dispersing agent and a nonphosphate builder. The additives used are both nonpolluting and nontoxic. Although the modified soaps are not yet being made commercially, the USDA scientists report they can be produced readily with the same equipment used to make present detergents. The supply of tallow, the scientists noted, is abundant and constantly being replenished and should be sufficient even if the new soaps should completely replace today's detergents. They added that the new supersoaps would not constitute a drain on the world's dwindling supplies of petroleum.

Commercial production of these modified soaps could provide consumers with an attractive alternative to either conventional phosphated or nonphosphated detergents. Concern over eutrophication of streams has caused some states and communities to ban or consider banning phosphate detergents altogether. Adding to the problem is that some of the proposed phosphate substitutes may be toxic, harmful to the skin, or destructive to flame retardance in fabrics.

The objections to conventional detergents do not apply to the new soap formulations. The supersoaps will not cause eutrophication of streams because they contain no phosphate or other chemicals that would fertilize the stream bed and promote algae growth. Furthermore, they are highly biodegradable.

The new soap formulations were tested on fish to determine their toxicity and on mice, guinea pigs, and rabbits to see if they irritated the eyes or skin. The results, according to the scientists, showed the supersoaps to be at least as safe as the phosphate-built detergents against which they were tested.

Fatty Acids

Fatty acids obtained from animal fats today are being used in ever increasing quantities in the manufacture of scores of familiar products and some not so familiar.[1] The list includes such things as abrasives, shav-

---

1. Werner R. Boehme, *Render*, February 1974, p. 20.

ing cream, asphalt tile, lubricants, candles, caulking compounds, cement additives, cleaners, cosmetics, deodorants, paints, polishes, perfumes, plastics, printing inks, synthetic rubber, and water repellent compounds. The importance of fatty acids to allied U.S. industries was noted recently when a looming beef shortage caused a large rubber manufacturing company to become concerned about a possible shortage of beef tallow.

GLAND EXTRACTS

Scattered through various parts of the animal body are a number of internally secreting, ductless, or endocrine glands. The substance secreted by each exercises some specific control over the conduct, character, and development of the body. Their functions are so interrelated that under- or over-secretion of any one of several of the glands will cause abnormalities. The activating principle is a secretion termed a *hormone*.

Thyroid

In the sheep the thyroid gland is dark with a long ellipsoidal outline measuring about 2 inches by ½ inch. It is located on the first five or six rings of the trachea. In the ox, the gland has two lateral lobes connected by an isthmus and is located just below the larynx. It is about 3 inches long and is dark colored in a calf. In swine the thyroid is triangle shaped, about 2 inches across, may be located some distance from the larynx, has no isthmus, and somewhat adjoins the esophagus. It is smaller in cattle than in humans, and its secretion is an iodine-containing compound termed *thyroxin*. A deficiency of thyroid tissue in the young produces cretins, which are young that are physically and mentally defective; in the adult it causes a condition known as *myxedema*, defined as severe thyroid deficiency (hypothyroidism) characterized by dry skin and hair and loss of physical and mental vigor.

A deficiency of iodine in the diet or water supply may cause a simple goitre. Goitre in humans and animals can be treated by supplying the necessary iodine. Over-secretion of the thyroid increases basal metabolism causing the afflicted to become nervous and thin. The action of thyroid secretions is interrelated with other glands.

The dessicated thyroid is used extensively in keeping hypothyroid patients from the slow-moving, slow-talking, inactive existence they would otherwise lead. It is one of the few glandular substances that is effective when taken orally. It requires 40 beef thyroids to make a pound (½ to ¾ ounce per gland). Hog thyroids are equally valuable. Thyroids are handled very similarly to pancreas.

Parathyroids

Parathyroids consists of four small glands the size of a grain of wheat, which are located close to the thyroid gland. Their secretions regulate the lime (calcium) content of the blood stream and maintain the tone of the nervous system. The complete removal of the parathyroids causes death within a few weeks. To secure one pound of parathyroid extract requires the slaughter of approximately 3,600 animals. Each parathyroid gland weighs approximately .002 of a pound. The use of a potent parathyroid extract enables patients lacking parathyroid secretion to keep alive.

Pituitary

Located at the base of the brain and well protected in a separate bone cavity, the pituitary gland is about the size of a pea and is grayish yellow in color. It is made up of an anterior and posterior lobe which have distinct functions. The *anterior lobe* is known to produce (1) the growth promoting hormone, (2) the thyroid stimulating hormone, (3) the mammary stimulating hormone or prolactin, (4) the gonad stimulating hormone, and (5) the adrenal cortex stimulating hormone (ACTH). The *posterior lobe* exerts principles that (1) control blood pressure and pulse rate, (2) regulate the contractile organs of the body, and (3) govern energy metabolism.

Pineal

The pineal gland is about one-third the size of the pituitary, is reddish in color, and is located in a brain cavity behind and just above the pituitary. Its secretion regulates child growth—hastening or retarding puberty and maturity.

Adrenals

The adrenals are also called the suprarenal glands and are two in number. They are bean shaped in the sheep, measure approximately 1 inch by ½ inch and may be some 2 inches from the kidney. In the ox, they are located near the center of the animal (medial), anterior (towards the front) of the kidney, and are triangular or heart shaped. In the pig, they are long and narrow and are located on the medial border of the kidney. They are located astride the kidneys in humans and are larger than most endocrine glands. They are reddish brown in color and are some-what bean-shaped. The cortex (outer portion) produces steroid secretions essential to life maintenance, a lack of these secretions causing

Addison's disease. The medulla (inner portion) of the gland produces epinephrine which constricts the blood vessels and increases heart action. The valuable drug epinephrine is secured from the adrenals and is used in surgical operations to arrest hemorrhage and stimulate heart action. It requires the adrenals of 13,000 head of cattle to produce one pound of epinephrine. Each adrenal gland weighs approximately ⅓₀ of a pound.

Thymus

The thymus gland has a commercial food value in the case of the veal thymus. It is cream in color and is located in the neck near the chest cavity. In the case of veal it has two lobes, the second lying within the chest cavity. The thymus functions primarily in youth in inhibiting the activity of the sex glands and is considered to be a source of factors affecting the ability of the body to resist infections or react to the presence of foreign bodies. It atrophies after the age of puberty.

Pancreas

The pancreas is more commonly known as the sweetbread but should not be confused with the commercial sweetbreads of veal (thymus gland). The pancreas has both internal and external secretions, the latter passing into the small intestines to effect the digestion of starch, protein, and fat. The internal secretion (insulin) regulates sugar metabolism. Failure of the pancreas to regulate this sugar metabolism results in the affliction known as diabetes.

Insulin, first isolated by Doctors Banting and Best, is secured from specialized groups of cells in the pancreas known as the islets of Langerhans and is used extensively in treating diabetes. Other extracts made from the pancreas, such as pancreatin, are used as a remedy for intestinal disorders.

Dr. Sanger and associates were able to establish the primary structure of insulin, that is, they determined the number and sequence of amino acids that make up the protein insulin. Thus it was theoretically possible to synthesize insulin from a "test-tube," and such a task has been accomplished. However, the procedure is detailed and costly and at present will not contribute significantly to the world supply of insulin for treating diabetics.

A great need for insulin has developed throughout the world and the supply has never been too great. It takes 20 pounds of pancreas or the glands from 40 beeves to make sufficient insulin to treat a diabetic for one year.

The following specifications for the collection and subsequent handling of pancreas for insulin manufacture are those of Eli Lilly & Co., Indianapolis, recently verified.

Grade "A"

1. Glands

   a. Pancreas glands are to be taken from healthy animals. The beef and calf pancreas gland is located in the ruffle fat and lies attached to the liver near the gut. The pork pancreas is located between the small and large intestine imbedded in the ruffle fat.
   b. Calf pancreas glands are those taken from calves not over six months old.

2. Collection, Trimming, and Delivery to Freezer

   a. Glands are to be plucked from the viscera as soon as possible. Avoid long exposure to water spray.
   b. Glands should be collected in small buckets, perforated to permit drainage, or in small buckets surrounded with cracked ice. The glands should never be allowed to stand in water or directly in contact with ice. Water may dissolve the insulin in the glands.
   c. Glands are to be clean and trimmed closely, with all surface fat and connective tissue removed. Particular care should be taken in removing fat from pork pancreas; this is best done by stripping with the fingers. It is important with all pancreas, particularly beef and calf, that all of the tail of the gland be saved as *this portion is richest in insulin.*
   d. Glands are to be trimmed promptly and delivered *directly* to the sharp freezer. Not more than one hour should elapse between removal of gland from viscera and placing on tray in the freezer.
   e. It is important in all of the above operations that glands be handled in batches in order of removal from viscera so that each gland will be frozen in minimum time.

3. Freezing

   a. Glands should be promptly spread on clean, prechilled trays in the freezing chamber at the lowest available temperature, 0° F or less if available, but not higher than 15° F in any case.
   b. Glands should be *individually* frozen so that no two glands touch.

c. Within 48 hours after freezing hard, glands should be removed from trays and either stored in temporary *covered* containers or packed in shipping cases.

Ox Gall

The gall bladder of the average beef contains about four ounces of gall. The galls should be slashed and the bile emptied into a barrel in the freezer where it is allowed to freeze. Each day's production is put on top of the previous day's output so the barrel consists of layers of frozen bile. The bile is shipped in the frozen state. Four beef galls yield a pound of bile.

Cortisone has been found to relieve pain by reducing inflammation in joints of sufferers of arthritis. The gall of 100 cattle (25 pounds) is needed to produce sufficient cortisone to treat the average patient for one week. Cortisone is also secured in small quantities from sheep and calves. The animal source of cortisone has now been replaced by a synthetic product.

Other

Pepsin, a digestive ferment, is secured from the lining of the pyloric end of pig stomachs and is used in medicine as an aid to protein digestion.

Rennin, a digestive ferment, is secured from the fourth stomach of suckling calves and is used extensively as a milk coagulant in cheese making.

Peptones of different kinds are prepared from lean muscle tissue and serve as easily assimilated forms of proteins or as cultural media.

Liver extract finds wide use in treating patients suffering from pernicious anemia.

Thromboplastin, made from the brains of cattle, is used as a blood coagulant in surgery.

BY-PRODUCTS DIGEST

Hides

Bull hides are heavier than steer hides, and steer hides are heavier than cow hides. Texas hides make the heaviest sole leather.

Conditions in a hide that depreciate its value are (1) excessive tare in the form of manure or dirt, (2) excessive moisture (green), (3) grub holes, (4) cut throats (kosher killed) due to deep cut in the throat, (5) cuts and scores, and (6) improper cure (hair slips).

Hides rank first in cash value as a by-product of cattle.

When speaking of beef hides, the term *native* means *unbranded*.

Skins are the pelts of small animals, wild or domestic, such as calves, sheep, goats, muskrats, foxes, minks, etc.

When a salted beef hide is being prepared for shipment, it should not be bound with baling wire. The wire will cause a rust stain which lowers the quality of the leather.

The leather made from beef hides is used for shoe soles, harnesses, belting, etc., but when split to reduce its thickness, it is used for shoe uppers, furniture and automobile upholstering, footballs, and bag and case leather.

"Shoddy" leather is made by grinding waste leather to a pulp and pressing it into solid sheets, either with or without the addition of a binding material.

Considerable hide trimmings are used in the manufacture of glue and gelatin.

Glue and Gelatin

Both glue and gelatin are colloidal proteins. They are chemically and physically similar and differ mainly in that gelatin is made from clean, sweet materials prepared under sanitary conditions to make it edible.

The raw materials used to produce gelatin and glue are high in collagen. They are connective tissue, skin or hide trimmings, sinews, horn piths, lips, ear tubes, pizzles, cartilage, beef and calf bones, mammary glands, heads of cattle, calves, and sheep, knuckles, and feet. Pigskins are a good source of gelatin.

Glue and Gelatin Stocks

The three main types of glue are hide glue, bone glue, and blood albumin glue. The latter is water resistant and is used widely in the manufacture of plywood.

The oldest and widest use for glue is in the furniture and veneer industry. Glue has so many varied uses that it has been said that glue holds the world together. It is used in sizing paper; in the manufacture of wool, silk, and other fabrics; in sizing straw hats; in sizing walls that are to be painted; in sizing barrels or casks that are to contain liquids; on the heads of matches to make an air tight cap over the phosphorus; in the manufacture of sand and emery paper to hold the abrasive on the paper; in the manufacture of dolls, toys, and ornaments; in the making of picture frames, mirror frames, rosettes; billiard balls, composition cork, imitation hard rubber, printing rolls, mother-of-pearl, gummed tape, paper boxes, kalsomine, automobile bodies, caskets, leather goods, bookbinding, and many other products.

The two types of gelatin according to their source are hide gelatin and bone gelatin.

Gelatin finds wide use in the manufacture of ice cream, in the making of certain pharmaceutical preparations and capsules for medicine, for coating pills, in making mayonnaise dressings and emulsion flavors, to clarify wine, beer, and vinegar, in making court plaster, in photography, in electroplating, as a bacteria culture medium, and for various other uses.

Blood

According to USDA, APHIS, hog blood shall not be used as an ingredient of meat food products. No blood which comes in contact with the surface of the body of an animal or is otherwise contaminated shall be collected for food purposes. Only blood from animals, the carcasses of which are inspected and passed, may be used for meat food products. The defibrination of blood intended for food purposes shall not be performed with the hands.

Blood contains around 17% ammonia of which 14% is nitrogen. If the blood is allowed to coagulate, the jelly-like fibrin (hemoglobin) is cooked and dried, and the residue is pressed into cakes. The cakes are finely ground and disposed of as blood meal or mixed with low grade tankage for stock feed. When mixed with potash or phosphoric acid, blood makes a very rich fertilizer. The serum is clarified and dried and sold as blood albumin.

One hundred pounds of beef blood treated with an anticoagulant and centrifuged will yield about 40 pounds of hemoglobin and 60 pounds of plasma, or 16 pounds of dried hemoglobin, 3.4 pounds of dried serum, and 3.5 pounds of wet fibrin.

Small amounts of the best grades of blood are collected, defibrinated, and the hemoglobin used in making blood sausage. Or the blood may be dried at low temperatures to prevent coagulation of the albumin, and the cakes dissolved in warm water and added to liquid sugar to remove the impurities from the sugar.

Blood albumin is used in fixing pigment colors in cloth, in finishing leather, in certain malt extracts, in clarifying liquors, and in the manufacture of glue. Dried blood or blood meal is a very concentrated stock food containing about 87% protein.

Inferior grades of blood are used in the manufacture of buttons and imitation tortoise shell articles. Blood and its products are finding added medicinal and therapeutic uses.

Miscellaneous By-Products

The degreasing of wool removes a wool oil that amounts to about 15% of the weight of the wool treated and produces some valuable products, including lanolin, which are used as bases for ointments and cosmetics, leather dressings, and fiber lubricants.

The potassium carbonate removed in the wash water in wool cleaning represents about one-fourth of the by-product value of degreasing.

A substitute for camel-hair brushes is made from the delicate hairs on the inside of the ears of cattle. Hog bristles for making brushes were formerly imported from China but are now being produced in the United States in increasing amounts. It requires considerable hand labor to collect the proper length hair which is found over the shoulder and back of the hog. The fine hair of the bulk of our domestic hogs is not suitable for brush making and is processed and curled for upholstering purposes.

Pure neat's-foot stock is made from the shin bones and feet of cattle. This stock is grained and pressed to secure the pure neat's-foot oil which is used in the leather and textile industry.

Edible tallow is made from beef fat not considered suitable for the manufacture of oleomargarine. It is refined and used in lard substitutes.

Inedible tallow and other greases are considered contaminated and are used for making soap and lubricants.

Stick is tankwater collected in evaporators and reduced to the consistency of molasses. It is mixed with tankage and dried.

Most of the residue from packing plants is made into stock food and used to supplement the necessary protein for hog and poultry rations. Very little goes into the manufacture of fertilizer. Dead animals are tanked (steam-pressure cooked) in specially sealed tanks and made into fertilizer.

Shin bones of cattle, with knuckles removed, are cooked to remove the meat and neat's-foot oil and are washed and air-dried. They are then sawed into flat slabs from which crochet needles, bone teething rings, pipestems, dice, chessmen, electrical bushings, washers, collar buttons, flat buttons, knife handles, and many other articles are made. Some other uses for bone are in case hardening steel, in the manufacture of bone black used as a bleach for oils, fats, waxes, sugar, or pharmaceutical preparations; as a stock food (ground bone meal, steamed bone meal) and as a fertilizer.

Cattle horns can be split into thin strips, pressed in heated molds of various patterns, and colored to make imitation tortoise shell. Horns are used for making napkin rings, goblets, tobacco boxes, knife and umbrella handles, and many other articles.

White hoofs are used for making imitation ivory products. Black hoofs find use in the manufacture of potassium cyanide for extracting gold.

Dry rendering is used almost exclusively in the manufacture of lard and in the extraction of edible and inedible fats and oils. The advantage over the wet method (live steam turned into and mixed with the contents of the tank) is that it eliminates the expense of handling tank water, cuts down objectionable odors, produces crackling about 10% richer in protein, produces a grease or tallow low in free fatty acid, is more rapid, and produces a residue that is more suitable for stock food.

HORSE MEAT

The human consumption of horse meat in the United States is very small, but it is used in the manufacture of pet foods. The Horse Meat Act was approved July 24, 1919, making Federal inspection necessary for horses slaughtered for interstate or foreign shipment if the meat is to be sold for human consumption. The slaughter establishment must be separate from those slaughtering other animals or where the meat products of other animals are handled. The act provides that such meat must be conspicuously labeled, marked, branded, or tagged "Horse meat" or "Horse meat Product." Horse meat is also regulated by the Federal Food, Drug and Cosmetic Act, and the use of horse meat in every state is regulated by the U.S. Wholesome Meat Act.

The average annual export of horse meat for the period 1930-1940 was 3 million pounds as against 41½ million pounds in 1946. The decline in horse population from 21½ million in 1919 to slightly over 3 million head in 1959 has made horse meat more difficult to get and has changed the United States from an exporter to an importer of horse meat. Countries desiring to export horse meat to the States legally must have certification of APHIS. The countries qualifying as of 1972 are Argentina, Canada, and Mexico. Total imports of horse meat from these countries in 1972 were 20,469,522 pounds.

Horse meat is important as human food in most European countries, the USSR, and Japan. The leading consumers in 1971 were Belgium and Luxembourg, 7 pounds per person; France, 4 pounds; the Netherlands, 3 pounds; and Sweden, 1 pound.

The horse meat business is not the highly profitable business it was in the early forties because the cost of the horse has risen to a point where the margins are about the same as in the meat packing industry. The meat is not the only source of revenue. Horse hides are used for leather; tallow for soap; hair, mane, and tail for hair goods; the glands for pharmaceuticals; and the edible offal as food for fish or carnivorous animals. Dead horses are converted into oils, glue, and fertilizer.

Table 10.5—Horses Slaughtered Under Federal Inspection (1943–1972)

Year	Number	Year	Number
1943	39,935	1952	357,086
1944	60,501	1953	270,533
1945	59,674	1954	247,258
1946	103,880	1955	196,106
1947	276,290	1956	175,537
1948	303,974	1959	88,100
1949	307,794	1964	38,447
1950	275,851	1972	72,419
1951	340,287		

CHAPTER 11

Federal Meat Grading and
Its Interpretations

FEDERAL MEAT GRADING

The Federal Meat Grading Service was established by the Sixty-eighth Congress of the United States on February 10, 1925. However, tentative standards were formulated for grades of dressed beef in 1916. They provided the basis for uniformly reporting the dressed beef markets according to grades, which work was inaugurated as a national service early in 1917. The grade specifications were improved from time to time as experience gained through their use indicated what changes were necessary. They were published first in mimeographed form in June 1923. After slight changes they were included in the Department Bulletin No. 1246 *Market Classes and Grades of Dressed Beef* which was published in August 1924. The official standards for grades of lamb and mutton carcasses were initially promulgated and made effective on February 16, 1931. Tentative standards for grades of pork carcasses and fresh pork cuts were issued by USDA in 1931. These tentative standards were slightly revised in 1933. Grade standards for veal and calf carcasses and vealers and slaughter calves were initially promulgated in 1928.

Federal meat grading is now administered by the Livestock Division of the Agricultural Marketing Service of the U.S. Department of Agriculture.

The Purpose of the Act

Producer and Processor

The act authorized the establishment of an inspection service for perishable farm products for the purpose of making available to individuals, organizations, and establishments, an agency that would certify the class, quality (grade), and condition of the products examined to conform with uniform standards.

Consumer

The Federal grade stamp on meat provides consumers with a reliable guide to quality. Each grade name is associated with a specific degree of quality, thus enabling consumers to utilize meat most efficiently by preparing it in the manner for which it is best suited. Federally graded meat is widely found in retail stores. Most retailers sell only the grade or grades that are requested or deemed to meet the needs of their customers. The grade name appearing on the grade stamp can be used to serve the consumer in two important ways: (1) as a guide to quality and (2) as a guide to preparation.

Meat of each grade will provide a satisfactory dish if appropriately cooked.

A consumer must learn, either by study or from experience, what government grade names mean and represent, and the same is true of packer brands that represent these grades. Quality in meat is quite variable and difficult for the average person to recognize in the retail cut. Because of this fact, the consumer has come to depend on items bearing brand names. If the particular brand meets his or her approval, a new customer has been added—until some better graded product is tried and accepted. The manufacturer of a food product may be unknown to the public, but the brand name of his product, if good, is on every tongue. There are so many brand names, however, that it would appear that the terminology used by the U.S. grading service would be a pleasant relief.

Inspection Requirements

Products, to be eligible for grading service, must be prepared under Federal inspection or other official inspection acceptable to the Administration.

Types of Service

The Federal Meat Grading Branch engages in two main types of activities (1) the grading and identification for grade of beef, veal, lamb, and mutton for sale on a grade basis through regular commercial channels and (2) the examination and acceptance, for conformance with specifications for grade and other factors, of meats offered for delivery to Federal, state, county, and municipal institutions which purchase meat on the basis of contract awards. This latter service covers all kinds of meats, meat products, and by-products.

However, effective October 1, 1965, vendors and others requesting acceptance service for certifying compliance of meat and meat food products with approved specifications must apply to the Meat Grading Branch, Livestock Division, Agricultural Marketing Service, USDA. The fee for doing this work is presently $13.80 per hour for work performed between 6 a.m. and 6 p.m. on Monday through Friday. Work on Saturday and Sunday between 6 a.m. and 6 p.m. costs $16 an hour and the rate for work on national holidays is $27.60 per hour. All fees are paid by those requesting the service.

BEEF CARCASS GRADING

Development of the Standards[1]

- Standards were first formulated in 1916.

- Standards were first published in 1923.

- Standards were slightly changed in 1924.

- Voluntary beef grading and stamping service was begun in May 1927.

- The official standards were amended in July 1939 to provide a single standard for the grading and labeling of steer, heifer, and cow beef according to similar inherent quality characteristics. The amendment also changed certain grade terms for steer, heifer, and cow beef from *Meduim, Common,* and *Low Cutter* to *Commercial, Utility,* and *Canner,* respectively.

- An amendment in November 1941 made similar changes in the grade terms for bull and stag beef and established the following grade terminology for all beef: *Prime, Choice, Good, Commercial, Utility, Cutter,* and *Canner.*

- Compulsory grading by the Office of Price Administration was in effect from 1941 to 1946 during World War II.

- An amendment in October 1949 eliminated all references to color of fat.

- In December 1950, the official standards for grades of steer, heifer,

---

1. *Official United States Standards for Grades of Carcass Beef,* Title 7, Chapter I, Part 53, Sections 53.100-53.105 of the Code of Federal Regulations, reprinted with amendments effective July 1, 1973.

and cow beef were amended by combining the Prime and Choice grades and designating them as Prime, renaming the Good grade as Choice, and dividing the Commercial grade into two grades by designating the beef produced from young animals included in the top half of the grade as Good while retaining the Commercial grade designation for the remainder of the beef in that guide.

- In June 1956, the official standards for grades of steer, heifer, and cow beef were amended by dividing the Commercial grade into two grades strictly on the basis of maturity with beef produced from young animals being designated as Standard while Commercial was retained as the grade name for beef produced from mature animals.

- In June 1965, the official standards for grades of steer, heifer, and cow beef were revised to place less emphasis on changes in maturity in the Prime, Choice, Good, and Standard grades.

  The rate of increase in required marbling to offset increasing maturity was changed, and the minimum marbling permitted was reduced for more mature carcasses by as much as 1 to 1½ degrees in Prime, 1 degree in Choice, and ¾ of a degree in Good and Standard.

  Consideration of the 2 degrees of marbling in excess of that described as abundant was eliminated.

  The manner of evaluating conformation was clarified by providing that carcasses may meet the conformation requirements for a grade either through a specified development of muscling or a specified development of muscling and fat combined.

  The requirement was established that all carcasses be ribbed prior to grading.

  Established standards for yield grades of carcasses and certain wholesale cuts of all classes of beef.

- In July 1973, the official standards were revised to provide separate quality grades for beef from young bulls. Research comparing the palatability of beef from steers and young bulls indicated that young bull beef was slightly less palatable and slightly more variable in palatability than steer beef. These palatability differences were considered sufficient to preclude the grading of young bull beef without a sex identification so this class was designated as *bullock*. The quality grade standards for bullock were essentially the same as those for steer, heifer, and cow beef but provided for only five grades—Prime, Choice, Good, Standard, and Utility. *Bull* was retained as the class designation for beef from more mature bulls, but the quality grades for such beef were eliminated. As a result, the yield grade standards only applied to the grading of *Bull* beef. The quality grade standards for *Stag* beef also were eliminated and beef formerly included in this class was redesignated as *Bullock* or *Bull,* dependent on its evidences of maturity.

Classes of Beef Carcasses

Class determination of beef carcasses is based on evidences of maturity and apparent sex condition at the time of slaughter. The classes of beef carcasses are steers, bullocks, bulls, heifers, and cows. Carcasses from males—steers, bullocks, and bulls—are distinguished from carcasses from females—heifers and cows—as follows:

Steer, bullock, and bull carcasses have a "pizzle muscle" (attachment of the penis) and related "pizzle eye" adjacent to the posterior end of the aitchbone. (Figures 11.1, 11.3.)

Steer, bullock, and bull carcasses have, if present, rather rough, irregular fat in the region of the cod. In heifer and cow carcasses, the fat in this region—if present—is much smoother. (Figures 11.1 and 11.2.)

Fig. 11.1–Steer carcass. The cod fat (A) to the left, the half-closed face of the gracilis muscle (B), and the pizzle ring (C) at the right of the aitchbone (D) identify this as a male.

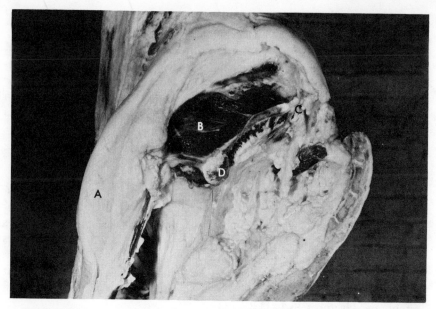

Fig. 11.2—Heifer carcass. Note the presence of the udder (A), the exposed face of the gracilis muscle (B), and the lack of a pizzle ring (C) at the right of the aitchbone (D).

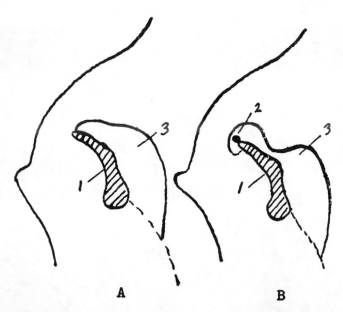

Fig. 11.3—A—The contour of the lean area of the gracilis muscle on heifer carcasses. B—The same area on steer carcasses. (1) Aitchbone, (2) pizzle eye, (3) lean area of gracilis. This shows the method of identifying steer from heifer rounds when the rump and shank have been removed.

In steer, bullock, and bull carcasses, the area of lean exposed immediately ventral to the aitchbone is much smaller than in heifer and cow carcasses. (Figures 11.1, 11.2, 11.3.)

Steer, bullock, and bull carcasses are distinguished by the following:

In steer carcasses, the "pizzle muscle" is relatively small, light red in color, and fine in texture, and the related "pizzle eye" is relatively small.

In bullock and bull carcasses, the "pizzle muscle" is relatively large, dark red in color, and coarse in texture, and the related "pizzle eye" is relatively large.

Bullock and bull carcasses usually have a noticeable crest.

Bullock and bull carcasses also usually have a noticeably developed small round muscle adjacent to the hipbone commonly referred to as the "jump muscle." However, in carcasses with a considerable amount of external fat the development of this muscle may be obscured.

Although the development of the secondary sex characteristics is given primary consideration in distinguishing steer carcasses from bullock or bull carcasses, this differentiation is also facilitated by consideration of the color and texture of the lean. In bullock and bull carcasses, the lean is frequently at least dark red in color with a dull, "muddy" appearance—and in some cases it may have an iridescent sheen. Also, it frequently has an "open" texture. In distinguishing between these classes when grading wholesale cuts in which the secondary sex characteristics are absent or normally not well developed—especially ribs and loins—consideration of the color and texture of the lean necessarily must receive the major emphasis.

The distinction between bullock and bull carcasses is based solely on their evidences of skeletal maturity. Carcasses with the maximum maturity permitted in the bullock class have slightly red and slightly soft chine bones, and the cartilages on the ends of the thoracic vertebrae have some evidences of ossification; the sacral vertebrae are completely fused; the cartilages on the ends of the lumbar vertebrae are nearly completely ossified; and the rib bones are slightly wide and slightly flat. Bull carcasses have evidences of more advanced maturity.

Heifer and cow carcasses are distinguished by the following:

Heifer carcasses have a relatively small pelvic cavity and a slightly curved aitchbone. In cow carcasses, the pelvic cavity is relatively large and the aitchbone is nearly straight.

In heifer carcasses, the udder usually will be present. In cow carcasses, the udder usually will have been removed. However, neither of these are requirements.

Two Considerations—Quality and Yield

The grade of a steer, heifer, cow, or bullock carcass is based on separate evaluations of two general considerations: (1) The indicated percent of trimmed, boneless, major retail cuts to be derived from the carcass, referred to as the *yield grade* and (2) the palatability-indicating characteristics of the lean and conformation, referred to as the *quality grade*. When graded by a Federal meat grader, the grade of a steer, heifer, cow, or bullock carcass may consist of the quality grade, the yield grade, or a combination of both the quality grade and yield grade. The grade of a bull carcass consists of the yield grade only.

The terms *quality grade* and *quality* are used throughout the standards. The term *quality* is used to refer only to the palatability-indicating characteristics of the lean. As such, it is one of the factors considered in determining the *quality grade*. Although the term *quality grade* is used to refer to an overall evaluation of a carcass based on (1) its quality and (2) its conformation, this is not intended to imply that variations in conformation are either directly or indirectly related to differences in palatability, since research has shown no relationship.

The carcass beef grade standards are written so that the quality and yield grade standards are contained in separate sections. Quality grades are applicable separately to carcasses from (1) steers, heifers, and cows and (2) bullocks. Eight quality grade designations—Prime, Choice, Good, Standard, Commercial, Utility, Cutter, and Canner—are applicable to steer and heifer carcasses. Except for Prime, the same designations apply to cow carcasses. The quality grade designations for bullock carcasses are Prime, Choice, Good, Standard, and Utility. There are five yield grades applicable to all classes of beef, denoted by numbers 1 through 5, with Yield Grade 1 representing the highest degree of yield.

When officially graded, bullock and bull beef will be further identified for their sex condition; steer, heifer, and cow beef will not be so identified. The designated grades of bullock beef are not necessarily comparable in quality or yield with a similarly designated grade of beef from steers, heifers, or cows. Neither is the yield of a designated yield grade of bull beef necessarily comparable with a similarly designated yield grade of steer, heifer, cow, or bullock beef.

Ribbing the Carcass

To determine the quality grade or yield grade of a carcass, it must be split down the back into two sides, and one side must be partially separated into a hindquarter and forequarter by cutting it with a saw and knife insofar as practicable, as follows: A saw cut perpendicular to both the long axis and split surface of the vertebral column is made across the twelfth thoracic vertebra at a point which leaves not more than one-half of this vertebra on the hindquarter. The knife cut across the rib-eye muscle starts—or terminates—opposite the above-described saw cut. From that point it extends across the rib-eye muscle perpendicular to the outside skin surface of the carcass at an angle toward the hindquarter which is slightly greater (more nearly horizontal) than the angle made by the thirteenth rib with the vertebral column of the hindquarter posterior to that point. As a result of this cut, the outer end of the cut surface of the rib-eye muscle is closer to the twelfth rib than is the end next to the chine bone. Beyond the rib eye, the knife cut shall continue between the twelfth and thirteenth ribs to a point which will adequately expose the distribution of fat and lean in this area. The knife cut may be made prior to or following the saw cut but must be smooth and even, such as would result from a single stroke of a very sharp knife.

Other methods of ribbing may prevent an accurate evaluation of quality grade and yield grade determining characteristics. Therefore, carcasses ribbed by other methods will be eligible for grading only if an accurate grade determination can be made by the official grader under the standards.

Beveling of the fat over the rib eye, application of pressure, or any other influences which alter the area of the rib eye or the thickness of fat over the rib eye may prevent an accurate yield grade determination. Therefore, carcasses subjected to such influences may not be eligible for a yield grade determination. Also carcasses with more than minor amounts of lean removed from the major sections of the round, loin, rib, or chuck will not be eligible for a yield grade determination.

Non-Carcass Grading

The quality and yield grade descriptions are intended primarily for beef carcasses. However, the quality grade standards also apply to the grading of hindquarters, forequarters, and individual primal cuts—rounds, loins, short loins, loin ends, ribs, and chucks. A portion of a primal cut as well as plates, flanks, shanks, and briskets likewise can be graded if attached by their natural attachments to a primal cut. Grade requirements for individual primal cuts or special cuts eligible for grading shall be based on requirements consistent with the normal development of grade characteristics in various parts of a carcass of the quality level involved.

Except for bulls, the yield standards also are applicable to the grading of hindquarters and forequarters, and to ribs, loins, short loins, and combinations of wholesale cuts which include either a rib or a short loin. Since bull carcasses are graded for yield only, they may be graded only as carcasses, sides, or hindquarters. This is because yield grades for forequarters and forequarter cuts and for trimmed hindquarters and trimmed hindquarter cuts include consideration of standard percentages of kidney, pelvic, and heart fat based on the quality grade.

Conformation and Quality

The quality grade of a beef carcass is based on separate evaluations of two general considerations: (1) The quality or the palatability-indicating characteristics of the lean and (2) the conformation of the carcass.

Conformation is the manner of formation of the carcass. The conformation descriptions included in each of the grade specifications refer to the thickness of muscling and to an overall degree of thickness and fullness of the carcass. Carcasses which meet the requirements for thickness of muscling specified for a grade will be considered to have conformation adequate for that grade despite the fact that, because of a lack of fatness, they may not have the overall degree of thickness and fullness described. Conformation is evaluated by averaging the conformation of the various parts of the carcass, considering not only the proportion that each part is of the carcass weight but also the general value of each part as compared with the other parts. Thus, although the chuck and round are nearly the same percentage of the carcass weight, the round is considered the more valuable cut. Therefore, in evaluating the overall conformation of a carcass, the development of the round is given more consideration than the development of the chuck. Similarly, since the loin is both a greater percentage of the carcass weight and also generally a more valuable cut than the rib, its conformation receives much more consideration than the conformation of the rib. Superior conformation implies a high proportion of meat to bone and a high proportion of the weight of the carcass in the more valuable parts. It is reflected in carcasses which are very thickly muscled, very full and thick in relation to their length, and which have a very plump, full, and well-rounded appearance. Inferior conformation implies a low proportion of meat to bone and a low proportion of the weight of the carcass in the more valuable parts. It is reflected in carcasses which are very thinly muscled, very narrow and thin in relation to their length, and which have a very angular, thin, sunken appearance.

Quality—Maturity

For steer, heifer, and cow beef, *quality* of the lean is evaluated by considering its *marbling* and firmness as observed in a cut surface in relation to the apparent *maturity* of the animal from which the carcass was produced. The *maturity* of the carcass is determined by evaluating the size, shape, and ossification of the bones and cartilages—especially the split chine bones—and the color and texture of the lean flesh. In the split chine bones, ossification changes occur at an earlier stage of maturity in the posterior portion of the vertebral column (sacral vertebrae) and at progressively later stages of maturity in the lumbar and thoracic vertebrae. The ossification changes that occur in the cartilages on the ends of the spilt thoracic vertebrate are especially useful in evaluating maturity, and these vertebrae are referred to frequently in the carcass beef standards. Unless otherwise specified in the standards, whenever the ossification of cartilages on the thoracic vertebrae is referred to, this shall be construed to refer to the cartilages attached to the thoracic vertebrate at the posterior end of the forequarter. The size and shape of the rib bones also are important considerations in evaluating differences in maturity. In the very youngest carcasses considered as beef (A-minus maturity), the cartilages on the ends of the chine bones show no ossification, cartilage is evident on all of the vertebrae of the spinal column, and the sacral vertebrae show distinct separation. In addition, the split vertebrae usually are soft and porous and very red in color. In such carcasses, the rib bones have only a slight tendency toward flatness. In progressively more mature carcasses, ossification changes become evident first in the bones and cartilages of the sacral vertebrae, then in the lumbar vertebrae, and still later in the thoracic vertebrae. In beef which is very advanced in maturity (E-plus maturity), all the split vertebrae will be devoid of red color, very hard and flinty, and the cartilages on the ends of all the vertebrae will be entirely ossified. Likewise, with advancing maturity, the rib bones will become progressively wider and flatter until in beef from very mature animals the ribs will be very wide and flat.

In steer, heifer, and cow carcasses, the range of maturity permitted within each of the grades varies considerably. The Prime, Choice, Good, and Standard grades are restricted to beef from young cattle; the Commercial grade is restricted to beef from cattle too mature for Good or Standard; and the Utility, Cutter, and Canner grades include beef from animals of all ages. By definition, bullock carcasses are restricted to those whose evidences of maturity do not exceed those specified for the juncture of the two youngest maturity groups referenced in the standards for steer, heifer, and cow carcasses (A maturity).

Quality—Color and Texture

In steer, heifer, and cow beef, the *color* and *texture* of the lean flesh also undergo progressive changes with advancing *maturity*. In the very youngest carcasses considered as *beef*, the lean flesh will be very fine in texture and light grayish red in color. In progressively more mature carcasses, the texture of the lean will become progressively coarser and the color of the lean will become progressively darker red. In very mature beef, the lean flesh will be very coarse in texture and very dark red in color. Since color of lean also is affected by variations in quality, references to color of lean in the standards for a given degree of maturity vary sightly with different levels of quality. In determining the maturity of a carcass in which the skeletal evidences of maturity are different from those indicated by the color and texture of the lean, slightly more emphasis is placed on the characteristics of the bones and cartilages than on the characteristics of the lean. In no case can the overall maturity of the carcass be considered more than one full maturity group different from that indicated by its bones and cartilages.

Bullock beef carcasses having darker colors of lean than specified in the standards for the quality level for which they would otherwise qualify are evaluated on the basis of skeletal characteristics only, and the final grade will be determined in accordance with the procedures specified in the standards for grading dark-cutting beef.

Dark-Cutting Beef

References to color of lean in the standards for steer, heifer, and cow beef involve only colors associated with changes in maturity. They are not intended to apply to colors of lean associated with so-called *dark-cutting beef*. Dark-cutting beef is believed to be the result of a reduced sugar content of the lean at the time of slaughter. As a result, this condition does not have the same significance in grading as do the darker shades of red associated with advancing maturity. The dark color of the lean associated with dark-cutting beef is present in varying degrees from that which is barely evident to so-called *black cutters* in which the lean is actually nearly black in color and usually has a gummy texture. Although there is little or no evidence which indicates that the dark-cutting condition has any adverse effect on palatability, it is considered in grading because of its effect on acceptability and value. Depending on the degree to which this characteristic is developed, the final grade of carcasses which otherwise would qualify for the Prime, Choice, or Good grades may be reduced as much as *one full grade*. In beef otherwise eligible for the Standard or Commercial grade, the final grade may be reduced as much as *one-half of a grade*. In the Utility, Cutter, and Canner grades, this condition is not considered.

Marbling (Intramuscular Fat)

The degrees of marbling, in order of descending quantity, are abundant, moderately abundant, slightly abundant, moderate, modest, small,

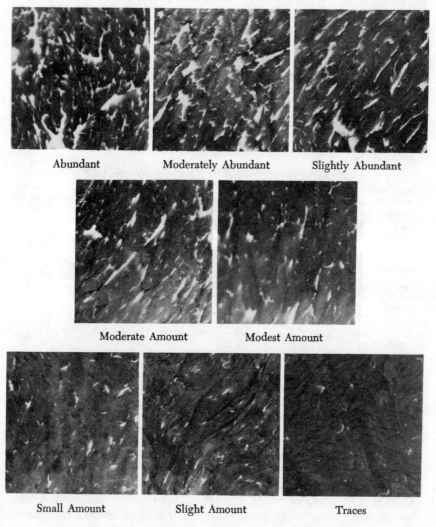

Fig. 11.4—Degrees of marbling. (Courtesy, USDA)

slight, traces, and practically devoid. Illustrations of the lower limits of eight of the nine degrees of marbling considered in grading beef appear in Figure 11.4.

Within any specified grade, the requirements for marbling and firmness increase progressively with evidences of advancing maturity. To facilitate the application of this principle, the standards recognize five different maturity groups and nine different degrees of marbling. The five maturity groups are identified in Figure 11.5 as A, B, C, D, and E in order of increasing maturity. The limits of these five maturity groups are specified in the grade descriptions for steer, heifer, and cow carcasses. The A maturity portion of the figure is the only portion applicable to bullock carcasses.

Relationship Between Marbling, Maturity, and Quality

The relationship between marbling, maturity, and quality (that part of the final grade that represents the palatability of the lean) is shown in Figure 11.5. From this figure it can be seen, for instance, that the mini-

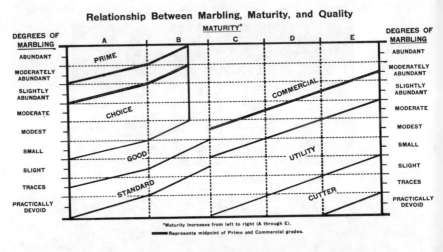

Fig. 11.5—Relationship between marbling, maturity, and quality.

mum marbling requirement for Choice varies from a minimum small amount for the very youngest carcasses classified as beef to a maximum modest amount for carcasses having the maximum maturity permitted in Choice. Likewise, in the Commercial grade, the minimum marbling requirement varies from a minimum small amount in beef from animals with the minimum maturity permitted to a maximum moderate amount in beef from very mature animals. No consideration is given to marbling beyond that considered maximum abundant. The marbling and other lean flesh characteristics specified for the various grades are based on their appearance in the rib-eye muscle of properly chilled carcasses that are ribbed between the twelfth and thirteenth ribs.

Quality + Conformation = Final Quality Grade

The final quality grade of a carcass is based on a composite evaluation of its conformation and quality. Since relatively few carcasses have an identical development of conformation and quality, each grade will include various combinations of development of these two characteristics. Examples of how conformation and quality are combined into the final quality grade are included in each of the grade descriptions. The principles governing these compensations are as follows: In each of the grades a superior development of quality is permitted to compensate for a deficient development of conformation, without limit, through the upper limit of quality. The rate of compensation in all grades is on an equal basis—a given degree of superior quality compensates for the same degree of deficient conformation. The reverse type of compensation—a superior development of conformation for an inferior development of quality—is not permitted in the Prime, Choice, and Commercial grades. In all other grades this type of compensation is permitted but only to the extent of one-third of a grade of deficient quality. The rate of compensation is also on an equal basis—a given degree of superior conformation compensates for the same degree of deficient quality.

Quality Specifications for Bullocks, Bulls, and Stags

Bullock by definition includes only carcasses within the A maturity range. Specifications for bullock beef are thus identical to those for steer and heifer beef in the Prime, Choice, Good, Standard, and Utility grades where spelled out for A maturity.

Bulls and stags (all exceeding A maturity) *are not* quality graded but may be yield graded.

Specifications for Official U.S. Standards for Grades of Carcass Beef (quality—steer, heifer, cow)[2]

---

2. *Official United States Standards for Grades of Carcass Beef,* Title 7, Chapter I, Part 53, Sections 53.100-53.105 of the Code of Federal Regulations, reprinted with amendments effective July 1, 1973.

Prime (Cow beef not eligible for Prime grade)

As the name implies, beef of this grade is highly acceptable and palatable. Prime grade beef is produced from young and well-fed beef-type cattle. The youth of the cattle and the careful intensive feeding which they have had combine to produce very high quality cuts of beef. Such cuts have liberal quantities of fat interspersed within the lean (marbling). These characteristics contribute greatly to the juiciness, tenderness, and flavor of the meat. Rib roasts and loin steaks of this grade are consistently tender, and cuts from the round and chuck should also be highly satisfactory.

Carcasses and wholesale cuts with minimum Prime grade conformation:

> Are thickly muscled throughout.
>
> Tend to be very wide.
>
> Are thick in relation to their length.
>
> Have loins and ribs which tend to be thick and full.
>
> Have rounds which tend to be plump (plumpness carries well down to the hocks).
>
> Have chucks which tend to be thick and necks and shanks which tend to be short.

(Minimum quality characteristics for two maturity groups which cover the entire range of maturity permitted in the Prime grade.)

> 1. Carcasses in the younger group (A maturity) (from the youngest eligible to those at the juncture of the two maturity groups):
>
>> Have slightly red and slightly soft chine bones.
>>
>> Have cartilages on the ends of the thoracic vertebrae which have some evidence of ossification.
>>
>> Have completely fused sacral vertebrae.
>>
>> Have cartilages on the ends of the lumbar vertebrae which are almost completely ossified.

Have rib bones which are slightly wide and slightly flat.

Have a rib-eye muscle which is fine in texture, light red in color, and moderately firm.

Minimum degree of marbling required—increases with maturity:

From minimum—Slightly Abundant

To maximum—Slightly Abundant

2. Carcasses in the older group (B maturity) (from those as representative of the juncture of the two groups to those at the maximum maturity permitted in the Prime grade):

Have chine bones tinged with red.

Have cartilages on the ends of the thoracic vertebrae which are partially ossified.

Have lean which tends to be fine in texture, light red in color, and firm.

Have moderate symmetry and uniformity in contour.

Minimum degree of marbling required—increases with maturity:

From minimum—Moderately Abundant

To maximum—Moderately Abundant

(Quality versus conformation)

A development of quality superior to that specified as minimum for the Prime grade may compensate, without limit, for a development of conformation inferior to that specified as minimum for Prime at an equal rate as indicated in the following example: A carcass which has mid-point Prime quality may have conformation equal to the mid-point of the Choice grade and remain eligible for Prime. However, regardless of the extent to which the conformation of a carcass exceeds the minimum of the grade, a carcass must have minimum Prime quality to be eligible for Prime.

Choice

This grade is preferred by most consumers because it is of high quality but usually has less fat than beef of the Prime grade. More of this grade of beef is stamped than of any other grade. Choice beef is usually available the year-round in substantial quantity. Roasts and steaks from the loin and rib are tender and juicy, and other cuts, such as those from the round or chuck which are more suitable for braising and pot roasting, should be tender with a well-developed flavor.

Carcasses and wholesale cuts with minimum Choice grade conformation:

> Are moderately thick-muscled throughout.
>
> Tend to be moderately wide.
>
> Are moderately thick in relation to their length.
>
> Have loins and ribs which tend to be moderately thick and full.
>
> Have rounds which tend to be moderately plump.
>
> Have chucks which tend to be moderately thick and necks and shanks which are moderately short.

(Minimum quality characteristics for two maturity groups which cover the entire range of maturity permitted in the Choice grade.)

1. Carcasses in the younger group (A maturity) (from the youngest eligible to those at the juncture of the two maturity groups):

> Similar to the younger group under Prime except that the rib-eye muscle is moderately red in color and slightly soft.

Minimum degree of marbling required—increases with maturity:

> From minimum—Small Amount
>
> To maximum—Small Amount

2. Carcasses in the older group (B maturity) (from those described above as representative of the juncture of the two groups to those at the maximum maturity permitted in the Choice grade):

> Have chine bone tinged with red.
>
> Have cartilages on the ends of the thoracic vertebrae which are partially ossified.
>
> Have a rib-eye muscle which is fine in texture and slightly firm.

Minimum degree of marbling required—increases with maturity:

> From minimum—Modest Amount

To maximum—Modest Amount

(Quality versus conformation)

A carcass which has mid-point Choice quality may have conformation equal to the mid-point of the Good grade and remain eligible for Choice. However, regardless of the extent to which the conformation of a carcass exceeds the minimum of the grade, a carcass must have minimum Choice quality to be eligible for Choice.

Good

This grade pleases thrifty consumers who seek beef with little fat but with an acceptable degree of quality. Although cuts of this grade lack the juiciness associated with a higher degree of fatness, their relative tenderness and high proportion of lean to fat make them the preference of many people.

Carcasses and wholesale cuts with minimum Good grade conformation:

> Are slightly thick-muscled throughout.
>
> Tend to be slightly wide and thick in relation to their length.
>
> Have loins and ribs which tend to be slightly thick and full.
>
> Have rounds which tend to be slightly plump.
>
> Have necks and shanks which tend to be slightly long and thin.

(Minimum quality characteristics for two maturity groups which cover the entire range of maturity permitted in the Good grade.)

1. Carcasses in the younger group (A maturity) (from the youngest eligible to those at the juncture of the two maturity groups):

   > Have slightly red and slighty soft chine bones.
   >
   > Have some ossification of cartilages on ends of thoracic vertebrae.
   >
   > Have sacral vertebrae which are completely fused.
   >
   > Have cartilages on the ends of the lumbar vertebrae which

are nearly completely ossified.

Have rib bones which are slightly wide and slightly flat.

Have a rib-eye muscle which is slightly light red in color, fine in texture, and moderately soft.

Minimum degree of marbling required—increases with maturity:

From minimum—Typical Traces

To maximum—Typical Slight Amount

2. Carcasses in the older group (B maturity) (from those described above as representative of the juncture of the two groups to those at the maximum permitted in the Good grade):

Have chine bones tinged with red.

Have cartilages on the ends of thoracic vertebrae which are moderately ossified.

Have a rib-eye muscle which is moderately fine in texture but slightly soft.

Have moderate symmetry and uniformity in contour.

Minimum degree of marbling required—increases with maturity:

From minimum—Typical Slight Amount

To maximum—Small Amount

(Quality versus conformation)

A carcass which has mid-point Good grade quality may have conformation equivalent to the mid-point of the Standard grade and remain eligible for Good. Also, a carcass which has at least one-third of a grade superior conformation to that specified as minimum for the grade may qualify for Good with a development of quality equivalent to the lower limit of the upper third of the Standard grade. Compensation of superior conformation for inferior quality is limited to one-third of a quality grade.

Standard

Standard grade beef has a very thin covering of fat and appeals to consumers whose primary concern is a high proportion of lean. When properly prepared, such beef is usually relatively tender. It is mild in flavor and lacks the juiciness usually found in beef with more marbling.

Carcasses and wholesale cuts with minimum Standard grade conformation:

Tend to be thinly muscled throughout.

Are slightly narrow and thin in relation to their length.

Have loins and ribs which tend to be flat and slightly thin fleshed.

Have rounds which tend to be thin and slightly concave.

Have chucks which tend to be flat and thin-fleshed.

(Minimum quality characteristics for two maturity groups which cover the entire range of maturity permitted in this grade):

1. Carcasses in the younger group (A maturity) (from the younger eligible to those at the juncture of the two maturity groups):

   Have slightly red and slightly soft chine bones.

   Have cartilages on the ends of the thoracic vertebrae with some evidence of ossification.

   Have sacral vertebrae which are completely fused.

   Have cartilages on the ends of lumbar vertebrae which are nearly ossified.

   Have rib bones which are slightly wide and slightly flat.

   Have a rib-eye muscle which is slightly dark red in color, fine in texture, but soft.

Minimum degree of marbling required—increases with maturity:

From minimum—Practically Devoid

To maximum—Practically Devoid

2. Carcasses in the older group (B maturity) (from those described above as representative of the juncture of the two groups to those at the maximum maturity permitted in the Standard grade):

   Have chine bones tinged with red.

   Have cartilages on ends of thoracic vertebrae which are moderately ossified.

   Have a rib-eye muscle which is moderately fine in texture, moderately dark red in color, and moderately soft.

Minimum degree of marbling required—increases with maturity:

From minimum—Traces

To minimum—Typical Slight Amount

(Quality versus conformation)

A carcass which has mid-point Standard quality may have conformation equal to the mid-point of the Utility grade and remain eligible
for Standard. Also, a carcass which has at least one-third of a grade
superior conformation to that specified as minimum for the grade may
qualify for Standard with a development of quality equal to the minimum of the upper third of the Utility grade. Compensation of superior
conformation for inferior quality is limited to one-third of a quality
grade.

Commercial

Beef that is graded Commercial is produced from older cattle and
usually lacks the tenderness of the higher grades. Cuts from this grade, if
carefully prepared, can be made into satisfactory and economical meat
dishes. Most cuts require long slow cooking with moist heat to make them
tender and to develop the rich, full beef flavor characteristic of mature
beef.

(Restricted to carcasses and wholesale cuts with evidences of more advanced maturity than permitted in the Good and Standard grades.)

Carcasses and wholesale cuts with minimum Commercial grade conformation:

Are slightly thin muscled throughout.

Because of the usually moderately heavy fat covering, tend to be
slightly thick but rather rough and irregular in contour.

Have rounds which tend to be thin and slightly concave.

Have loins which tend to be moderately wide but slightly
sunken.

Have rather prominent hips.

Have ribs which tend to be slightly thick and full.

Have chucks which are slightly thin or shelly.

Have plates and briskets which are wide and spready.

Have necks and shanks which are slightly long and thin.

(Three maturity groups are recognized in the Commercial grade.)

1. Carcasses in the youngest group (C maturity):

Range from those of maturity barely more advanced than the maximum for the Good and Standard grades to those with moderately hard, rather white chine bones.

Have cartilages on the ends of the thoracic vertebrae which show considerable ossification, but the outlines of the cartilages are still plainly visible.

Have rib bones which are moderately wide and flat.

Have a rib-eye muscle which is moderately dark, slightly coarse in texture, and slightly firm.

Minimum degree of marbling required—increases with maturity:

From minimum—Small Amount

To maximum—Small Amount

Intermediate group (D maturity) determined by interpolation.

2. Carcasses in the most mature group (E maturity):

Have hard, white chine bones.

Have cartilages on the ends of the thoracic vertebrae, the outlines of which are barely visible.

Have rib bones which are wide and flat.

Rib-eye muscle which is firm, dark red in color, and coarse-textured.

Minimum degree of marbling—increases with maturity:

From minimum—Moderate Amount

To maximum—Moderate Amount

(Quality versus conformation)

A carcass which has mid-point Commercial quality may have conformation equal to the midpoint of the Utility grade and remain eligible for Commercial. However, regardless of the extent to which the conformation of a carcass exceeds the minimum of the Commercial grade, the carcass must have quality to the minimum of the Commercial grade to be eligible for Commercial.

Utility

Beef of this grade is produced mostly from cattle somewhat advanced in age and is usually lacking in natural tenderness and juiciness. The cuts of this grade, as they appear in the retail markets, carry very little fat but provide a palatable, economical source of lean meat for pot roasting, stewing, boiling, or ground-meat dishes. For satisfactory results, long, slow cooking by moist heat is essential.

Carcasses and wholesale cuts with minimum Utility grade conformation:

>Are thinly muscled throughout.
>
>Are very narrow in relation to their length.
>
>Are decidedly rangy, angular, and irregular in contours.
>
>Have loins and ribs which are flat and thinly fleshed.
>
>Have rounds which tend to be very thin and concave.
>
>Have chucks which are thin and flat and necks and shanks which are long and tapering.
>
>Have hips and shoulder joints which are prominent.

(Five maturity groups are recognized. Minimum quality requirements are here described for the first [youngest (A)], the third [intermediate (C)], and the fifth [most mature (E)]. The requirements for the second and fourth groups are determined by interpolation between the requirements described for their adjoining groups.)

1. Carcasses in the youngest group (A maturity):

>Have slightly red and slightly soft chine bones.
>
>Have cartilages on the ends of the thoracic vertebrae which have some evidence of ossification.
>
>Have sacral vertebrae which are completely fused.
>
>Have lumbar vertebrae of which the ends are nearly com-

pletely ossified.

Have slightly flat rib bones.

Have a rib-eye muscle which is slightly dark red in color, fine in texture, slightly watery, and *devoid of marbling.*

2. Carcasses in the third maturity group (C maturity):

Have moderately hard, rather white chine bones.

Have cartilages on the ends of the thoracic vertebrae which show considerable ossification, but the outlines of the cartilages are still plainly visible.

Have rib bones which are moderately wide and flat.

Have a rib-eye muscle which is moderately soft, dark red in color, and slightly coarse in texture.

Marbling—*practically devoid.*

3. Carcasses in the fifth or oldest maturity group (E maturity):

Have hard, white chine bones, and the outlines of the cartilages on the ends of the thoracic vertebrae are barely visible.

Have rib bones which are wide and flat.

Have a rib-eye muscle which is slightly firm, but very dark in color, and coarse in texture.

Have a *slight amount* of marbling.

(Quality versus conformation)

A carcass which has mid-point Utility quality may have conformation equal to the mid-point of the Cutter grade and remain eligible for Utility. Also, a carcass which has at least one-third of a grade superior conformation to that specified for the minimum of the grade may qualify for Utility with a development of quality equal to the lower limit of the upper third of the Cutter grade. Compensation of superior conformation for inferior quality is limited to one-third of a quality grade.

Cutter

Carcasses and wholesale cuts with minimum Cutter grade conformation:

Are very thinly muscled throughout.

Are rangy, angular, and irregular in contour.

Have loins and ribs which are very flat, thin, and shallow.

Have rounds which are very thin and very concave.

Have chucks which are very flat, thin, and shallow.

Have very long and tapering necks and shanks.

Have hips and shoulder joints which are very prominent.

(Five maturity groups are recognized. In all groups the rib-eye muscle is devoid of marbling, is soft and watery, and dark red in color.)

Since this grade of beef is not presented to the buying public in our retail markets, it will not be discussed beyond this point.

Canner

This grade includes only those carcasses that are inferior to the minimum requirements specified for the Cutter grade.

Live and Carcass Illustrations of Beef Quality Grades

These live and carcass pictures for beef quality grades were generously provided by the University of Illinois Animal Science and Vo Ag Services Departments and by the National Live Stock and Meat Board. The carcass pictures appear in color in the *Meat Evaluation Handbook,*

Fig. 11.6—The round inspection stamp and the grade stamp. (Courtesy, AMS, USDA)

published by the Meat Board, and were originally secured by Meat Board Staff and American Meat Science Association members who worked tirelessly to produce a most useful handbook. The handbook is highly recommended for the serious student of meat judging and grading.

The beef carcass quality grades are based on conformation, marbling, and maturity (see above discussion). In live cattle, the traits of maturity (age) and conformation are rather easily recognized after some training and experience. Marbling, however, is very difficult to estimate on a live animal without the use of supplemental information, such as length of time on feed, composition of ration, and genetic background. Thus many cattle are bought on "reputation," that is, buyers learn to know the way various feeders feed a certain kind of cattle in order to produce carcasses of a given grade.

Some characteristics can be observed on live cattle, which relate to overall fatness and therefore indirectly to marbling, but there are some "fat" cattle that don't marble and some "lean" cattle that do marble. Therefore, the pictures depicting especially the live grades of Prime, Choice, and Good must be recognized as typical examples only, and furthermore, the final carcass grade is not known until the carcass is ribbed and the marbling evaluated. Certainly breeds and types other than those shown for each grade qualify daily in the United States for the various grades.

Yield Grades[3]

Yield grades indicate the quantity of meat, i.e., the amount of retail, consumer-ready, ready-to-cook, or edible meat that a carcass contains. Whichever term you choose, the final amount available for eating is extremely important. Do not confuse yield grade with dressing percent, often called *yield*. Yield grade refers to the amount of edible product from the carcass. Dressing percent (*yield*) refers to the amount of carcass from a live animal.

The *lower* the number of the yield grade, the *higher* the percent of the carcass in boneless, closely trimmed retail cuts from the round, loin, rib, and chuck as shown in Table 11.1.

Determination of a Yield Grade

Yield grade refers to the percent of trimmed, retail cuts that the

---

3. *Official United States Standards for Grades of Carcass Beef,* Title 7, Chapter I, Part 53, Sections 53.100-53.105 of the Code of Federal Regulations, reprinted with amendments effective July 1, 1973.

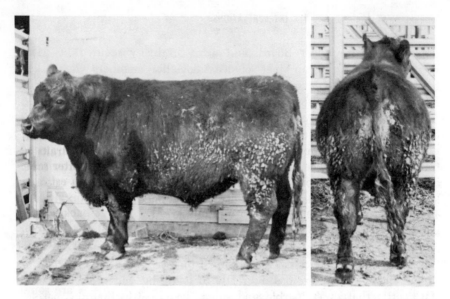

Fig. 11.7—A 1,090-pound Prime steer. From the side, the fullness of his brisket and the fore and rear flanks is evidence of his having been fed. Fullness here represents fat. From the rear, his width through his middle and fullness of twist again indicate feed, fat, and the potential to marble.

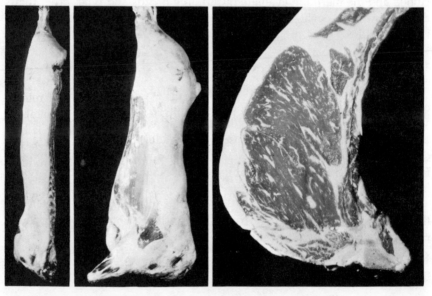

Fig. 11.8—U.S. Prime beef carcass. The carcass is wide and thick in relation to its length and is thickly muscled throughout—note the plumpness in the round and the thickness in the loin, rib, and chuck—thus, it has average Prime grade conformation. This typical A maturity carcass has a light red color of lean, red porous chine bones, large cartilaginous "buttons" on the thoracic vertebrae, and the sacral vertebrae are nearly completely fused, all traits which cannot be seen in these photos. The

moderately abundant marbling and firm rib-eye muscle combine to indicate average Prime quality. The combination of average Prime conformation and average Prime quality results in an average Prime carcass. Note the lack of waste fat over the eye, indicating that external fat is *not* always a prerequisite for marbling.

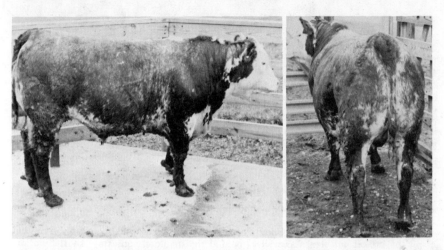

Fig. 11.9—A 1,150-pound Choice steer. From the side, this steer appears to be more upstanding, but his brisket and fore flank are moderately full, indicating some fatness. From the rear, he appears to be trim in the twist and lower round but shows evidence of some fatness over the edge of his loin.

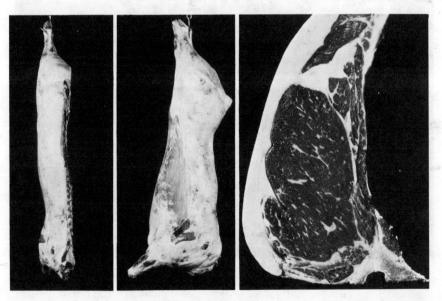

Fig. 11.10—U.S. Choice beef carcass. The rib-eye muscle of this typical A maturity carcass displays average Choice quality. It has a weak, moderate amount of marbling and slightly firm lean. This quality, combined with average Choice conformation—evidenced by a moderately plump round and a moderately thick loin, rib, and chuck—results in an average Choice grade carcass.

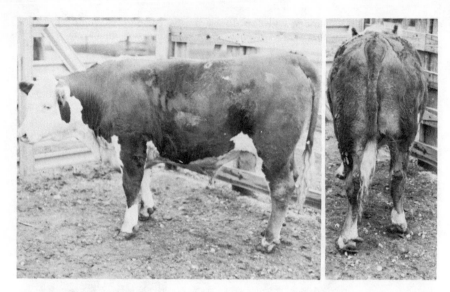

Fig. 11.11—A 980-pound Good steer. The steer's light weight and his trimness about the brisket and flanks as well as behind the shoulders indicate a short time on feed. The steer is narrow behind, lacking muscling and bulge to the round which will lower his conformation grade.

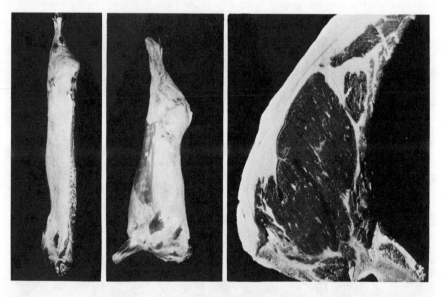

Fig. 11.12—U.S. Good beef carcass. The slightly plump rounds and the slightly thick and full loins, ribs, and chucks of this carcass make its conformation average Good. This very young (A-minus maturity) carcass has distinct separation of the sacral vertebrae, red porous chine bones, and a very light red color of lean, none of which can be seen in these illustrations. The slight amount of marbling in the moderately soft rib-eye muscle combined with average Good grade conformation qualifies it for average Good.

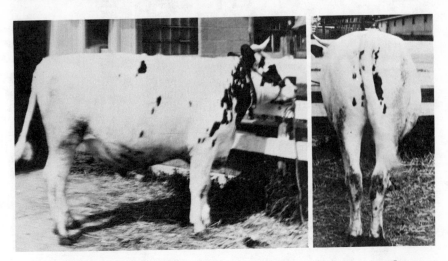

Fig. 11.13—A 1,125-pound Standard steer. Young steers of dairy breeding predominate here, although young cattle of any breed which are somewhat under finished and upstanding qualify for the Standard grade. On the other hand, many dairy steers move up to the Good grade, while some even move up to the Choice grade, conformation being the factor which holds them back. The steer is narrow and upstanding behind and shows little evidence of external finish.

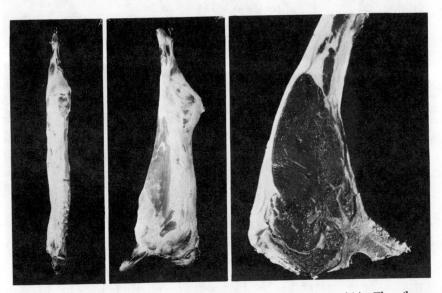

Fig. 11.14—This carcass is in the younger maturity group (A). The rib-eye muscle, which is moderately soft and has traces of marbling, is typical of average Standard grade quality. Its conformation is typical of the Standard grade as it is slightly thin-fleshed throughout. The combination of conformation and quality, both typical of average Standard, qualifies the carcass for average Standard grade.

Fig. 11.15–A 1,120-pound Commercial cow. The advanced age of this cow is apparent from her angular conformation. The fullness in her brisket and behind her shoulders indicates a well-finished cow. From the rear, her angular conformation is more obvious. Yet she has sufficient thickness to qualify for the Commercial grade.

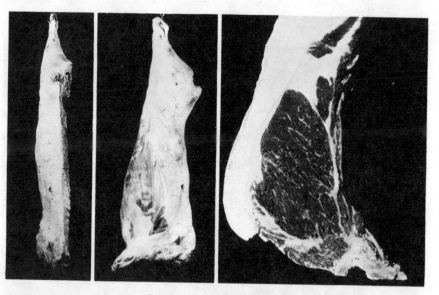

Fig. 11.16–U.S. Commercial beef carcass. This very hard-boned carcass with cartilages on the ends of the chine bones which are completely ossified and flinty is E-plus maturity. This is also indicated by the dark red, coarse-textured, rib-eye muscle. The moderately abundant amount of marbling indicates average Commercial grade quality. Average Commercial grade quality combined with average Commercial grade conformation—rounds that are slightly thin, slightly sunken and moderately wide loins, and slightly thick ribs and chucks—qualifies this carcass for average Commercial.

Fig. 11.17–An 840-pound Utility cow. From the side, her extreme angularity from front to rear is obvious. Note her protruding ribs indicating practically a complete void of cover. From the rear, concave rounds and sunken sirloin indicate Utility conformation. Normally such cows are dry before going to market; this cow was slaughtered to obtain an active udder as part of a research project, thus her obviously preponderant udder.

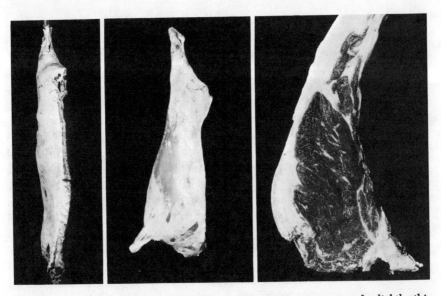

Fig. 11.18–U.S. Utility beef carcass. The slightly concave round, slightly thin sunken loin, and the flat, thinly-fleshed rib of this carcass qualifies its conformation as average Utility. The modest amount of marbling in the dark red, coarse-textured, rib-eye muscle of this E-plus maturity carcass, together with its average Utility conformation, qualifies it for average Utility.

Table 11.1—Beef Yield Grade Retail Yield Equivalents

Yield Grade	Percent of Warm Carcass in Closely Trimmed Primal Cuts
1	52.6 – 54.6
2	50.3 – 52.3
3	48.0 – 50.0
4	45.7 – 47.7
5	43.5 – 45.4

chuck, rib, loin, and round will yield collectively or as separate wholesale cuts. The flank, shank, brisket, and plate are not included in determining yield grade.

The determination is made on (1) the amount of external fat, (2) the amount of kidney, pelvic, and heart fat, (3) the area of the rib-eye muscle, and (4) the carcass weight.

1. The amount of *external fat* on a carcass is evaluated in terms of thickness of this fat over the rib-eye muscle measured perpendicular to the outside surface at a point three-fourths of the length of the rib eye from its chine bone end (Figure 11.19). This measurement may be adjusted, as necessary, to reflect unusual amounts of fat on other parts of the carcass. In determining the amount of this adjustment, if any, particular attention is given to the amount of fat in such areas as the brisket, plate, flank, cod or udder, inside round, rump, and hips in relation to the actual thickness of fat over the rib eye. Thus, in a carcass which is fatter over other areas than is indicated by the fat measurement over the rib eye, the measurement is adjusted upward. Conversely, in a carcass which has less fat over the other areas than is indicated by the fat measurement over the rib eye, the measurement is adjusted downward. In many carcasses no such adjustment is necessary; however, an adjustment in the thickness of fat measurement of one-tenth or two-tenths of an inch is not uncommon. In some carcasses a greater adjustment may be necessary. As the amount of external fat increases, the percent of retail cuts decreases. Each one-tenth-inch change in adjusted fat thickness over the rib eye changes the yield grade by 25% of a yield grade.

2. The amount of *kidney, pelvic, and heart fat* considered in determining the yield grade includes the kidney knob (kidney and surrounding fat), the lumbar and pelvic fat in the loin and round, and the heart fat in the chuck and brisket area which are removed in making closely trimmed retail cuts (Note Chapter 13). The amount of these fats is evaluated subjectively and expressed as a percent of the carcass weight. As the amount of kidney, pelvic, and heart fat increases, the percent of retail cuts decreases. A change of 1% of the carcass weight in these fats changes the yield grade by 20% of a yield grade.

3. The *area of the rib eye* is determined where this muscle is exposed by ribbing (Figure 11.19). This area usually is estimated subjectively; however, it may be measured. Area of rib-eye measurements may be made by means of a grid calibrated in tenths of a square inch or by a compensating planimeter measurement of an acetate tracing. An increase in the area of rib eye increases the percent of retail cuts. A change of 1 square inch in area of rib eye changes the yield grade by approximately 30% of a yield grade.

4. *Hot carcass weight* (or chilled carcass weight × 102%) is used in

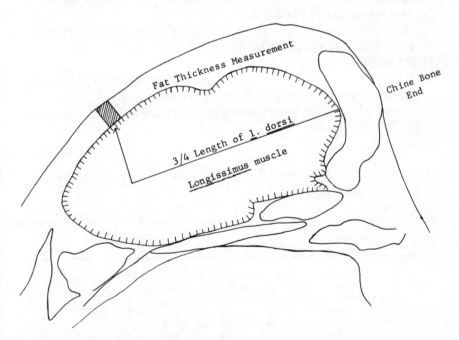

Fig. 11.19—Showing where fat thickness and rib-eye area are measured. (Courtesy, American Meat Science Association)

determining the yield grade. As carcass weight increases, the percent of retail cuts decreases. A change of 100 pounds in hot carcass weight changes the yield grade by approximately 38% of a yield grade.

The Standards include a mathematical equation for determining yield grade group. This group is expressed as a whole number; any fractional part of a designation is always dropped. For example, if the computation results in a designation of 3.9, the final yield grade is 3—it is not rounded to 4. *Equation:* 2.50 + (2.50 × adjusted fat thickness, inches) + (0.20 × percent kidney, pelvic, and heart fat) + (0.0038 × hot carcass weight, pounds) − (0.32 × area rib eye, square inches).

For forequarters and forequarter cuts and trimmed hindquarters and trimmed hindquarter cuts, use the standard percentages of kidney, pelvic, and heart fat, applicable to the quality grade of the quarter or cut in the equation as shown in Table 11.2.

Example: Let us suppose that we have a 610-pound (hotweight) Prime grade carcass that has .7 of an inch of fat thickness over the rib eye (other external fat covering normal), has, according to the above table, 4.5 percent of its carcass weight in kidney, pelvic, and heart fat, and has 10.4 square inches of rib eye.

Use the equation: 2.50 + (2.50 × .7) + (0.20 × 4.5) + (0.0038 × 610) − (0.32 × 10.4). 2.50 + 1.75 + .9 + 2.32 − 3.33 = 4.14. Result— Yield Grade 4.

Hot carcass weight is determined by multiplying the chilled weight of the cut by an appropriate factor as applicable to the cut.

The Federal meat grader learns to rather accurately determine the

Table 11.2—Standard Kidney, Pelvic, and Heart Fat Percentage by
Quality Grades

Grade	Fat Percentage
Prime – – – – – – – – – – – – – – – – –	4.5
Choice – – – – – – – – – – – – – – – –	3.5
Good – – – – – – – – – – – – – – – – –	3.0
Standard – – – – – – – – – – – – – – –	2.0
Commercial – – – – – – – – – – – – – –	4.0
Utility – – – – – – – – – – – – – – – –	2.0
Cutter and Canner – – – – – – – – – –	1.5

Table 11.3—Hot Weight Determination from Cut Weights

	Factor
Forequarter - - - - - - - - - - - - - - -	3.90
Hindquarter - - - - - - - - - - - - - - -	4.25
(IMP Specifications for Fresh Beef—Series 100)	
Rib - - - - - - - - - - - - - - - - - - -	22.50
Loin, full, trimmed - - - - - - - - - - -	12.75
Short Loin, trimmed - - - - - - - - - - -	29.10

yield grade rating for a beef carcass by a visual appraisal, aided by a pocket scale graduated in tenths of an inch and the preliminary yield grades associated with fat thickness. He is provided with a card that contains the following:

1. Determine a *Preliminary yield grade* from a schedule. (Table 11.4)
   The fat thickness is a single measurement of the fat over the rib eye three-fourths of the length of the rib eye from its chine bone end. This measurement may be adjusted, either upward or downward as necessary, to reflect unusual amounts of fat on other parts of the carcass or cut.
2. Determine the Final Yield Grade (1 to 5) by adjusting the pre-

Table 11.4—Preliminary Yield Grade by Fat Thickness

Thickness of Fat over Rib Eye	Preliminary Yield Grade
(in.)	
.2 - - - - - - - - - - - - - - - - -	2.5
.4 - - - - - - - - - - - - - - - - -	3.0
.6 - - - - - - - - - - - - - - - - -	3.5
.8 - - - - - - - - - - - - - - - - -	4.0
1.0 - - - - - - - - - - - - - - - - -	4.5
1.2 - - - - - - - - - - - - - - - - -	5.0
1.4 - - - - - - - - - - - - - - - - -	5.5
1.6 - - - - - - - - - - - - - - - - -	6.0

liminary yield grade, as necessary, for variations in kidney fat from 3.5% and for variations in area of rib eye from the weight-area of rib-eye schedule. (See Table 11.5.) Such adjustments are rounded to the nearest tenth of a grade.

Rate of adjustment for area of rib eye in relation to weight:

For each square inch more than area indicated in the weight-area of rib-eye schedule, subtract .3 of a grade from the preliminary yield grade.

Table 11.5—Carcass and Wholesale Cut Weight—Area of Rib-Eye Schedule[1,2]

Warm Carcass Weight	Area of Rib Eye	Chilled Weight					
		Side	Fore-quarter	Hind-quarter	Rib	Loin	Short Loin
(lbs.)	(sq. in.)	— — — — — — — — — — — —(lbs.)— — — — — — — — — — — —					
350	8.0	172	90	82	16	27	12
375	8.3	184	96	88	17	29	13
400	8.6	196	103	94	18	31	14
425	8.9	208	109	100	19	33	15
450	9.2	220	115	106	20	35	15
475	9.5	233	122	112	21	37	16
500	9.8	245	128	118	22	39	17
525	10.1	257	135	124	23	41	18
550	10.4	270	141	129	24	43	19
575	10.7	282	147	135	26	45	20
600	11.0	294	154	141	27	47	21
625	11.3	306	160	147	28	49	21
650	11.6	319	167	153	29	51	22
675	11.9	331	173	159	30	53	23
700	12.2	343	179	165	31	55	24
725	12.5	355	186	171	32	57	25
750	12.8	368	192	176	33	59	26
775	13.1	380	199	182	34	61	27
800	13.4	392	205	188	36	63	27
825	13.7	404	212	194	37	65	28
850	14.0	417	218	200	38	67	29
875	14.3	429	224	206	39	69	30

(Continued)

For each square inch less than area indicated in the weight-area of rib-eye schedule, add .3 of a grade to the preliminary yield grade.

Rate of adjustment for percent of kidney, pelvic, and heart fat:

Carcasses

For each percent of kidney, pelvic, and heart fat more than 3.5%, add .2 of a grade to the preliminary yield grade. For each percent of kidney, pelvic, and heart fat less than 3.5%, subtract .2 of a grade from the preliminary yield grade.

Table 11.5 (Continued)

Warm Carcass Weight	Area of Rib Eye	Chilled Weight					
		Side	Fore-quarter	Hind-quarter	Rib	Loin	Short Loin
(lbs.)	(sq. in.)	- - - - - - - - - - - -(lbs.)- - - - - - - - - - - - - - -					
900	14.6	441	231	212	40	71	31
925	14.9	453	237	218	41	73	32
950	15.2	466	244	224	42	75	33
975	15.5	478	250	229	43	76	34
1,000	15.8	490	256	235	44	78	34
1,025	16.1	502	263	241	46	80	35
1,050	16.4	515	269	247	47	82	36
1,075	16.7	527	276	253	48	84	37
1,100	17.0	539	282	259	49	86	38
1,125	17.3	551	288	265	50	88	39
1,150	17.6	564	295	271	51	90	40

1. The combined effect of carcass weight and area of rib eye on yield grade is the same for all combinations indicated by the schedule.

2. Guide to rib-eye area for other weights of carcasses between the 25-pound gradations:

Warm Carcass Weight	Area of Rib Eye		
		600–608 lbs.	11.0 sq. in.
600	11.0	609–616 lbs.	11.1 sq. in.
625	11.3	617–624 lbs.	11.2 sq. in.
		625–633 lbs.	11.3 sq. in.

Cuts

In yield grading forequarters, trimmed hindquarters, or cuts eligible for grading which do not include the kidney, pelvic, and heart fat, the standard adjustment for those fats shall be made according to the quality grade as shown in Table 11.6.

For untrimmed hindquarters or untrimmed hindquarter cuts, the quantity of kidney and pelvic fat is estimated as a percent of the hot side weight.

"Shortcut" Method for Yield Grade Calculation

1. An average beef carcass with a yield grade of 3.5 would have the following credentials:
   a. Carcass weight—600 pounds
   b. Loin-eye area—11.00 square inches
   c. Fat thickness—0.6 inch
   d. Percent of KPH fat—3.5%
2. Factors that affect yield grade
   a. *Carcass weight*
      (1) Heavier weight makes higher-numbered yield grade
      (2) Every *100 lbs. of carcass* is worth *0.4 Yield Grade*
   b. *Loin-eye area*
      (1) Larger loin-eye area makes a lower-numbered yield grade
      (2) Every *inch of loin-eye area* is worth *0.3 Yield Grade*
   c. *Fat thickness*
      (1) More fat thickness makes a higher-numbered yield grade

Table 11.6—Yield Grade Adjustment for Missing KPHF

Grade	Standard Adjustment
Prime	.2
Choice	none
Good	-.1
Standard	-.3
Commercial	.1
Utility	-.3
Cutter and Canner	-.4

(2) Each *0.1 inch of fat* is worth *0.25 Yield Grade*

d. *Kidney, Pelvic, and Heart Fat* (KPH)

    (1) More KPH fat makes a higher-numbered yield grade

    (2) Each *percent of KPH* fat is worth *0.2 Yield Grade*

3. Yield grade can be calculated on any carcass by adjusting the 3.5 base according to how each factor above (1, a-d) varies from the average.

4. Example:

	Carcass	Difference from "Average"	Adjustment
Weight	700	100	+0.4 (1 × .4)
Loin-eye area	13.00	2.0	−0.6 (2 × .3)
Fat thickness	0.50	0.1	−0.25 (1 × .25)
Percent of KPH fat	2.5	1.0	−0.2 (1 × .20)
		Total Adjustment	−0.65

Yield Grade = 3.5 − 0.65 = 2.85 = 2.8

Specifications for Official U.S. Standards for Grades of Carcass Beef (Yield)

The following descriptions provide a guide to the characteristics of carcasses in each yield grade to aid in determining yield grades subjectively.

Yield Grade 1

Carcass has a thin layer of external fat over the ribs, loins, rumps, and clods and slight deposits of fat in the flanks and cod or udder; a very thin layer of fat over the outside of the rounds and over the tops of the shoulders and neck.

Muscles are usually visible through the fat in many areas of the carcass.

(Description of two different weight carcasses near the borderline of Yield Grades 1 and 2. These descriptions facilitate the subjective determination of the yield grade without making detailed measurements and computations. The yield grade for most beef carcasses can be determined accurately on the basis of a visual appraisal by a trained and experienced grader.)

1. A 500-pound carcass might have .3 inch of fat over the rib eye, 11.5 square inches of rib eye, and 2.5% of its weight in kidney, pelvic, and heart fat.
2. An 800-pound carcass might have .4 inch of fat over the rib eye, 16.0 square inches of rib eye and 2.5% of its weight in kidney, pelvic, and heart fat.

Yield Grade 2

Carcass is nearly completely covered with fat, but the lean is plainly visible through the fat over the outside of the rounds, the tops of the shoulders, and the necks.

There is a slightly thin layer of fat over the loins, ribs, and inside rounds, with a slightly thick layer of fat over the rumps, hips, and clods.

Small deposits of fat occur in the flanks and cod or udder.

1. A 500-pound carcass (near the borderline of Yield Grades 2 and 3) might have .5 inch of fat over the rib eye, and 3.5% of its weight in kidney, pelvic, and heart fat.
2. An 800-pound carcass might have .6 inch of fat over the rib eye, 15 square inches of rib eye and 3.5% of its weight in kidney, pelvic, and heart fat.

Yield Grade 3

Carcass is usually completely covered with fat, and the lean usually is visible through the fat only on the necks and lower part of the outside of the round.

There is a slightly thick layer of fat over the loins, ribs, and inside rounds with a moderately thick layer over the rumps, hips, and clods.

Slightly large deposits of fat occur in the flanks and cod or udder.

1. A 500-pound carcass (near the borderline of Yield Grades 3 and 4) might have .7 inch of fat over the rib eye, 9.5 square inches of rib eye, and 4% of its weight in kidney, pelvic, and heart fat.
2. An 800-pound carcass might have .8 inch of fat over the rib eye, 14 square inches of rib eye, and 4.5% of its weight in kidney, pelvic, and heart fat.

Yield Grade 4

A carcass in this group is usually completely covered with fat. The only muscles visible are those on the shanks and over the outside of the plates and flanks.

There is a moderately thick layer of fat over the loins, ribs, and inside rounds and a thick covering of fat over the rumps, hips, and clods.

Large deposits of fat occur in the flanks and cod or udder.

1. A 500-pound carcass (near the borderline of Yield Grades 4 and 5) might have 1 inch of fat over the rib eye, 9 square inches of rib eye, and 4.5% of its carcass weight in kidney, pelvic, and heart fat.
2. An 800-pound carcass might have 1.1 inches of fat over the rib eye, 13.5 square inches of rib eye, and 5% of its weight in kidney, pelvic, and heart fat.

Yield Grade 5

A carcass in this group has more fat on all the various parts, a smaller area of rib eye, and more kidney, pelvic, and heart fat than a carcass in Yield Grade 4.

Yields and Value Differences Between Yield Grades

Value differences between yield grades naturally fluctuate from week to week and month to month due to overall meat price fluctuations. Nevertheless, Table 11.7 vividly presents yield and value differences between yield grades which should make one aware of their economic importance.

Live and Carcass Illustrations of Beef Yield Grades

These live and carcass pictures for yield grades were generously provided by the University of Illinois Animal Science and Vo Ag Services Departments and by the National Live Stock and Meat Board. The carcass pictures appear in color in the *Meat Evaluation Handbook,* published by the Meat Board, and were originally secured by Meat Board Staff and American Meat Science Association members who worked tirelessly to produce a most useful handbook. The handbook is highly recommended for the serious student of meat judging and grading.

Beef carcass yield grades are based on four factors (see above discussion): (1) carcass weight, (2) loin-eye area, (3) external fat thick-

Table 11.7—Comparison of Yields of Retail Cuts and Retail Sales Values for Choice Beef Carcasses, by Yield Grades[1,2,3]

Retail Cut	Jan. 1973 Price per Pound	Yield Grade 1		Yield Grade 2		Yield Grade 3		Yield Grade 4		Yield Grade 5	
		% of Carcass	Value/ Cwt. Carcass	% of Carcass	Value/ Cwt. Carcass	% of Carcass	Value/ Cwt. Carcass	% of Carcass	Value/ Cwt. Carcass	% of Carcass	Value/ Cwt. Carcass
Rump, boneless	$1.54	3.7	$5.70	3.5	$5.39	3.3	$5.08	3.1	$4.77	2.9	$4.47
Inside round, boneless	1.72	4.9	8.43	4.5	7.74	4.1	7.05	3.7	6.36	3.3	5.68
Outside round, boneless	1.63	4.8	7.82	4.6	7.50	4.4	7.17	4.2	6.85	4.0	6.52
Round tip, boneless	1.62	2.7	4.37	2.6	4.21	2.5	4.05	2.4	3.89	2.3	3.73
Sirloin, bone-in	1.62	9.1	14.74	8.7	14.09	8.3	13.45	7.9	12.80	7.5	12.15
Short loin, bone-in	1.87	5.3	9.91	5.2	9.72	5.1	9.54	5.0	9.35	4.9	9.16
Blade chuck, bone-in	.85	9.9	8.42	9.4	7.99	8.9	7.57	8.4	7.14	7.9	6.72
Rib, short cut (7"), bone-in	1.47	6.3	9.26	6.2	9.11	6.1	8.97	6.0	8.82	5.9	8.67
Chuck, arm boneless	1.15	6.4	7.36	6.1	7.02	5.8	6.67	5.5	6.33	5.2	5.98
Brisket, boneless	1.32	2.5	3.30	2.3	3.04	2.1	2.77	1.9	2.50	1.7	2.24

(Continued)

Table 11.7 (Continued)

Retail Cut	Jan. 1973 Price per Pound	Yield Grade 1		Yield Grade 2		Yield Grade 3		Yield Grade 4		Yield Grade 5	
		% of Carcass	Value/ Cwt. Carcass	% of Carcass	Value/ Cwt. Carcass	% of Carcass	Value/ Cwt. Carcass	% of Carcass	Value/ Cwt. Carcass	% of Carcass	Value/ Cwt. Carcass
Flank steak	1.82	.5	.91	.5	.91	.5	.91	.5	.91	.5	.91
Lean trim	1.01	12.3	12.42	11.3	11.41	10.3	10.40	9.3	9.39	8.3	8.38
Ground beef	.79	13.3	10.52	12.2	9.65	11.1	8.77	10.0	7.90	8.9	7.03
Kidney	.47	.3	.14	.3	.14	.3	.14	.3	.14	.3	.14
Fat	.02	7.6	.15	12.7	.25	17.8	.36	22.9	.46	28.0	.56
Bone	.01	10.4	.10	9.9	.10	9.4	.09	8.9	.09	8.4	.08
Total		100.0	$103.55	100.0	$98.27	100.0	$92.99	100.0	$87.70	100.0	$82.42

1. Difference in retail value between yield grades—$5.28 per cwt. of carcass in January 1973.

2. Difference in retail value between yield grades—$6.28 per cwt. of carcass in January 1974.

3. These comparisons reflect average yields of retail cuts from beef carcasses typical of the midpoint of each of the USDA yield grades and average prices (including sale priced items) for USDA Choice beef during January 1973 and January 1974, as furnished to the Economic Research Service, U.S. Dept. of Agriculture by a large number of selected retailers throughout the country.

ness, and (4) percent kidney, pelvic, and heart fat. Since these final yield grade factors are more objective (i.e., may be actually measured) than are those for the quality grades, live appraisal for yield grade is somewhat more straightforward than live appraisal for quality grades.

For instance, we look at certain key areas in the live animal for indications of trimness and muscling. Those animals which are deep and full in both flanks and brisket, are very deep in the twist, and are wide and flat over the top of the back will be *fat*, because those places fill up with fat as an animal becomes over fat. Muscling indicators in the live animal are width through the lower round in the area of the stifle joint, width through the chest, leg placement well spaced on all four corners, evidence of forearm muscling, and a rounding, muscular appearance over the loin and back. Muscles are not square, but rounded. Squareness over the back indicates fatness, not muscling.

Muscling and fatness are the two big yield grade factors, and they can be reasonably appraised. Carcass weight is, of course, a function of live weight and can easily be considered when evaluating the live animal. Kidney, pelvic, and heart fat is somewhat difficult to estimate. Cattle with wasty middles may have excessive internal fats, but this is easily confused with *fill* (feed in the digestive tract, primarily in the stomach). Thus an estimate of kidney, pelvic, and heart fat based on overall fatness and considering quality grade is probably the most useful.

In actual evaluations, movement of the animal is extremely helpful in evaluating muscling and trimness. Obviously, these pictures don't provide movement, and thus serve only as a general guide to evaluation. The student should always observe animals in motion when evaluating. Oftentimes, judges like to get their hands on an animal to feel the fatness, but such an opportunity is so rare and out of place in the general flow of cattle to market that only this mention is made here.

Fig. 11.20—A 1,020-pound Yield Grade 1 steer. From the side, trimness in his flank and brisket is apparent. Muscling in the shoulder and bulge to the lower round can be observed from this view. From the rear, note the leg placement squarely on the corners. He lacks depth of twist, indicating trimness, but is wide and thick through the lower round, indicating muscling. Due to the influence of carcass weight in the yield grade calculation, the great majority of animals qualifying for Yield Grade 1 weigh 1,025 pounds or less.

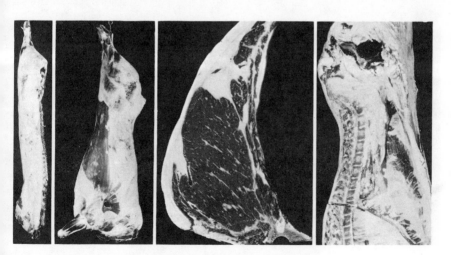

Fig. 11.21—Yield Grade 1 beef carcass

Carcass weight....................645 pounds
External fat thickness..............2 inch
Rib-eye area......................13.9 square inches
Kidney, pelvic, and heart fat........2.5%
Yield Grade.......................1.5
Quality Grade....................High Choice

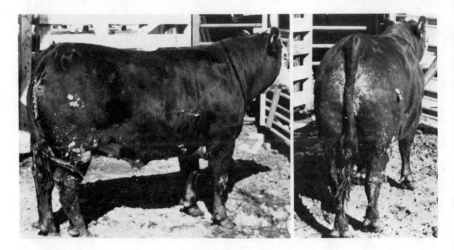

Fig. 11.22—A 975-pound Yield Grade 2 steer. From the side, this steer shows considerable forearm muscling and is moderately trim in the rear flank. His stance from behind is somewhat closed although he does show width through the center of his rounds and a muscular turn to his loin.

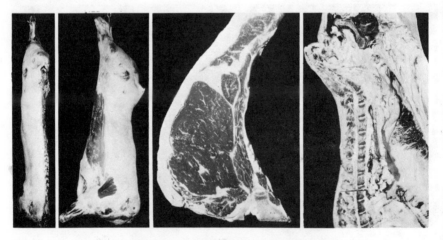

Fig. 11.23—Yield Grade 2 beef carcass.

Carcass weight...................605 pounds
External fat thickness..............4 inch
Rib-eye area......................12.3 square inches
Kidney, pelvic, and heart fat........3.0%
Yield Grade......................2.5
Quality Grade....................Average Choice

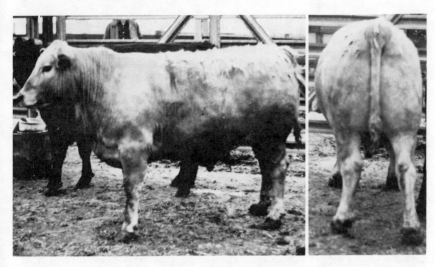

Fig. 11.24—A 1,120-pound Yield Grade 3 steer. From the side, this steer appears upstanding but does show some flesh in his brisket. Forearm and rear quarter muscling are evident. From the rear, evidences of excess fat appear around the tail head, and his turn of loin indicates possible excess finish. Muscling from this view appears adequate but not exceptional.

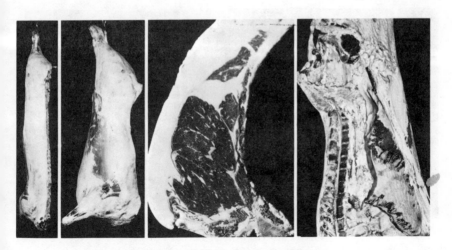

Fig. 11.25—Yield Grade 3 beef carcass.

Carcass weight....................700 pounds
External fat thickness..............6 inch
Rib-eye area.....................11.8 square inches
Kidney, pelvic, and heart fat........3.5%
Yield Grade.....................3.6
Quality Grade...................Average Choice

Fig. 11.26—A 1,060-pound Yield Grade 4 steer. From the side, excessive development of the brisket is apparent. The steer appears very heavy in the front quarter and lacks muscle in the valuable hind quarter. From the rear, his broad, flat topped back indicates excessive finish.

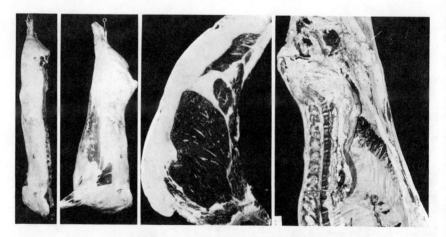

Fig. 11.27—Yield Grade 4 beef carcass.

Carcass weight.....................665 pounds
External fat thickness...............9 inch
Rib-eye area.......................10.5 square inches
Kidney, pelvic, and heart fat........3.5%
Yield Grade.......................4.6
Quality Grade....................Average Choice

Fig. 11.28—A 1,200-pound Yield Grade 5 steer. This big steer from the side appears to have adequate muscling, but excessive fat is especially evident over the tail head and sirloin. From the rear, he is much wider in his middle and up over his back than he is through his rounds, indicating excessive fat. His rear stance is closed, giving evidence of poor muscling.

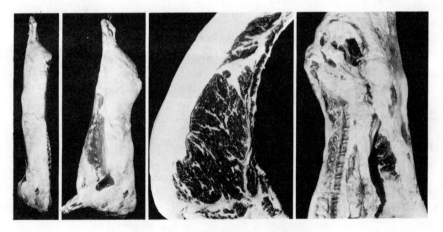

Fig. 11.29—Yield Grade 5 beef carcass.

Carcass weight..................750 pounds
External fat thickness..............1.1 inch
Rib-eye area.....................10.9 square inches
Kidney, pelvic, and heart fat........5.0%
Yield Grade.....................5.6
Quality Grade...................High Choice

VEAL AND CALF CARCASS GRADING

Per capita consumption of veal and calf has fallen from 6.1 pounds in 1960 to 1.8 pounds in 1973 (Table 1.3), while commercial veal and calf slaughter has fallen from a high of 12,746,000 in 1954 to the present low of 3,052,900. The high demand for beef has caused the onset of the practice of castrating and feeding male dairy calves for subsequent slaughter as beef steers. Most of the more thickly muscled calves are selected for further feeding, leaving calves with less well developed conformation for the veal and calf market.

Thus, in 1971, the most recent change in veal and calf standards was made which (1) increased the emphasis placed on the color of lean in classing veal, (2) reduced the conformation requirements one full grade in both veal and calf, (3) reduced the quality requirements by varying degrees from a maximum of one grade for veal to no change for the oldest calves, and (4) eliminated the Cull grade for both classes leaving Prime, Choice, Good, Standard, and Utility as the carcass grades for veal and calf.

Changes in standards for grades of veal and calf carcasses previously made effective March 10, 1951, coincided with revisions made in the live grades and (1) combined the former Choice and Prime grades under the name *Prime*, (2) renamed the Good grade *Choice*, (3) established a new grade called *Good* which included meat from the top half of the former Commercial grade, (4) continued the remainder of the Commercial grade as *Commercial*, and (5) left the Utility and Cull grades unchanged.

A further revision was made in October 1956, changing the grade name *Commercial* to *Standard* and making certain changes in the phrasing of the standards designed to facilitate their interpretations.

Differentiation Between Veal, Calf, and Beef Carcasses[4]

Differentiation between veal, calf, and beef carcasses is made primarily on the basis of the color of the lean, although such factors as texture of the lean; character of the fat; color, shape, size, and ossification of the bones and cartilages; and the general contour of the carcass are also given consideration. Typical veal carcasses have a grayish pink color of lean that is very smooth and velvety in texture, and they also have a slightly soft, pliable character of fat and marrow and very red rib bones. By contrast, typical calf carcasses have a grayish red color

---

4. *Federal Register*, 7 CFR Part 53, August 7, 1971.

of lean, a flakier type of fat, and somewhat wider rib bones with less pronounced evidences of red color.

Classes of Veal and Calf Carcasses

Class determination is based on the apparent sex condition of the animal at the time of slaughter. Hence, there are three classes of veal and calf carcasses—steers, heifers, and bulls. While recognition may sometimes be given to these different classes on the market, especially calf carcasses from bulls that are approaching beef in maturity, the char-

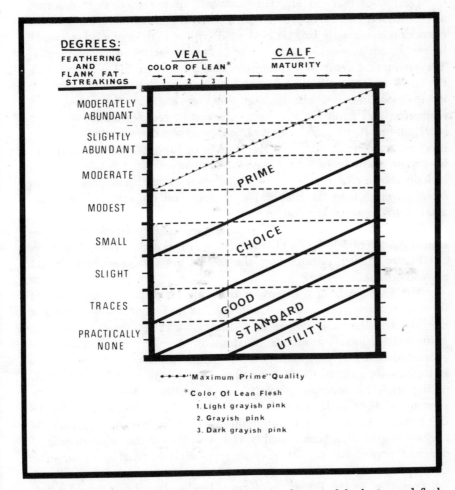

Fig. 11.30—Quality grade equivalent of various degrees of feathering and flank fat streakings in relation to color of lean (veal) or maturity (calf).

acteristics of such carcasses are not sufficiently different from those of steers and heifers to warrant the development of separate standards for them. Therefore, the grade standards which follow are equally applicable to all classes of veal and calf carcasses.

Application of Standards

Veal and calf carcasses are graded on a composite evaluation of *conformation* and quality. *Conformation,* or the manner of formation of the carcass, refers to its thickness or fullness.

Quality of lean—in all veal carcasses, all unribbed calf carcasses, and in ribbed calf carcasses in which their degree of marbling is not a consideration—usually can be evaluated with a high degree of accuracy by giving equal consideration to the following factors, as available: (1) The amount of feathering (fat intermingled within the lean between the ribs) and (2) the quantity of fat streakings within and upon the inside flank muscles. (In making these evaluations, the amounts of feathering and flank fat streakings are considered in relation to color [veal] and maturity [calf].) In addition, however, consideration also may be given to other factors if, in the opinion of the grader, this will result in a more accurate quality assessment. Examples of such other factors include firmness of the lean, the distribution of feathering, the amount of fat covering over the diaphragm or skirt, and the amount and character of the external and kidney and pelvic fat.

When grading ribbed calf carcasses, the quality evaluation of the lean is based entirely on its characteristics as exposed in the cut surface.

Figure 11.30 illustrates how the factors are combined to arrive at a quality grade.

The *final grade* of a carcass is based on a composite evaluation of its conformation and quality. Conformation and quality often are not developed to the same degree in a carcass, and it is obvious that each grade will include various combinations of development of these two characteristics. The principles governing the compensations of variations in the development of quality and conformation are as follows: In each of the grades, a superior development of quality is permitted to compensate, without limit, for a deficient development of conformation. In this instance, the rate of compensation in all grades is on an equal basis— a given degree of superior quality compensates for the same degree of deficient conformation. The reverse type of compensation—a superior development of conformation for an inferior development of quality—is not permitted in the Prime and Choice grades. In all other grades this type of compensation is permitted but only to the extent of one-third

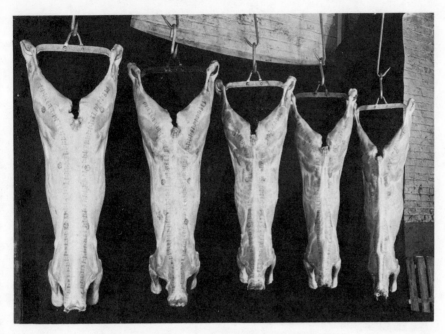

Fig. 11.31—Five grades of veal carcasses (left to right): Prime, Choice, Good, Standard, and Utility.

of a grade of deficient quality. The rate of this type of compensation is also on an equal basis—a given degree of superior conformation compensates for the same degree of deficient quality.

LAMB, YEARLING MUTTON, AND MUTTON CARCASS GRADING

Development of the Standards[5]

- In February 1931 grades for lamb and mutton carcasses were made effective.

- The standards were amended in October 1940 so as to change the grade designations Medium and Common to *Commercial* and *Utility*, respectively.

- In April 1951, the official standards were again amended when Prime and Choice grades were combined and designated as *Prime*.

---

5. *Service and Regulatory Announcements No. 123*, Agricultural Marketing Service, U.S. Dept. of Agriculture.

The Good grade was renamed *Choice,* which also became the highest grade for carcasses of mutton older than yearlings.

The top two-thirds of the Commercial grade was designated as *Good.* The lower one-third of the Commercial grade was combined with the top two-thirds of the Utility grade and designated as *Utility,* thereby eliminating the Commercial grade name. The lower one-third of the Utility grade was combined with the Cull grade and designated as *Cull.*

• In February 1957, the standards for grades of lamb carcasses were amended by reducing the quality requirements for Prime and Choice grade carcasses from more mature lambs.

The quality requirements for the Good grade were increased slightly, particularly for carcasses from very young lambs.

Carcasses with quality indications equivalent to the lower limit of the upper third of the Good grade were permitted to be graded *Choice* provided they had a development of conformation equivalent to the mid-point of the Choice grade or better.

Practically all references to quantity of external and kidney and pelvic fats were also eliminated.

• In March 1960, both the conformation and quality requirements for the Prime and Choice grades were reduced about one-half grade. In addition, a minimum degree of external fat covering was prescribed for the Prime and Choice grades.

The emphasis placed on internal factors considered in evaluating quality was decreased by reducing the emphasis on feathering between the ribs, eliminating consideration of overflow fat, and increasing the emphasis on firmness of fat and lean.

• On March 1, 1969, yield grades were adopted for lamb, yearling mutton, and mutton carcasses.

Differentiation Between Lamb, Yearling Mutton, and Mutton Carcasses

Differentiation between lamb, yearling mutton, and mutton carcasses is made on the basis of differences that occur in the development of their muscular and skeletal systems.

Typical *lamb carcasses* tend to have slightly wide and moderately flat rib bones, a light red color and fine texture of lean, and must have break joints on both front shanks (note Chapter 6).

Lambs are further subdivided by apparent evidences of maturity as shown in Table 11.8.

Table 11.8—Lamb Maturity Indicators

	Young Lambs	Mature Lambs
	(A maturity)	(B maturity)
Rib bones	Moderately narrow slightly flat	Slightly wide moderately flat
Break joints	Moderately red moist and porous	Slightly red dry and hard
Color of inside flank muscles	Slightly dark pink	Light red

Typical *yearling mutton carcasses* have moderately wide rib bones which tend to be flat and a slightly dark red color and slightly coarse texture of lean. Yearling mutton carcasses may have either break joints or spool (Figure 6.6) joints on their front shanks.

Typical *mutton carcasses* have wide, flat rib bones and a dark red color and coarse texture of lean. They always have spool joints on their front shanks. Regardless of their other characteristics, carcasses from which the front shanks have been removed will be assumed to have had spool joints and will be classed as yearling mutton or mutton on the basis of their other characteristics. In determining the maturity class of ovine carcasses, more consideration is given to the characteristics of the flesh than is given to the characteristics of the skeleton.

Two Considerations—Quality and Yield

The grade of a lamb, yearling mutton, or mutton carcass is based on separate evaluations of two general considerations: (1) The indicated percent of trimmed, boneless major retail cuts to be derived from the carcass, referred to as the *yield grade* and (2) the palatability-indicating characteristics of the lean and conformation, referred to as the *quality grade*. When graded by a Federal meat grader, the grade of a lamb, yearling mutton, or mutton carcass may consist of the quality grade, the yield grade, or a combination of both the quality grade and the yield grade.

The terms *quality grade* and *quality* are used throughout the standards. The term *quality* is used to refer only to the palatability-indicating characteristics of the lean. As such, it is one of the factors considered in determining the quality grade. Although the term *quality grade* is used to refer to an overall evaluation of a carcass based on (1) its quality and (2) its conformation, this is not intended to imply that variations in conformation are either directly or indirectly related to differences in palatability, since research has shown no relationship.

Conformation is the manner of formation of the carcass with particular reference to the relative development of the muscular and skeletal systems, although it is also influenced, to some extent, by the quantity and distribution of external finish.

Quality of the lean flesh is best evaluated from consideration of its texture, firmness, and marbling, as observed in a cut surface, in relation to the apparent maturity of the animal from which the carcass was produced. However, in grading carcasses, direct observation of these characteristics is not possible. Therefore, the quality of the lean is evaluated indirectly by giving equal consideration to (1) the quantity of fat intermingled within the lean between the ribs called *feathering*, (2) the streaking of fat within and upon the inside flank muscles, and (3) the firmness of the fat and lean—all in relation to the apparent evidence of maturity.

Apparent *sex condition* of the animal at the time of slaughter is not normally considered in ovine carcass grading. However, carcasses which have thick, heavy necks and shoulders, typical of uncastrated males, are discounted in grade in accord with the extent to which these characteristics are developed. Such discounts may vary from less than one-half grade in carcasses from young lambs, in which such characteristics are barely noticeable, to as much as two full grades in carcasses from mature rams, in which such characteristics are very pronounced.

Lamb Carcass Quality Grades

Prime

Carcasses possessing the minimum qualifications for the Prime grade are moderately wide and thick in relation to their length and have moderately wide and thick backs, moderately plump and full legs, and moderately thick and full shoulders.

Requirements for quantities of interior fats and for firmness of lean and fat vary with changes in maturity.

Young lambs—modest amount of feathering between the ribs.
Mature lambs—moderate amount of feathering between the ribs.
Young lambs—small quantity of fat streaking on inside flank muscle.
Mature lambs—modest amount of fat streaking on inside flank muscle.

The lean flesh and the exterior finish should be relatively firm and the flanks moderately full and firm. The minimum external fat requirements for Prime are at least a very thin covering of external fat over the top of the shoulders and the outsides of the upper parts of the legs, and the back must have at least a thin covering of fat; that is, the muscles of the back may be no more than barely visible through the fat.

A development of quality which is superior to that specified as minimum for Prime may compensate, on an equal basis, for a development of conformation which is inferior to that specified as minimum for Prime. For example, a carcass which has evidence of quality equivalent to the mid-point of the Prime grade may have conformation equivalent to the mid-point of the Choice grade and remain eligible for Prime. However, in no instance may a carcass be graded Prime which has a conformation inferior to that specified as minimum for the Choice grade.

Choice

To minimize repetition, substitute the word *slightly* for *moderately* in the description of the Prime grade to this point. A carcass which has conformation equivalent to at least the mid-point of the Choice grade may have quality equivalent to the minimum for the upper third of the Good grade and remain eligible for Choice. Superior quality may compensate on an equal basis for a conformation which is inferior to that specified as minimum for Choice. For example, top Choice quality in a carcass with top Good conformation makes it eligible for the Choice grade. However, in no instance may a carcass be graded Choice which has a conformation inferior to that specified for the Good grade.

Good

Lamb carcasses possessing minimum qualifications for the Good grade are moderately narrow in relation to their length and have slightly thin, tapering legs and slightly narrow, thin back and shoulders. The young lambs have traces of feathering between the ribs, but no fat streaking on the inside flank muscle. Their lean flesh and exterior finish are slightly firm, and their flanks are slightly thin and soft.

The more mature lambs have a slight amount of feathering, and traces of fat streaking on the inside flank muscles. Also, their lean flesh and external finish tend to be moderately firm, and their flanks tend to be slightly full and firm.

A carcass which has conformation equivalent to the midpoint of the Good grade and quality equivalent to the minimum for the upper one-third of the Utility grade is eligible for Good. Also, a quality which is superior to that specified as the minimum for the Good grade may compensate for a conformation which is inferior to that specified as minimum for Good on the basis of one-half grade of superior quality for one-third grade of deficient conformation. However, in no instance may a carcass be graded Good which has a conformation inferior to that specified as minimum for the Utility grade.

Utility

Lamb carcasses of this grade are very angular and very narrow in relation to their length and have thin, slightly concave legs, very narrow and sunken backs, and narrow, sharp shoulders. Hips and shoulder joints are plainly visible. Although evidences of quality vary slightly with changes in maturity, the differences are very small. The lean of the inside flank and between the ribs is dark red in color, and the carcass is soft and slightly watery.

A carcass with average Utility conformation and top Cull quality qualifies for the Utility grade. Also, quality superior to that specified as minimum for the Utility grade may compensate for conformation which is inferior to that specified as minimum for Utility on the basis of one-half grade of superior quality for one-third grade of deficient conformation.

Cull

You know them when you see them.

Yearling and Mutton Carcasses

The grades are Prime, Choice, Good, Utility, and Cull for yearlings, and Choice, Good, Utility, and Cull for mutton carcasses.

Live and Carcass Illustrations of Lamb Quality Grades

These live and carcass pictures for lamb quality grades were generously provided by the University of Illinois Department of Animal Science and by the National Live Stock and Meat Board. The carcass pictures appear in color in the *Meat Evaluation Handbook,* published by the Meat Board, and were originally secured by Meat Board Staff and American Meat Science members who worked tirelessly to produce a most useful handbook. It is highly recommended for the serious student of meat judging and grading.

Lamb carcass quality grading is based on conformation, maturity, and evidences of quality as seen in feathering between the ribs, flank lacing, and flank fullness and firmness (see above discussion). Conformation can be readily determined in live lambs, and maturity can be checked by mouthing. However, the quality traits must be estimated in the live animal by evaluation of overall finish or fatness. Sight alone is often deceiving, especially when evaluating wooled lambs, so most buyers will "wade through" the group making spot checks of fatness over the rump, ribs, and back on a number of the lambs.

Review live lamb classification and grading as it was discussed in Chapter 6. Note in Table 11.12 that about 73% of *all* lamb carcasses are quality graded.

Yield Grades[6]

Yield grades indicate the quantity of meat, i.e., the amount of retail, consumer-ready, read-to-cook, or edible meat that a carcass contains. Whichever term you choose, the final amount available for eating is extremely important. Do not confuse yield grade with dressing percent, often called *yield*. Yield grade refers to the amount of edible product from the carcass. Dressing percent (*yield*) refers to the amount of carcass from a live animal.

The *lower* the number of the yield grade, the *higher* the percent of the carcass in boneless, closely trimmed retail cuts from the leg, loin, rack, and shoulder.

Table 11.9—Lamb Yield Grade Retail Yield Equivalents

Yield Grade	Percent of Warm Carcass in Closely Trimmed Primal Cuts
1	47.6 – 49.4
2	45.8 – 47.2
3	44.0 – 45.4
4	42.2 – 43.6
5	40.4 – 41.8

---

6. *Federal Register*, Title 7, Chapter I, Part 53, Subpart B, CMS, USDA, January 8, 1969.

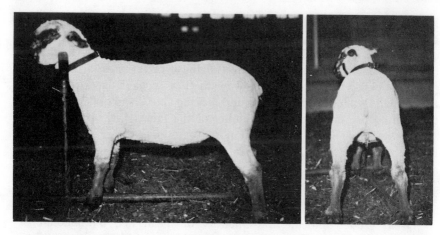

Fig. 11.32—A Prime wether. Recall that 12% of lambs graded qualify for this grade. From the side, this black faced lamb appears moderately low set, blocky, and thick fleshed. The shoulders and hips are moderately smooth. From the rear, he is moderately wide over the back, loin, and rump. The twist is moderately deep and full, and the legs are moderately large and plump.

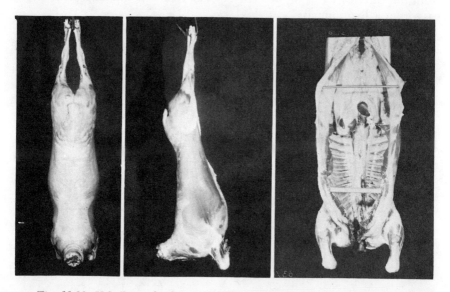

Fig. 11.33—U.S. Prime lamb carcass. This lamb carcass has typical A maturity as indicated by the moderately narrow, slightly flat rib bones and the slightly dark pink color of the inside flank muscles. Its plump, full legs, wide, thick back, and thick, full shoulders qualify its conformation for average Prime. The moderate amount of feathering between the ribs, the modest streakings of fat in the inside flank muscles, and the moderately full and firm flanks combine to indicate average Prime quality. When the conformation and quality grades are combined, this carcass qualifies for average Prime.

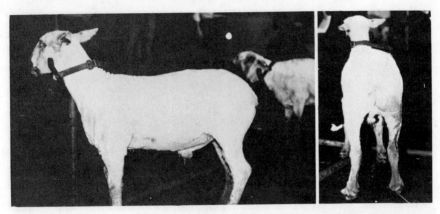

Fig. 11.34—A Choice wether. Recall that 87% of lambs graded qualified for this grade, so the one individual shown here is only that *one* of many breeds and types that annually qualify for this grade. From the side, this crossbred lamb is not lowset and blocky but is thick fleshed. The shoulders and hips show some prominence, indicating that he may be carrying a thin fat covering. From the rear, he is not as wide over the back, loin, and rump as the Prime lamb nor is his leg as fully developed.

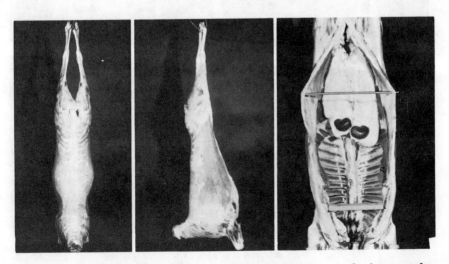

Fig. 11.35—U.S. Choice lamb carcass. This typical A maturity lamb carcass has average Choice conformation as evidenced by slightly plump and full legs, a slightly wide and thick back, and slightly thick and full shoulders. The small amount of feathering and slight streakings of fat in the inside flank muscles coupled with slightly full and firm flanks combine to meet the quality requirements for average Choice. With average Choice conformation and quality, the final grade of this carcass is average Choice.

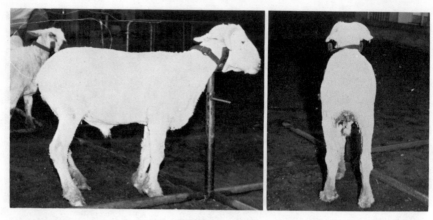

Fig. 11.36—A Good wether. Recall that less than 1% of lambs graded qualify for this grade. From the side, this western lamb is moderately rangy, upstanding, and thin fleshed. His hips and shoulders are moderately prominent. From the rear, he is slightly narrow over the back, loin, and rump. The twist is slightly shallow, and the legs are slightly small and thin.

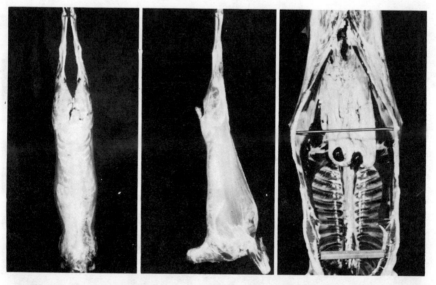

Fig. 11.37—U.S. Good lamb carcass. This is a more mature lamb carcass (B-minus maturity) as indicated by the slightly wide, moderately flat rib bones, and light red color of the inside flank muscles. It has average Good conformation in that the legs tend to be slightly thin and tapering, and the back and shoulders tend to be slightly narrow and thin. Likewise, average Good quality is indicated by the weak slight amount of feathering between the ribs, the strong traces of streakings of fat in the inside flank muscles, and the slightly full and firm flanks. Average Good conformation and average Good quality combine to qualify this carcass for average Good.

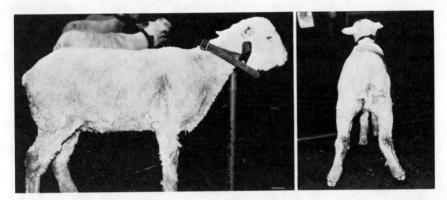

Fig. 11.38—A Utility ewe lamb. Such a lamb represents less than 1% of all the lambs graded. This is a very rangy and angular lamb that is very thin fleshed. She is very narrow over the back, loin, and rump and very shallow in the twist. The legs are very small and present a slightly concave appearance.

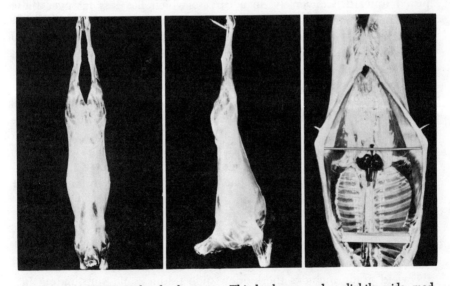

Fig. 11.39—U.S. Utility lamb carcass. This lamb carcass has slightly wide, moderately flat rib bones and light red color of the inside flank muscles, indicating B-minus maturity. It has low Utility quality since there is practically no feathering between the ribs and no fat streakings in the inside flank muscles, and the flanks are soft and watery. This carcass is slightly narrow and thin, qualifying it for average Good conformation. Therefore, when the average Good conformation and the low Utility are combined, this carcass qualifies for average Utility.

The yield grade of an ovine carcass is determined by considering three characteristics: The amount of external fat, the amount of kidney and pelvic fat, and the conformation grade of the legs.

External Fat

The amount of *external fat* for carcasses with a normal distribution of this fat is evaluated in terms of its actual thickness over the center of the rib-eye muscle and is measured perpendicular to the outside surface between the twelfth and thirteenth ribs. On intact carcasses, fat thickness is measured by probing. This measurement may be adjusted, as necessary, to reflect unusual amounts of fat on other parts of the carcass. In determining the amount of this adjustment, if any, particular attention is given to the amount of external fat on those parts where fat is deposited at a faster-than-average rate, particularly the rump, outside of the shoulders, breast, flank, and cod or udder. Thus, in a carcass which is fatter over these other parts than is normally associated with the actual fat thickness over the rib eye, the measurement is adjusted upward. Conversely, in a carcass which has less fat over these other parts than is normally associated with the actual fat thickness over the rib eye, the measurement is adjusted downward. In many carcasses, no such adjustment is necessary; however, an adjustment in the thickness of fat measurement of 0.05 or 0.10 inch is not uncommon. In some carcasses, a greater adjustment may be necessary. As a guide in making these adjustments, the standards for each yield grade include an additional related measurement—body wall thickness, which is measured five inches laterally from the middle of the backbone between the twelfth and thirteenth ribs. As the amount of external fat increases, the percent of retail cuts decreases—each 0.05 inch change in adjusted fat thickness over the rib eye changes the yield grade by one-third of a grade.

Kidney and Pelvic Fat

The amount of kidney and pelvic fat considered in determining the yield grade includes the kidney knob (kidney and surrounding fat) and the lumbar and pelvic fat in the loin and leg which are removed in making closely trimmed retail cuts. The amount of these fats is evaluated subjectively and expressed as a percent of the carcass weight. As the amount of kidney and pelvic fat increases, the percent of retail cuts decreases—a change of 1% of the carcass weight in kidney and pelvic fat changes the yield grade by one-fourth of a grade.

The yield grade of a hindsaddle, hindquarter, foresaddle, forequarter, or a cut eligible for grading also is determined, except that if the portion being graded does not include kidney and pelvic fat or if the portion is a trimmed cut (a cut from which most of the kidney and pelvic fat has been removed), the standard percentages of kidney and pelvic fat (Table 11.10) as applicable to the quality grade of the portion also shall be used in the equation.

Table 11.10—Yield Grade Adjustment When Kidney and Pelvic Fat Are Not Present

Grade	KPF Percent
Prime	4.5
Choice	3.5
Good	3.0
Utility	2.0
Cull	1.5

Leg Conformation

The conformation grade of the legs is evaluated as described in the quality standards. The evaluation is made in terms of thirds of grades and coded using 15 for high Prime and 1 for low Cull. An increase in the conformation grade of the legs increases the percent of retail cuts—a change of one-third of a grade changes the yield grade by 5% of a grade.

The Yield Grade Equation

The yield grade of an ovine carcass or side is determined on the basis of the following equation: Yield Grade = 1.66 − (0.05 × leg conformation grade code) + (0.25 × percent kidney and pelvic fat) + (6.66 × adjusted fat thickness over the rib eye in inches). The application of this equation usually results in a fractional grade. However, in normal grading operations any fractional part of a yield grade is dropped. For example, if the computation results in a *Yield Grade* of 3.9, the final Yield Grade is 3—it is not rounded to 4.

Yield Grade Descriptions

The following descriptions provide a guide to the characteristics of carcasses in each yield grade to aid in determining yield grades subjectively.

Yield Grade 1

A carcass in Yield Grade 1 usually has only a thin layer of external fat over the back and loin and slight deposits of fat in the flanks and cod or udder. There is usually a very thin layer of fat over the top of the shoulders and the outside of the legs. Muscles are usually plainly visible on most areas of the carcass.

A carcass of this yield grade which is near the borderline of Yield Grade 1 and Yield Grade 2 might have 0.1 inch of fat over the rib eye, 1.5 per cent of its weight in kidney and pelvic fat, and an average Prime leg conformation grade. Such a carcass with normal fat distribution would also have a body wall thickness of 0.5 inch.

Yield Grade 2

A carcass in Yield Grade 2 usually has a slightly thin layer of fat over the back and loin and the muscles of the back are not visible. The top of the shoulders and the outside of the legs have a thin covering of fat and the muscles are slightly visible. There are usually small deposits of fat in the flanks and cod or udder.

A carcass of this yield grade which is near the borderline of Yield Grade 2 and Yield Grade 3 might have 0.2 inch of fat over the rib eye, 2.5% of its weight in kidney and pelvic fat, and a low Prime leg conformation grade. Such a carcass with normal fat distribution would also have a body wall thickness of 0.7 inch.

Yield Grade 3

A carcass in Yield Grade 3 usually has a slightly thick covering of fat over the back. The top of the shoulders are completely covered with fat, although the muscles are still barely visible. The legs are nearly completely covered, although the muscles on the outside of the lower legs are visible. There usually are slightly large deposits of fat in the flanks and cod or udder.

A carcass of this yield grade which is near the borderline of Yield Grade 3 and Yield Grade 4 might have 0.3 inch of fat over the ribeye, 3.5 percent of its weight in kidney and pelvic fat, and a high Choice leg conformation grade. Such a carcass with normal fat distribution would also have a body wall thickness of 0.9 inch.

Yield Grade 4

A carcass in Yield Grade 4 usually is completely covered with fat. There usually is a moderately thick covering of fat over the back and a slightly thick covering over the shoulder and legs. There usually are large deposits of fat in the flanks and cod or udder.

A carcass in this yield grade which is near the borderline of Yield Grade 4 and Yield Grade 5 might have 0.4 inch of fat over the rib eye, 4.5% of its weight in kidney and pelvic fat, and an average Choice leg conformation grade. Such a carcass with normal fat distribution would also have a body wall thickness of 1.1 inches.

Yield Grade 5

A carcass in Yield Grade 5 usually has more external and kidney and pelvic fat and a lower conformation grade of leg than a carcass in Yield Grade 4.

"Shortcut" Method for Yield Grade Calculation.

1. An average lamb carcass with a yield grade of 3.5 would have the following credentials:
   a. Fat thickness—0.24 inch
   b. Percent of KPH fat—3.5%
   c. Leg conformation score—12 (high Choice)
2. Factors that affect yield grade
   a. *Fat thickness*
      (1) More fat thickness makes a higher-numbered yield grade
      (2) Each *0.1 inch of fat* is worth *0.67 Yield Grade*
   b. *Kidney, Pelvic, and Heart Fat* (KPH)
      (1) More KPH fat makes a higher-numbered yield grade
      (2) Each *percent of KPH* fat is worth *0.25 Yield Grade*
   c. *Leg conformation*
      (1) Higher leg conformation makes a lower-numbered yield grade
      (2) Each *leg score* is worth *0.05 Yield Grade*
3. Yield grade can be calculated on any carcass by adjusting the 3.5 base according to how each factor above (1, a-c) varies from the average.

4. Example:

	Carcass	Difference from "Average"	Adjustment
Fat thickness	0.14	0.1	−.67 (1 × .67)
Percent of KPH fat	2.5	1.0	−.25 (1 × .25)
Leg score	14	2	−.10 (2 × .05)
		Total Adjustment	−1.02
		Yield Grade = 3.5 − 1.02 = 2.48 = 2.5	

Yields and Value Differences Between Yield Grades

Value differences between yield grades naturally fluctuate from week to week and month to month due to overall meat price fluctuations. Nevertheless, Table 11.11 vividly presents yield and value differences between yield grades which should make one aware of their economic importance.

Live and Carcass Illustrations of Lamb Yield Grades

These live and carcass pictures for lamb yield grades were generously provided by the University of Illinois Department of Animal Science and by the National Live Stock and Meat Board. The carcass pictures appear in color in the *Meat Evaluation Handbook,* published by the Meat Board, and were originally secured by Meat Board Staff and American Meat Science members who worked tirelessly to produce a most useful handbook. It is highly recommended for the serious student of meat judging and grading.

Lamb carcass yield grading is based on leg conformation, external fat thickness, and kidney and pelvic fat percent (see preceding discussion). Fat thickness is by far the most important factor, each 1/10 change representing 2/3 of one yield grade. Thus the appraisal of fatness must be made as accurately as possible meaning a "hands-on" approach. A light touch over the back, ribs, and rump with closed fingers can reveal a tremendous amount of yield grading information.

Table 11.11—Comparison of Yields of Retail Cuts and Retail Sales Values for Choice Lamb Carcasses, by Yield Grades[1,2,3]

Retail Cut (Bone-in)	Jan. 1973 Price per Pound	Yield Grade 1		Yield Grade 2		Yield Grade 3		Yield Grade 4		Yield Grade 5	
		% of Carcass	Value/ Cwt. Carcass	% of Carcass	Value/ Cwt. Carcass	% of Carcass	Value/ Cwt. Carcass	% of Carcass	Value/ Cwt. Carcass	% of Carcass	Value/ Cwt. Carcass
Leg, short cut	$1.17	23.6	$27.61	22.2	$25.97	20.8	$24.34	19.4	$22.70	18.0	$21.06
Sirloin	1.65	6.7	11.06	6.4	10.56	6.1	10.07	5.8	9.57	5.5	9.08
Short loin	2.03	10.4	21.11	10.1	20.50	9.8	19.89	9.5	19.29	9.2	18.68
Back	1.84	8.1	14.91	7.9	14.55	7.7	14.17	7.5	13.80	7.3	13.43
Shoulder	1.08	24.9	26.89	23.8	25.70	22.7	24.51	21.6	23.32	20.5	22.13
Neck	.60	2.2	1.32	2.1	1.26	2.0	1.20	1.9	1.14	1.8	1.08
Breast	.46	9.8	4.51	9.8	4.51	9.8	4.51	9.8	4.51	9.8	4.51
Foreshank	.77	3.5	2.70	3.4	2.62	3.3	2.54	3.2	2.46	3.1	2.39

(Continued)

Table 11.11 (Continued)

Retail Cut (Bone-in)	Jan. 1973 Price per Pound	Yield Grade 1		Yield Grade 2		Yield Grade 3		Yield Grade 4		Yield Grade 5	
		% of Carcass	Value/ Cwt. Carcass	% of Carcass	Value/ Cwt. Carcass	% of Carcass	Value/ Cwt. Carcass	% of Carcass	Value/ Cwt. Carcass	% of Carcass	Value/ Cwt. Carcass
Flank	.94	2.3	2.16	2.3	2.16	2.3	2.16	2.3	2.16	2.3	2.16
Kidney	.72	0.5	.36	0.5	.36	0.5	.36	0.5	.36	0.5	.36
Fat	.02	4.6	.09	8.2	.16	11.8	.24	15.4	.31	19.0	.38
Bone	.01	3.4	.03	3.3	.03	3.2	.03	3.1	.03	3.0	.03
Total		100.0	$112.75	100.0	$108.38	100.0	$104.02	100.0	$99.65	100.0	$95.29

1. Difference in retail value between yield grades—$4.36 per cwt. of carcass in January 1973.

2. Difference in retail value between yield grades—$5.16 per cwt. of carcass in January 1974.

3. These comparisons reflect average yields of retail cuts from lamb carcasses typical of the midpoint of each of the USDA yield grades and average prices (including sale priced items) for USDA Choice lamb during January 1973 and January 1974, as furnished to the Economic Research Service, U.S. Dept. of Agriculture by a large number of selected retailers throughout the country.

Table 11.12—Percent of Commercial Production Quality and Yield Graded 1965–1973[1]

| Year | Percent of Commercial Production Quality Graded | | | Beef Yield Graded[2] | |
	Beef	Veal	Lamb and Mutton	As Percent of Commercial Production	As Percent of Beef Quality Graded
1965	57.3	19.3	56.3	1.4	2.9
1966	61.8	19.5	60.3	2.3	3.6
1967	63.7	21.2	63.2	5.7	9.0
1968	63.3	18.1	66.3	11.2	17.5
1969	63.9	15.4	69.1	13.0	20.3
1970	64.9	13.5	74.2	16.5	25.4
1971	64.3	10.9	76.8	18.8	29.3
1972	61.1	8.9	74.4	25.6	42.0
1973	57.7	6.8	72.7	34.5	59.9

1. Livestock Division, Agricultural Marketing Service, U.S. Dept. of Agriculture.

2. Yield grades became effective June 1, 1965.

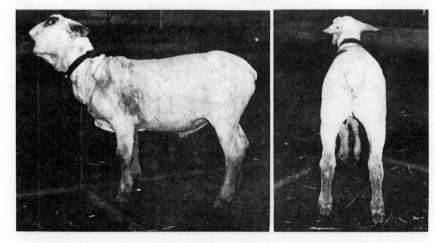

Fig. 11.40—A Yield Grade 1 wether. Only a very small percentage of market lambs qualify for this grade, since it requires a high degree of trimness and muscling. This crossbred lamb is restricted just behind the shoulders, indicating that this area has not filled with fat. Also he is especially trim in the breast and flank. From the rear, leanness is apparent by observing the lack of fullness in the twist. Excellent muscling is indicated by his being wider and thicker through the center of his leg than he is over his back.

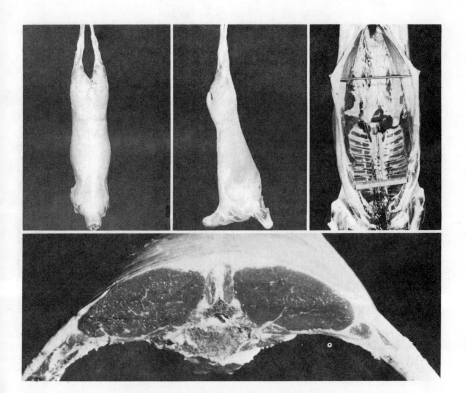

Fig. 11.41—A Yield Grade 1 lamb carcass.

External fat thickness.......... .05 inch
Kidney and pelvic fat.......... 1.5%
Leg conformation grade........ Low Prime
Yield Grade.................. 1.7

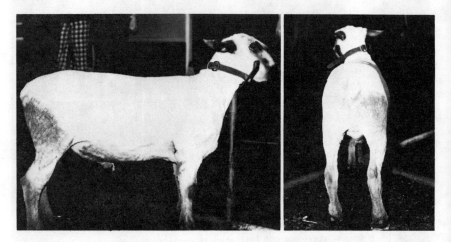

Fig. 11.42—A Yield Grade 2 wether. From the side, this wether is very trim in his breast and flank, but is uniformly smooth behind the shoulders, indicating that this area is somewhat filled with fat. This well muscled lamb is wider through the center of his legs than up over his top, but is carrying more finish in his twist than the Yield Grade 1 lamb.

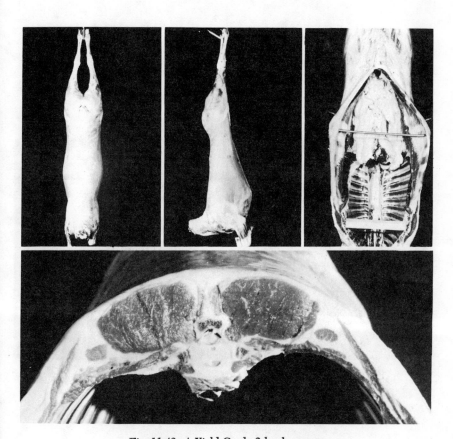

Fig. 11.43—A Yield Grade 2 lamb carcass.

External fat thickness.......... .10 inch
Kidney and pelvic fat.......... 3.0%
Leg conformation grade........ Average Prime
Yield Grade.................. 2.4

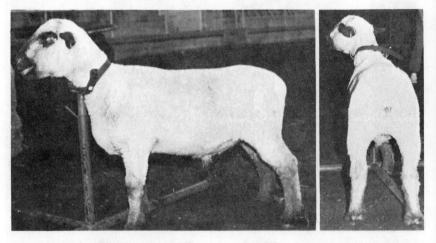

Fig. 11.44—A Yield Grade 3 wether. From the side, increased deposits of fat can be observed in the areas previously discussed, and from the rear view as well.

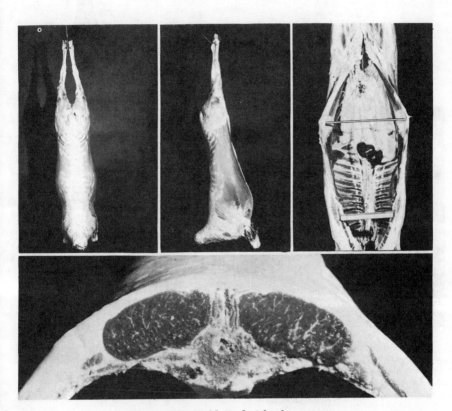

Fig. 11.45—A Yield Grade 3 lamb carcass.

External fat thickness.......... .25 inch
Kidney and pelvic fat......... 3.5%
Leg conformation grade....... High Choice
Yield Grade................. 3.6

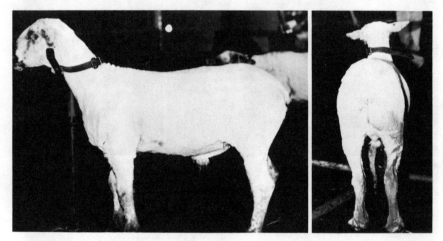

Fig. 11.46—A Yield Grade 4 wether. Although this wether is long, upstanding, and appears trim in the breast region, the overall smooth appearance from shoulder to sirloin and rump gives evidence of his overall fatness. From the rear, he is narrow and light muscled in his legs, and his twist is filled with fat.

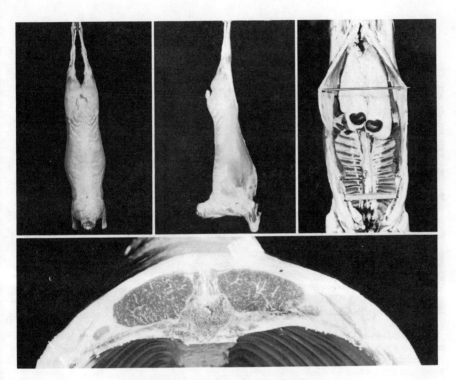

Fig. 11.47—A Yield Grade 4 lamb carcass.

External fat thickness.......... .35 inch
Kidney and pelvic fat.......... 4.5%
Leg conformation grade........ Low Choice
Yield Grade.................. 4.6

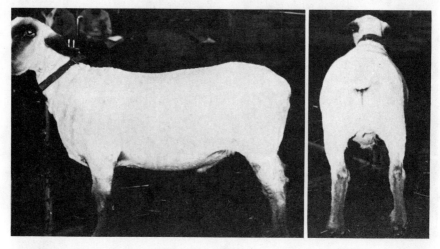

Fig. 11.48—A Yield Grade 5 wether. The heavy middle on this wether is an indication of excessive kidney fat. His fullness of flank and breast portray his overall fatness. Although the lamb stands wide behind and has plump, heavy legs, the depth of twist and squareness of dock indicate fatness.

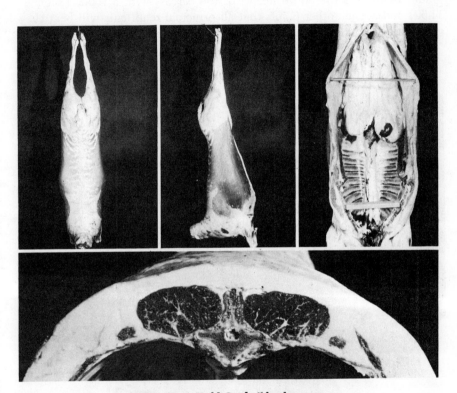

Fig. 11.49—A Yield Grade 5 lamb carcass.

External fat thickness.......... .45 inch
Kidney and pelvic fat.......... 5.5%
Leg conformation grade........ Average Choice
Yield Grade.................. 5.5

Applying the Grade Stamp

The Federal meat grader weighs all the factors that have been discussed, decides upon the grade, and makes an identifying mark with a stamp designating the grade: xxx for Prime, xx for Choice, etc. After the grading task is ended, the grader or his assistant applies the ribbon grade stamp over the entire length of the carcass with a roller (Figure 11.50) and at such other points that all principal retail cuts will bear the grade label. That is why Federally graded beef and lamb are often

Fig. 11.50—Applying the grade stamp. Note the round inspection stamp adjacent to the rolled grade stamp. (Courtesy, Livestock Division, Agricultural Marketing Service, U.S. Dept. of Agriculture)

referred to as "rolled." The grade designations are in full grades. The Cutter and Canner beef grades are not rolled. If the buyer wishes to know whether the rolled beef of the grade he is buying is in the top, middle, or low bracket of the grade, he can demand a grading certificate which will so indicate.

PORK CARCASS GRADING

Development of the Standards[7]

Tentative standards for grades of pork carcasses and fresh pork cuts were issued by USDA in 1931. These tentative standards were slightly revised in 1933.

New standards for grades of barrow and gilt carcasses were proposed by USDA in 1949. These standards represented the first application of objective measurements as guides to grades for pork carcasses. Slight revisions were made in the proposed standards prior to adoption, as the Official United States Standards for Grades of Barrow and Gilt Carcasses, effective September 12, 1952.

The official standards were amended in July 1955, by changing the grade designations Choice No. 1, Choice No. 2, and Choice No. 3 to U.S. No. 1, U.S. No. 2, and U.S. No. 3, respectively. In addition, the backfat thickness requirements were reduced for each grade and the descriptive specifications were reworded slightly to reflect the reduced fat thickness requirements and to allow more uniform interpretation of the standards.

On April 1, 1968, the official standards were again revised to reflect the improvements made since 1955 in pork carcasses. The minimum backfat thickness requirement for the U.S. No. 1 grade was eliminated and a new U.S. No. 1 grade was established to properly identify the superior pork carcasses then being produced. The former No. 1, No. 2, and No. 3 grades were renamed No. 2, No. 3, and No. 4 respectively. The former Medium and Cull grades were combined and renamed U.S. Utility. Also, the maximum allowable adjustment for variations-from-normal fat distribution and muscling was changed from one-half to one full grade to more adequately reflect the effect of these factors on yields of cuts.

Pork Carcass Classes

The five classes of pork carcasses, comparable to the same five classes of slaughter hogs, are barrow, gilt, sow, stag, and boar.

---

7. *Marketing Bulletin No. 49*, Agricultural Marketing Service, U.S. Dept. of Agriculture.

"Because of the relationships between sex and/or sex condition in pork and the acceptability of the prepared meats to the consumer, separate standards have been developed for (1) barrow and gilt carcasses and (2) sow carcasses. There are no official standards for grades of stag and boar carcasses.

"The determination of sex condition is based on the following:

- Barrow carcasses are identified by a small 'pizzle eye' (Figure 11.1—beef) and the typical pocket in the split edge of the belly where the preputial sheath was removed.

- Gilt carcasses are recognized by the smooth split edge of the belly, the absence of the 'pizzle eye,' and the lack of development of mammary tissue.

- Sow carcasses exhibit the smooth split edge of the belly characteristic of females. They differ from gilts in that mammary tissue has developed in connection with advanced pregnancy or lactation.

- Stag carcasses have the pocket in the split edge of the belly typical of males, and the 'pizzle eye' is larger and more prominent than in barrows. In addition, other distinguishing characteristics that often may be noted are rather heavy shoulders, thick skin over the shoulders, large bones and joints, and a dark red color of lean.

- Boar carcasses have the same distinguishing characteristics as stag carcasses but to a more pronounced degree."[8]

Grades for Barrow and Gilt Carcasses

Differences in barrow and gilt carcasses due to sex condition are minor, and the grade standards are equally applicable for grading both classes.

Grades for barrow and gilt carcasses are based on two general conditions: (1) quality-indicating characteristics of the lean and (2) expected combined yields of the four lean cuts (ham, loin, picnic shoulder, and Boston shoulder).

Quality

With respect to quality, two general levels are considered: one for carcasses with characteristics which indicate that the lean in the four

---

8. *Meat Evaluation Handbook*, National Live Stock and Meat Board.

lean cuts will have an acceptable quality and one for carcasses with characteristics which indicate that the lean will have an unacceptable quality.

The quality of the lean is best evaluated by a direct observation of its characteristics in a cut surface and when a cut surface of major muscles is available, this shall be used as the basis for the quality determination. The standards describe the characteristics of the loin-eye muscle at the tenth rib. However, when this surface is not available, other exposed major muscle surfaces can be used for the quality determination based on the normal development of the characteristics in relation to those described for the loin-eye muscle at the tenth rib.

When a major muscle cut surface is not available, the quality of the lean shall be evaluated indirectly based on quality-indicating characteristics that are evident in carcasses. These include firmness of the fat and lean, amount of feathering between the ribs, and color of the lean. The standards describe a development of each of these factors that is normally associated with the lower limit of acceptable lean quality. The degree of external fatness, as such, is not considered in evaluating the quality of the lean.

Carcasses which have characteristics indicating that the lean in the four lean cuts will not have an acceptable quality or bellies too thin to be suitable for bacon production are graded U.S. Utility. Also graded U.S. Utility—regardless of their development of other quality-indicating characteristics—are carcasses which are soft and oily. Belly thickness is determined by an overall evaluation of its thickness with primary consideration being given to the thickness along the navel edge and thickness of the belly pocket.

A numerical system for designating pork quality as observed in the cut surfaces of major muscles was published by the University of Wisconsin in 1963 in *Special Bulletin 9, Pork Quality Standards,* and although not used as such in Federal descriptions, these standards are widely recognized in the industry today. Table 11.13 lists the scores and the somewhat modified but widely recognized terms used to describe the various levels of quality.

Yield

Four grades—U.S. No. 1, U.S. No. 2, U.S. No. 3, and U.S. No. 4—are provided for carcasses which have indications of an acceptable lean quality and acceptable belly thickness. These grades are based entirely on the expected carcass yields of the four lean cuts and no consideration

Table 11.13—Scoring System Widely Used to Indicate Pork Quality

Marbling	Color and Firmness
1. Practically devoid	1. Very pale, soft, and watery
2. Traces to small amount	2. Pale, moderately soft, and watery
3. Moderate	3. Grayish pink, moderately firm, and dry
4. Slightly abundant	4. Somewhat dark, quite firm, and dry
5. Very abundant	5. Dark, very firm, and dry

is given to a development of quality superior to that described as minimum for these grades. The expected yields of the four lean cuts for each of these four grades are shown in Table 11.14.

The yields shown in Table 11.14 are based on cutting and trimming methods used by the U.S. Department of Agriculture in developing the standards. (These methods generally specify a quarter inch fat trim and copies may be obtained from the Livestock Division, Agricultural Marketing Service, USDA, Washington, D.C. 20250.) Other cutting and trimming methods may result in different yields. For example, if more fat is left on the four lean cuts than prescribed in the USDA methods, the yield for each grade will be higher than indicated. However, such a method of trimming, if applied uniformly, should result in similar differences in yields between grades.

Carcasses vary in their yields of the four lean cuts because of varia-

Table 11.14—Expected Yields of the Four Lean Cuts Based on Chilled Carcass Weight, by Grade

Grade	Yield
U.S. No. 1 — — — — — — — — — — —	53% and over
U.S. No. 2 — — — — — — — — — — —	50% to 52.9%
U.S. No. 3 — — — — — — — — — — —	47% to 49.9%
U.S. No. 4 — — — — — — — — — — —	Less than 47%

tions in their degree of fatness and in their degree of muscling (thickness of muscling in relation to skeletal size). Since many carcasses have a normal distribution of fat and a normal development of muscling for their degree of fatness, in determining their grade the actual average thickness of backfat and the carcass length or weight are the only factors considered.

These relationships are illustrated in Figure 11.51 for carcasses either 27 to 36 inches long or weighing 120 to 255 pounds. For carcasses of other lengths or weights, average backfat thickness requirements for the various grades can be determined by an extension of the lines in this figure. Note: (In cases where length and backfat thickness indicate a different grade than weight and backfat, the grade shall be determined by using length.)

Objective Measures

In these standards, the actual average thickness of backfat is an average of three measurements including the skin made opposite the

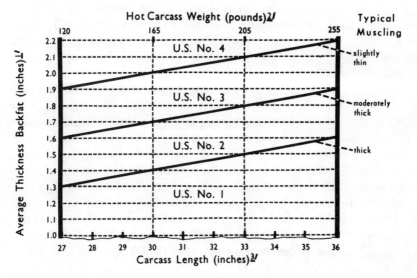

1/ An average of three measurements including the skin made opposite the first and last ribs and the last lumbar vertebra. It also reflects adjustment, as appropriate, to compensate for variations - from - normal fat distribution.
2/ Carcass weight is based on a hot packer style carcass.
3/ Carcass length is measured from the anterior point of the aitch bone to the anterior edge of the first rib.

Fig. 11.51—Relationship between average thickness of backfat, carcass length or weight, and grade for carcasses with muscling typical of their degree of fatness.

first and last ribs and the last lumbar vertebra; carcass length is measured from the anterior point of the aitch bone to the anterior edge of the first rib next to the first vertebra (see Figure 11.52), and hot carcass weight (or chilled carcass weight multiplied by 102 percent) is based on an entire carcass dressed packer style—split into two sides down the back, jowls attached, and head, ham facings, and leaf fat removed. When carcasses are not dressed according to packer style or when, through condemnations or for other reasons, portions of the carcass have been removed, appropriate adjustments shall be made in carcass weight.

Degree of Muscling

The degree of muscling specified for each of the four grades decreases progressively from the U.S. No. 1 grade through the U.S. No. 4 grade. This reflects the fact that among carcasses of the same weight, fatter carcasses normally have a lesser degree of muscling. For purposes of these standards, six degrees of muscling are recognized: very thick, thick, moderately thick, slightly thin, thin, and very thin. These are intended to cover the entire range of muscling present among pork carcasses currently being produced. (Figure 11.53 illustrates five of the six degrees of muscling; the very thin degree is not shown.) The degrees which are typical for carcasses at the minimum of the U.S. No. 1, No. 2, No. 3, and No. 4 grades are, respectively: thick, moderately thick, slightly thin, and thin.

For carcasses having a development of muscling which is different from that normally associated with their degree of fatness, the average backfat thickness-carcass length or carcass weight relationships for the various grades are different than shown in Figure 11.51. Consideration is given such unusual developments of muscling as follows: In each grade, a superior development of muscling is permitted to compensate for a greater average backfat thickness at the rate of 1/10 inch greater backfat thickness for a full degree of superior muscling. Except for the U.S. No. 1 grade, the reverse type of compensation is also permitted at the same rate. In the U.S. No. 1 grade, this type of compensation is limited to one full degree of inferior muscling; carcasses which have less than moderately thick muscling but which would otherwise qualify for the U.S. No. 1 grade are graded U.S. No 2.

In no case, however, may the combined effect of variations-from-normal fat distribution and muscling alter the final grade more than one full grade from that indicated by the actual average backfat thickness and carcass length and weight.

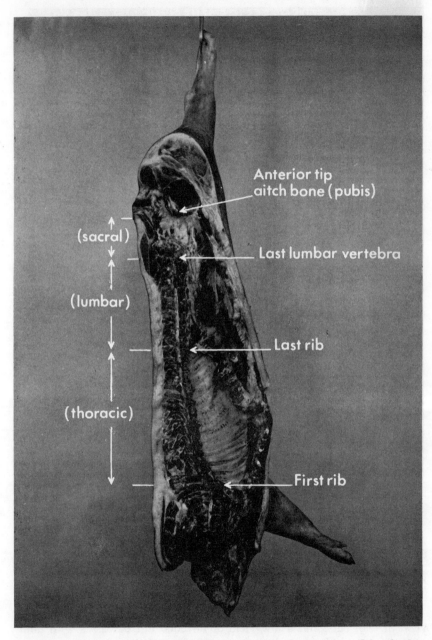

Fig. 11.52—Back fat is measured opposite the first rib, last rib, and last lumbar vertebra, added and averaged. Length is measured from the first rib to the anterior (front) tip of the aitch bone. (Courtesy, University of Illinois)

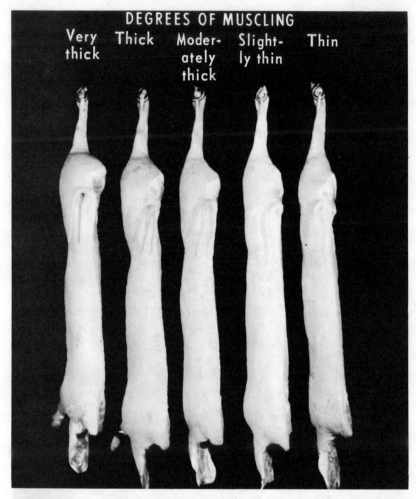

Fig. 11.53—Degrees of muscling. (Courtesy, Livestock Division, Agricultural Service, U.S. Dept. of Agriculture)

Specifications for Grades of Barrow and Gilt Carcasses

U.S. No. 1

Carcasses in this grade have an acceptable quality of lean, a high yield of lean cuts, and a low yield of fat cuts. For carcasses with minimum acceptable lean quality, the cut surface of the loin-eye muscle at the tenth rib will be slightly firm, have a slight amount of marbling, and be grayish pink to moderately dark red in color. However, for intact carcasses, minimum acceptable quality of lean is indicated by a slight amount of feathering, fat that is slightly firm, and lean that is slightly firm and grayish pink to moderately dark red in color. The belly is at least slightly thick.

Carcasses near the borderline between the U.S. No. 1 and U.S. No. 2 grades are thickly muscled in the hams, loins, and shoulders. The lower portion of the ham toward the hock is covered with a thin layer of fat, the back is well rounded, the area at the juncture of the lower part of the shoulder and the belly is depressed in relation to the shoulder and the belly, and the area directly anterior to the hipbone is depressed in relation to the loin and ham. The maximum actual average thickness of backfat for carcasses in this grade will vary depending upon the distribution of fat, the development of muscling, and the carcass length or weight. For carcasses with a distribution of fat and development of muscling as described herein, the maximum average thickness of backfat increases from 1.3 to 1.6 inches with increases in either carcass length from 27 to 36 inches or carcass weight from 120 to 255 pounds (see Figure 11.51).

A development of muscling superior to that specified as minimum for the U.S. No. 1 grade may compensate for a development of fatness which is greater than that indicated in Figure 11.51 as maximum for the U.S. No. 1 grade at the rate of one full degree of muscling for 1/10 of an inch increase in thickness of backfat. For example, a carcass which is 30 inches long and which has very thick muscling may have an average thickness of backfat of 1.5 inches and remain eligible for the U.S. No. 1 grade. The reverse type of compensation is also permitted—at the same rate—except that in no case may a carcass be graded U.S. No. 1 with less than moderately thick muscling. Also, in no case may the combined effect of variations in muscling and fat distribution from those described herein alter the final grade more than one full grade from that indicated by the actual average backfat thickness and either carcass length or weight.

U.S. No. 2

Carcasses in this grade have an acceptable quality of lean, a slightly high yield of lean cuts, and a slightly low yield of fat cuts. For carcasses with minimum acceptable lean quality, the cut surface of the loin-eye muscle at the tenth rib will be slightly firm, have a slight amount of marbling and be grayish pink to moderately dark red in color. However, for intact carcasses, minimum acceptable quality of lean is indicated by a slight amount of feathering, fat that is slightly firm, and lean that is slightly firm and grayish pink to moderately dark red in color. The belly is at least slightly thick.

Carcasses near the borderline between the U.S. No. 2 and U.S. No. 3 grades are moderately thickly muscled in the hams, loins, and shoulders. The lower portion of the ham toward the hock is covered with a slightly thin layer of fat and the back is slightly well rounded. The area at the juncture of the lower part of the shoulder and belly is slightly depressed in relation to the shoulder and belly, and the area directly anterior to the hipbone is slightly depressed in relation to the loin and ham. The maximum actual average thickness of backfat for carcasses in this grade will vary depending upon the distribution of fat, the development of muscling, and the carcass length or weight. For carcasses with a distribution of fat and development of muscling as described herein, the maximum average thickness of backfat increases from 1.6 to 1.9 inches with increases in either carcass length from 27 to 36 inches or carcass weight from 120 to 255 pounds (see Figure 11.51).

A development of muscling superior to that specified as minimum for the U.S. No. 2 grade may compensate for a development of fatness which is greater than that indicated in Figure 11.51 as maximum for the U.S. No. 2 grade at the rate of one full degree of muscling for 1/10 of an inch increase in thickness of backfat. For example, a carcass which is 30 inches long and which has thick muscling may have an average thickness of backfat of 1.8 inches and remain eligible for the U.S. No. 2 grade. The reverse type of compensation is also permitted at the same rate. For example, a carcass which is 30 inches long and which has an average thickness of backfat of 1.6 inches may have slightly thin muscling and remain eligible for the U.S. No. 2 grade. In no case may the combined effect of variations in muscling and fat distribution from those described herein alter the final grade more than one full grade from that indicated by the actual average backfat thickness and either length or weight.

U.S. No. 3

Carcasses in this grade have an acceptable quality of lean, a slightly low yield of lean cuts, and a slightly high yield of fat cuts. For carcasses with minimum acceptable lean quality, the cut surface of the loin-eye muscle at the tenth rib will be at least slightly firm, have a slight amount of marbling, and be grayish pink to moderately dark red in color. However, for intact carcasses, minimum acceptable quality of lean is indicated by a slight amount of feathering, fat that is slightly firm, and lean that is slightly firm and grayish pink to moderately dark red in color. The belly is at least slightly thick.

Carcasses near the borderline between the U.S. No. 3 and U.S. No. 4

grades are slightly thinly muscled in the hams, loins, and shoulders. The lower portion of the ham toward the hock is covered with a slightly thick layer of fat. The back is slightly flat, and the edge of the loin is slightly full, resulting in a slight break from the back into the side. In the area at the juncture of the lower part of the shoulder and the belly there is only a slight depression in relation to the shoulder and the belly. In the area directly anterior to the hipbone there is only a very slight depression in relation to the loin and ham. The maximum actual average thickness of backfat for carcasses in this grade will vary dependent upon the distribution of fat, the development of muscling, and the carcass length or weight. For carcasses with a distribution of fat and development of muscling as described herein, the maximum average thickness of backfat increases from 1.9 to 2.2 inches with increases in either carcass length from 27 to 36 inches or carcass weight from 120 to 255 pounds (see Figure 11.51).

A development of muscling superior to that specified as minimum for the U.S. No. 3 grade may compensate for a development of fatness which is greater than that indicated in Figure 11.51 as maximum for the U.S. No. 3 grade at the rate of one full degree of muscling for 1/10 of an inch increase in thickness of backfat. For example, a carcass which is 30 inches long and which has moderately thick muscling may have an average thickness of backfat of 2.1 inches and remain eligible for the U.S. No. 3 grade. The reverse type of compensation is also permitted at the same rate. For example, a carcass which is 30 inches long and which has an average thickness of backfat of 1.9 inches may have thin muscling and remain eligible for the U.S. No. 3 grade. In no case may the combined effect of variations in muscling and fat distribution from those described herein alter the final grade more than one full grade from that indicated by the actual average backfat thickness and either carcass length or weight.

U.S. No. 4

Carcasses in this grade have an acceptable quality of lean but a lower expected yield of lean cuts than carcasses in the U.S. No. 3 grade.

U.S. Utility

Included in this grade are all carcasses which have characteristics that indicate they will have a lesser development of lean quality than described as minimum for the U.S. No. 1, U.S. No. 2, U.S. No. 3, and U.S. No. 4 grades. Also included are all carcasses which do not have acceptable belly thickness and all carcasses—regardless of their development of other quality-indicating characteristics—which are soft and oily.

Live and Carcass Illustrations of Pork Carcass Grades

Illustrations depicting live and carcass representatives of the various pork carcass grades are provided by the University of Illinois Animal Science and Vo Ag Services Departments.

Grade Standards for Sow Carcasses

The establishment of U. S. standards for grades of slaughter sows and sow carcasses became effective Sept., 1, 1956.

The grades are based on differences in yields of lean cuts and fat cuts and differences in quality of pork. In developing the standards, sow carcass data were studied to establish relationships between measurements and carcass differences important in grading. As a result, these standards include average backfat thickness measurements as objective guides to grade. These principles are similar to those which have received widespread acceptance in the standards for barrows and gilts, adopted in 1952.

The five grades for sows and sow carcasses are U.S. No. 1, U.S. No. 2, U.S. No. 3, Medium, and Cull. The U.S. No. 1 grade includes sows and carcasses with about the minimum finish required to produce pork cuts of acceptable palatability. The U.S. No. 2 and U.S. No. 3 grades represent overfinish with resulting lower yields of lean and higher yields of fat. Medium and Cull are underfinished grades producing pork with low palatability.

The backfat measurements which qualify sow carcasses for the various grades are listed in Table 11.15.

Table 11.15—Backfat Measurement Guides to Grades for Sow Carcasses

Average Back Fat Thickness	Grade
(in.)	
1.5 to 1.9	U.S. No. 1
1.9 to 2.3	U.S. No. 2
2.3 or more	U.S. No. 3
1.1 to 1.5	Medium
Less than 1.1	Cull

Fig. 11.54—A U.S. No. 1 grade barrow. This U.S. No. 1 grade barrow is adequate in length, very trim in his middle and jowl, and well muscled and firm through his ham. From the rear, he is wider through the ham than any place else in his body and is free of evidence of excess fat at the root of the tail and in the crotch. From the top, he shows evidence of a large loin eye with a minimum of finish. He shows this by a bold spring of rib and a round turn (from side to side) over the top. His shoulder is free of evidence of excess fat and is wider through the center of his shoulder than over his top. Meaty hogs are wider through their hams and shoulders than through their backs and loins.

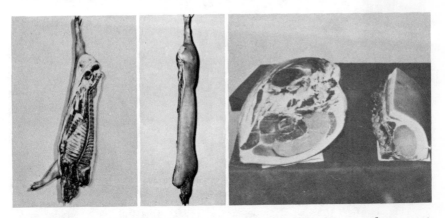

Fig. 11.55—A U.S. No. 1 grade carcass. (Left) This U.S. No. 1 grade carcass is 31.4 inches long, has 1.03 inches of backfat, and is trim over the ham face and in the belly. Acceptable quality is indicated by the bright, greyish pink, lean, and white, firm fat. (Center) This U.S. No. 1 grade carcass is thickly muscled as evidenced by the thick, bulging ham and shoulder. The loin is smoothly turned, indicating muscling and trimness. (Right) Further evidence of thick muscling in this U.S. No. 1 grade carcass is the 5.5 square inch loin eye exposed at the tenth rib and the thick, deep, full ham. The cut, lean surface scored 3 in color, 2 in firmness, and also 2 in marbling.

Fig. 11.56—A U.S. No. 2 grade barrow. This U.S. No. 2 grade barrow is adequate in length but shows some evidence of fat through his jowl and middle. He is also not as well muscled through his ham as the U.S. No. 1 grade barrow. From the rear, he shows some evidence of a cushion of fat at the root of the tail and in the crotch area. He is also almost as wide over his back as he is through the center of his hams and shoulders. From the top, he is not as round (from side to side) as the U.S. No. 1 grade barrow, and he tends to be broader and flatter over his back.

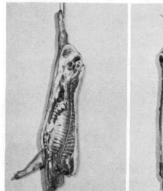

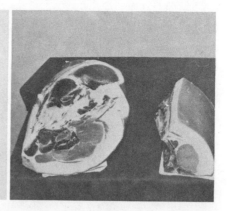

Fig. 11.57—A U.S. No. 2 grade carcass. (Left) This U.S. No. 2 grade carcass is 29.1 inches long, has 1.4 inches of backfat, and shows slightly more waste fat over the ham face and in the belly than the U.S. No. 1 grade carcass. Color and firmness of lean and fat are acceptable. (Center) This carcass shows moderately thick muscling as indicated by the ham, which is somewhat lacking at the heel and the shoulder, which lacks prominence when compared with the U.S. No. 1 grade carcass. (Right) The bright, firm, well marbled loin eye is very appealing. The 4.2 square inch loin eye and the ham face look smaller due to the waste backfat surrounding them.

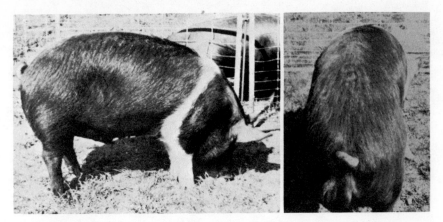

Fig. 11.58—A U.S. No. 3 grade barrow. This U.S. No. 3 grade barrow is a heavy pig and appears short for his size. He is heavy through his middle and very heavy in his jowl. Both of these factors indicate that he may be carrying excessive amounts of fat. He is also not as well developed or muscular in the ham as either the No. 1 or No. 2 barrows. From the rear, this animal shows evidence of carrying excessive fat. There is a large cushion of fat along the root of the tail, and the center of his back is about as wide as the center of his hams or shoulders. From the top, he is broad and flat over his back and has an obvious roll of fat along the edge of his loin.

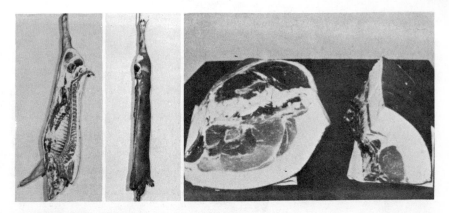

Fig. 11.59—A U.S. No. 3 grade carcass. (Left) This U.S. No. 3 grade carcass is 31.5 inches long and has 1.8 inches of average backfat. (Center) This carcass has slightly thin muscling. Note that the loin is turned sharply, indicating fat. Also that the ham and shoulder are about the same thickness as the loin. This is an indication of a lack of muscling in these two cuts. (Right) Carcass fatness is obvious at the cross section of the loin at the tenth rib and the butt face of the ham. The ratio of lean to fat is low. This 3.7-square-inch loin eye scored 3 in color, firmness, and marbling.

Fig. 11.60—A U.S. No. 4 grade barrow. This U.S. No. 4 grade barrow is very short and fat. It is extremely heavy in its middle and jowl. He shows evidence of very excessive finish by the roll of fat along the lower part of his shoulder and the pad of fat along the root of his tail. From the rear, this animal shows evidence of being extremely fat. There is an extremely large pad of fat along the root of the deeply countersunk tail and a great deal of fat in the crotch and at the base of the ham. From the top, this animal is wider through the center of his back than through the center of his hams and shoulders. He also has a very large roll of fat along the edge of his loin.

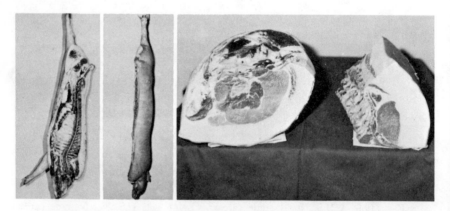

Fig. 11.61—A U.S. No. 4 grade carcass. (Left) This U.S. No. 4 grade Carcass is 30.9 inches long and has 2.2 inches of backfat. (Center) This carcass has slightly thin muscling, as indicated by the thin, narrow, peaked ham. The apparent thickness of shoulder is due to fat. (Right) The ratio of lean to fat is very low. In fact, in this loin view, the backfat is thicker than the loin eye, which measures 4.0 square inches. The color score was 4, being dark in the loin especially. Firmness score was 3.0, while the marbling score was 4.

A GALLERY OF CHAMPIONS

Livestock shows have been held up by some as being instrumental in livestock improvement, while these same shows have been maligned as gaudy theatrical affairs benefiting only the few who can afford to attend and "play the game." Whatever one's personal persuasion might be, in the long run, exhibiting one's best in any business makes good sense. Hopefully, the educational aspects of the shows make them all worthwhile.

Recently, modern shows have put more emphasis on growability and efficiency of production so that money and time is not wasted fitting animals by the use of restricted feeding, exercise, or other nonproductive practices.

Pictured in this section are the champions as named on foot in the 1973 Illinois State Fair. For comparison, the third place steer at the 1933 International Livestock Exposition, Chicago, is included (it appeared in many earlier editions of this book). The current champions were slaughtered one to two months after the State Fair when pictures and carcass data were taken to really see "How the Champions Cut."

Fig. 11.62—Third place steer (Slaughter Class), 1933 International Livestock Exposition, Chicago. Today we would say he was "modern in type."

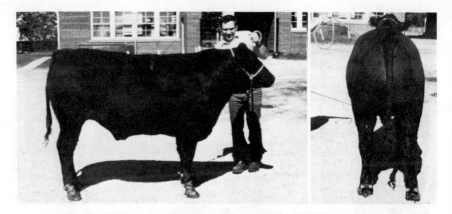

Fig. 11.63–Frosty, the 1973 Illinois Champion, strikingly similar to the 1933 steer in general conformation, is probably more heavily muscled and leaner than the early version. From the rear, Frosty shows excellent width through the stifle, his muscular rounds being his widest dimension. He weighed 1,215 pounds just before slaughter.

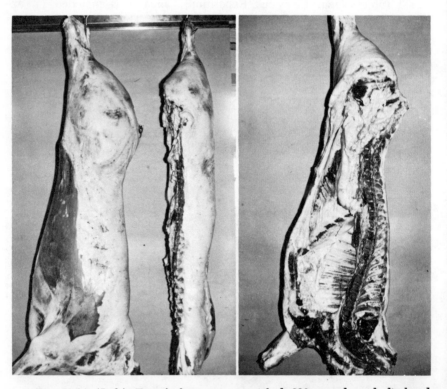

Fig. 11.64–(Left) Frosty's hot carcass weighed 820 pounds and displayed average Prime conformation with typical A maturity. Note the lean muscle showing through on his rounds. (Right) Frosty did carry an above average amount of kidney, pelvic, and heart fat internally; it calculated 4.4% of his carcass weight.

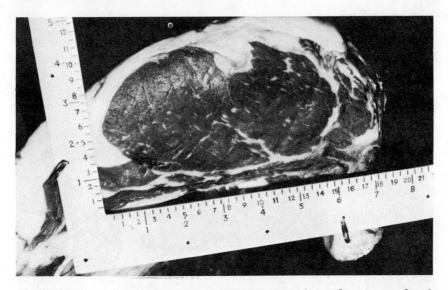

Fig. 11.65–Frosty's rib eye measured 14.0 square inches and was covered with 0.4 inch of fat. Thus his USDA yield grade calculated 3.2. His bright, cherry red rib-eye muscle contained modest amounts of marbling, qualifying him for average Choice quality grade.

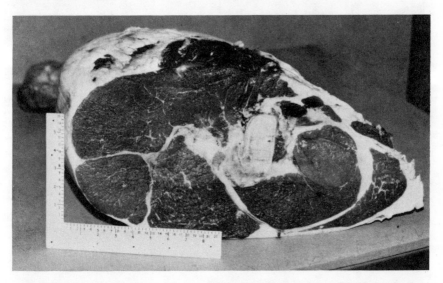

Fig. 11.66–This is a view of one of Frosty's *untrimmed* rounds. Obviously there was very little trimming to do. One side of Frosty was boned out completely and yielded 63.1% of that side weight in closely trimmed boneless roasts and lean trim, 23.1% fat trim, and 14.0% bone. The other side yielded 67.3% of its weight in retail cuts with some bone left in the loin, rib, and chuck, 21.1% fat trim, and 10.6% remaining bone trim.

Fig. 11.67—Weiner, a crossbred barrow, was named grand champion barrow and weighed 285 pounds when this picture was taken two months after the show. His leanness over the ham and shoulder is still obvious from the side. Even at this weight, his excellent muscling through the ham and loin are obvious from the rear.

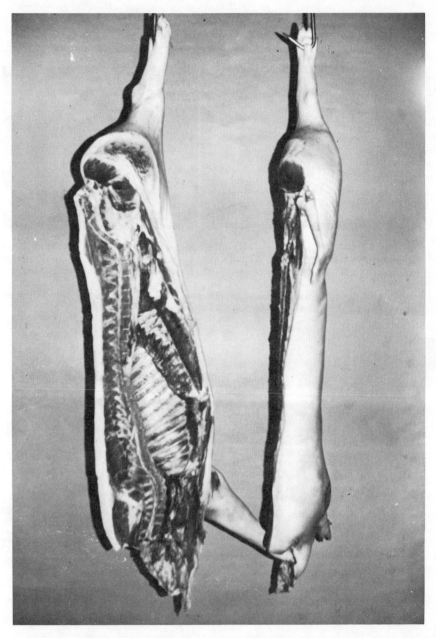

Fig. 11.68—Weiner's carcass, weighing 222 pounds, was 33.6 inches long, carried 1.07 inches of fat down the midline, and displayed thick muscling. Thus he qualified as a very high U.S. No. 1.

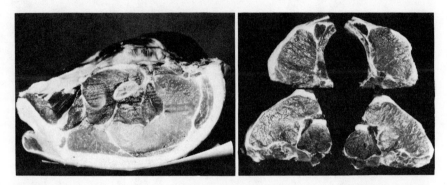

Fig. 11.69—(Left) Weiner's untrimmed ham appears lean and muscular. After all cuts were closely trimmed, Weiner's carcass yielded 42.3% ham and loin, 61.3% four lean cuts, 73.2% five primal cuts, 14.3% miscellaneous cuts, and 12.5% fat trim. (Right) Weiner's loin eye measured 6.78 square inches at the tenth rib, and his muscle quality scores were 3 for color, firmness, and marbling, ideal for quality as can be seen in these center rib and loin chops.

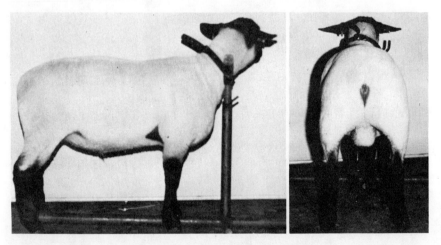

Fig. 11.70—A Suffolk wether garnered championship honors in the wether show. His weight when slaughtered one month after the show was 112 pounds.

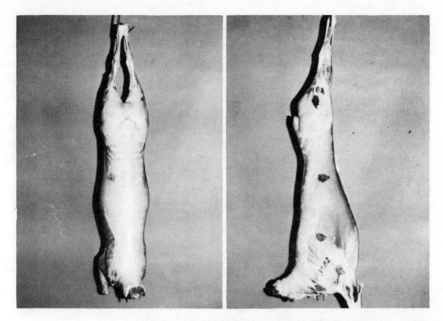

Fig. 11.71—This lamb's leg conformation was high Prime, and his overall conformation was average Prime. The hot carcass weighed 62 pounds.

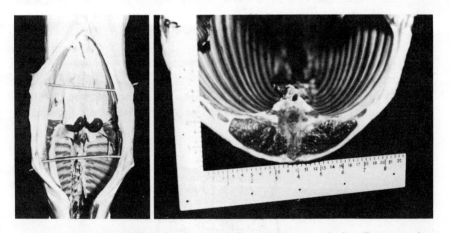

Fig. 11.72—The lamb had only 2.2% kidney fat, but yet had sufficient quality to grade high Choice. The loin eye measured 2.42 square inches or 3.90 square inches per hundredweight of carcass. He had 0.19 inch of fat over his eye and 0.50 inch at the lower rib. His calculated yield grade was 2.8. The carcass yielded 77.3% of closely trimmed retail product when bone was left in the rack and loin, 75.8% with the bone out of the loin, 9.1% trimmed fat, and 16.8% bone.

What Makes Progress?

These are champions of one modern prestigious show, but they are by no means yet the ultimate in meat animal production. We must continue to improve by openly comparing our best with that of others. The U.S. Department of Agriculture Agricultural Marketing Service, through the Federal Grading Branch of its Livestock Division, gives us a set of uniform standards on which to make comparisons, and thus have been instrumental in fostering improvement. For the meat animal industry to continue to flourish, it must encourage the development of animals that produce high quality edible product most efficiently.

USDA'S ACCEPTANCE SERVICE AND PRODUCT EXAMINATION SERVICE

In addition to grading carcasses and cuts, the meat graders of the Livestock Division of the U.S. Department of Agriculture Agricultural Marketing Service provide two more services to the meat industry. Both services are paid for by the segment of the meat industry using them, and both are becoming more widely used in the U.S.

Acceptance Service for Meat and Meat Products[9]

Since 1923, the Federal Meat Grading Service has assisted organizations such as government agencies, private institutions, and other purveyors of meals in their meat procurement programs. This service involves (1) assisting the purchaser in the development of specifications to assure accurate and uniform interpretation and (2) examining the product to assure its compliance with the specifications. Upon acceptance, each piece or package is stamped, as illustrated below, and the purchaser is furnished with an official certificate containing pertinent information about the product.

---

9. *Marketing Bulletin No. 47*, Agricultural Marketing Service, U.S. Dept. of Agriculture.

The Meat Acceptance Service is based on USDA approved Institutional Meat Purchase Specifications, commonly called IMPS. IMP specifications are available for fresh beef, fresh lamb and mutton, fresh veal and calf, fresh pork, cured pork, cured beef, edible by-products, sausage products, and portion-cut meat products. Each item is numbered and belongs to a series according to the product—Series 100 for instance is fresh beef, and Item 104 is a rib, oven ready. IMP specifications can be purchased from the Government Printing Office.

Purchasers, be they hospitals, schools, restaurants, hotels, air lines, or steamship lines, may ask suppliers to submit bids on products based on IMP specifications.

When the purchaser requests delivery, the supplier asks the nearest USDA meat grading office to have a grader examine the product. The meat grader is responsible for accepting the product and certifying that it is in compliance with specifications.

The Federal grader stamps each acceptable meat item, or the sealed carton in which it is contained, with a shield-shaped stamp bearing the words, "USDA Accepted as Specified." This assures the purchaser that all products delivered to him met the requirements of the specifications at the time of acceptance.

This method of meat procurement assures the purchaser of a wholesome product (only meat that has passed inspection for wholesomeness will be examined for "acceptance"), of the grade, trim, weight, and other options requested. This system also encourages competitive bidding and usually results in overall lower costs, permits long-range meal planning, and eliminates controversies between the buyer and seller over compliance of product.

Product Examination Service[10]

If a business involves meat shipments, there may be times when it is necessary to have an impartial expert officially establish a shipment's physical condition. This service is available to meat packers, wholesalers, brokers, carriers, and their insurance agents—in short, to anyone with a financial interest in the meat shipment who may want to substantiate a damage claim, protect against one, or save the time and expense of examining it himself. Product examinations are made on request, and a fee is charged for the service. The examination may be performed wherever the meat shipment is located—in packing plants, warehouses, trucks, or railroad cars—provided the meat is accessible to the meat grader.

---

10. *Marketing Bulletin No. 55*, Agricultural Marketing Service, U.S. Dept. of Agriculture.

During an examination, the grader impartially documents the facts about the physical condition of a meat or meat products shipment. The meat involved may be fresh or frozen carcasses or wholesale cuts of beef, pork, lamb, veal, or calf; sausage; smoked or cured meats; etc. The grader issues an official certificate attesting to the physical condition of the shipment. Such certificates are accepted as *prima facie* evidence by all Federal and most state courts.

In a product examination, the meat grader reports only on physical conditions that can be accurately determined and described. For example, he can examine meat or meat products for extent and kind of damage, freezer burn, thawing and refreezing, cleanliness, freshness, temperature, weight ranges, and fat thickness. He can also determine the temperature of the conveyance and any container damage. Management should specify the factors to be determined by the examination, and whether it is to be conducted by random sample or 100% examination of the product.

NOTE: Meat that is unwholesome is not eligible for product examination. If there is any question about the meat being fit for human consumption, the meat grader will refer the problem to USDA's Animal and Plant Health Inspection Service (APHIS) or, if appropriate, to state and local authorities having jurisdiction over the wholesomeness of meat.

THE MEAT GRADER

Government meat graders are appointed from a list of eligibles submitted by the Civil Service Commission. To qualify, a candidate must have had at least three years of suitable practical experience in wholesale meat marketing and grading. A maximum of three years of appropriate college training (courses in meat and livestock judging) can be substituted for practical experience at the rate of one year of study for nine months of required experience. Before being given a permanent appointment as grader, the candidate must serve a probationary period of one year, during which time he is given intensive training in the application of standards, and his work is reviewed very carefully by a grading supervisor to ascertain his ability to do the job in strict conformance with the Federal standards. The government takes precautions to obtain competent men of high integrity.

During 1973 there were 370 Federal meat graders listed in the salary range of GS-5 to GS-11 and 43 supervisory grading personnel at the GS-12 and GS-13 levels.

Trainees are employed at the GS-5 grade with an annual salary of $8,055. They participate in an intensive training program for five to six months before assuming a grading or reporting assignment. That training is accomplished at group meetings and assignments at two different field offices. Trainees are paid travel and subsistence allowances in addition to salary for approximately three months of the training period—while attending meetings and training at the first field office. They are eligible for promotion to the GS-7 ($9,969) a year after their original employment. They are eligible for promotion to the GS-9 grade ($12,167), which is the journeyman level for most grader and reporter positions, after a year of satisfactory performance at the GS-7 grade. Higher grade positions usually involve supervisory duties; selections for these openings are based on merit. Every grader's work is identified by a code in his grade stamp by means of a letter of the alphabet.

COST OF THE GRADING SERVICE

1. The rate for grading service is presently $13.80 per hour. The fees for service shall be based on the time required to render the service, including the time required for the preparation of certificates and travel of the official grader in connection with the performance of the service.
2. Fees for grading performed on a weekly contract basis shall be $552 per calendar week (less any allowable credits) to cover up to 40 hours of weekly grading service, and at the regular rate prescribed in paragraph one of this section for grading time in excess of 40 hours per week between the hours of 6:00 a.m. and 6:00 p.m. Monday through Friday. The fee increases to $16 per hour from 6:00 a.m. to 6:00 p.m. on Saturday or Sunday and to $27.60 per hour on a national holiday.

THE STAMP INK IS HARMLESS

The ink used in stamping meat, whether it is the inspection stamp or the grade stamp, is made from a vegetable dye that is absolutely harmless and need not be trimmed off the meat.

Violet No. 1 may no longer be used as the stamp ink. The U.S. Food and Drug Administration banned its use because of *suspected* cancer-inducing properties shown by unpublished Japanese research, although U.S. researchers have continually shown it to be safe, the latest confirmation coming in November 1972.

Presently another vegetable dye, Purple GL-31, is being used under USDA and FDA authority and is deemed safe and harmless.

PACKERS AND STOCKYARDS ACT

The purpose of the Packers and Stockyards Act, passed in 1921, is to provide for uniform and reasonable rates and practices, and to prevent unfair, unjustly discriminatory, or deceptive practices. This is particularly helpful to farmers who are unable to supervise the sale of their livestock personally. Federal supervision under the act extends to trade practices, commissions, feed and yardage rate charges, weighing and scale testing, and to other services rendered at the posted stockyards. Millions of dollars are saved livestock producers annually through this supervision. This act was amended in 1935 to bring within its scope certain poultry markets designated by the Secretary of Agriculture.

An amendment to the Packers and Stockyards Act in 1957 made the act applicable to all public markets, market agencies, and dealers handling livestock in interstate commerce.

In February 1968, the Packers and Stockyards Act was further amended to accommodate the growing number of carcass weight and grade sales. This amendment provided that.[11]

1. Each packer purchasing livestock on a carcass grade, carcass weight, or carcass grade and weight basis shall, prior to such purchase, make known to the seller, or to his duly authorized agent, the details of the purchase contract. Such details shall include, when applicable, expected date and place of slaughter, carcass price, condemnation terms, description of the carcass trim, grading to be used, accounting, and any special conditions.

2. Each packer purchasing livestock on a carcass grade, carcass weight, or carcass grade and weight basis, shall maintain the identity of each seller's livestock and the carcasses therefrom and shall, after determination of the amount of the purchase price, transmit or deliver to the seller, or his duly authorized agent, a true written account of such purchase showing the number, weight, and price of the carcasses of each grade (identifying the grade) and of the ungraded carcasses, an explanation of any condemnations, and any other information affecting final accounting. Packers purchasing livestock on such a basis shall

---

11. *Federal Register*, Vol. 33, F. R. No. 28, February 9, 1968.

maintain sufficient records to substantiate the settlement of each transaction.

3. When livestock are purchased by a packer on a carcass weight or carcass grade and weight basis, purchase and settlement therefore shall be on the basis of carcass price. This paragraph does not apply to purchases of livestock by a packer on a guaranteed yield basis.

4. Settlement and final payment for livestock purchased by a packer on a carcass weight or carcass grade and weight basis shall be on actual (hot) carcass weights determined before shrouding. The hooks, rollers, and gambrels, or other similar equipment used at a packing establishment in connection with the weighing of carcasses of the same species of livestock shall be uniform in weight. The tare weight shall include only the weight of such equipment.

5. Settlement and final payment for livestock purchased by a packer on a USDA carcass grade shall be on an official (final—not preliminary) grade. If settlement and final payment are based upon any grades other than official USDA grades, such other grades shall be set forth in detailed written specifications which shall be made available to the seller or his duly authorized agent. For purposes of settlement and final payment for livestock purchased on a grade or grade and weight basis, carcasses shall be final graded before the close of the second business day following the day the livestock are slaughtered.

New regulations recently enacted under the Packers and Stockyards Act, among other things, prohibit certain dual ownership relationships between custom feedlots and packing plants. Also required are the registration and bonding of custom feedlots. Before any changes are made, the U.S. Department of Agriculture holds hearings throughout the country. Then after careful consideration of all the views and comments received, and the facts available, the Packers and Stockyards Administration will decide for or against the proposed changes.

CARCASS GRADING AT COLLEGIATE AND NONCOLLEGIATE LEVELS

A full discussion on collegiate meat judging and evaluation contests appears in Chapter 21. This section will deal only with carcass *grading* as it relates to intercollegiate and other contests.

Beginning in 1971, lamb carcass quality grading was eliminated from most intercollegiate contests, although it could be retained at the discretion of the competing schools. In 1973, no intercollegiate contest had competition in lamb carcass quality grading. There are at least two reasons why lamb quality grading was dropped:

1. Lamb slaughter has become so concentrated and localized that many schools were unable to find a source of lamb carcasses nearby to practice grade, thus felt unable to compete in a contest.
2. As indicated earlier in this chapter, 87% of all lambs graded grade Choice, and 12% grade Prime, leaving only 1% for the Good, Utility, and Cull grades. There just wasn't enough variety to make a good contest.

Beef Carcass Grading

Out of 1,000 points per contestant per contest, 200 arise from quality grading 20 beef carcasses, and 100 arise from yield grading 10 beef carcasses. In scoring quality grading, if the contestant hits the grade exactly to the 1/3 of a grade, the score is 10; if missed by 1/3 grade, the score is 8; if missed by 2/3 grade, the score is 5; and if missed by 1 full grade or more, the score is 0. In scoring yield grades, the student is penalized one point for each 1/10 yield grade missed, so a perfect score of 10 per carcass results when the contestant yield graded the carcass exactly to the 1/10 of a yield grade, while if it was missed by a full yield grade, a score of 0 would result. It is often said that whichever team wins beef grading will also win the contest. Thus beef grading is important to overall placing, accounting alone for 30% of the total score. The contestant is allowed 1 minute to quality grade each of 20 carcasses and 1½ minutes to yield grade each of 10 carcasses in a standard contest.

Beef carcass quality grading is the act of determining, by visual examination of a carcass, the features and qualities that make it eligible to be classified under one of the Federal grades. It also involves the ability to identify sex, since steer, heifer, cow, bull, and stag carcasses have physical characteristics for which separate grade standards have been provided.

Meat packers may segregate carcasses by sex, so in many instances a carcass grader is working on one particular sex at a time. This is not the case in contest judging where mixing of the sexes is practiced.

A full grade designation is not acceptable in contest grading since it would involve the contestants in too many ties. Designation of the particular segment of the grade for which it qualifies such as High (top), Average (middle), or Low (minimum) is required. This makes it very important that, as a first step in learning to grade, one study rather closely the specifications set up for each grade.

One has read that there are certain important factors to consider when grading beef, lamb, pork, or veal. These are: stage of maturity (age), marbling, and conformation, for quality grading, and finish (external fat covering and body cavity fat), loin-eye area, and carcass weight, for yield grading.

Why begin with age? Because meat fibers from older animals are less tender. The evidences of quality may be as prominent in the carcass of a 4-year-old heifer or steer carcass as in a 20-month-old steer carcass, but what one cannot see too plainly, when looking at a cross section of the rib-eye muscle, is the difference in the fiber. Connective tissue (collagen) increases in thickness with age. Each cell wall is made up of collagen; bundles of muscle cells are sheathed in collagen, and entire muscles are wrapped in collagen. Broil a steak from this four-year-old and good teeth will pass between the fibrous-covered cells; the flavor will probably be high, but one must keep chewing away on the bolus of meat. The best set of teeth are defeated when it comes to grinding the connective tissues. Don't condemn such meat, because it can be made tender, but not without giving it special treatment. Therefore, if one does not first determine the age of the carcass, no beginning has been made.

Here We Go Again!

The grade standards for beef that went into effect in 1965 make it necessary to place more emphasis on the stage of maturity of the carcass and primal cuts than heretofore. Previously the term, *quality,* referred only to palatability—indicating characteristics of the lean (marbling, texture, firmness, color) without reference to conformation. Presently—and with tongue in cheek—conformation is considered in quality grading, as it should be, even though it does not imply that variations in conformation are either directly or indirectly related to differences in palatability. Lest the expression—with tongue in cheek—would be misinterpreted, it simply refers to the author's expression of wonderment; wondering when the next change will come and wondering if our forebears were off-base when they said, "You can't beat a young dairy heifer or anything young for good eating." This might infer that we oldsters must be downgraded because of stage of maturity. Take heed, therefore, and consider the following.

Quality Characteristics

Marbling is essential for quality. Note the different degrees of marbling in the illustrations in Fig. 11.4 and, with practice, a mental picture can be developed. (Refer to the graph in Fig. 11.5, "Relationship Between Marbling, Maturity, and Quality.")

Firmness is desirable but it is not a characteristic of young animals which have a higher moisture content. Marbling (if the fat is firm) will enhance firmness. Aged cows have a rather firm lean but it tends to be gummy.

Color of the lean will vary with the stage of maturity from a bright cherry red in the younger beef to the darker shades of red in the more mature beef. Where the dark color exists in beef that is not mature (dark cutters), a condition resulting from a reduced sugar content at the time of slaughter, the final grade of carcasses which otherwise would qualify for the Prime, Choice, or Good grades may be reduced as much as one full grade. Although this dark color does not have any adverse effect on palatability, it is considered in grading because of its effect on acceptability and value.

Texture

The surface of the lean should be smooth and fine in appearance. If there is cell definition, it indicates that an excess of collagen is present, giving it a coarse texture.

Size of the Rib-Eye Muscle

The rib eye is the framed picture that you study for color, marbling, firmness, texture, rib conformation, and external fat covering. The rib eye should have a size proportionate to the weight of the carcass. (See Table 11.5.)

Conformation

Conformation (shape) is a very important asset or liability, depending upon whether it is good or bad. It is the most important factor (aside from excessive fat) in the yield grade or yield of trimmed, boneless, major retail cuts to be derived from the carcass or primal cuts. Attention should be focused on those parts of the carcass which yield the more valuable cuts such as the loin, round, and rib. Briefly, a greater proportionate weight in the hindquarter and a neat, trim forequarter are desirable.

Internal and External Carcass Fat

Referring to the yield grades, note that for Yield Grade 1 it lists 0.3 inch of external fat covering the rib-eye muscle and 2.5% of kidney, pelvic, and heart fat for a 500-pound carcass as against over 1 inch of fat over the rib eye and over 4.5% of its carcass weight in kidney, pelvic, and heart fat for Yield Grade 4. Estimates are, of course, subjective since no mechanical aids are permitted in a contest.

With these facts in mind, and the carcasses to be graded hanging before you, *evaluate, estimate, be progressive—not aggressive, and be smart.* To be the latter, one must remember the compensation values of conformation for quality and vice versa for each grade. The principles governing these compensations are as follows: In each of the grades, a superior development of quality is permitted to compensate for a deficient development of conformation, without limit, through the upper limit of quality. The rate of compensation in all grades is on an equal basis—a given degree of superior quality compensates for the same degree of deficient conformation.

The reverse type of compensation—a superior development of conformation for an inferior development of quality—is not permitted in the Prime, Choice, and Commercial grades. In all other grades, this type of compensation is permitted, but only to the extent of one-third of a grade of deficient quality. The rate of compensation is also on an equal basis—a given degree of superior conformation compensates for the same degree of deficient quality.

You must be able to weigh values that may be minor, yet have considerable bearing on the final grade when they are marginal; for example, smoothness and uniformity of external finish, or the amount of that finish in excess of that shown covering the rib eye.

PART TWO

PART TWO

CHAPTER 12

Pork Identification and Fabrication and Rendering Lard

The method of cutting pork is practically the same in all sections of the United States. In the past, conventional methods were to let the pork carcass thoroughly chill after slaughter for approximately 24 hours at 33° to 38° F, thus allowing the carcass to become firm in order to make possible a neat job of cutting. This is still the most popular procedure and most widely followed.

However, less than one-third of the pork processed in the United States is sold as fresh product, the remaining two-thirds being cured and smoked (thus being heated, actually "reheated") during processing (Chapter 17). Therefore, meat researchers are investigating the possibility of cutting pork before the animal heat has been removed in order to save the energy of cooling and the energy of reheating during processing. In this book, only this mention will be made of the hot processing possibility, but it is one development in the pork industry to be watched in the future.

Pork does not normally leave the packing plant in carcass form but is fabricated at the plant. Historically this procedure differed from that used in beef, veal, and lamb distribution where whole carcasses were shipped from the packing plant to distribution centers. Now more fabrication of carcasses of all these species as well as pork is taking place right in the plant where the animals are slaughtered.

IDENTIFICATION

Presently in the United States, there are estimated to be more than 1,000 meat names to identify the approximately 300 fresh cuts of beef, pork, lamb, and veal offered for sale at the retail level. Because of this situation, the Industrial Cooperative Meat Identification Standards Committee (ICMISC) was formed in mid 1972, composed of representatives of the entire meat industry, including meat packers and processors and all different sizes of grocery and supermarket operations. Livestock producers were represented through the National Live Stock and Meat Board.

This committee worked diligently to produce a most needed document for the U.S. meat industry. It is entitled *Uniform Retail Meat Identity Standards* and is published and distributed at cost by:

> Department of Merchandising
> National Live Stock and Meat Board
> 36 South Wabash Avenue
> Chicago, Illinois 60603

This document includes a master list of 314 identifications for retail cuts of all species and is designed to serve all marketing areas in the United States.

The meat label information recommended by the ICMISC includes:

1. The kind (species) of meat—Beef, Pork, Lamb, or Veal. It is listed first on every label.
2. The primal (wholesale) cut—Loin, Leg (Ham), Shoulder, Chuck, etc.—tells where the meat comes from on the animal.
3. The retail cut—Blade Roast, Spareribs, Loin Chops, etc.—tells what part of the primal cut the meat comes from.
4. Ground beef—Not Less Than X% Lean—tells what percentage of lean in ground beef the retailer will guarantee. "X" in this case may be any figure the retailer wishes to put there. According to Federal law, ground beef and hamburger must be at least 70% lean, but the area between 70% and 100% is entirely up to the retailer.

The retailer may put his own familiar "fanciful" name on a label after any of these four items, if he wishes. Further, if cooking instructions are given, chances for the consumer to "go wrong" are significantly lessened.

This uniform identity system is strictly voluntary, not government controlled in any way. Hopefully, it will be widely accepted in the United States so legislation will not be required. Some states already had identification laws on the books before these standards were published. In order for the system to be truly "uniform" and thus serve *all* the people, regardless of where they move or relocate in the United States, it must be widely used.

Copies of the standards are available from the publisher (National Live Stock and Meat Board) at cost.

In this text, the *Uniform Retail Meat Identity Standards* are used. Also some of the more common "fanciful" names are added where appropriate.

FABRICATION

The skeletal structure of the porcine in relation to an outline of the wholesale cuts is shown in Figure 12.1 and a more detailed chart of wholesale and retail cuts appears as Figure 12.2. Use these two figures for reference as the discussion moves through cutting a pork carcass. Figures 12.3 through 12.88 appear through the courtesy of the University of Illinois.

Mr. Jasper Lewis of the University of Illinois Meats Science staff is shown in many of the figures carrying out the major fabrication steps.

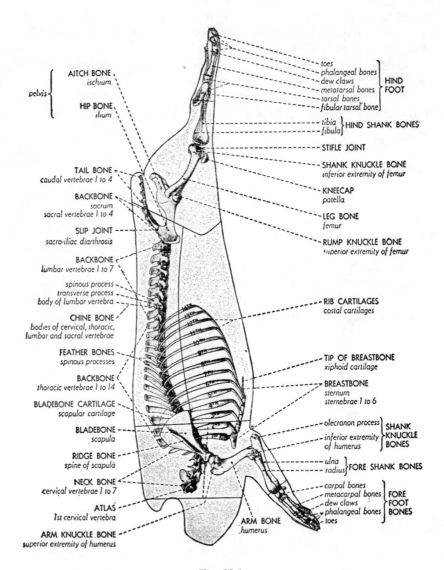

Fig. 12.1

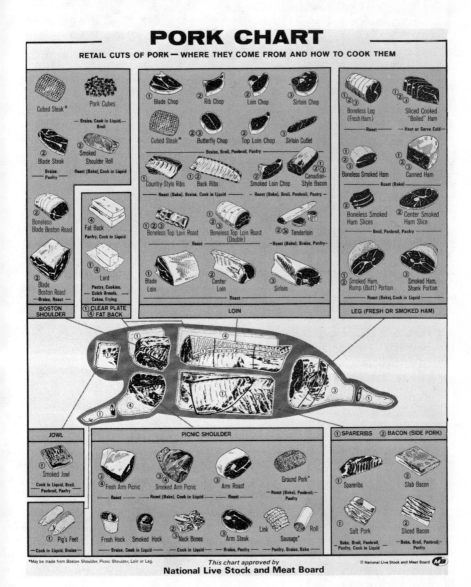

Fig. 12.2

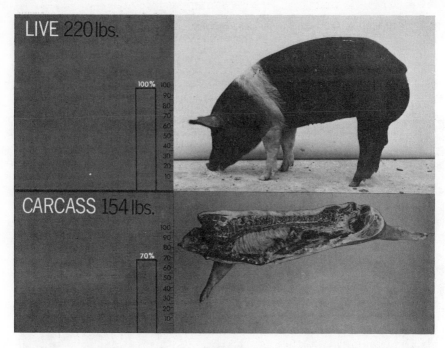

Fig. 12.3

Figure 12.3. Generally, when hogs are finished for market they will weigh *approximately* 220 pounds. After slaughter, the resulting carcass represents approximately 70% of the live weight. Therefore, a 220-pound live hog will produce a carcass weighing approximately 154 pounds.

Figure 12.4. Before leaving the slaughter floor, hog carcasses are generally split into right and left sides of approximately equal weight—in this case, 77 pounds each. In many packing houses, hog carcasses are not completely split but are hung on a single hook or gambrel, and the sides are attached by the fatback only.

Fig. 12.4

Figure 12.5. Generally, the hams are faced; that is, the collar fat or the fat about the inside of the ham is trimmed away on the kill floor. Note the difference between a faced ham and an unfaced ham. The kidney fat, which is called leaf fat in pork, is removed on the kill floor. The dotted lines indicate where the leaf fat was located. This procedure differs from lamb and beef slaughter where the kidneys and kidney fat are left intact in the carcass.

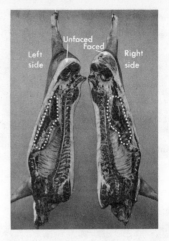

Fig. 12.5

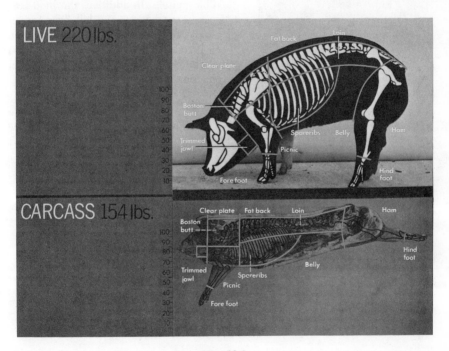

Fig. 12.6

Figure 12.6. The wholesale cuts of pork sometimes double as retail cuts. The leg (ham) and the loin are the two most valuable lean, primal cuts, with the Boston shoulder (butt) and the picnic shoulder being of less value. The belly is the fifth primal cut. Therefore, the five primal cuts are the leg (ham), loin, Boston shoulder (butt), picnic shoulder, and belly, the first four being further recognized as the four lean cuts. Other cuts may be known as minor cuts.

389

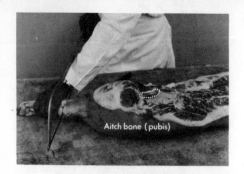

Fig. 12.7

Figure 12.7. The first step in fabricating a pork carcass is to remove the hind foot. Note the location of the aitch bone or *pubis* and orient yourself to the position of the carcass positioned on a block as related to the previous views of it hanging on a rail.

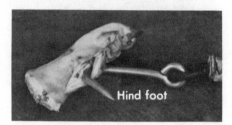

Fig. 12.8

Figure 12.8. The hind foot is generally not used for human consumption since it does contain an exceptionally high proportion of bone and very little edible muscle. In addition, the hind feet must be opened on the kill floor for insertion of the gambrel or hook in the tendon to hang the carcass. This also detracts from its desirability as a human food product.

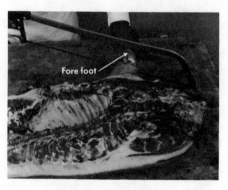

Fig. 12.9

Figure 12.9. The next step is the removal of the fore foot at the junction between the fore shank bone and the fore foot bone.

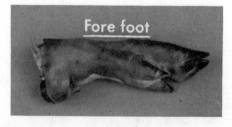

Fig. 12.10

Figure 12.10. The fore foot, unlike the hind foot, has a larger percentage of edible tissue composed largely of muscle and a lower percentage of tendon and bone. The fore foot is generally easier to clean and process and is therefore utilized for human consumption as pickled pigs' feet.

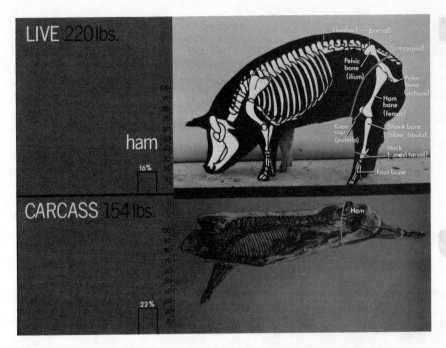

Fig. 12.11

Figure 12.11. The leg (ham) is the largest single cut in the pork carcass comprising, on the average, 16% of the live weight and 22% of the carcass weight. Note its location on the live animal and the carcass. Note the skeletal designations for future reference.

Figure 12.12. Caution should be used in removing the ham so that the *femoral* artery which provides a natural method for applying cure is not destroyed. Previous steps must be taken on the slaughter floor to remove the kidney and pelvic fat with care so that the femoral artery is not destroyed. When removing the ham from the carcass, be careful not to cut off the *femoral* artery too short. (Note Chapter 17)

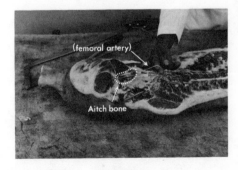

Fig. 12.12

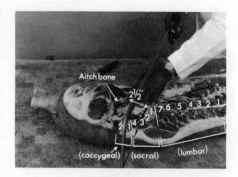

Fig. 12.13

Figure 12.13. The ham is removed from the carcass at a point approximately 2½ inches cranial or forward from the tip of the aitch bone. The cut is made perpendicular to the long axis of the ham and usually cuts between the third and fourth *sacral* vertebrae.

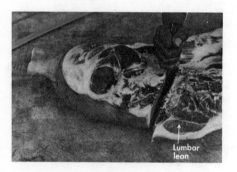

Fig. 12.14

Figure 12.14. After the bone has been severed with a saw, the knife is used to complete the removal of the ham. Note the *lumbar* lean which may be used as an indication of the overall leanness and muscling of intact carcasses.

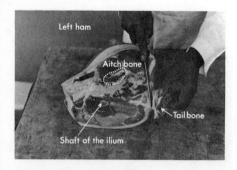

Fig. 12.15

Figure 12.15. To further trim the ham once it is removed, the first step is to remove the tail bone. Note the location of the aitch or pelvic bone as well as the shaft of the *ilium* which is the round portion of the pelvic bone. Do not confuse this round bone with the round ham bone or *femur* which is located caudal or (to the rear) of the aitch bone.

392

Figure 12.16. On this right ham, the flank side is trimmed, being especially careful to remove the lymph glands. The large muscle in the face of every ham is the *gluteus medius* or top sirloin.

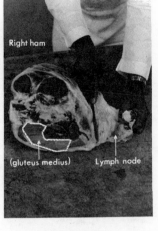

Fig. 12.16

Figure 12.17. The most common ham is a ham which is skinned approximately three-fourths of the distance from the rump (butt) face and is called a skinned ham. The skin is removed as well as a certain amount of the fat.

Fig. 12.17

Figure 12.18. The idea is to bevel the fat in a uniform manner so that the fat will measure approximately one-quarter of an inch in thickness at the rump (butt) face. Different amounts of fat are trimmed, according to the market potential for the pork leg. All legs are not trimmed this close.

Fig. 12.18

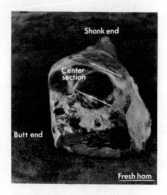

Fig. 12.19

Figure 12.19. A pork leg (fresh ham) is composed of a shank portion, a rump (butt) portion, and the center section and may be sold whole, either fresh or cured and smoked. The center section is the most valuable portion of the ham and often center slices are removed for sale.

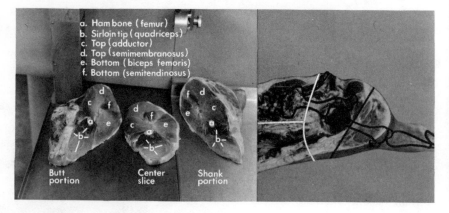

Fig. 12.20

Figure 12.20. On this fresh ham you can see the desirability of a center slice, with only a small cross section of the ham bone (*femur*) present. The shank portion is less desirable from a palatability standpoint since there are more connective tissues in that lower portion of the ham. The rump (butt) portion is more palatable, but notice the larger pelvic bone present in this portion which makes carving difficult. The location of the cut for the center slice is indicated by a dark line in the carcass diagram to the right. If the word *portion* is used in describing either the rump or shank parts, this indicates that center slices have been removed. However, if the parts are designated shank half or rump half, the center section must be included in the half you buy.

Nowadays few consumers care to purchase a whole ham, except for very special occasions, due to its size and total cost. Also, the large pelvic bone present in a bone-in leg may cause considerable grief for the modern housewife in terms of carving and serving. Thus more processors and packers are removing the bone before it is merchandized; that is, fabricating a boneless leg (ham). This is a very simple task for the processor, but usually a near impossible one for the housewife or her husband. Furthermore, a boneless leg (ham) may be easily merchandized in smaller portions.

394

Figure 12.21. In boning a leg (ham), approach it from the butt face and clear out the pelvic bone (aitch bone).

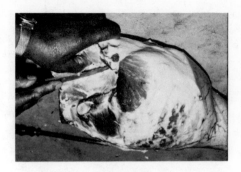

Fig. 12.21

Figure 12.22. Note the ball of the *femur* or ham bone which has been exposed. By loosening the meat surrounding the femur without cutting to the outside, we are using the procedure known as tunnel boning.

Fig. 12.22

Figure 12.23. From the shank end of the ham, the shank bones are loosened.

Fig. 12.23

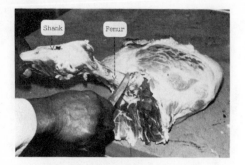

Figure 12.24.   Since the *femur* or ham bone had been loosened from the rump end of the ham, it is a rather simple matter to remove the shank bone and the ham bone intact after loosening this shank end.

Fig. 12.24

Figure 12.25.   The introduction of a jet-netter and the elastic net have made the tying of roasts with the string and butcher's knot outdated. Using the jet-netter, it is a simple and quick operation to tie any boneless roast.

Fig. 12.25

Figure 12.26.   A boneless fresh ham may be somewhat difficult to identify. However, its main identifying feature is its size, which is much larger than any other boneless pork cut.

Fig. 12.26

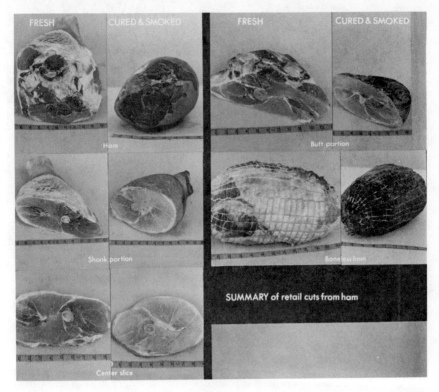

Fig. 12.27

Figure 12.27.   A summary of the retail cuts from the ham. The leg (ham) itself is a wholesale cut and at the same time a retail cut. In Chapter 17, you will be introduced to cured and smoked products. Here the identical cut is pictured; on the left in fresh form, on the right in cured and smoked form. The exterior of cured and smoked products takes on a highly appetizing brownish cast which results from heating and smoking for a 16-hour period. The cut surface of a cured and smoked product appears to be pink in color, which is a result of the action of the nitrites in the curing mix with the myoglobin pigment of the meat under the influence of heat to give the characteristic cured meat color which will be discussed in Chapter 17. A bone-in ham is usually hung in the smokehouse shank down in a stockinet (a porous cloth tube), which helps form the ham into a desirable shape. The more desirable symmetrical appearance of the cured ham and its component parts is obvious.

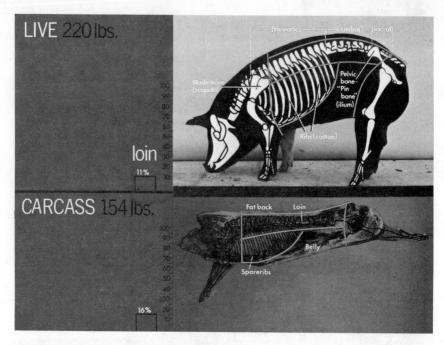

Fig. 12.28

Figure 12.28. The primal, lean cut, which is usually the most valuable cut in the pork carcass, is the loin. The loin comprises approximately 11% of the live weight of a hog and 16% of its carcass weight. These percentage figures are strictly averages, and the more mascular, minimumly finished hogs will have a considerably higher percentage of their carcass or live weight represented by the ham and the loin. The pork loin encompasses a longer area of the ·carcass than does the beef or lamb loin. The pork loin includes the area of the ribs, so in fact, you may have a retail cut properly named a rib chop from the loin in pork. This is definitely not possible in beef and lamb. The pork loin encompasses the *sacral, lumbar,* and a good portion of the *thoracic* areas of the vertebral column.

Figure 12.29. The first step in removing the loin from the pork carcass is to separate it from the shoulder. This is often done by cutting across the third rib, although variations are made (note later section in this chapter).

Fig. 12.29

Figure 12.30. After the bone has been cut with a saw, a final severance is made with a knife. Note that this separation is made at right angles to the long axis of the carcass.

Fig. 12.30

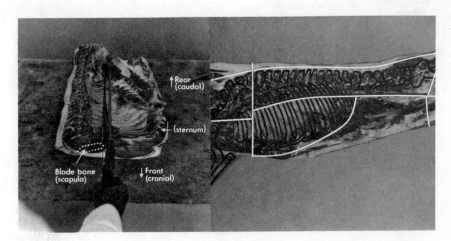

Fig. 12.31

Figure 12.31. The spareribs and belly are separated from the loin, which at this point still has the fatback remaining intact. Note in the skeletal diagram, the line indicating where the ribs will be severed, separatng the loin from the spareribs. Orient yourself with the blade bone or *scapula* on the front or cranial end of the carcass and the sirloin end to the rear.

Figure 12.32. After the ribs have been cut with a saw, the separation is completed from the sirloin end with a knife.

Viewing from the rear, the belly, with the spareribs intact, is on your left, the loin on your right. Recall the top sirloin or *gluteus medius* muscle which we identified in the rump (butt) face of the ham. The rump (butt) face of the ham actually joined this sirloin end of the loin. The tenderloin, or *psoas* muscle, is evident from this view.

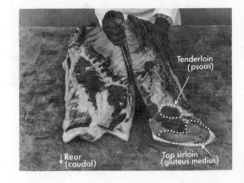

Fig. 12.32

399

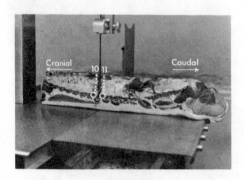

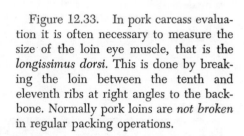

Figure 12.33. In pork carcass evaluation it is often necessary to measure the size of the loin eye muscle, that is the *longissimus dorsi*. This is done by breaking the loin between the tenth and eleventh ribs at right angles to the backbone. Normally pork loins are *not broken* in regular packing operations.

Fig. 12.33

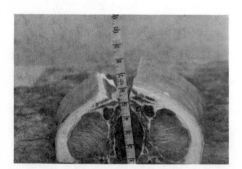

Fig. 12.34

Figure 12.34. If possible, we like to break the loin with the fatback intact so that when we measure loin eye area the loin maintains its natural size and shape, but in a packing house situation, where disassembly proceeds at about 11 pork carcasses per minute, the loin is pulled away from the fatback rapidly with a U-shaped loin knife so that it is impossible to break the loin with the fat intact. It is important that the loin is cut exactly perpendicular to its long axis to avoid making an error in its measurement. Some pork carcass evaluators break or "rib" the loin while the carcass is hanging, somewhat similar to the procedure in ribbing a beef carcass (Chapter 13). Two disadvantages to this technique are: (1) The belly is sometimes damaged by cutting into it from the side near the loin and (2) it is difficult to maintain a cut across the loin muscle exactly perpendicular to its long axis, thus inflating its true size.

Figure 12.35. The fatback is removed from the loin. Since this loin has been broken between the tenth and eleventh ribs, it is here removed from the blade portion or blade end of the loin, containing ribs 3 through 10. Note the characteristic blade bone, or *scapula*, and the cartilage present on the end of the blade bone. In trimming the blade end of the loin down to the point where only ¼ inch of outside fat remains, one exposes the false lean or *trapezius* muscle. In order to accomplish the proper job of trimming, this particular muscle must be exposed.

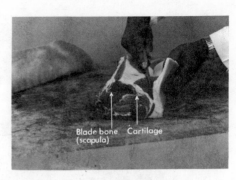

Fig. 12.35

Figure 12.36. In commercial practice, the loin is pulled from the belly and spareribs with a U-shaped loin knife and therefore comes out in one whole piece rather than in two sections as we have done here under laboratory conditions to properly evaluate the loin eye area. When loins are removed under packing house conditions with a loin pulling knife, sometimes the muscle is scored; that is, instead of only removing the fat, the knife penetrates into the loin muscle itself. This is very undesirable, since it destroys a part of the most valuable edible portion of the carcass. Under the laboratory conditions shown in this figure, the fatback is removed very carefully without scoring the loin.

Fig. 12.36

Figure 12.37. The fatback is processed into lard, although some areas still prefer *chunks* of fatback to be used in certain types of cooking, but the demand at present is very small for such use. This fat makes very high quality rendered lard.

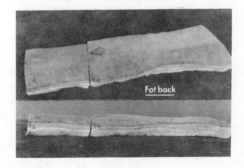

Fig. 12.37

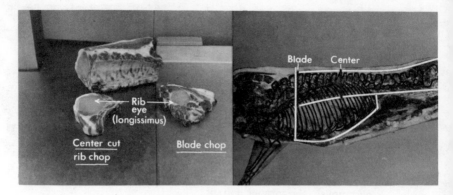

Fig. 12.38

Figure 12.38. Beginning at the cranial (front) portion of the loin, a retail chop called a blade chop is removed. The blade chop is identified by the presence of the blade bone and the attached cartilage. The center-cut rib chop in this figure came from the tenth rib, but the area from the fifth rib through the last rib would be the area for the center-cut rib chops. Notice the prevalent use of the term *chop* which originated from the use of a cleaver to *chop* the meat into small pieces. Now we use modern saws to make chops, but previously anything small enough to be *chopped* with a cleaver was designated a chop, while anything larger that had to be separated with a saw was called a steak. Thus, today we have pork and lamb chops but beef steaks.

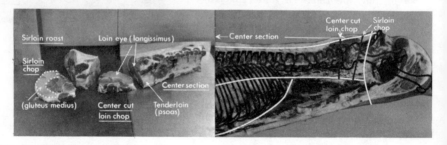

Fig. 12.39

Figure 12.39. The center-cut loin chop in this example has been removed from the area of the seventh (rear most) *lumbar* vertebra. All chops removed cranial (to the front) of this seventh *lumbar* vertabra up to the last rib are called center-cut loin chops and are identified by the presence of the tenderloin muscle and absence of a rib. In other words, all chops removed from the *lumbar* area of the vertebral column would be termed *center-cut loin chops*. From the caudal (rear) end of the loin, the rear-most chop removed is termed a *sirloin chop*. This chop is removed from the face which was directly connected to the rump (butt) face of the ham.

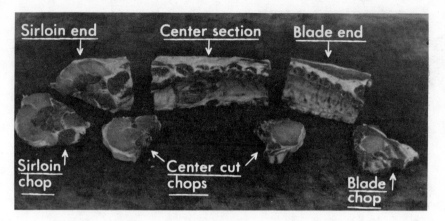

Fig. 12.40

Figure 12.40. In review, here are the component retail cuts from the loin: the blade chop from the blade end, center-cut chops which may be either center-cut rib chops or center-cut loin chops, and a sirloin chop. The pork loin chop contains a bonus—the tenderloin, which is indeed a tasty morsel!

Figure 12.41. Several innovations can be made with pork chops, one of them being a pocket chop. Ordinarily, regular bone-in pork chops are cut approximately ¾ to 1 inch thick, but for a pocket chop, they may be cut slightly thicker. Immediately adjacent to the rib, in the loin eye muscle, a slit is made which can be filled with dressing. The use of the rib chop is most appropriate for a pocket chop since the slit can be made under the rib and is hardly noticeable when the chops are served.

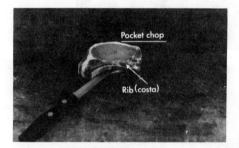

Fig. 12.41

The pork loin may be boned, although it is definitely more widely merchandised as bone-in chops and roasts. Boning the main portion of the loin does not normally present a problem if one first carefully removes the tenderloin (composed of the *psoas* major and *psoas* minor). The small minor is removed from the major for pork trim. From the blade end, it is an easy matter to remove the remaining *scapular* cartilage by keeping the knife flat and close to the cartilage. By using the same technique, the backbone and remaining portion of the ribs are removed. After removing the chine (body) and feather bones (dorsal processes), only back ribs remain, an excellent cut for barbecuing.

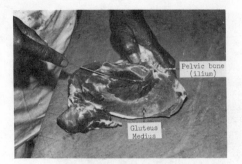

Fig. 12.42

Figure 12.42. The one somewhat difficult portion of the loin to bone is the sirloin end, because it contains a portion of the pelvic bone. Start by entering from the ham side and stay close to the bone.

Fig. 12.43

Figure 12.43. By continuing close to the bone, it is followed around in the same initial direction. It can be separated from the backbone through the *sacroiliac* joint and each removed separately, or they may be removed as one bone.

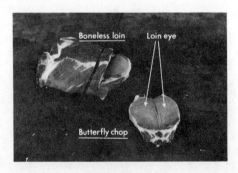

Fig. 12.44

Figure 12.44. A popular chop made from a boneless loin is a butterfly chop. This is in reality a double chop, since a normal ¾ inch thickness of cut is made but not completed. Again, a second normal thickness beyond that is made and the cut is completed. The double chop thus removed is folded out and becomes a very desirable boneless butterfly chop.

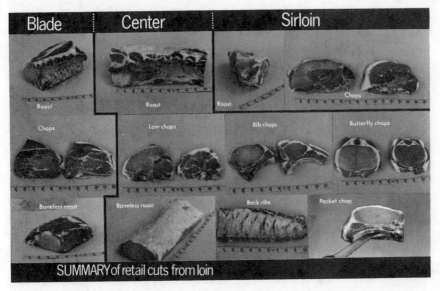

Fig. 12.45

Figure 12.45.   In summary, there are a multitude of retail cuts from the pork loin. Remember, the most forward portion of the loin is termed blade end. From the blade end, we may remove blade chops, or the blade end may be boned and the result is a boneless blade end roast. The most variety arises from the center section of the loin. The center itself may be utilized as a roast, but more often it is cut into chops, center-cut loin chops, and the center-cut rib chops. Also a rib chop may be made into a pocket chop. The boneless loin may be made into butterfly chops or simply left as a boneless loin. The boneless loin from large packing sows, that is, those weighing over 360 pounds alive, is often times cured and utilized as Canadian bacon. When one bones out the loin, a portion of the bone which is removed is very desirable for barbecuing. This is known as the back ribs. Finally, the sirloin end may be utilized intact as a bone-in roast or may be cut into chops, but more desirably, it is boned and two of them put together for a boneless sirloin roast, not shown in this summary.

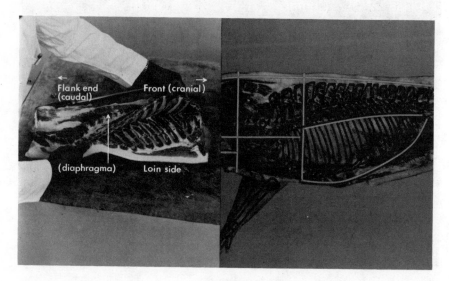

Fig. 12.46

Figure 12.46. When the spareribs are removed from the belly, the idea is to leave as small an amount of meat on the spareribs as is possible; thus, the name *spare* ribs. Also, one must be certain to remove all portions of the bone and cartilage including the *sternum* with the spareribs, since these make very unpalatable bacon. The loin side of the belly is that side which was attached to the loin. The length of the ribs themselves on the spareribs is a function of where the cut was made in separating the loin and spareribs. Recall our earlier discussion concerning separating the loin from the spareribs and belly (figures 12.31 and 12.32). Modern cutting methods dictate that the largest portion of the rib cage be left on the spareribs. Actually, pricewise, spareribs sometimes exceed loins in retail price. This is a matter of supply and demand since loins account for approximately 16% of the carcass weight while spareribs account for only 3% of the carcass weight.

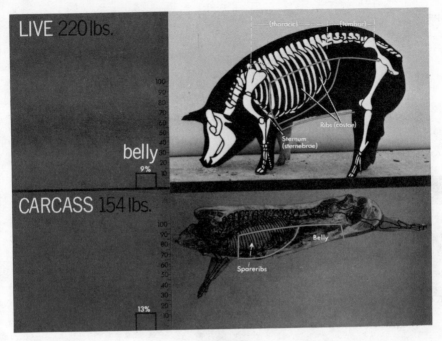

Fig. 12.47

Figure 12.47. The remaining portion after the removal of the spareribs is the fifth primal cut, called the belly. The belly comprises 9% of the live weight and approximately 13% of the carcass weight.

Figure 12.48. Once the spareribs have been removed, all that remains to be done to the belly is to simply square it up. First of all, the flank end is squared, next the loin side is trimmed, and finally the teat line is removed so that no rudimentary mammary glands are left in the bacon slab. Less expensive bacon is not trimmed so closely, and thus these mammary "seeds" may be found in such bacon.

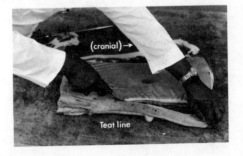

Fig. 12.48

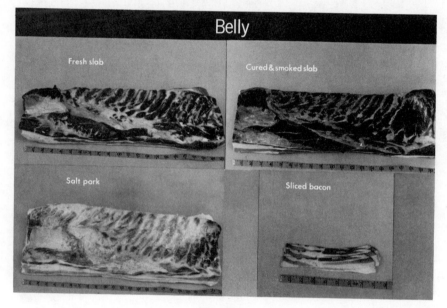

Fig. 12.49

Figure 12.49. The most common use of the belly is to cure and smoke it, which results in a cured and smoked slab. The most popular form of bacon is, of course, sliced bacon. Some people do prefer fresh slab bacon or fresh side pork. This also may be sliced. Others prefer the belly dry-cured or salted, which is called salt pork.

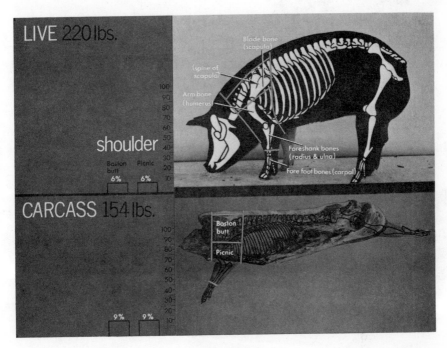

Fig. 12.50

Figure 12.50. The pork shoulder is composed of two primal, lean cuts, namely, the Boston shoulder (butt) and the picnic shoulder. Often the Boston shoulder (butt) and the picnic are nearly equal in weight, although the picnic is usually slightly heavier than the Boston shoulder (butt). The skeleton plays a very important role in identifying retail cuts from the Boston shoulder (butt) and the picnic, as indicated.

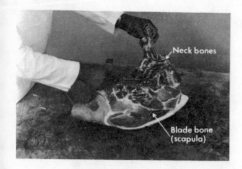

Fig. 12.51

Figure 12.51. The first step in fabricating the rough shoulder is to remove the neck bones. Neck bones make somewhat desirable, but less expensive, spareribs. Utilized as such, they can be very delicious barbecued.

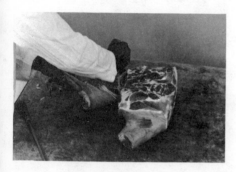

Fig. 12.52

Figure 12.52. The jowl is removed by beginning with the fat collar immediately above the fore shank and continuing straight across the cranial portion of the shoulder parallel with the cut which separated the shoulder from the loin, belly, and spareribs.

Fig. 12.53

Figure 12.53. The rough-cut jowl, after removal, is trimmed into the square-cut jowl. The square-cut jowl is utilized as cured and smoked jowl bacon squares. The bulk is utilized in sausage and loaf manufacture.

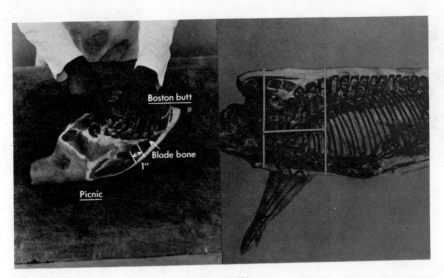

Fig. 12.54

Figure 12.54. The remaining portion, after removal of the neck bones and jowl, is called the fresh pork shoulder or New York shoulder. In this form it is a wholesale cut. At the same time, however, it is composed of two other wholesale cuts, the Boston shoulder (butt) and the picnic. The Boston butt is separated from the picnic by cutting at right angles to the long axis of the shoulder at a distance approximately 1 inch below the exposed surface of the blade bone. Note in the diagram to the right the bone structures that must be severed to make the separation.

Figure 12.55. A cut is made first with a saw to sever the bone, and then the cut is completed with a knife. Note that the blade bone is now exposed on two adjacent surfaces of the Boston shoulder (butt).

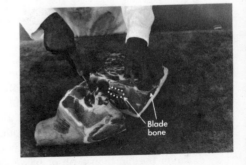

Fig. 12.55

411

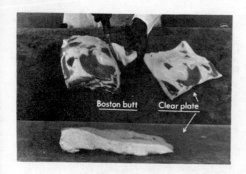

Fig. 12.56

Figure 12.56. The clear plate and any additional excess fat is removed from the Boston shoulder (butt). The clear plate is actually an extension of the fatback which was removed from the loin. Note again the false lean or *trapezius* muscle.

The clear plate is utilized much as the fatback is, mainly for rendering into high quality lard.

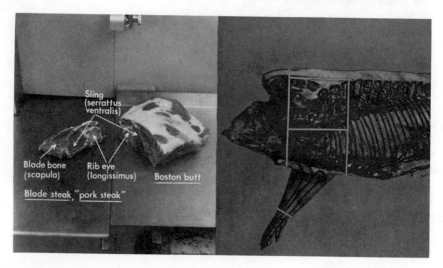

Fig. 12.57

Figure 12.57. The Boston butt is a wholesale cut and also a retail cut. The most popular retail cut of the Boston shoulder (butt) is the pork shoulder blade steak which is removed with a saw across the edge which contains the blade bone. Note the location of the cut in the diagram to the right. The identifying feature of the pork shoulder blade steak is the blade bone or *scapula*. Observe also the extension of the rib eye or the *longissimus* muscle. Note that we now refer to the pork shoulder *steak* or blade *steak*. This is a larger portion than a rib or blade chop and must be removed with a saw, thus the term *steak* is used.

Figure 12.58. The blade chop from the loin is very easily confused with the blade steak from the Boston shoulder (butt). The key to identifying them is the presence of a large amount of cartilage in the blade chop from the loin. This results from the fact that the chop is removed farther down on the blade bone, where the cartilage is more pronounced. The blade bone in the blade steak is much heavier, and a very small portion of cartilage is present. Also, the overall size of the blade steak is usually greater than that of the blade chop.

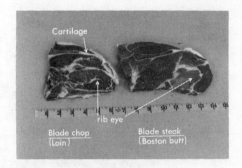

Fig. 12.58

Figure 12.59. Of all the boning operations, perhaps boning the Boston shoulder (butt) is the most simple. The one bone in the Boston butt is the blade bone or *scapula*. On the upper side of the blade bone is the spine of the *scapula* protruding from the broad flat area of the bone.

The boneless Boston butt is highly desirable, especially when cured and smoked. In this form it often rivals the boneless, cured, and smoked ham and generally may be sold at a slightly lower price.

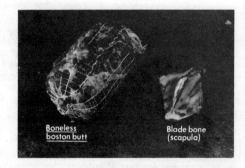

Fig. 12.59

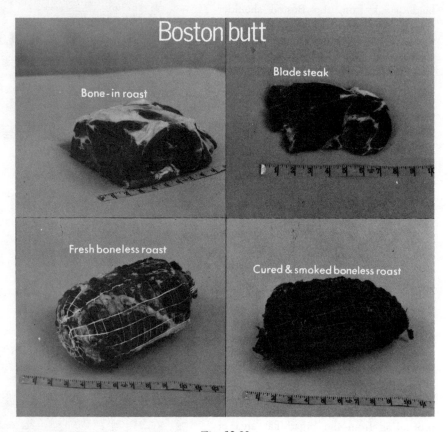

Fig. 12.60

Figure 12.60.   In summary, the retail cuts of the Boston shoulder (butt) are the fresh bone-in Boston shoulder roast, the blade steak removed from the fresh Boston shoulder, the fresh boneless roast, and the cured and smoked boneless roast.

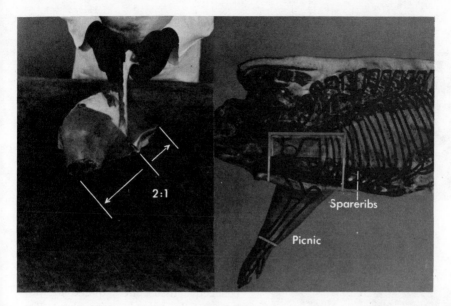

Fig. 12.61

Figure 12.61. The remaining portion of the shoulder is the one other lean cut called the pork shoulder picnic. In some parts of the country, it is called the *cala* because this type of cut originated in California. Most modern fabricators do remove approxmately one-third of the skin.

The fresh picnic shoulder also doubles as a wholesale cut and a retail cut.

Figure 12.62. The shoulder hock may be removed from the picnic shoulder and as such it makes a separate retail cut. It may be sold fresh or it may be cured and smoked.

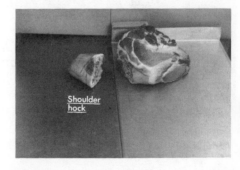

Fig. 12.62

415

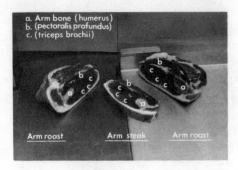

a. Arm bone (humerus)
b. (pectoralis profundus)
c. (triceps brachii)

Arm roast   Arm steak   Arm roast

Fig. 12.63

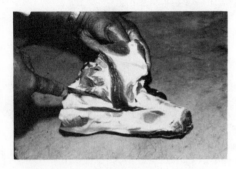

Fig. 12.64

Foreshank bone

Humerus

Fig. 12.65

Figure 12.63. The remainder of the picnic shoulder may be cut into arm roasts or arm steaks. The arm steak has a characteristic of an arm roast or steak of beef or an arm chop of lamb. The key to species identification comes mainly through the characteristic color of pork, lamb and beef, and cut size differences. Pork arm steaks are usually removed from the center of the picnic, the roasts being that portion left at either end. Many times the picnic will be sold only as a roast, either fresh or cured and smoked. The picnic shoulder is less desirable from a palatability standpoint than the Boston butt, since it is located lower on the live animal where smaller muscles, held together with large amounts of connective tissue, are required to work more as the animal moves about. The more that muscles are used in the live animal, the less palatable they are.

Figure 12.64. A major portion of the bone in the shoulder is located in the picnic. The bones are the fore shank bone which is the *tibia* and *fibula* fused together and the arm bone or *humerus*. Tunnel boning is not employed here but rather a cut is made from the outside to the bones.

Figure 12.65. The fore shank bone may be separated from the arm bone in its removal. The arm bone is then removed. Note the size of the arm bone. Because of the large amount of bone and connective tissue in a wholesale picnic as contrasted with the Boston butt, the picnic has less value.

416

Figure 12.66. Because of the large proportion of bone (the arm and shank bones) in the picnic shoulder, much more convenience is gained in boning the picnic than is gained by boning the Boston shoulder (butt) which contains only the blade bone. Often, picnics are boned out to obtain high quality sausage material.

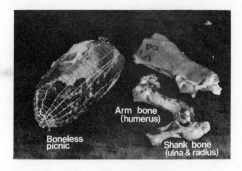

Fig. 12.66

Fig. 12.67

Figure 12.67.   The picnic shoulder itself in fresh or cured and smoked form is a retail cut. The cured and smoked picnic gains its symmetrical shape from being hung in a stockinet as it is heated and smoked in the smokehouse. The shoulder hock can be removed either from the fresh picnic or from the cured, smoked picnic. The arm steak, arm roast, and boneless picnic shown here fresh may also be utilized as cured and smoked product.

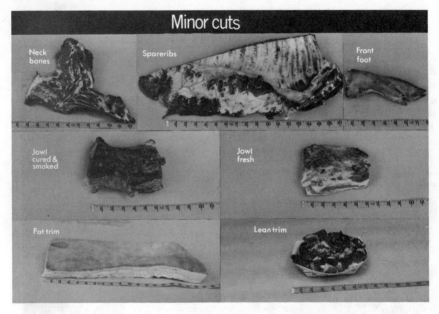

Fig. 12.68

Figure 12.68.   Discussion to this point has covered the four lean cuts— the leg (ham), loin, Boston shoulder (butt), and picnic shoulder as well as the other primal cut—the belly. Those remaining cuts of a pork carcass other than the primal cuts might be classified as minor cuts. Foremost among them would be the spareribs. Also of great importance is the lean trim. Pork trimmings fulfill a terrifically vital role in the fabrication of processed meats such as the multitude of sausage products and sandwich loaves, frankfurters, etc. (see Chapter 16). Fat trim is generally processed into lard. The neck bones serve as a substitute for spareribs, and the jowl serves as a rather inexpensive form of slab bacon.

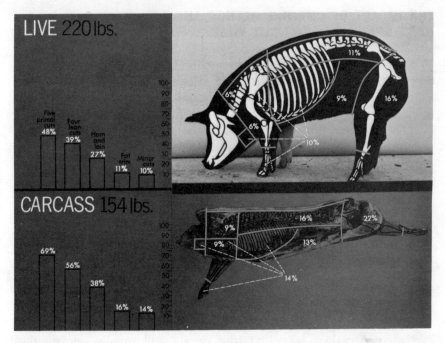

Fig. 12.69

Figure 12.69. In summary, first focus your attention on the center column. The leg (ham) and loin compose 27% of the live animal and 38% of its carcass. Check these figures by adding 16 and 11 for the leg (ham) and loin respectively as shown on the live animal to get 27 and by adding 22 and 16 on the carcass to get 38. The percentages listed on the cuts on the live animal and carcass thus represent the percentage yield of each of those cuts. To obtain the four lean cut percentages, simply add the Boston shoulder (butt) and picnic shoulder to the leg (ham) and loin percentages to come up with a total of 39% of the live weight for the four lean cuts and 56% of the carcass weight. When one adds the fifth primal cut, the belly, the percentage for the five primal cuts amounts to 48% of the live weight and 69% of the carcass weight. Fat trim comprises 11% of the live weight and 16% of the carcass, while minor cuts comprise 10% of the live weight and 14% of the carcass weight. It must be stressed that these are average figures taken from a so-called average hog. This hog would probably have approximately 1.3 inches of average backfat, be approximately 30 inches long, and have an area of loin eye in the neighborhood of 4½ square inches.

More muscular and trimmer hogs would yield considerably higher percentages of the lean cuts than these figures, while less well muscled or fatter hogs would yield lower figures.

THE IMPACT OF CUTTING METHOD AND
USDA GRADE ON LEAN CUT YIELD

Almost all of the progress in producing the modern, meaty hog dates from the time breeders began selecting herd replacements and using carcass data on their hogs. Today, nearly everyone uses cut-out information at one time or another in selecting replacements.

There is one problem with that, though. Many people think that once a hog is dead, the carcass is measured and that's it. But *there are big differences in the way hogs are evaluated for slaughter data,* depending on which plant is doing the work. How the cuts are taken and how they are trimmed can make 5% or even 7% difference in cut-out from identical hogs.

While one way is not necessarily *better* than the other, you should know how your packer does it if you are going to get the most out of the data.

The differences crop up in the way the packer cuts up carcasses and trims the cuts. A given packer may also change the way he cuts and trims from day to day, depending on the relative prices of the various cuts. In general, however, he follows the same overall method pretty consistently. Those that trim closely will usually operate that way; those with a market that doesn't mind more fat usually leave more on.

Backfat, length, and loin eye will generally be consistent with either method. *But weights and percentages can vary tremendously*—never compare those figures from two different packers or processors. To illustrate this point, we slaughtered and processed two hogs of quite different types.

Figure 12.70. The hog on the left is an overfat No. 3, weighing 208 pounds; the hog on the right, a meaty USDA No. 1, weighing 234 pounds. Notice the flat top and abrupt, sharp turn over the loin of the white pig indicating considerable amount of fat over that loin.

Fig. 12.70

Figure 12.71. As we view the pigs over the top from the rear, we see that the Hampshire gilt has considerably more ham development as well as a groove down her back indicating a high degree of muscling and, at the same time, only a moderate amount of finish as compared to the white barrow on the left.

Fig. 12.71

Figure 12.72. From the side, differences in ham development are quite apparent. Note also the heavy shoulders of the white barrow, as compared to the Hampshire gilt which has a larger proportion of her body in the more valuable ham and loin.

Fig. 12.72

Figure 12.73. After slaughter, both carcasses were carefully split so that as nearly as possible each half weighed the same. The overfat carcass was 30.1 inches long, had an average backfat thickness of 1.87 inches, and had slightly thin muscling. The meaty hog had a carcass length of 30.2 inches with an average backfat thickness of 1.10 inches and displayed very thick muscling.

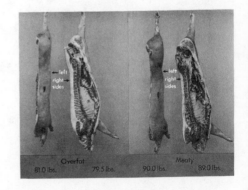

Fig. 12.73

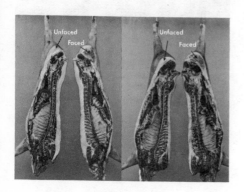

Fig. 12.74

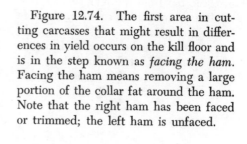

Figure 12.74. The first area in cutting carcasses that might result in differences in yield occurs on the kill floor and is in the step known as *facing the ham*. Facing the ham means removing a large portion of the collar fat around the ham. Note that the right ham has been faced or trimmed; the left ham is unfaced.

Fig. 12.75

Figure 12.75. What is the impact of cutting method on lean cut yield of these two very different types of hogs, the meaty hog on the right, which produced a carcass with considerably less fatness and more muscling, especially in the ham versus the overfat pig on the left, which is heavy in backfat and lacks muscling? The carcass halves were cut up using two rather sharply contrasting methods. Both methods are used by packing plants. The first method, called the *maximum trim method,* means that the maximum amount of fat is trimmed away and results in lower percentages (based on carcass weight) of the four lean cuts [leg (ham), loin, Boston shoulder (butt), and picnic shoulder]. The second method called the *minimum trim method,* means that very little fat is trimmed away which results in higher percentage figures.

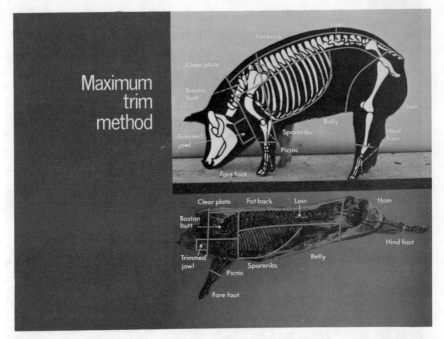

Fig. 12.76

Figure 12.76.   Frst, examine the maximum trim method in detail, observing where differences in cutting methods exist. Note the location of the hind foot removal. By leaving a long shank on the ham and removing less hind foot, the weight of the ham is increased. Secondly, examine the point at which the ham is separated from the loin. Depending on prices for hams and loins, the packer can make this cut farther forward, resulting in more ham and less loin, or conversely, farther to the rear resulting in more loin and less ham. Next, note the line separating the rough shoulder [composed of the Boston shoulder (butt), picnic shoulder, clear plate, jowl, and fore foot] from the loin, spareribs, belly and fatback. The critical point is the separation between the shoulder (picnic–Boston) and the loin. In this maximum trim, the cut is made across the third rib, leaving 2½ ribs on the shoulder. Since shoulders are usually less valuable than loins, this cut is sometimes made farther forward into the shoulder, that is, at the first rib, making a heavier but less desirable loin. The removal of the front foot may also vary. The final cutting difference we want to point out is the technique used in separating the spareribs from the loin. Note here how the cutting line follows the curvature of the back, resulting in a loin with very short ribs. The more this line is straightened out, the longer the rib length of the loin becomes, thus shortening the length of ribs in the spareribs.

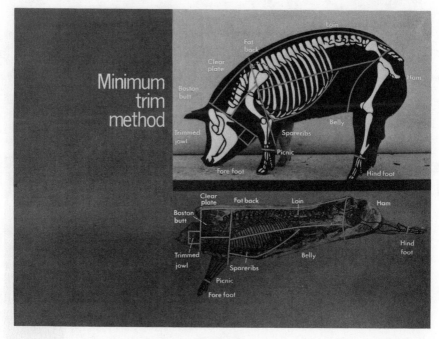

Fig. 12.77

Figure 12.77. Remember, when considering the minimum trim, this method results in a higher percentage of trimmed lean cuts, but the cuts are actually fatter or *less* lean. Note the location of the hind foot removal. Compare with the maximum trim in Figure 12.76. The hind foot is usually not used for human consumption since it has very little muscle (meat) attached. Therefore, any part of the foot left on the ham is added weight to the ham, but makes the ham less desirable. Again notice the ham/loin junction, in this case moved slightly to the rear, making a smaller ham and a longer loin. Observe the shoulder/loin separation. The cut is made directly over the first rib, making a longer, heavier loin than would result from cutting across the third rib. Furthermore, the front shank is left longer on the picnic with this minimum trim method. Front feet are used for smoked or pickled pigs feet, and thus, the price differential between them and picnics is not as great as the price difference between hind feet and ham. Finally, notice the straight line separating the loin from the spareribs and belly. It is obvious that a much greater portion of the ribs will be left on the loin than is the case with the maximum trim (Figure 12.76).

Figure 12.78. Now let us return to the overfat and meaty animals and demonstrate the impact of cutting method on each lean cut in more detail.

With the leg (ham), note the shank length, short with maximum trim, and long with minimum trim. Secondly, note the length of the rump (butt) portion, that portion to your right of the aitch bone, indicated by brackets. With the minimum trim, we can see that more ham was left on the loin thus resulting in a shorter length of (rump) butt as you view the ham.

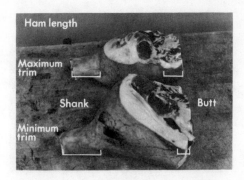

Fig. 12.78

Figure 12.79. As viewed from the rump (butt) end, the untrimmed hams further exemplify the differences in the meaty hog and the overfat hog. Note that the right ham is faced in each case, the left ham is unfaced. This is more obvious in the overfat hams.

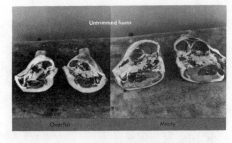

Fig. 12.79

Figure 12.80. There can be a considerable difference in the way hams are trimmed. In a minimum trim, only the skin and a little fat are removed. With the maximum trim, the skin is removed farther down towards the shank, more fat is removed, and the remaining fat is beveled down to a mere ¼ inch. This is easily seen as you view the skinned hams from the outside. Note that in the case of the overfat carcass, the maximum trim resulted in a 2-pound lighter ham, a difference of 2.6 percent of carcass weight. In the meaty hog, the differences in ham length cancelled out the differences in trim so that the maximum trim ham weighed exactly the same as the minimum trim ham.

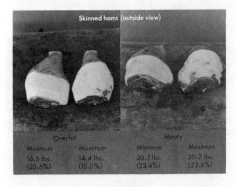

Fig. 12.80

425

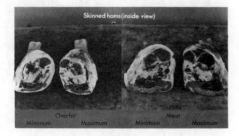

Fig. 12.81

Figure 12.81. When the ham is viewed as ordinarily seen from the inside—the differences in trim are not nearly as apparent. Therefore, one must be aware of what he is looking for to determine differences in cutting methods.

Although it is not the purpose of this presentation to discuss pork quality, mention must be made of the obvious differences in the quality of hams from these two hogs. Unfortunately, the hams from the overfat hog excell considerably in quality, being firmer in the lean surface, possessing a more uniform greyish-pink color and a higher level of marbling than the muscular hams which must be criticized for being extremely pale and soft and lacking marbling.

Fig. 12.82

Figure 12.82. The cutting method is quite noticeable by the length of loin. In both cases, the overfat loins on the left and the meaty loins on the right, a minimum trim gives a longer loin. The extra length comes from the additional one-half to two ribs left on the loin as seen on the front portion of the loin.

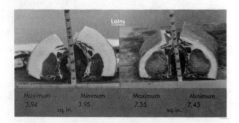

Fig. 12.83

Figure 12.83. Rib length left on the loin after the spareribs and belly have been removed varies according to cutting method. When using the minimum trim, a longer rib is left than in the maximum trim, resulting in more weight in the loin for the minimum trim. It is interesting to note here at the tenth rib, the loin eye areas of the two individuals used in this test—3.9 square inches versus 7.4 square inches. Even though the two sides of a pork carcass are mirror images of one another, it is practically impossible to get *exactly* the same measurements of loin eye area or backfat thickness between the two sides because of human error. Again notice the quality differences in favor of the less muscular loin.

Figure 12.84. In the trimmed loins, it is obvious that more fat is removed with the maximum trim, leaving only one-fourth of an inch. In fact, some of the surface muscles near the blade or front end of the loin are exposed. The difference in cutting methods is shown most dramatically in the weights of the trimmed loins. Notice that the fat hog differences due to trimming methods were 5.4 pounds or 6.4% of the carcass weight—19.8% for minimum trim versus 13.4% for the maximum trim. Differences in loin weight were even greater for the meaty hog with a minimum trim loin weight of 23 pounds versus a maximum trim loin weight of 16.2 pounds.

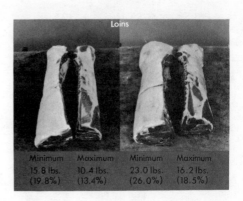

Fig. 12.84

Figure 12.85. The minimum trim Boston shoulder (butt) actually weighed less than the maximum trim from the meaty hog because of the fact that the cut separating the shoulder from the loin was made a distance of 1½ ribs farther forward, thus subtracting from the weight of the Boston shoulder (butt) and picnic shoulder while adding to the weight of the loin. However, with the overfat hog, the difference in fatness overshadowed this difference in cutting location on the weight of the Boston shoulder (butt). At any rate, we can see that there are considerable differences due to cutting methods in the weight and percentages of the Boston shoulder (butt), but that these differences may tend to cancel out when both loins and Boston shoulders are considered to establish lean cut percentages of hog carcasses.

Fig. 12.85

Fig. 12.86

Figure 12.86. In looking at the picnic shoulder, that cut which is the lower portion of the shoulder, the influence of the number of ribs left on the loin does not appear to be as great as was the case with the Boston shoulder (butt), since the minimum trim picnic weighs slightly more in both cases than the maximum trim picnic shoulder. This difference is due largely to differences in amount of fat and skin trimmed; considerably more is trimmed in the maximum method. The overfat hog has an additional advantage as compared to the meaty hog, as it gained 0.2% due to cutting method while the meaty hog only gained 0.1%.

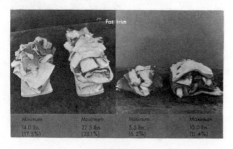

Fig. 12.87

Figure 12.87. Observe the total amount of fat trimmed from each carcass during the complete processing of the carcass into its five primal cuts (including the belly) and the minor cuts such as spareribs, neck bones, jowl, etc. This is total fat trim in the carcass. As would be expected with a maximum trim, there are larger amounts of fat trim as compared to the minimum trim which leaves more fat on the four lean cuts. It is certainly an eye opener to see the tremendous difference in fat trim, especially in the overfat hog.

	Overfat		Meaty	
	*Minimum	*Maximum	*Minimum	*Maximum
Ham	20.6	18.0	23.4	23.6
Loin	19.8	13.4	26.0	18.5
Ham & loin	40.4	31.4	49.4	42.1
Boston butt	7.9	7.4	9.6	10.1
Picnic	7.0	6.8	9.6	9.5
Four lean cuts	55.3	45.6	68.6	61.7
Fat trim	17.5	28.1	6.2	11.4

*Percent of carcass

Fig. 12.88

Figure 12.88. In summary, review the figures which resulted from this comparison of cutting methods. The most popular method of evaluating hog carcasses is by percent ham and loin, that is the percent of the carcass represented as ham and loin. However, some data is still reported in terms of four lean cuts. Recall again the definition of minimum and maximum trim. Minimum trim means a type of fabrication which leaves as much fat as the market can bear on the leg (ham), loin, Boston shoulder (butt), and picnic shoulder, whereas the maximum trim removes the maximum amount of fat leaving only that which is necessary to insure palatability for the consumer. We are comparing an overfat hog with a meaty hog. The leg (ham) figures are lower in the overfat hog than they are in the properly finished, muscular, meaty hog. The differences due to cutting methods were not great in the meaty hog because of the fact that ham length differences equalled the difference in trim. However, this was not the case in the overfat leg (ham) where fatness overshadowed cutting differences. The differences in loin weight are very apparent and are perhaps the most dramatic point of the presentation. Since the common criterion generally reported is percent ham and loin, notice the difference of 9% in the overfat hog and 7.3% in the meaty hog due to cutting method! This is evidence that a fat hog can generally benefit more by the use of a minimum trim method than can a properly finished hog. Boston butt and picnic figures are presented. Note that differences due to cutting method are of the same magnitude whether expressed as percent four lean cuts or as percent ham and loin. The fat trim figures are also dramatic and parallel very closely in an opposite trend, the four lean cuts and percent ham and loin figures.

Since these differences do exist, how can a person evaluate a set of carcass figures and tell what kind of a cutting method was used in securing the data? Here are some guidelines to keep in mind: (1) the percent ham and loin or four lean cuts should increase as backfat declines and decrease as backfat increases. If this is not generally true, that is, hogs that have 1.3 to 1.4 inches of backfat have about as high a percent ham and loin as hogs with 1.0 or 1.1 inches, a maximum trim method was *not* used; (2) the general level of the percent and loin that is secured will tell you something. If a maximum trim is being used, hogs that have 1.0 to 1.1 inches of backfat and have approximately 5.5 square inches of loin eye will have 40%, 41%, or possibly 42% ham and loin. If such hogs cut 43% to 46% ham and loin, a minimum type trim method was used.

Finally, remember three things when checking carcass data: *First,* never compare percentage figures secured at different packing plants. *Second,* don't attach too much significance to small differences between hogs. If we could get a 7% to 9% difference between two sides of the same hog due to cutting methods, differences of up to 1% between different hogs can easily exist due to differences in how the carcasses were split, cut, and trimmed within the same plant, even if every effort was put forth to be consistent. Remember, most large commercial operations cut approximately 11 hogs per *minute* (660/hour) when in normal production. A slip of the knife can come quite easily under such conditions. *Third,* in spite of all this, carcass data properly evaluated has been and will continue to be the basis of much of the future improvement in the hog business.

LARD

Trends in Lard Production and Consumption

Lard production and consumption has continued a steady decline since 1950 (Table 12.1). The cyclic hog slaughter trends indicated in the first column are not borne out entirely in the second column showing total lard production. This is because a dramatic change has come about in composition of our market hogs away from the "lard bucket" types toward the lean, muscular, fast growing market animals which are bred to produce lean edible products. The third column shows lard production per slaughtered hog which demonstrates the progress that has been made.

The decrease in production coupled with increased competition from fats of vegetable origin has resulted in a steady decrease in consumption since 1950.

Table 12.1—Trends in U.S. Lard Production and Consumption[1]

Year	Total Hog Slaughter	Total Lard Production	Lard Production per Hog (Col. 2/Col. 1)	Consumption[2]		Civilian Population July 1
				Total	Per Person	
	(1,000 hd.)	(mil. lbs.)	(lbs.)	(mil. lbs.)	(lb.)	(mil.)
1950	79,263	2,631	33.2	1,891	12.6	150.2
1951	85,540	2,863	33.5	1,855	12.3	151.1
1952	86,572	2,881	33.3	1,817	11.8	153.4
1953	74,368	2,355	31.7	1,772	11.4	156.0
1954	71,495	2,330	32.6	1,627	10.2	159.1
1955	81,051	2,660	32.6	1,639	10.1	162.3
1956	85,064	2,757	32.4	1,623	9.8	165.4
1957	78,636	2,547	32.4	1,589	9.4	168.4
1958	76,822	2,426	31.6	1,640	9.6	171.5
1959	87,606	2,780	31.7	1,536	8.8	174.5
1960	84,150	2,562	30.4	1,358	7.6	178.1
1961	81,970	2,514	30.7	1,393	7.7	181.1
1962	83,424	2,476	29.7	1,314	7.2	183.6
1963	87,117	2,473	28.4	1,190	6.4	186.4
1964	86,284	2,473	28.7	1,193	6.3	189.1
1965	76,458	2,045	26.7	1,225	6.4	191.5
1966	75,382	1,929	25.6	1,071	5.5	193.3
1967	83,420	2,076	24.9	1,055	5.4	195.2
1968	86,417	2,062	23.9	1,106	5.6	197.0
1969	84,968	1,904	22.4	1,011	5.1	199.1
1970	86,924	1,913	22.0	939	4.7	201.6
1971	95,527	1,960	20.5	880	4.3	204.2
1972	85,669	1,558	18.2	795	3.8	206.5

1. Livestock and Meat Statistics, Livestock Division, Agricultural Marketing Service, U.S. Dept. of Agriculture, Stat. Bul. No. 522.

2. As lard direct only and not including lard used in manufactured foodstuffs.

Official Definitions[1]

319.702   Lard, Leaf Lard

Lard is the fat rendered from fresh, clean, sound, fatty tissue from hogs with or without lard stearin or hydrogenated lard. The fatty tissues shall not include bones, detached skin, head skin, ears, tails, organs, windpipes, large blood vessels, scrap fat, skimmings, settings, pressings, and similar materials, and the fatty tissues shall be reasonably free from muscle tissue and blood. *Leaf lard* is lard prepared from fresh leaf fat.

319.703   Rendered Animal Fat or Mixture Thereof

1. *Rendered Animal Fat,* or any mixture of fats containing edible rendered animal fat, shall contain no added water, except that *Puff Pastry Shortening* may contain not more than 10% of water.
2. *Rendered Pork Fat* is fat, other than lard, rendered from clean, sound carcasses, parts of carcasses, or edible organs from hogs, except that stomachs, bones from the head, and bones from cured or cooked pork are not included. The tissues rendered are usually fresh, but may be cured, cooked, or otherwise prepared and may contain some meat food products. Rendered pork fat may be hardened by the use of lard stearin and/or hydrogenated lard and/or rendered pork fat stearin and/or hydrogenated rendered pork fat.

Rendering the Pork Fat

Lard rendered on the farm usually is a combination of leaf and trimming fat which is cooked either with or without the rind (skin). Killing fat (intestinal fat) is usually rendered separately for soap making purposes. Removal of the skin (rinding) is optional. Lard yield based on rinded fat should average 80% to 85% as compared to 75% to 78% for unrinded fat when extracted by the ordinary hand press method.

The fat should be cut into pieces of uniform size, not over an inch square, or run through a chopper. The smaller the pieces, the more rapid and thorough the rendering. The fat is usually rendered the day after slaughtering. The longer the fat is held before it is rendered, the greater will be the free fatty acid content of the lard. This lowers the keeping quality as well as the smoke point of the lard. The smoke point (250° to 425° F, depending upon its free fatty acid content) is the temperature at which lard begins to give off smoke in cooking.

---

1. *Meat and Poultry Inspection Regulations,* USDA, APHIS.

Overcooking lard increases the free fatty acid content, lowers its keeping quality, develops a more pronounced flavor and odor, and darkens the color. Particles of meat adhering to the fat will also cause a discoloration. The steam pressure employed in rendering lard in steam jacketed kettles varies from 30 to 50 pounds. The temperature of the lard, when rendering, should not exceed 240° F. The longer lard is hot, the more free fatty acid is formed; therefore, quick cooling, to inhibit this action, is a recommended practice. Lard should not be rendered in copper or rusty iron kettles, or run through brass valves or fittings, because some of the copper and rust are dissolved and combined with the fats, forming oxidative salts that will lower the stability of the lard. Stainless steel is considered an ideal receptacle for rendering. Rust-free iron kettles are in general use; aluminum is very satisfactory.

If steam jacketed kettles are not available for the process of rendering, and the job is done with an open fire, it will be necessary to stir the fat frequently and watch the fire closely to avoid scorching the lard. Continual agitation by stirring gives the most rapid and thorough rendering. The lard is ready to be "drawn off" when the cracklings have become amber in color and no more moisture rises from the lard.

Pressing and Cooling

The lard press should be sweet and clean. A slight coating of last year's rancid lard on the press or old, ill-smelling containers will lower the quality and hasten the deterioration of the new batch. Lard containers should be scrubbed thoroughly and dried. Several thicknesses of cheese cloth are sufficient to strain out the sediment.

If lard is allowed to cool without any stirring, the lard oil in it tends to separate from the stearin and causes a grainy texture, a characteristic of country lard. To get a smooth lard, set it away in a cool place, and when it becomes creamy, stir it well with a paddle and let it harden. Pork packers plasticize lard by cooling it rapidly on a chill roll or in a Votator chilling machine. Rapid chilling and agitating cause the formation of small crystals which produce a firm, smooth lard. The lard storage temperature should be 40° F.

Packing House Lard

Pork packers have three grades of pork fat: (1) the killing fats (intestinal), (2) the leaf fats, and (3) the cutting fats. Usually these are rendered within 24 hours after the hogs have been slaughtered.

The three most important sources of lard obtained from a hog carcass are (1) leaf fat, (2) fat trimmings, and (3) fat backs and plates. About

75% of the fat backs are rendered for lard, the other 25% being marketed fresh, frozen, or cured.

A market weight hog grading U. S. No. 1 yields about 8 pounds of lard per 100 pounds live weight, whereas the same weight hog grading U. S. No. 3 yields about 16 pounds, or 50% more lard.

Kettle-rendered Lard

Steam jacketed kettles with mechanical agitators are used in this method. Leaf fat rendered by this process is known as *open kettle-rendered leaf lard* and is the highest grade of commercial lard outside of the neutral lards or the new processed lards. Trimming fats go into kettle-rendered lard.

Steam-rendered Lard

This process consists of bringing live steam into direct contact with the fat in a closed vertical tank or cylinder under a pressure of 30 to 50 pounds. Mostly killing and trimming fats are used. If it is bleached with fuller's earth and refined, it is known as *refined lard*.

Dry-processed Rendered Lard

In this process, fats are cooked in horizontal steam jacketed tanks under a vacuum. The three kinds of fat may be rendered separately, or all kinds of pork fat may be converted into lard under this method.

Neutral Lard

This consists generally of leaf or back fats that are rendered in a water jacketed kettle by slowly melting them at 126° F. Neutral lard is white in color, bland in flavor, and finds wide use in the manufacture of butter substitutes.

Lard Substitutes

Substitutes are made of a combination of (1) lard and other animal fats (lard compound), (2) vegetable oils with animal fats, and (3) hydrogenated vegetable oils, the most prominent of which are cottonseed, soya bean, peanut, and coconut oil.

Lard Oil and Stearin

Fat may be stored at high temperatures, usually 90° to 100° F to permit the liquid (lard oil) to separate from the solid (stearin). Stearin is the white solid material composed of glycerin and stearic acid left after the pressing operation forces out the lard oil. Lard oil consists mainly of olein and is made from prime steam lard. It is used in the manufacture of margarine, as a burning oil, and as a lubricant for thread-cutting machines.

Modern Lard

One of the accomplishments of the packing industry during the period of World War II was the improvement made in lard to meet the competition of vegetable shortenings. This new type of lard is no longer rendered pork fat as such. It has been given new treatments and new names.

The processing necessary to produce this new lard has added to its cost and, like all improvements, must be paid for by the consumer. Because the average housewife objected to the blue color, (which is the natural color of pure lard), the manufacturer had to decolorize it; because she objected to its odor, he had to deodorize it; so that it would not become too soft at room temperature, he had to add hydrogenated lard flakes and raise its melting point; in order that it would keep on the shelf as well as well as in the refrigerator, he had to give it added stability by adding an antioxidant; and, finally, he had to place it in a container that would preserve these added qualities.

Lard as a Shortening

Pure lard is a natural fat—nothing has been added and nothing removed. This is an important factor in its digestibility and nutritive value. All fats are highly digestible, but their ease of digestion is reported to depend on their melting point. In order to convert liquid vegetable oils to lard-like consistency and give them increased stability, manufacturers use the hydrogenation process to raise the melting point. Lard is practically liquid at body temperature; hydrogenated fats are not.

Fats contain varying amounts of linoleic and arachidonic fatty acids, which are essential to the human body. Since the body cannot synthesize these fatty acids, they must be supplied in the diet. In hydrogenation, linoleic acid, the nutritionally valuable substance, is converted to a more saturated acid to make fat more resistant to the development of rancidity. The lard that consumers buy is not hydrogenated but does contain an adequate amount of the acid.

Lard is composed of a mixture of liquid and solid fats which gives it a wider plastic range under lower temperatures than hydrogenated fats. This makes it possible to use lard right out of the refrigerator.

Repeated tests have indicated that lard has greater shortening value than hydrogenated fats. By shortness is meant the force necessary to break a standard cracker or pie crust. The lower the breaking strength, the greater the shortening value. This shortening ability results in a flakier and lighter crust.

Antioxidants for Animal Fats

APHIS, USDA has to approve any antioxidant used in animal fats sold in interstate commerce. To date, these approved antioxidants, which must be tasteless, odorless, and non-toxic and must stabilize the fat by retarding rancidity as claimed, are: (1) BHA (butylated hydroxyanisole), (2) BHT (butylated hydroxytoluene), (3) glycine, (4) propyl gallate, (5) resin guaiac, and (6) tocopherols.

An illustration of the use of (4) is the combination of propyl gallate, lecithin, corn oil, and citric acid marketed by Griffith Laboratories of Chicago, Illinois, under the trade name of G-4. It is sold in both regular and concentrated form, the recommended amount being 2 ounces of the regular to 100 pounds of lard or fat and 6 to 8 ounces of the concentrate to 1,000 pounds of fat. It is also available with salt (5¾ ounces of antioxidant to 100 pounds of salt). This is recommended by the company in seasoning sausage, fried pork skins, potato chips, nut meats, popcorn, peanut butter, etc.

A.M.I.F.–72, developed by H. R. Kraybill and staff of the American Meat Institute, has butylated hydroxyanisole as its main ingredient and, when used alone, is not unusually effective in increasing the stability of lard as measured by the Active Oxygen Method, but it does have the unusual property of "carrying through" and protecting the foods made with lard from becoming rancid. However, when 70 parts of propylene glycol, 6 parts of propyl gallate, and 4 parts of citric acid are added to 20 parts of butylated hydroxyanisole (BHA), it has very definite antioxidant qualities.

It is commercially available under the trade name Tenox II, made and sold by Tennessee Eastman Corporation, Kingsport, Tennessee. The recommendations are for the use of 1 pint of Tenox for each 2,000 pounds of lard. Add the Tenox II to the melted lard and stir thoroughly to insure complete distribution.

Stabilizing Home-Rendered Lard

To improve the keeping quality of home-rendered lard, the U.S. Department of Agriculture's Eastern Regional Research Laboratory has recommended the addition of 2 to 3 pounds of hydrogenated vegetable shortening to every 50 pounds of lard at rendering time, just before settling and separating the cracklings. The shortening should be stirred into the hot lard to get a thorough mix. The vegetable oils used in making vegetable shortening contain vitamin E (tocopherol), which is an antioxidant. The addition of the antioxidant to home-rendered lard in this manner provides a cheap and easy method for farmers to follow without tangling with vexatious chemical terms.

Scoring Lard

Texture (20 points)

Lard that is allowed to cool slowly without any stirring at the cream stage will become grainy because the lard oil separates from the stearin. This is characteristic of home-rendered lard. However, a smooth, velvety lard is desirable, from the standpoint of both appearance and plasticity.

Odor (30 points)

Lard should have the sweet characteristic lard odor, and strong or rancid odors should be scored down.

Color (25 points)

Off color in lard may be due to scorching or to the presence of meat proteins caused by lean meat in the fat trimmings. Both are considered objectionable. A chalk or white color is ideal, and any shading into cream or tan must be scored down.

Body (25 points)

Ordinary room temperature (60° to 70° F) should find lard fairly firm. Oily, soft lard is scored down.

Lard as a Treatment for Eczema

Finnerud and Kesler of Rush Medical College, Chicago, studied a number of eczema cases in the clinic and hospitalized some for a period of two to seven weeks. After determining the unsaturated fatty acid content of the blood of normal patients and comparing it with those afflicted with eczema, they discovered that half of the afflicted patients had blood with low fatty acid content. Lard was administered through the diet and the patients whose blood had been found to have a low, unsaturated fatty acid content showed an increase. All the patients improved markedly under the treatment, which suggests that there was an unsaturated fatty acid deficiency that could be rectified by the addition of lard to the diet.

CHAPTER 13

Beef Identification and Fabrication

IDENTIFICATION

The *Uniform Retail Meat Identity Standards*[1] (see Chapter 12) will again be used as the basis for identification in this chapter.

FABRICATION

The skeletal structure of the bovine in relation to an outline of the wholesale cuts is shown in Figure 13.1 and a more detailed chart of wholesale and retail cuts appears as Figure 13.2. Use these two figures for reference as the discussion moves through cutting a beef carcass.

Figures 13.3 through 13.90 appear through the courtesy of the University of Illinois.

More Detailed References

The Agricultural Marketing Service, U. S. Department of Agriculture, has prepared a series of Institutional Meat Purchase Specifications titled as follows:

—for Fresh Beef - Series 100
—for Fresh Lamb and Mutton - Series 200
—for Fresh Veal and Calf - Series 300
—for Fresh Pork - Series 400

---

1. National Live Stock and Meat Board.

–for Cured, Cured and Smoked, and Fully-Cooked Pork
Products - Series 500
–for Cured, Dried and Smoked Beef Products - Series 600
–for Edible By-Products - Series 700

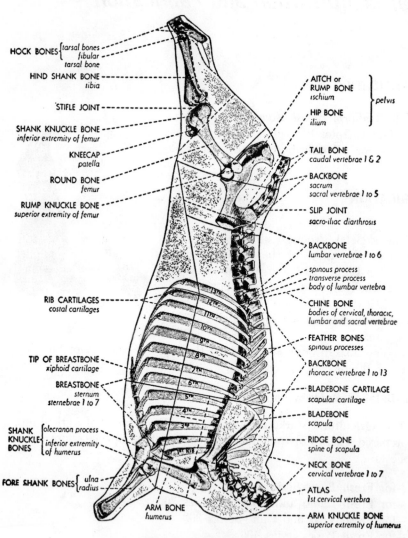

HOCK BONES { *tarsal bones*
fibular
tarsal bone

HIND SHANK BONE
tibia

'STIFLE JOINT

SHANK KNUCKLE BONE
inferior extremity of femur

KNEECAP
patella

ROUND BONE
femur

RUMP KNUCKLE BONE
superior extremity of femur

RIB CARTILAGES
costal cartilages

TIP OF BREASTBONE
xiphoid cartilage

BREASTBONE
sternum
sternebrae 1 to 7

SHANK { *olecranon process*
KNUCKLE { *inferior extremity*
BONES { *of humerus*

FORE SHANK BONES { *ulna*
{ *radius*

ARM BONE
humerus

AITCH or
RUMP BONE
ischium } pelvis

HIP BONE
ilium

TAIL BONE
caudal vertebrae 1 & 2

BACKBONE
sacrum
sacral vertebrae 1 to 5

SLIP JOINT
sacro-iliac diarthrosis

BACKBONE
lumbar vertebrae 1 to 6

spinous process
transverse process
body of lumbar vertebra

CHINE BONE
bodies of cervical, thoracic,
lumbar and sacral vertebrae

FEATHER BONES
spinous processes

BACKBONE
thoracic vertebrae 1 to 13

BLADEBONE CARTILAGE
scapular cartilage

BLADEBONE
scapula

RIDGE BONE
spine of scapula

NECK BONE
cervical vertebrae 1 to 7

ATLAS
1st cervical vertebra

ARM KNUCKLE BONE
superior extremity of humerus

Fig. 13.1–Bovine anatomy.

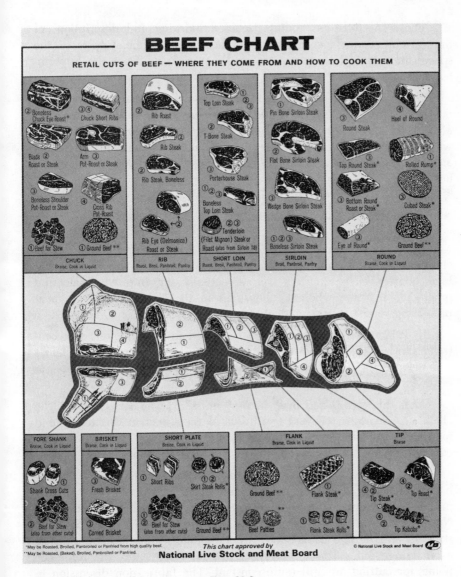

Fig. 13.2

—for Sausage Products - Series 800
—for Portion-Cut Meat Products - Series 1,000

These specifications contain detailed indexing and descriptions of the various products customarily purchased in volume. Copies of the specifications for these products may be purchased from the Superintendent of Documents.

The National Association of Meat Purveyors, Tucson, Arizona, has published two Meat Buyers Guides, *Meat Buyers Guide to Standardized Meat Cuts* and *Meat Buyers Guide to Portion Control Meat Cuts,* in which excellent descriptive color pictures and accompanying discussion are presented for the Series 100, 200, 300, 400, and 1,000 USDA specifications.

New Developments in Beef Handling and Distribution

Prior to 1966, most beef was distributed in carcass form, i.e., generally trucked or shipped by rail from the packing house in fore and hind quarters. The quarters were eventually cut into wholesale and retail cuts in some wholesale house or in the "back room", (a meat processing room) of many retail stores.

In 1972 more than half the beef shipped to supermarkets was centrally fabricated either at the packing house or at a meat warehouse and the prefabricated primal and subprimal cuts delivered to stores in boxes instead of in the conventional carcass form.

Thus the term *Boxed Beef,* or *Beef in a Box,* was born. In 1972, the chain supermarkets received two-thirds of their beef in this form,[2] and food chain executives expect the figure to rise to over 70% by 1977 with carcass shipments dropping to 14% of the total beef shipments.

This chapter will cover modern fabrication techniques currently being used in many different situations. Many plants now have highly mechanized cutting lines which speed up fabrication considerably. Nevertheless, the animal is still put together the same way, i.e., the skeleton and muscle connections are the same as in the year one, so even though our cattle are carrying less fat waste now, the reference points for cutting are still quite constant. The fabrication discussion in this chapter should thus be applicable to all modern day beef fabrication situations.

---

2. Seth T. Shaw in *The National Provisioner,* November 3, 1973.

Fig. 13.3

The First Steps

Figure 13.3. For demonstration purposes let us assume that generally, when beef animals are finished for market, they will weigh approximately 1,000 pounds. After slaughter, the resulting carcass represents approximately 60% of the live weight. Therefore, this particular 1,000-pound live animal will have a carcass weighing approximately 600 pounds.

Figure 13.4. Before leaving the slaughter floor, beef carcasses are split into right and left sides, each side then weighing about 300 pounds.

Fig. 13.4

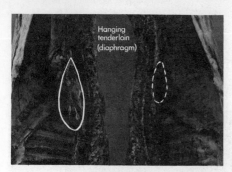

Fig. 13.5

Figure 13.5. In this close-up, where the left side of the carcass is on your left, note that the hanging tenderloin, or diaphragm muscle, is present in the left side, but absent in the right. It is customary to trim the diaphragm on the kill floor so that the major portion of it remains on the left side of the carcass. This hanging tenderloin is removed as an initial step in the fabrication process. It must be clear that this is the *hanging* tenderloin and not actually the tenderloin of the carcass. This hanging tenderloin is a portion of the diaphragm muscle, which is a very active muscle in the live animal and, therefore, leaves something to be desired in terms of palatability. It is placed in the lean trim where it fulfills its retail role most logically as ground beef. Note that the kidney fat just above the diaphragm is more obvious in the left side than in the right. In the live animal, the rumen pushes the kidney fat close to the body wall on the right side, thus it is called the tight side while the left is called the loose side.

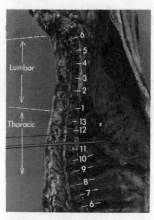

Fig. 13.6

Figure 13.6. To be properly evaluated and merchandised, beef sides must be separated into forequarters and hindquarters, a practice called ribbing or quartering. This is normally done by severing the half carcass between the twelfth and thirteenth ribs, although some local areas modify the number of ribs left on the hindquarter. In actual practice, rather than counting the ribs in a posterior direction from front to rear to find the twelfth rib, the exposed bodies of the *lumbar* and *thoracic* vertebrae are counted in an anterior direction or from the rear to the front. Counting off six *lumbar*, Nos. 6 through 1 and 1½ *thoracic* vertebrae, Nos. 13 and 12 in this figure, a total of 7½ vertebrae, to arrive at a point midway between the twelfth and thirteenth ribs. These exposed vertebrae are much easier to locate and to count than are the ribs. A saw is used to sever the backbone, and a knife is used to complete the cut, leaving a portion of the flank attached to the plate in order that the entire half carcass may still hang from a rail. For shipping and further processing, the separation into forequarters and hindquarters is completed by easily severing this plate-flank attachment with a knife. The ribbing procedure may be reversed by inserting the knife at the desired spot below the rib-eye muscle and making a smooth cut toward the backbone. The first method is preferred for making a most nearly perpendicular cut across the rib-eye muscle in order to measure its true size.

444

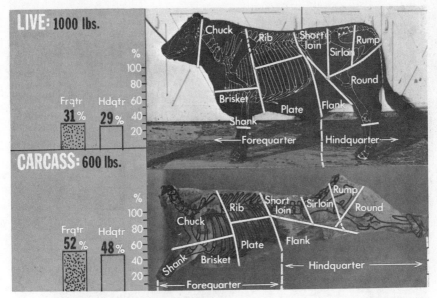

Fig. 13.7

Figure 13.7.   Each carcass side or half is divided into quarters. The fore-quarter, composed of the following wholesale cuts—the primal chuck and rib, and the rough brisket, plate and shank—is usually the heavier quarter representing about 52% of the carcass weight or 31% of the live weight when one rib is left on the hindquarter. The hindquarter, composed of the following wholesale cuts—the primal round, subprimal rump, sirloin, shortloin, and rough flank represents approximately 48% of the carcass weight and 29% of the live weight.

Hindquarter

Figure 13.8.   After removal of the hanging tenderloin, the next step in fabricating a beef carcass is to remove the kidney, pelvic, and heart fat. This fat is situated on the inside of the body cavity as indicated in this figure and covers the valuable tenderloin muscle. Thus care must be taken in its removal so as to avoid scoring the tenderloin. Edible beef tallow is utilized today for oleomargarine manufacture and other shortening products while inedible fats are utilized for the manufacture of feeds, soaps, and lubricants (see Chapter 10). The raw material in any case has small value when compared to edible meat.

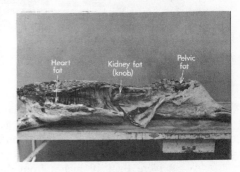

Fig. 13.8

445

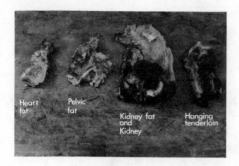

Fig. 13.9

Figure 13.9. Note the relative sizes of the fat deposits and hanging tenderloin as removed from the carcass. Note that the kidney itself is included within the kidney knob or kidney fat.

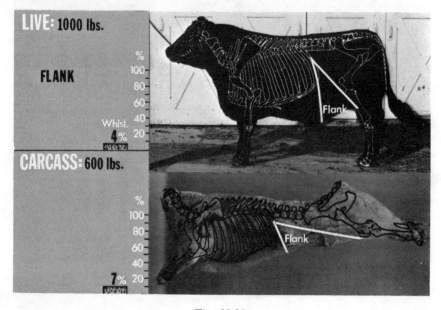

Fig. 13.10

Figure 13.10. After kidney fat removal, the next step is the removal of the wholesale flank. This wholesale cut represents 4% of the live weight of an animal and 7% of its carcass weight. The flank is removed by following the contour of the round and removing the cod or udder fat with the flank. Towards the front, the cut is marked lateral to the loin-eye muscle not more than 10 inches from the backbone where a saw must be used to sever the thirteenth rib. Separation of the flank is completed with a knife. Being one of the four rough wholesale cuts in a beef carcass, discussion of its retail fabrication will be handled later with the other three rough cuts from the forequarter.

446

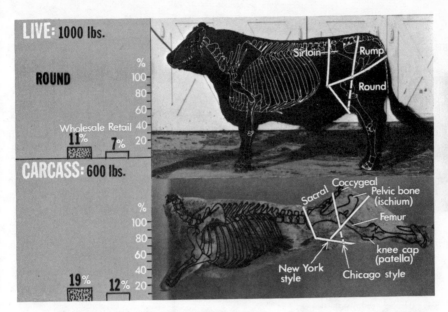

Fig. 13.11

Figure 13.11.   There are several possible methods of removing the primal round from the hindquarter. They result in (1) the Chicago Round which includes only half of the tip (knuckle), (2) the New York Round which includes none of the tip, and (3) the Diamond Round which includes all of the tip. Note the lines indicating each method of cutting, both in the live animal where the wholesale cuts are named and in the carcass where the skeletal structures are named. The tip or knuckle is the triangular cut in front of the *femur*. With the New York style of cutting, a cut is made adjacent to and parallel with the *ischiatic* portion of the pelvic bone. Therefore, when this cut is made as indicated in the diagram, we are able to remove that group of muscles, in front of the large *femur* bone in the round, known as the round (sirloin) tip muscles (*quadriceps*). Alternately, if we would employ the Chicago style by cutting on a line connecting the last *sacral* vertebrae with the proximal (closest) head of the *femur*, we would cut right through the round (sirloin) tip and ruin a very desirable roast. Such a cut is indicated by the dotted line in this figure. Therefore, to avoid ruining this tip roast, we recommend and will describe in detail the New York style of cutting the round. (In wholesale form, the round, thus removed by the New York style of cutting, approximates 11% of the live weight and 19% of the carcass weight. Retail roasts and steaks from the round make up approximately 7% of the live weight and 12% of the carcass weight.)

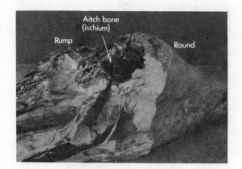

Fig. 13.12

Figure 13.12. The knife is poised *caudal* (to the rear) of the *ischium* (*ischiatic portion*) of the pelvic bone. A saw is needed before the separation can be completed, as the *femur* bone must be cut.

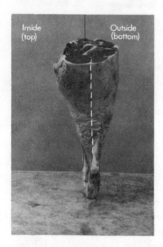

Fig. 13.13

Figure 13.13. The nomenclature of the retail cuts from the round can be explained very logically if one knows the origin of the names. The outside round is that portion which is toward the outside of the animal as indicated in this figure where you can visualize the animal walking directly away from you. The inside round is that portion of the round toward the animal's midline. The outside round became known as the bottom round because in cutting, the round is usually placed on the table or block with the outside next to the table. Therefore, it was called bottom round. The inside being on top was thus called top round.

Figure 13.14. Note this wholesale primal round as removed from the hindquarter by the New York style of cutting. This is the way it appears to the meat cutter as he approaches it to fabricate it into its subprimals and retail cuts. Notice that the eye of the round is the *semitendinosus* muscle, while the remainder of the bottom round is the *biceps femoris* muscle. Two muscles compose the top round also. They are the *semimembranosus* and the *adductor*. The tip is composed of four muscles, commonly called *quadriceps*. In fabricating this round into its four subprimals, a technique known as muscle boning will be employed. In so doing, the muscles and muscle groups are separated into subprimal and retail cuts by following the natural seams as much as possible. The muscles are taken apart in much the same manner as nature put them together. Muscles grouped naturally together for function in the live animal are more uniform in palatability and thus form much more desirable retail cuts.

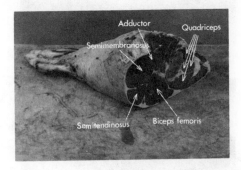

Fig. 13.14

Figure 13.15. The first step in muscle boning the round is the removal of the hind shank bone or *tibia*. Muscles of the lower round are anchored to this bone through strong connective tissues which must be severed. The large tendon on the back of the shank is the *Achilles* tendon in which was inserted a hook on a trolley to suspend the carcass on a rail. The *tibia* or shank bone is followed with a knife up into the round to the stifle joint. This is the knee joint of the animal where the *tibia* joins the large bone of the round, the *femur*. When this joint is severed with a knife, remaining connective tissue attachments to the *tibia* are loosened and the shank bone is removed. Since this is the knee joint, the knee cap or *patella* is present. It remains in the round for the time being.

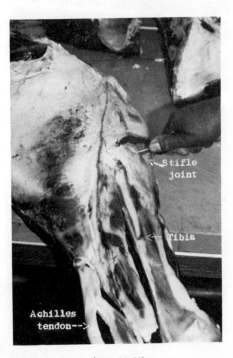

Fig. 13.15

449

Fig. 13.16

Figure 13.16 The *quadriceps* muscles which compose the round tip and lie to the cranial (front) side of the *femur* are removed by entering through the natural seam which separates the round tip from the top or inside round on one side and from the bottom or outside round on the other. From this cranial view, you can see the cross section of the rump knucklebone, the cranial or proximal end of the *femur*.

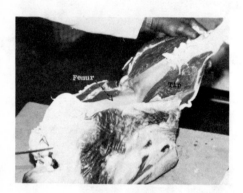

Fig. 13.17

Figure 13.17. Entering once again from the stifle joint near the *patella*, at the shank knuckle bone which is the caudal or distal end of the *femur*, one can loosen the connections sufficiently so that it is possible to grasp the tip in one hand and the knuckle of the *femur* in the other to separate the two. Final separation is made with a knife. From the rough tip, the *patella* or knee cap is removed.

Fig. 13.18

Figure 13.18. The outside or cap muscles may be removed to make a highly desirable retail cut, the cap off ("bald") or round (sirloin) tip roast and steak. This cut is located at the junction of the sirloin tip and the round tip but is officially named round tip, since it is a subprimal of the primal round. The term *sirloin tip* is well recognized by industry but often confusing to consumers. This cut makes an excellent roast, and may be cut into steaks if the animal had sufficient (at least high Choice) quality. The tip is usually the most tender roast from the round, due to its location in the live animal, in front of the large round bone (*femur*). Also in this position, the muscle fibers are stretched when the carcass is hung up in the conventional manner, thus making the roast more tender (see Chapter 19).

Figure 13.19. From the shank knuckle or stifle joint, the large *femur* bone is being removed. With older methods of cutting, this large bone was left in the retail round steaks. Noting the size of this bone, don't you agree that it is unwise to leave it in the round and later have it occupy valuable freezer space?

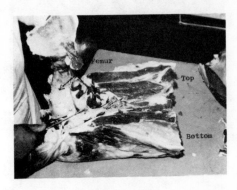

Fig. 13.19

Figure 13.20. The bottom round on your left is separated from the top round on your right by following the natural seam which separates them. The top round subprimal is trimmed on the newly separated face as well as on the inside or top surface, where there is usually a portion of the lean that has been darkened due to exposure to air for several days during marketing or aging.

Fig. 13.20

Figure 13.21. Steaks, preferably for moist heat cookery (braising), can be cut from the top round. The top round is composed of two major muscles, the *semimembranosus* and the *adductor*. The top round roasts and steaks appear very solid and homogeneous, thus the muscle separation is difficult to see. The top round is generally considered to be the second most tender round roast although some research has disputed this.

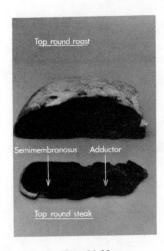

Fig. 13.21

451

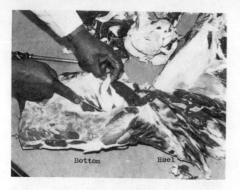

Fig. 13.22

Figure 13.22. Especially important in trimming the bottom round subprimal is the removal of the *popliteal* lymph node and its surrounding fat deposit, which is located on the center top of the roast between the *semitendinosus* or eye and the *biceps femoris* muscles. The heel of the round is separated from the lower portion of the bottom round.

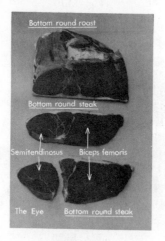

Fig. 13.23

Figure 13.23. Steaks may also be cut from the bottom round. They may be cut thicker than the top round steaks and make ideal material for swissing. Steaks and roasts from the bottom round can be most easily identified by the distinct eye of the round, the *semitendinosus* muscle. The other large muscle in the bottom round, sometimes alone called the bottom round is the *biceps femoris*.

Fig. 13.24

Figure 13.24. Bottom round steaks from lower grading cattle may be utilized as cubed (minute) steaks, by passing them through a mechanical tenderizer, a desirable method of merchandising the lower quality bottom round steaks.

Figure 13.25. The heel or *Pikes Peak* roast should be utilized with moist heat cookery since it contains high amounts of connective tissues, because of its location in the live animal, at the lower portion of the round. The main muscle of the heel roast is the *gastrocnemius* muscle.

Fig. 13.25

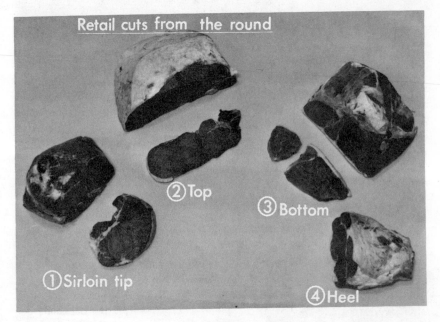

Fig. 13.26

Figure 13.26. The four subprimal cuts from the round beginning with the round (sirloin) tip are displayed in a clockwise manner from the most palatable to the least palatable, although all are desirable if properly prepared.

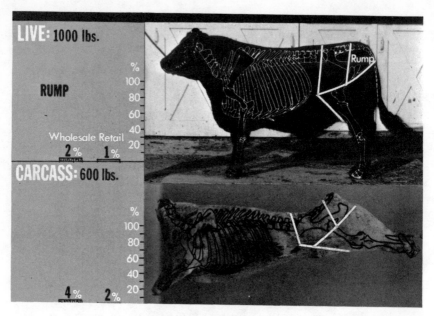

Fig. 13.27

Figure 13.27. Using this style of cutting (New York), the rump was left on the loin when the round was removed from the carcass. However, in industry, the rump is considered a part of the round. Thus when rounds are quoted and traded, it is done with the assumption that the rump is a part of the round. Here we consider it a separate cut for purposes of clarity. The rump, when considered a wholesale cut by itself, represents 2% of the live weight and 4% of the carcass weight, while in retail form, the boneless roast represents 1% of the live weight and 2% of the carcass weight.

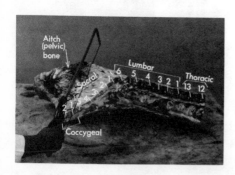

Fig. 13.28

Figure 13.28. The rump is here separated from the loin by making a cut on an imaginary line connecting two points: (1) a point on the backbone between the fifth *sacral* vertebra and the first *coccygeal* (tail) vertebra and (2) the anterior (front) tip of the proximal (inward) end of the *femur*. This cut is identical to the Chicago style separation described earlier and indicated in figures 13.11 and 13.12, except that now the sirloin tip has been removed and will not be cut in two by this separation.

Figure 13.29. The beef round rump roast (standing rump) normally has the knuckle from the *femur* removed, but still contains the large pelvic bone which creates difficulty in carving and serving for the consumer. Note in Figure 13.27, the large portion of the pelvic bone contained in the rump area.

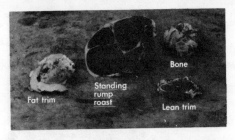

Fig. 13.29

Figure 13.30. It is more appropriate for the butcher or meat cutter to bone the rump and ultimately much more satisfying to the consumer to be able to effortlessly carve an exquisite roast for company. The pelvic bone (aitch bone) is "cleared" by following closely on either side with the knife.

Fig. 13.30

Figure 13.31. The knuckle (from *femur*) is separated from the pelvic bone.

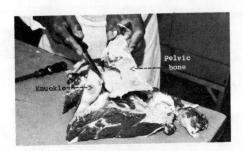

Fig. 13.31

Figure 13.32. Note the size of the pelvic bone as its last attachments are severed. The knuckle remains momentarily until the rump is made completely boneless.

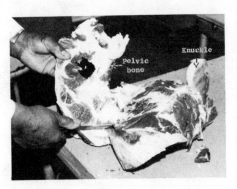

Fig. 13.32

Fig. 13.33

Figure 13.33. The boneless rump is rather diffuse so it must be tied for ease of cooking and slicing. Any boneless roast can be very easily and quickly passed through the tube of a Jet Netter to become closely wrapped in this elastic net. The finished roast, thus neatly tied, in Illinois has acquired the name *football roast* since it resembles very closely the shape of a football. However, this is only a fanciful name, and is not accepted by the Uniform Meat Identity Standards. The jet net is left on during roasting and may be removed quite easily before the roast is served.

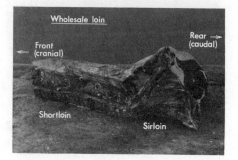

Fig. 13.34

Figure 13.34. The wholesale primal loin is composed of two subprimals—the sirloin and the shortloin.

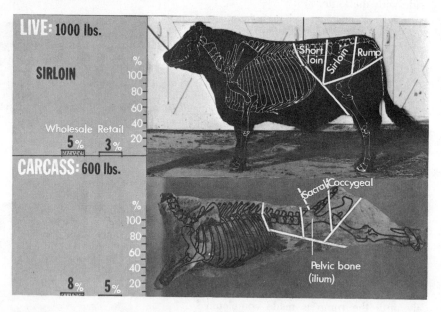

Fig. 13.35

Figure 13.35. The sirloin subprimal wholesale weight approximates 5% of the live weight and 8% of the carcass weight. Steak yield from the sirloin equals about 3% of the live weight and 5% of carcass weight.

Figure 13.36. The separation of the sirloin from the shortloin is achieved by making a cut between the fifth and sixth *lumbar* vertebrae which nicks the cranial or front portion of the pelvic girdle. After the backbone has been separated with a saw, the cut is completed with a knife. Normally, when fabricating full loins into bone-in steaks, the sirloin and shortloin will not be separated as indicated here but rather the whole loin will be sawed into steaks from this sirloin end.

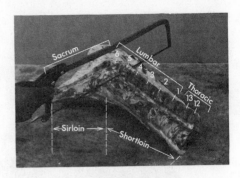

Fig. 13.36

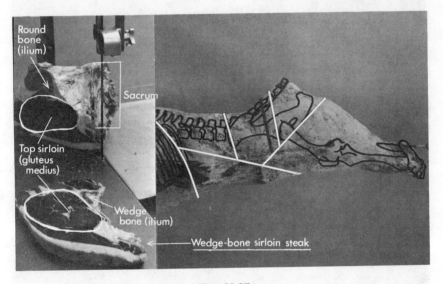

Fig. 13.37

Figure 13.37. The sirloin is cut on a band saw into steaks which may differ considerably from one another in their value due to the amount of bone they contain. The ICMISC recommends four names for the various sirloin steaks, based on the shape of the pelvic bone each contains. Beginning at the caudal (rear) end of the sirloin, the first steak removed is sometimes called a butt-bone sirloin steak, because the pelvic bone has a depression where the *femur* (round bone) engaged the pelvic bone. However, this steak and one or two more cranial (toward the front) from this steak are called wedge-bone sirloin steaks, because that portion of the *ilium* (pelvic bone) has the characteristic wedge shape. The heavy dark line in the diagram to the right indicates steak location. Note the top sirloin or *gluteus medius* muscle. This muscle carries throughout the whole sirloin and may be removed and sold as a boneless top sirloin roast or cut into top sirloin steaks. Note on the remaining portion of the sirloin the round bone, *ilium* and the *sacrum*.

457

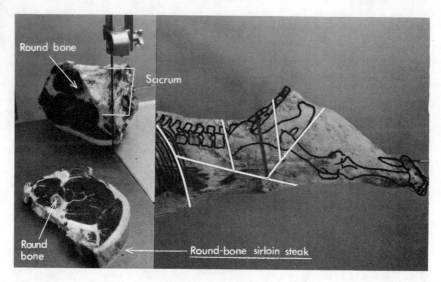

Fig. 13.38

Figure 13.38. Proceeding further in a cranial direction, the next steak is the round-bone sirloin steak which receives its name from the fact that the shaft of the *ilium* is almost round at this point. Note again in the remaining portion of the sirloin, the round bone, and the *sacrum*.

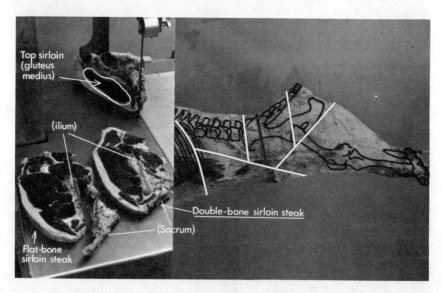

Fig. 13.39

Figure 13.39. Proceeding further in a cranial direction, we approach that portion of the sirloin which contains the backbone or *sacrum* joined to the pelvic bone or *ilium,* thus known as the *sacroiliac* joint. Since there are two bones in this particular steak, it has received the name *double-bone sirloin steak.* In modern methods of merchandising, the backbone or *sacrum* is removed leaving only the *ilium* present, thus a flat-bone sirloin steak, indicated on the left. Note the top sirloin or *gluteus medius* muscle which persists throughout the sirloin.

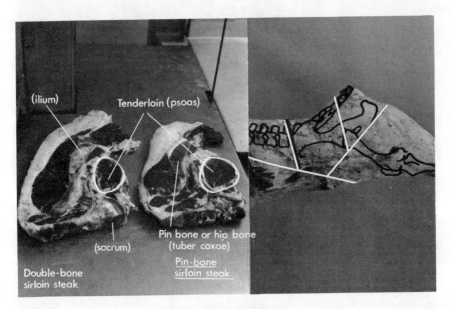

Fig. 13.40

Figure 13.40.   The most cranial steak of the sirloin is the pin-bone sirloin steak. The pin bone or hip bone (*tuber coxae*) is quite prominent at this location as can be evidenced in the steak on the saw. There is usually one pin-bone sirloin steak and the steak immediately caudal (to the rear) of it is a (double bone) flat-boned sirloin steak. The tenderloin (*psoas*) muscle appears quite prominently in the pin-bone sirloin steak.

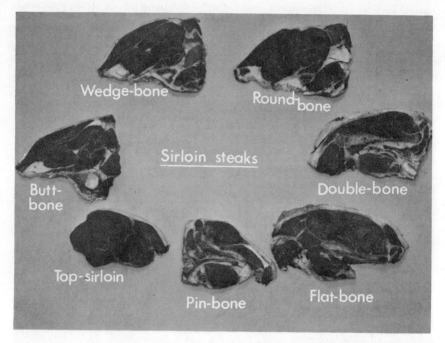

Fig. 13.41

Figure 13.41. Observing all possible steaks from the sirloin in one figure, one can readily see that the round-bone sirloin steak possesses the least amount of bone waste, whereas the pin-bone sirloin has an extremely large amount of bone in relation to the amount of meat, thus there is considerable value difference between types of sirloin steaks.

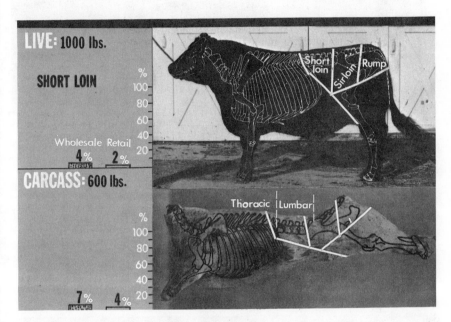

LIVE: 1000 lbs.

SHORT LOIN

%
100-
80-
60-
40-
Wholesale Retail 20-
4% 2%

CARCASS: 600 lbs.

%
100-
80-
60-
40-
7% 4% 20-

Thoracic Lumbar
Short Loin Sirloin Rump

Fig. 13.42

Figure 13.42. The shortloin is that subprimal of the primal loin remaining after the removal of the sirloin. The shortloin is composed of the *lumbar* section of the hind quarter. As a wholesale subprimal cut the shortloin equals 4% of the live weight and 7% of the carcass weight. Steak yield from the shortloin will equal approximately 2% of the live weight and 4% of the carcass weight. Note that one rib remains on the cranial end of the shortloin.

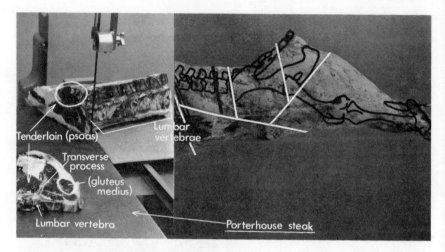

Fig. 13.43

Figure 13.43.   Beginning to saw from the sirloin or caudal end, the first steaks off the shortloin are the porterhouse steaks. Porterhouse steaks may be identified by the large size of the tenderloin (*psoas*) muscle ventral (below) the *transverse* (T) vertebral processes. The real key to identifying the porterhouse steak is, however, the presence of an additional muscle dorsal (above) to the *longissimus,* which is actually an extension of the top sirloin, the *gluteus medius* muscle.

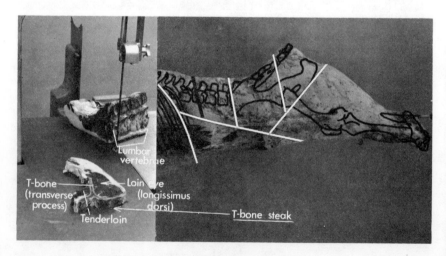

Fig. 13.44

Figure 13.44. Moving forward in the shortloin, as the tenderloin decreases in size and the *gluteus medius* disappears, the steaks become T-bone steaks. The characteristic T being formed by the *transverse* processes of the lumbar vertebrae.

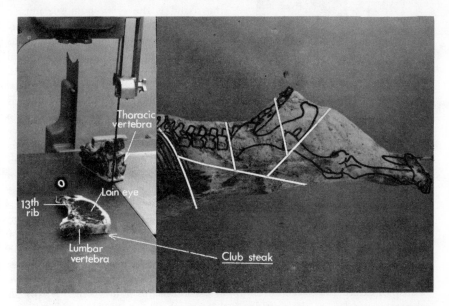

Fig. 13.45

Figure 13.45. Proceeding forward, where the tenderloin disappears and a rib or a portion of an obliquely split rib appears, the steaks are properly named top-loin steaks. Previously this particular steak was called a club steak, but the term *club* was so widely used, oftentimes inappropriately, for many other cuts from other locations on the carcass that ICMISC decided to use the universal descriptive term *top-loin steak*. Note the large loin-eye (*longissimus*) muscle and the portion of the split rib.

Figure 13.46. In an alternate method of fabricating the entire shortloin, the tenderloin muscle, *not* the hanging tenderloin, may be removed and processed as a fillet. Care must be taken in removing this tenderloin muscle.

Fig. 13.46

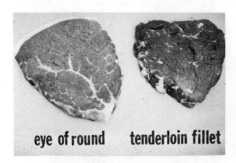

eye of round   tenderloin fillet

Fig. 13.47

Figure 13.47. The tenderloin fillet is the most palatable muscle in the beef carcass but may be easily confused with the eye of the round which is quite similar in appearance. Recall that the eye of the round is the *semitendinosus* muscle from the bottom or outside round. During the animal's life, this *semitendinosus* muscle is used every time the animal takes a step as he moves from place to place. On the other hand, the *psoas* muscle of which the tenderloin fillet is composed, lying on the inside of the transverse processes of the loin does very little work in the animal other than perhaps aid in some small way the maintenance of the animal's posture or aid him as he turns his body to a slight degree. The eye of the round is considerably less tender than the tenderloin fillet, and this fact is related to the function of the respective muscles within the live animal. To differentiate these two steaks, note the coarse structure of the eye of the round as compared to the fine texture of the tenderloin fillet. Here is a simple lesson in muscle structure. The muscle bundles are much larger in the eye of the round, thus causing the coarser texture. Another identifying hint is the fact that the eye of the round displays a strip of external fat, seen in the upper portion of this figure, which is normal, since this cut lies to the outside of the animal. The tenderloin fillet, on the other hand, from the inside of the animal has no surface containing subcutaneous fat.

Fat trim   Lean trim   Bone-in strip loin "New York strip"   Bone

Fig. 13.48

Figure 13.48. Further fabrication of the shortloin by this alternative method involves removing the chine bones or body of the lumbar vertebrae of the backbone, trimming the "tail" of the shortloin to approximately 1 inch lateral to the loin-eye muscle (the shortloin tail is adjacent to the flank in the intact carcass), and trimming away the external fat in excess of 0.25 to 0.3 of an inch. The above trimming is subject to market demand and specifications. The resulting subprimal then is called a top-loin or strip-loin bone-in or a *New York* strip.

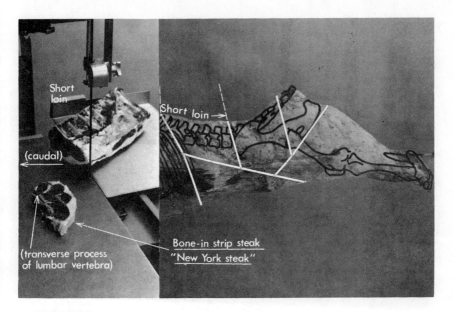

Fig. 13.49

Figure 13.49.　Any steak then from this top-loin bone-in or strip loin would be officially called a top-loin steak. It may be called a bone-in strip steak or a New York steak unofficially. Note the *transverse* process of the *lumbar* vertebrae. The dorsal process of this vertebrae also remains. This particular steak is actually a porterhouse steak without the bone and tenderloin muscle, as indicated by the small *gluteus medius* muscle above the eye. If the remaining bone is removed (the *transverse* process and that remaining portion of the *dorsal* process), the resulting steak would be officially a top-loin steak, boneless or unofficially a boneless strip steak, sometimes called a *Kansas City* steak.

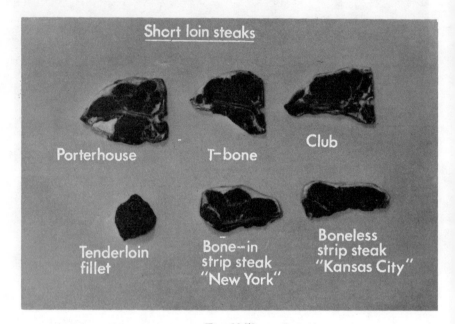

Fig. 13.50

Figure 13.50.   In a summary of the shortloin steaks, recall that these steaks represent only 2% of the live weight and 4% of the carcass weight, not a very large percentage in either case. The Porterhouse, T-bone, and Club steaks are a result of a typical fabrication method. The top-loin and top-loin boneless (*New York* and *Kansas City*) steaks and tenderloin fillet are results of an alternate method of fabrication in which bone is removed.

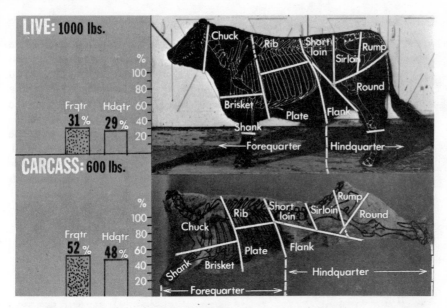

Fig. 13.51

Forequarter

Figure 13.51. The forequarter represents approximately 52% of the carcass weight and approximately 31% of the live weight. The forequarter is composed of the following wholesale cuts, the chuck and rib, which are primal cuts, and the brisket, shank, and plate, which are rough cuts.

Figure 13.52. The rib and plate are severed from the chuck, brisket, and shank by making a cut between the fifth and sixth ribs. The ribs are counted and the cut marked from the inside after which the cut is made from the outside of the forequarter, following closely the fifth rib to insure a square-cut chuck. This separation is then completed with a saw.

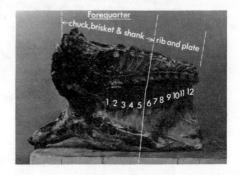

Fig. 13.52

467

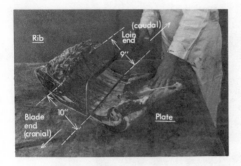

Fig. 13.53

Figure 13.53. The wholesale plate is separated from the wholesale primal rib by a cut which is approximately 10 inches from the chine (backbone) at the large (blade) end and 9 inches from the chine at the small (loin) end. The blade end is thus called because the blade cartilage from the blade bone is exposed, while the loin end is thus named because it is adjacent to the loin from the hindquarter.

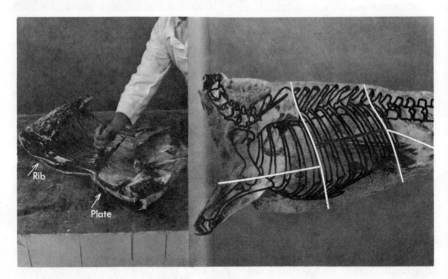

Fig. 13.54

Figure 13.54. The completion of the separation of the rib and plate is done with a knife. Note in the diagram the particular location of this cut indicated by a heavy dark line.

468

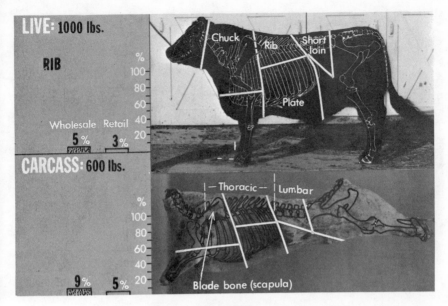

Fig. 13.55

Figure 13.55. The primal rib in wholesale form represents 5% of live weight and 9% of the carcass weight. Steaks and roasts trimmed for retail trade from the rib amount to approximately 3% of the live weight and 5% of the carcass weight.

Figure 13.56. In a typical blade-end view of a wholesale rib, note the blade cartilage. It has been separated from the blade bone itself which remains on the chuck.

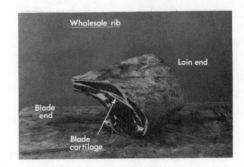

Fig. 13.56

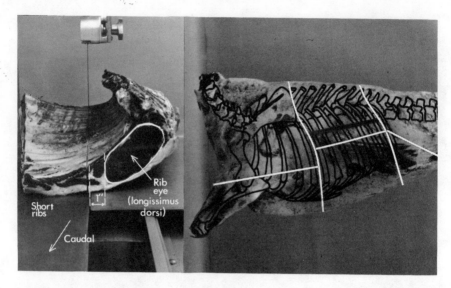

Fig. 13.57

Figure 13.57. Fabrication of the rib is begun by removing with a saw the ends of all rib bones on a line approximately 1 inch from the lateral edge of the *longissimus* dorsi (now called the rib eye). The location of this cut depends on market demand, so may be located at a greater distance from the eye, giving more weight but at the same time more "waste" to the rib roast. The cut is indicated in the carcass diagram by a dark heavy line.

Figure 13.58. The resulting rib ends which are removed may be made into short ribs. These particular short ribs look very lean and meaty.

Fig. 13.58

Figure 13.59. As with the short-loin, the bodies of the vertebrae (chine bones), are removed on the saw. Note the blade cartilage and the neck leader or *ligamentum nuchae*.

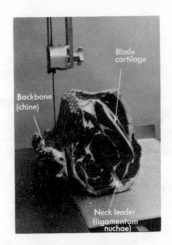

Fig. 13.59

Figure 13.60. In further process-ing this rib, some of which is optional, the feather bones or *dorsal* processes of the *thoracic* vertebrae are removed. Since the main portion or the bodies of the *thoracic* vertebrae have already been re-moved, the only bones remaining are the ribs themselves.

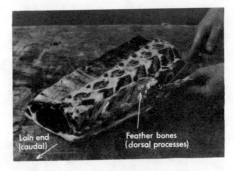

Fig. 13.60

Figures 13.61. It is essential that the neck leader (*ligamentum nuchae*) be removed, since it is composed almost entirely of elastin connective tissue, thus is absolutely impossible to make palata-ble by means of cookery.

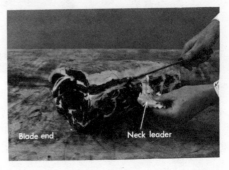

Fig. 13.61

471

Fig. 13.62

Figure 13.62. Finally, outside fat in excess of 0.3 inch is removed, resulting in a finished short standing rib roast so named for its short length of ribs remaining. Officially this would be labeled "extra trim." The components which were removed from the wholesale rib to get this standing rib roast were the body and *dorsal* processes of the *thoracic* vertebrae (bone), the neck leader, and the fat trim. In this view of the standing rib roast, note the natural rack formed by the ribs which remain in the roast. This roast would be placed in the oven inverted on this natural rack for roasting.

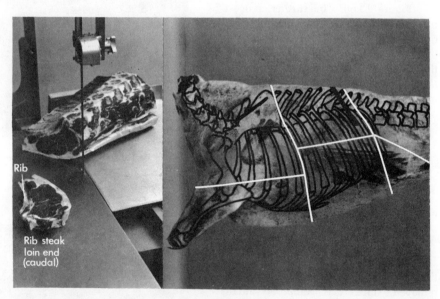

Fig. 13.63

Figure 13.63. Rib steaks removed from this standing rib roast from the loin (small) end are called rib steaks, small end.

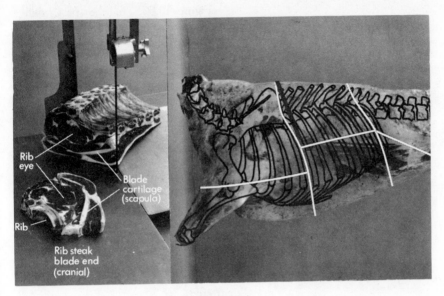

Fig. 13.64

Figure 13.64. Rib steaks removed from the blade (large) end are called rib steaks, large end. Note the number of accessory muscles contained in this steak which make it less palatable and more usable as a roast.

Figure 13.65. Steaks from the rib do vary in value. In this close comparison between a steak from the small (loin) end and one from the large (blade) end, the steak from the loin end is more desirable in that it has a larger rib-eye muscle and less intermuscular (seam) fat. Both of these cuts are called rib steaks, but now the new uniform labeling standards identify them for their value differences.

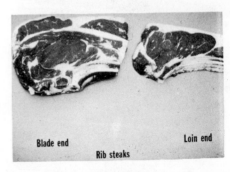

Fig. 13.65

Fig. 13.66

Figure 13.66. In the past, difficulty was frequently encountered in distinguishing a club steak from the shortloin, on the left (now called top-loin steak) and a rib steak from the loin end of the rib, on the right. The two identifying characteristics of the rib steak used to differentiate it from the top-loin (club) steak are (1) the rib steak has a cap muscle (*spinalis dorsi*) which the club steak does not have and (2) a full longitudinal section of the rib may be present in a rib steak as shown here, while possibly only an oblique or partial section of the rib may be present in a top-loin (club) steak. A club (top-loin) steak from the shortloin has this portion of a rib, because there is one rib left on the hindquarter when the carcass is quartered.

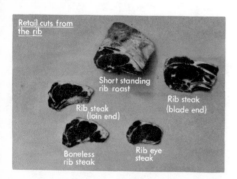

Fig. 13.67

Figure 13.67. When the rib bone itself is removed from a rib steak, the resulting steak is called boneless. If the rib bone and all cap muscles except the *spinalis dorsi* are removed, the resulting steaks are called rib eye or *Delmonico* steaks. These retail roasts and steaks from the rib equal only about 3% of the live weight and 5% of the carcass weight of a beef animal. The short standing rib roast here is resting on its natural rack.

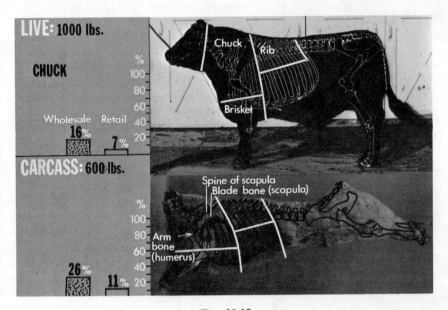

Fig. 13.68

Figure 13.68. Returning to that portion of the forequarter remaining after the removal of the rib and plate, the primal chuck is separated from the brisket and shank by a cut parallel to the top side of the chuck which severs the *distal* (far) end of the *humerus* (arm) bone. This cut must be completed with a saw, as the *humerus* bone must be severed. The chuck is the largest wholesale primal cut in the beef animal and as such represents 16% of the live weight and 26% of the carcass weight. However, the boneless retail roasts secured from the chuck represent only 7% of the live weight and 11% of the carcass weight. This does not mean that the portion of the chuck not represented by roasts is all waste, since there are considerable amounts of lean trim and some miscellaneous cuts secured from the chuck in addition to these roasts.

Fig. 13.69

Figure 13.69. This is a chuck from the animal's right side. Visualize the rib having been removed from the blade face and the brisket and shank removed from the arm face. The chuck may be processed by either of two methods. The method in most general use leaves the *humerus* bone and the blade bone (*scapula*) in the roasts resulting in about a 4% higher roast yield on a carcass basis or raising the 11% quoted earlier (Figure 13.68) to 15%. With the second method, an institutional method, all bone is removed from the roasts resulting in inside (chuck eye) and outside (shoulder) chuck roasts.

Fig. 13.70

Figure 13.70. In both methods, the rib cage and neck bones are first removed from the chuck.

Fig. 13.71

Figure 13.71. The neck leader (*ligamentum nuchae*) is removed. This piece of connective tissue (seen earlier in the rib) is sometimes called the backstrap and is responsible for holding the animal's head erect. As discussed earlier, it is impossible to make this piece of connective tissue palatable.

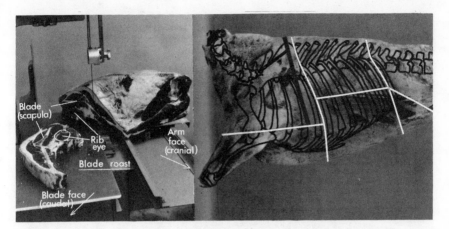

Fig. 13.72

Figure 13.72. For the most commonly used bone-in method, the square-cut chuck thus prepared is placed on a saw and two or three blade roasts are removed. The blade bone (*scapula*) appears in these roasts, thus the name blade roast. Note that the rib eye still remains in the chuck although it is somewhat small in size at this point.

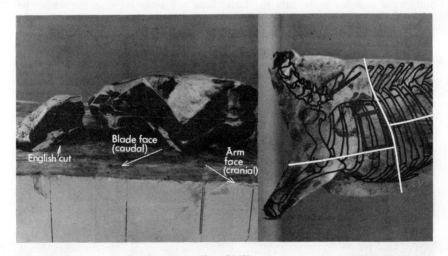

Fig. 13.73

Figure 13.73. The square corner of the square-cut chuck is called the cross-rib pot roast, formerly known as the English cut, but as such was a somewhat confusing name.

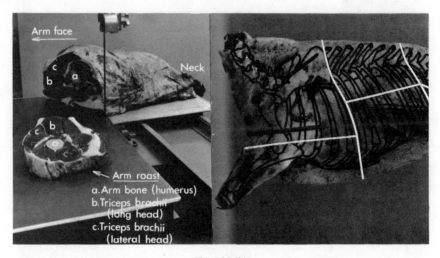

Fig. 13.74

Figure 13.74. Next, the chuck is turned 90 degrees, or a right angle, and several arm roasts are cut. Notice in the diagram the location of the cut, which is at right angles to the blade cuts. The arm bone (*humerus*) is very evident in these cuts, thus the name arm roasts. Note that there are fewer and larger muscles in the arm roast and thus less seam fat than occurs in the blade roasts. The main muscle systems of the arm roasts are the *triceps brachii*, long head and *triceps brachii*, lateral head.

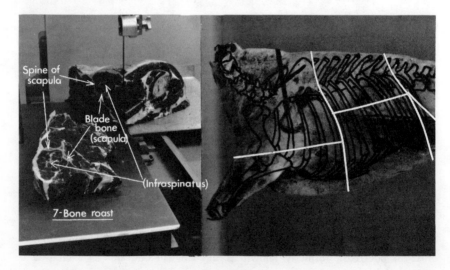

Fig. 13.75

Figure 13.75. After the removal of several arm roasts, the remaining portion of the chuck is returned to its original position and more blade roasts are removed. Proceeding forward (cranially) the spine of the *scapula* (blade) bone becomes evident in the blade roast. The spine of the *scapula* forms, in fact, a characteristic seven configuration and these roasts are thus known as seven-bone roasts.

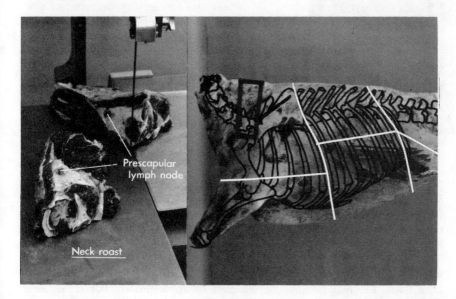

Fig. 13.76

Figure 13.76. The last roast taken is called the neck pot roast, and is perhaps the least desirable of the chuck roasts. It is essential that the *prescapular* lymph node be removed, since there is a large fat deposit surrounding this lymph node.

Figure 13.77. These retail cuts from the chuck result from the most common method of fabricating, leaving the arm and blade bones in the roasts. Notice that the lymph node has been removed from the neck pot roast. These bone-in retail cuts equal approximately 9% of the live weight of the animal and 15% of the carcass.

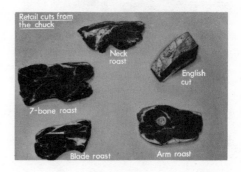

Fig. 13.77

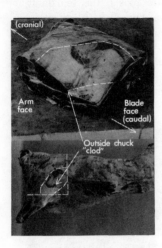

Fig. 13.78

Figure 13.78. An alternate method of fabricating this primal is to muscle bone the chuck, resulting in two large boneless roasts. This is sometimes termed an *Institutional Method* since the boneless roasts are ideal for use in large institutions such as hospitals and dormitories where uniform servings in terms of size and quality are essential. One roast, the shoulder pot roast, was formerly called the outside or arm chuck. Clod was also a name in popular use for this subprimal, but since the term *clod* is quite nondescriptive, ICMISC recommends that it not be used. The shoulder pot roast (outside chuck) is the large muscle group which lies behind the lower end of the arm bone and below the spine of the *scapula.*

In removing the boneless shoulder (outside) enter caudal to (behind) the *humerus* and follow this bone closely to its juncture with the *scapula.* Then follow the spine of the *scapula* toward the adjacent side. As the outside chuck is trimmed away, the *scapula* (blade bone) is exposed. The boneless chuck thus removed is trimmed of excess intermuscular (seam) fat so that the lean tissue on the inner surface is exposed. The edges of the roast are squared up. The thin or upper end is trimmed considerably, resulting in a more uniform roast. External fat may be trimmed to approximately 0.3 of an inch depending on specifications.

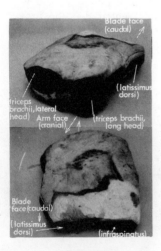

Fig. 13.79

Figure 13.79. In these two views of the completely fabricated boneless (outside) chuck, the upper view exposes the arm face. Scientific names for the various muscles are given. Note some are muscles of the arm roasts, indicated earlier in the retail fabrication method description (Figure 13.74). The lower half of this figure shows the same roast pictured from the opposite end. An identifying trait of the outside chuck is the appearance of the red, thin external muscle—sometimes commonly called the false lean or "rose" muscle. It is the *cutaneous trunci* muscle. The fat covering this muscle is sometimes called the "frosting over the rose."

Figure 13.80. The second roast, the chuck eye, commonly called the inside chuck or chuck roll is an extension of the rib-eye muscle with surrounding muscles included.

To isolate the inside chuck or chuck eye, first the large arm bone (*humerus*) is removed. The large end of the bone inside the chuck is the arm-bone knuckle and attaches to the *scapula*. The *scapula* (blade) bone is next removed. First, the ridge or spine of the scapula is cleared. Then connections under the blade bone are severed and the entire blade bone is lifted out. Those muscles interspersed with considerable amounts of connective tissue which originally lay below or inside the *humerus* and *scapula* are next removed. At right angles and parallel with the back of the animal, the external muscles and fat of the neck region are removed by following the natural seam which joins them to the inside chuck roll, and the roll is trimmed of thin edges and excess fat.

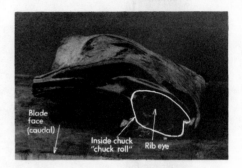

Fig. 13.80

Figure 13.81. In this view of the finished inside chuck roll, from the *caudal* (tail) end, the roast is turned over so the inside surface which was removed from the first five ribs is exposed and you can see where the ribs were once located. This serves as a useful key in identifying this inside chuck roll. Yield of roasts with this boneless method of cutting is somewhat less than that using the retail bone-in method and approximates 7% of the live weight and 11% of carcass weight.

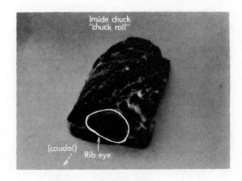

Fig. 13.81

481

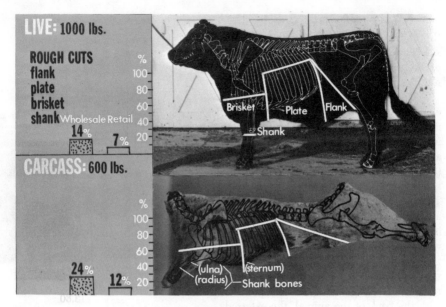

ROUGH CUTS %
flank 100-
plate 80-
brisket 60-
shank Wholesale Retail 40-
14% 7% 20-

CARCASS: 600 lbs.

%
100-
80-
60-
40-
24% 12% 20-

(ulna) (sternum)
(radius) Shank bones

Brisket Plate Flank
Shank

Fig. 13.82

Figure 13.82. The shank, brisket, and plate of the forequarter and the flank from the hindquarter are termed *rough cuts*. Wholesale percentages of these four cuts in total equal approximately 14% of the live weight and 24% of the carcass weight. Various retail cuts may be fabricated from these rough cuts, although through the use of modern retailing methods, much of this product is utilized as ground beef or stew beef. Retail yield in this form approximates 7% of live weight and 12% of carcass weight.

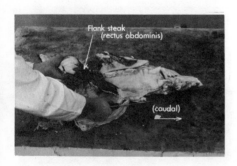

Flank steak
(rectus abdominis)

(caudal)

Fig. 13.83

Figure 13.83. From each flank, only one flank steak may be removed. This is composed of the *rectus abdominus* muscle. After removal, this flank steak is usually scored by cutting the surface lightly at right angles. The remainder of the flank is trimmed of waste fat and utilized for ground beef.

Fig. 13.84

Figure 13.84. The wholesale plate is directly ventral to the rib. The diaphragm may be removed from the plate. This muscle is commonly called the skirt in this location of the carcass. However, it is merely an extension of the hanging tenderloin, which, as you recall, was also the diaphragm muscle and was removed from the left side of the carcass as one of the preliminary steps to fabrication.

Figure 13.85. This skirt muscle can be fabricated into skirt-steak rolls (pin-wheel steaks). These skirt-steak rolls look quite desirable, and when they come from high quality beef and are properly prepared, they are. However, upon unrolling one, one can see that it is merely a thin muscle. This diaphragm muscle works quite regularly in the live animal (every time he breathes) and thus its palatability may leave something to be desired.

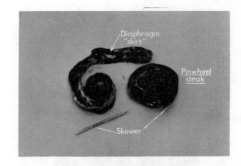

Fig. 13.85

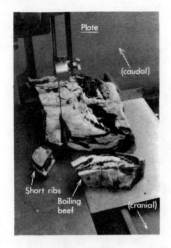

Fig. 13.86

Figure 13.86. Short ribs can be removed from ribs 6, 7, and 8 (counting from the front). These short ribs are adjacent to but ventral to those short ribs removed from the wholesale rib. Other options from the plate are boiling beef, beef spare ribs, and a boneless plate. These may be cured and sold as beef bacon, rolled and sold fresh, or sold as ground beef.

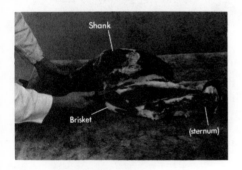

Fig. 13.87

Figure 13.87. The shank is separated from the brisket by cutting through the natural seam which separates them. The brisket may yield a boneless brisket roast if the sternum is removed. This boneless roast may be processed into corned beef.

Fig. 13.88

Figure 13.88. The wholesale foreshank is easily identified. Shank cross cuts may be obtained from the fore shank. The prominent shank bones are the *radius* and *ulna*. The shank, being very lean, is often boned and placed into lean trim for ground beef.

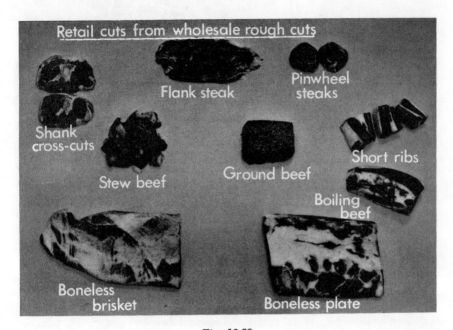

Fig. 13.89

Figure 13.89. In this recap of many possible retail cuts from the rough wholesale cuts, note that any or all of these cuts may be fabricated into stew beef or ground beef depending upon retail demands. Retail yield of these rough cuts, being largely in the form of ground beef or beef stew, approximates 7% of the live animal and 12% of the carcass.

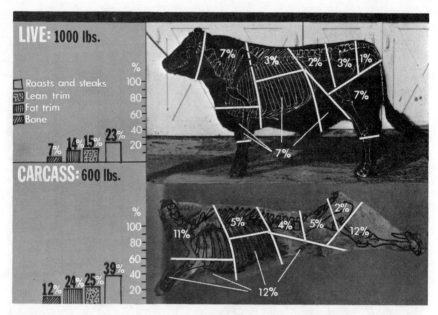

Fig. 13.90

Figure 13.90. In recapping the process of fabricating a beef carcass, note what portion of the live animal and carcass is actually available for retail sale and consumption. Total roasts and steaks fabricated and closely trimmed as shown previously in this presentation make up approximately 23% of the live weight of the animal. This 23% figure is obtained by adding the percentages listed in the six primal cuts—7% in the round, 1% in the rump, 3% in the sirloin, 2% in the shortloin, 3% in the rib, and 7% in the chuck, totaling 23% of the live weight of the animal in these roasts and steaks. Identical figures were presented as each wholesale cut was fabricated. Similar figures may be added in the carcass diagram, summing to a total of 39% of the carcass weight in the closely trimmed steaks and roasts. Now note in the live diagram the figure 7% which is directed toward all four rough cuts—the shank, brisket, plate, and flank. This 7% means that 7% of the live weight of the animal is represented in retail yield or in this case, lean trim from these four rough cuts. Likewise, the 12% figure in the carcass diagram has the same connotation.

Now notice the graph to the left of the diagrams. In the case of the live animal there is lean trim which approximates 15% of the live weight. You will recall that 7% of this 15% came from the rough cuts. The remaining 8% results from the trimming of the primal cuts to get the roasts and steaks which are accounted for in the 23% roast and steak yield. Likewise, in the carcass diagram as well, the 25% figure for total lean trim is made up of the 12% of the carcass weight obtained from the rough cuts while the remaining 13% comes from the trimmings of the primal roasts and steaks. Therefore, total retail yield, which would be a sum of these two figures approximates 38% of the live weight of the beef animal or 64% of its carcass weight.

It should be stressed that these are average yield figures and may vary considerably, due to methods of fabrication and the makeup of the animal itself, in terms of muscling and fat. These average figures are the result of the fabrication methods shown here. An animal which might yield this percentage of retail product might very well be our 1,000-pound live animal which might have a 600-pound carcass that might have approximately 11 square inches of loin eye at the twelfth rib, possess about 3.5% of its carcass weight in kidney, pelvic, and heart fat and carry about 0.6 of an inch of subcutaneous fat over the loin eye at the twelfth rib. What is the USDA yield grade of this steer? Check Chapter 11 if you do not remember how to calculate this yield grade.

Animals differing in fatness and muscling may cause this 38% live figure to vary from 33% to 45%, while the carcass figure of 64% may vary from 55% to 75%.

Note further in the graphs in this figure that the remaining components of the carcass of a beef animal are fat trim, which approximates 14% of the live weight and 24% of the carcass weight, and bone trim, which represents 7% of the live weight and 12% of the carcass weight. Thus, we can account for the gross composition of the carcass produced by this 1,000-pound live animal. Perhaps it will not be so difficult for you now to rationalize the retail price of beef cuts in comparison to the price of live animals, when you realize the relatively small percentage of the live animal which is represented in high quality edible meat.

CHAPTER 14

Lamb Identification and Fabrication

The reader may wonder, *why* include a chapter on lamb fabrication and identification when lamb is so unimportant in the United States today? Granted, those livestock producers engaged in breeding, feeding, and managing sheep and lambs as their major livestock enterprise are in a definite minority in the livestock industry. Also in the United States in 1973, it was estimated that the annual per capita lamb consumption (carcass weight) was only about 2.8 pounds compared with 62 pounds of pork and 111 pounds of beef. Therefore, if lamb production and consumption is so insignificant, why spend time learning about lamb carcasses and cuts?

The answer to this question can be found by examining the reasons for the relative unimportance of lamb in the United States today. The crux of the matter is the lack of demand for lamb at the consumer level. Only a minor segment of the population eats lamb at all. Those that do, probably eat it quite regularly and thus consume a considerable amount. But this is not reflected in total consumption based on the total population. Simply stated, the vast majority of the population is ignorant of the many attributes of lamb and thus ignores it completely when planning menus and when selecting and purchasing meat for the family's enjoyment and nutrition.

The number one objective of this chapter is, then, to allow you to become knowledgeable about the composition of a lamb carcass in terms of the identity, relative value, and palatability of its wholesale and retail cuts. Once you are informed, you can use this information as a producer to help establish guidelines for the type of livestock that must be produced to gain consumer acceptance. Or as a member of the meat industry team working between the producer and the consumer, you will be prepared to improve the processing, distribution, and retailing of meat products, including lamb. As an educator, you will have the background to inform others of the facts about lamb. As a consumer, you will be able to spend your food dollar more wisely and improve the quality and variety of your meat menu.

Lamb has long been noted for its delicacy of flavor and for its tenderness. Starting in biblical times, and carrying on to this modern age, reference has continually been made to the desirability of lamb meat. It is featured frequently for gourmet dining at home and in hotels and restaurants. However, many people have had unpleasant experiences with lamb or mutton due to a lack of knowledge on their part, or perhaps even on the part of those responsible for the processing, fabrication, merchandising, preparing, or serving the ovine meat, be it lamb or mutton.

IDENTIFICATION

The *Uniform Retail Meat Identity Standards*[1] (see Chapter 12) will again be used as the basis for identification in this chapter.

FABRICATION

The skeletal structure of the ovine in relation to an outline of the wholesale cuts is shown in Figure 14.1, and a more detailed chart of wholesale and retail cuts appears as Figure 14.2. Use these two figures for reference as the discussion moves through cutting a lamb carcass.

Figures 14.3 through 14.64 appear through the courtesy of the University of Illinois.

More Detailed References

In addition to those references indicated in Chapter 13, the following is especially appropriate for lamb: *How to Cut Today's New Lamb for Greater Sales and Profits,* published by the American Lamb Council, 200 Clayton Street, Denver, Colorado 80206 and the National Live Stock and Meat Board Lamb Committee. The publication can be obtained from the American Lamb Council.

---

1. National Live Stock and Meat Board.

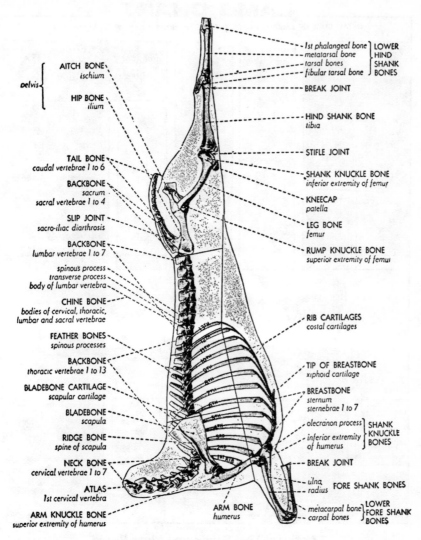

AITCH BONE
ischium

pelvis

HIP BONE
ilium

TAIL BONE
caudal vertebrae 1 to 6

BACKBONE
sacrum
sacral vertebrae 1 to 4

SLIP JOINT
sacro-iliac diarthrosis

BACKBONE
lumbar vertebrae 1 to 7

spinous process
transverse process
body of lumbar vertebra

CHINE BONE
bodies of cervical, thoracic,
lumbar and sacral vertebrae

FEATHER BONES
spinous processes

BACKBONE
thoracic vertebrae 1 to 13

BLADEBONE CARTILAGE
scapular cartilage

BLADEBONE
scapula

RIDGE BONE
spine of scapula

NECK BONE
cervical vertebrae 1 to 7

ATLAS
1st cervical vertebra

ARM KNUCKLE BONE
superior extremity of humerus

ARM BONE
humerus

1st phalangeal bone   LOWER
metatarsal bone   HIND
tarsal bones   SHANK
fibular tarsal bone   BONES

BREAK JOINT

HIND SHANK BONE
tibia

STIFLE JOINT

SHANK KNUCKLE BONE
inferior extremity of femur

KNEECAP
patella

LEG BONE
femur

RUMP KNUCKLE BONE
superior extremity of femur

RIB CARTILAGES
costal cartilages

TIP OF BREASTBONE
xiphoid cartilage

BREASTBONE
sternum
sternebrae 1 to 7

olecranon process   SHANK
inferior extremity   KNUCKLE
of humerus   BONES

BREAK JOINT

ulna   FORE SHANK BONES
radius

metacarpal bone   LOWER
carpal bones   FORE SHANK
                  BONES

Fig. 14.1—Ovine anatomy.

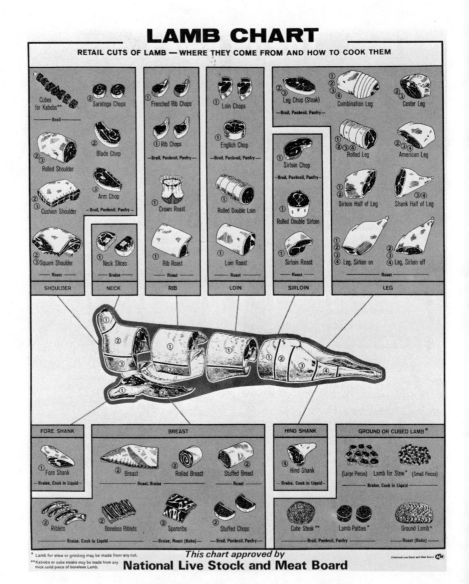

Fig. 14.2

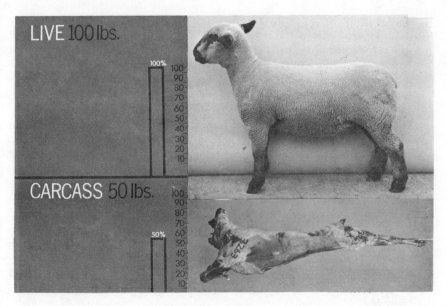

Fig. 14.3

The First Steps

Figure 14.3. For demonstration purposes, let us assume that generally, when lambs are finished for market, they will weigh approximately 100 pounds. Perhaps in the future, we will be seeing larger lambs, that is, lambs being ready for market at 150 pounds. However, the trend now is still for lambs to be marketed at 100 pounds. After slaughter, the resulting carcass represents approximately 50% of the live weight. Therefore, this particular 100-pound live animal will have a carcass weight of approximately 50 pounds.

Figure 14.4. Unlike beef or pork carcasses, lamb carcasses are not split before leaving the slaughter floor. The reason for this is the fact that lamb carcasses, being light in weight, can be cooled and handled as whole carcasses very readily. This is not the case with beef and pork.

Normally in industry, lamb carcasses are not ribbed before shipment, that is, they are not separated into foresaddles and hindsaddles. The reason for this is the fact that lamb carcasses weigh only approximately 50 pounds and are very easily handled in whole-carcass form. However, some packers are processing more lamb into primal and

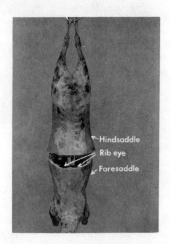

Fig. 14.4

subprimal cuts at the plant, and in order to properly evaluate a lamb carcass for subcutaneous fat thickness and loineye area in classroom, laboratory, or carcass contest situations, the carcasses must be ribbed. When this is done, the foresaddles and hindsaddles are separated between the twelfth and thirteenth ribs. Since the lamb carcass is not split longitudinally, the backbone cannot be seen, so the ribber must count ribs from the inside to find the twelfth rib.

Normally, the knife is inserted toward the outside to mark between the twelfth and thirteenth ribs. A cut is then made in a manner so as to bisect the loineye muscle (*longissimus dorsi*) at right angles to its long axis so that there is no distortion in its cross-sectional size. One skilled with a knife may cut through the muscle and the cartilagenous connection between *thoracic* vertebrae thus completing the separation without a saw. However, the use of a saw has proven very beneficial in neatly severing the backbone.

After the carcass has been ribbed, the rib eye and fat cover over the rib eye are easily measured. The terms hind*saddle* and fore*saddle* are used because the carcass has not been split. For fabrication, the hindsaddle is easily separated from the foresaddle by severing the attachment between the two, which is the flank muscle.

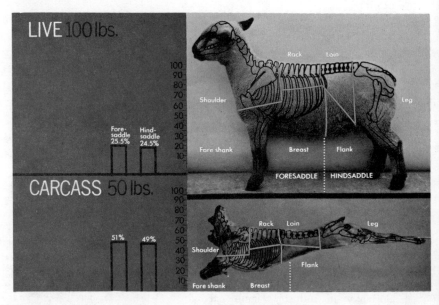

Fig. 14.5

Figure 14.5. The foresaddle comprises slightly more than half of the carcass weight as is the case with the beef forequarter. The foresaddle, composed of the shoulder, rack, fore shank, and breast comprises 51% of the carcass and 25.5% of the live animal while the hindsaddle composed of the loin, leg and flank comprises 49% of the carcass weight and 24.5% of the live weight. The leg, loin, rack, and shoulder are the primal cuts of lamb.

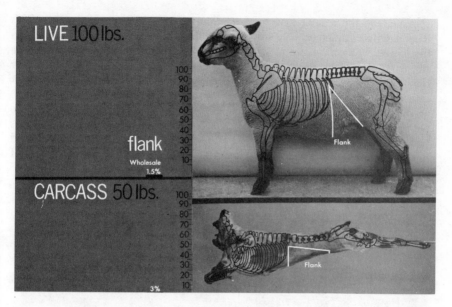

Fig. 14.6

Hindsaddle

Figure 14.6. The first step in the fabrication of the hindsaddle is the removal of the one rough cut from the hindsaddle, the flank. The flank in wholesale form comprises 1.5% of the live weight or 3% of the carcass weight. Possible retail cuts from the flank will be discussed later.

Figure 14.7. There are several modifications in the way in which the flank is removed. The modern method is to remove as much of the flank from the loin as possible, since the loin is much more palatable than the flank. In so doing, a measurement may be made laterally or away from the end of the loin eye a distance equal to one-half the width of the loin eye itself. In industry, a three-inch distance from the eye is common, but this leaves a rather long, undesirable "tail" on each loin chop. The flank muscles are just not palatable compared to the loin eye itself. Thus, a close trim here means a satisfied consumer.

When making a double or kidney chop, much more flank must be left on

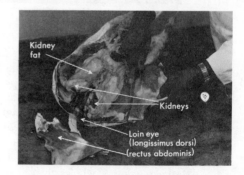

Fig. 14.7

495

the loin, and the separation is made farther into the flank, as shown here. This flank can be completely removed with a knife because of the wide flank left on the loin allowing the knife to go outside or lateral to the end of the thirteenth rib. A saw would be required in a closer trim to the loin eye in order to sever the thirteenth rib. The *longissimus dorsi* is called loin eye here because it is located in the loin. It is called the rib eye when it is viewed on the rib (rack) of the foresaddle. The largest, flat, straight muscle in the flank is called the *rectus abdominis*. In beef, this muscle becomes the flank steak, but in lamb its size, texture, and flavor dictate its use as ground lamb. Kidneys are enclosed in the cranial (front) portion of the kidney fat. The kidneys and kidney fat together are sometimes called the kidney knob.

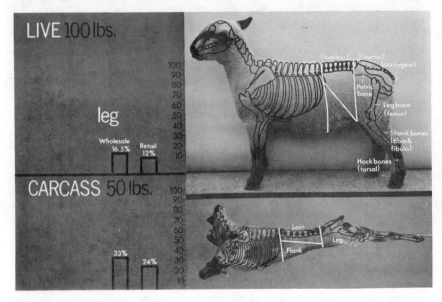

Fig. 14.8

Figure 14.8. The largest wholesale and retail cut in the lamb carcass is the leg. In wholesale form, it comprises 33% of the carcass and 16.5% of the live lamb. Note that these carcass and live percentage figures have a relationship of 2 to 1, since the carcass weight is exactly one-half of the live weight. The retail leg of lamb, fabricated with the bone in, comprises about 24% of the carcass and 12% of the live weight. A boneless leg would account for a smaller proportion of the carcass and live weight. A retail cut is ready for the consumer, while a wholesale primal cut may contain several subprimals or retail cuts and, as such, usually requires additional fabrication before being ready for the consumer. Exact percentages are unimportant, but relative weights are meaningful to establish a concept of live animal and carcass composition in terms of wholesale and retail cuts.

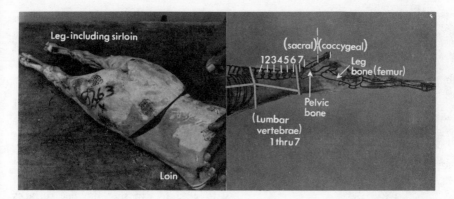

Fig. 14.9

Figure 14.9. In severing the leg from the loin, the sirloin is normally included with the leg. The resulting primal cut may be termed a *long-cut leg;* however, simply *leg-o-lamb,* or *leg of lamb,* implies the whole leg with sirloin. This lamb *pelvic* limb fabrication differs from beef fabrication where the round, including the rump and sirloin, is at least two separate cuts, and pork fabrication, where the sirloin is left with the loin rather than with the leg (ham). The separation in lamb is made at the seventh or last lumbar vertebra. Skeletal landmarks which are keys to cut identification are *sacral* (small of back) and *coccygeal* (tail) sections of the vertebral column, the pelvic bone, and the leg bone (*femur*).

After the muscle connections between the leg and the loin are severed with a knife, the separation of the backbone is completed with a saw.

Figure 14.10. The cranial (front) face of the leg presents these muscle and bone cross sections. Starting with the bone: (e) is the seventh *lumbar* vertebra which is dark (red) in color, indicating that this was a young lamb; its central portion or body extends out into the *transverse* processes which form the characteristic T in the loin chops. (d) The pin bone (*ilium* of the pelvic bone) is white because the cranial end of it is composed of cartilage. Muscle (c) is the tenderloin, the most tender muscle in the carcass; (b) is the largest muscle, the *longissimus dorsi,* here called the loin eye; (a) is the top sirloin muscle (*gluteus medius*). The Latin names are universal throughout the world, thus

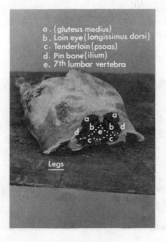

Fig. 14.10

497

Fig. 14.11

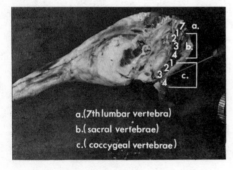

a.(7th lumbar vertebra)
b.(sacral vertebrae)
c.(coccygeal vertebrae)

Fig. 14.12

State inspection stamp

Fig. 14.13

their inclusion. Common names can vary even between sections of our own country. The new ISMISC standards should eliminate this variation.

Figure 14.11. In order to fabricate this pair of legs, it is necessary to split them. The aitch bone or *pubic* bone can normally be split with a knife in a young animal, since it is joined in cartilage. Once the aitch bone has been split, the remaining muscles can also be split with a knife exposing the cut surfaces of the aitch bone. Then the *sacral* and *coccygeal* portions of the vertebral column must be severed with a saw to complete the separation of the pair of legs.

A lamb carcass usually has a small amount of pelvic fat in the pelvic cavity located between the aitch bone and the backbone and it is removed when fabricating a leg of lamb.

Figure 14.12. There are three common types of lamb legs: The Frenched, American, and boneless. The first fabrication step in any case is the removal of the tail bone, composed of a number of the *coccygeal* vertebrae, the actual number depending on how long the tail was in the live lamb. Ordinarily, three tail vertebrae are left on the leg.

Figure 14.13. Outside fat is trimmed where needed until the remaining fat cover on the leg does not exceed ¼ inch. The fell or thin membrane separating the pelt from the subcutaneous fat is not removed unless absolutely necessary in trimming since this fell holds the shape of the leg and helps retain moisture and juices during cooking. When the flank side of the leg is trimmed, special care must be taken to remove the *prefemoral* lymph node. A state or Federal inspection stamp appears on every wholesale cut.

Figure 14.14. The large tendon at the rear of the leg, the *Achilles* tendon, is severed at its origin in preparation for the hock removal. In a Frenched leg, after the tendon is loosened, the muscle is severed about 1½ inches above the hock joint and cleared away from the bone. Slightly above the hock joint is the break joint. It is scored with a knife and may be broken across the edge of the cutting table. The hock bone or trotter is thus removed.

The break joint or *epiphyseal* plate is the area of growth in the long bones, so in young animals it is cartilaginous and easily broken, while in older animals where the bones have ceased growing, the *epiphyseal* plate has turned completely to bone and is tightly fused. The break joint is located above the hock joint, that joint which allows the animal to flex its leg and walk.

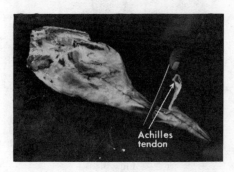

Fig. 14.14

Figure 14.15. The exposed shank bone is composed of the *tibia* and *fibula* which are fused together in the ovine. The Frenched leg is so named because the shank bone (*tibia* and *fibula*) is bare and exposed. When any bone is exposed, it is termed *Frenched*. The components of the wholesale leg, removed to become the retail Frenched leg, are the fat trim including the *prefemoral* lymph node, the tail bones, and the hock bones including the *Achilles* tendon.

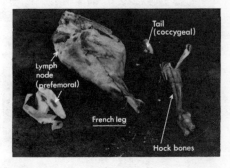

Fig. 14.15

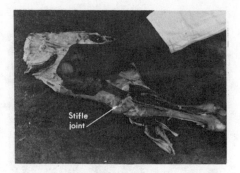

Fig. 14.16

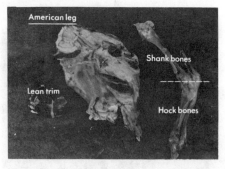

Fig. 14.17

Figure 14.16. In fabrication of the American leg, after the shank muscle and *Achilles* tendon are loosened from the shank bone as was done in the fabrication of the Frenched leg, the stifle joint is entered from the caudal (tail) side. This is the knee joint which joins the shank bone with the large leg bone, the *femur*, which are now separated by passing a knife through the joint. Note the abundant amount of connective tissue in the shank muscle as indicated by the white or silvery streaks.

The shank muscle (largely *gastrocnemius*) may be left attached to the American leg after the shank bone (*tibiafibula*) has been removed, and an attempt has been made to stuff the shank muscle into the small cavity next to the *femur*, created when the shank bone was removed at the stifle joint. However, the preferred method is to cut away and separate the shank muscle from the leg and utilize it as ground lamb since it does contain large amounts of connective tissue and is considerably less palatable than the leg itself. The kneecap or *patella* is normally left in an American leg.

Figure 14.17. The main portion of the American leg is identical to the Frenched leg. The reason an American leg is more valuable than the Frenched leg is that more bone has been removed, that is, the shank bone as well as the hock bone. Also, the unpalatable shank meat has been removed.

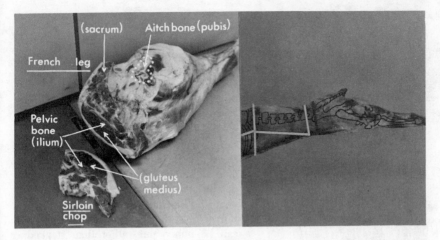

Fig. 14.18

Figure 14.18. The sirloin is normally left on the wholesale primal leg of lamb. Thus, sirloin chops can be removed from a leg of lamb. The location of the chop removal from the leg is indicated by a heavy dark line in the carcass diagram above. The largest muscle in a sirloin chop is the top sirloin or *gluteus medius* muscle. Note the presence of the flat pelvic bone in this sirloin chop.

Figure 14.19. The whole leg may be sawed into chops and slices (steaks) starting at this cranial (front) end. The result would be four to six sirloin chops, depending on how thick they were cut. These chops are identical to beef sirloin steaks in bone and muscle structure, differing of course in size and color. A wedge-shaped area corresponding to the rump in beef and containing the main portion of the pelvic bone most logically should be removed before the rest of the leg can be cut into leg slices (steaks). A sirloin half and/or a center roast of lamb leg can contain the rump section as indicated in the figure, i.e., it can go with either retail cut, but not both out of the same leg. It cannot be sliced or steaked because of the pelvic bone but makes excellent kabobs after the bone is removed. The center roast and most of the shank half can then be sliced.

Fig. 14.19

501

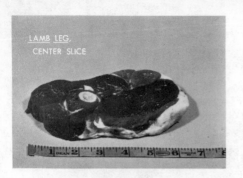

Fig. 14.20

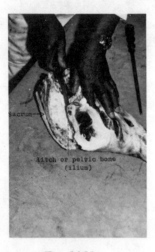

Fig. 14.21

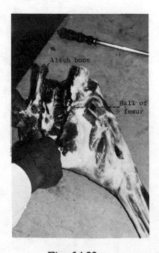

Fig. 14.22

Figure 14.20. The resulting center-leg slices (steaks) contain the full cross section of the leg composed of three muscle systems which may differ considerably in palatability: the top (nearest tape), bottom (away from tape), and tip (to your left). Such steaks would normally be broiled, and under these short time, high heat cooking conditions, there is a high possibility that a portion of each steak such as the bottom would not be palatable and would lack tenderness and juiciness. To avoid the possibility of such an occurrence, the leg can be boned out rather than steaked. The boneless leg would be roasted and, as such, is almost certain to be highly palatable. There is a considerable amount of bone (the whole pelvic bone and the *femur*) left in the Frenched and American legs. These bones can cause considerable inconvenience to the modern housewife when such a roast is being served. By boning the leg and jet-netting the resulting boneless roast before offering it to the consumer, any grief connected in serving a leg of lamb is eliminated.

Figure 14.21. The pelvic bone is removed by first entering the slip joint (*sacroiliac*) where the pelvic bone (*ilium*) is separated from the backbone (*sacrum*) . . .

Figure 14.22. . . . then it is separated from the *femur*.

Figure 14.23. The *proximal* (inward) end of the *femur* is loosened . . .

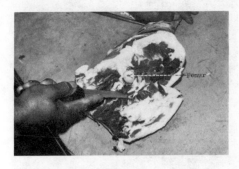

Fig. 14.23

Figure 14.24. . . . so the *femur* can be pulled out from the shank end without cutting through any muscles in the leg. This technique is called tunnel boning. After all bone is removed, the sirloin end is trimmed uniformly and the shank meat (*gastrocnemius* muscle) is removed.

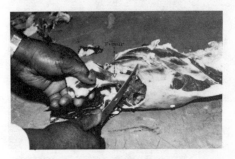

Fig. 14.24

Figure 14.25. A considerable amount of bone is removed in the process of boning a leg of lamb. . Only the hock bone (trotter) is removed in preparing a Frenched leg. Only the hock and shank bones are removed in fabricating an American leg.

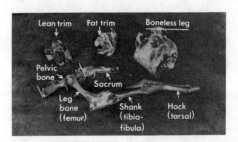

Fig. 14.25

Figure 14.26. The boneless leg, as any boneless roast, needs to be tied so that it can be roasted in a uniform manner and easily sliced after cooking. The introduction of a jet-netter and the elastic net have made the tying of roasts with the old-fashioned string and butcher's knot outdated. Using the jet-netter is a simple and quick operation to tie any boneless roast. A boneless leg of lamb is identified by its size and shape. Since it is a long cut leg containing the sirloin, one can recognize the boneless leg by its length. Keys to species identification are cut size and color. Lamb fat is much harder than beef or pork fat. Also, the fell will be present on lamb roasts. No such membrane is present on beef or pork cuts.

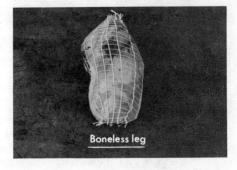

Fig. 14.26

Fig. 14.27

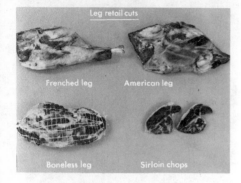

Fig. 14.28

Figure 14.27. A view of a cross section of the boneless leg of lamb cut exactly through the middle, makes it obvious that a boneless leg of lamb is packed with value. This cut is 99.9% edible, no waste.

Figure 14.28. To review the retail cuts from the leg, remember the Frenched leg, so named because of the exposed shank bone, the American leg differing from the Frenched leg in that the shank bone has been removed, the boneless leg which is preferred because of its value and convenience and the sirloin chops. Also note Figure 14.20 for leg slices.

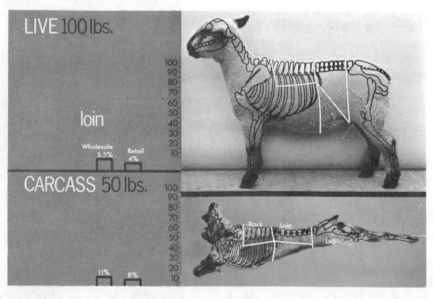

Fig. 14.29

Figure 14.29. The loin is the most valuable wholesale and retail cut in a lamb carcass since it contains the most tender muscles of the carcass. The main reason for the high retail price of lamb loin chops is the fact that there are so few of them from each animal. Only 4% of the live animal ends up as tender, juicy loin chops.

504

Figure 14.30. The composition of the loin varies slightly from end to end. At the seventh *lumbar* vertebra (the caudal end) the *longissimus dorsi* or loin eye is oval in shape, the tenderloin is at its maximum size, and the *gluteus medius* (top sirloin muscle) is present. From a cranial view, the loin eye is obviously larger and more symmetrically shaped. The tenderloin is not present since it originates at the last rib as a very thin muscle and gets progressively larger until it reaches its maximum size at the seventh *lumbar* vertebra. The hanging tenderloin is not to be confused with the actual tenderloin. Since the hanging tenderloin is a part of the diaphragm muscle, it is considerably less tender than the actual tenderloin muscle because of its constant activity in the live animal.

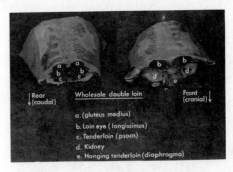

Fig. 14.30

Figure 14.31. Occasionally, double loin chops are made. If the kidney is left in the loin, they are called kidney chops; another name is English chop. A 2- to 3-inch chop is cut from the rib (cranial) end of the loin before the double loin is split. After cutting the muscle with a steak knife, the separation is completed with a saw. The resulting double or kidney chop is in demand mainly because of its uniqueness, rather than for its utility, since it does contain large amounts of subcutaneous and kidney fat. Also the kidneys and flank muscles are present, neither of which compare favorably at all with the quality of the loin eye muscle itself.

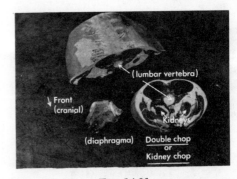

Fig. 14.31

Figure 14.32. The most popular method for fabricating the loin is to make individual, single loin chops. In

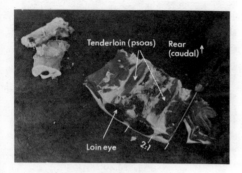

Fig. 14.32

order to do this the kidney fat must be removed. Recall its location in the live lamb and its carcass.

As in beef, lamb kidneys and kidney fat are left in the lamb carcass. Perhaps the reason for this is largely custom; however, the kidney fat does protect the valuable tenderloin muscle, which lies next to the backbone on the inside of the carcass, from discoloration and dehydration during the 3- to 6-day period between slaughter and fabrication.

The kidney and pelvic fat is a major internal fat deposit in a lamb and its carcass. Lamb fat has little or no value as such to today's consumer. Edible lamb tallow may be utilized in oleomargarine and other shortening manufacture, while inedible fats are utilized for the manufacture of feeds, soaps, and lubricants. The raw material in either case has little value when compared to edible meat.

Working now with the double loin from which one double chop has already been removed, the remainder of the kidney and kidney fat has been carefully cut away so that the tenderloin is exposed. The extra flank muscle originally left attached to the loin for the purpose of making a double chop is now removed by cutting along a line which is located one-half the length of the loin eye, lateral or away from the edge of the eye, thus the two to one ratio designation, a close trim by industry standards.

Fig. 14.33

Figure 14.33. The double loin may be split on a band saw. The transverse processes of the *lumbar* vertebrae form the characteristic T of loin chops, just as they form the T in the T-bone steak of beef. Each *lumbar* vertebra is split exactly in the middle, resulting in two loin roasts, each the mirror image of the other.

506

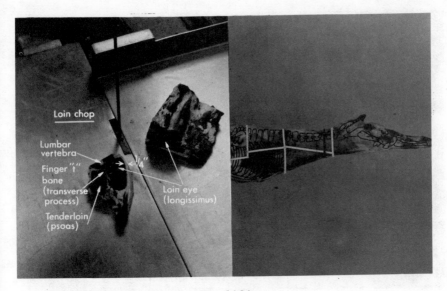

Fig. 14.34

Figure 14.34. The fell membrance separating the pelt from the subcutaneous fat is removed from the loin except for the specific area containing inspection and grading stamps. Since the loin will be made into chops which will be broiled, i.e., cooked with very high heat for a short time, the fell will shrink and distort the shape of the chop. The fell is left intact on leg roasts to hold in the juices during the slower roasting process.

The term *chop* originally was used for any piece of meat which was fabricated by the use of the cleaver, that is, it was chopped off with a cleaver. Only relatively small cuts could thus be fabricated, while larger cuts called steaks were removed with a saw. This is why all lamb cuts except leg slices (steaks) are called chops, for instance loin chops, rack chops, arm chops, and blade chops. In modern times, even chops are fabricated by the use of an electric band saw. The main identification key for the loin chop is the presence of the tenderloin muscle.

Figure 14.35. Loin retail cuts are loin chops, kidney or double chops sometimes called English chops, and the loin roast. By far the most popular retail cut from the loin is the loin chop. Recall that the retail loin chops represent only 4% of the weight of a live lamb.

Fig. 14.35

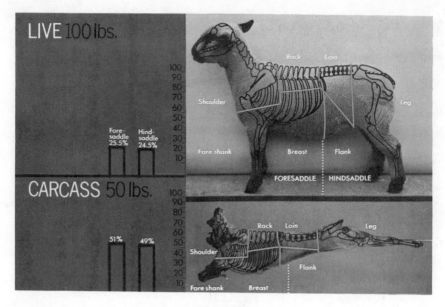

Fig. 14.36

Foresaddle

Figure 14.36. The foresaddle, which represents slightly more than one-half of the carcass weight, is composed of the primal rib (rack), shoulder, and the rough cuts, the foreshank and breast. Recall that the separation between foresaddles and hindsaddles is made between the twelfth and thirteenth ribs.

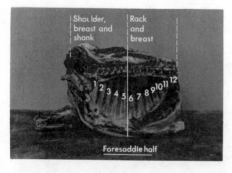

Fig. 14.37

Figure 14.37. The separation of the foresaddle half into the portion containing the shoulder and the portion containing the rib (rack) is made between the fifth and sixth ribs leaving a seven-rib rack just as the beef chuck is separated from the beef rib. Some lamb fabricators cut an eight-rib rack, that is, cutting between the fourth and fifth ribs to make a longer rack. However, the cranial portion of the rack near the shoulder is less desirable than the caudal portion near the loin since it contains more connective tissue and the *longissimus dorsi* or rib-eye muscle is much smaller. This front chop should be left on the shoulder to insure uniform palatability within each cut.

508

Figure 14.38. A knife is inserted between the fifth and sixth ribs and a cut made through the muscle of one side down to the backbone. Then a saw is used to sever the backbone, and the knife is used again to complete the separation through the muscles of the opposite side.

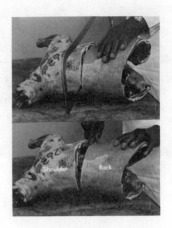

Fig. 14.38

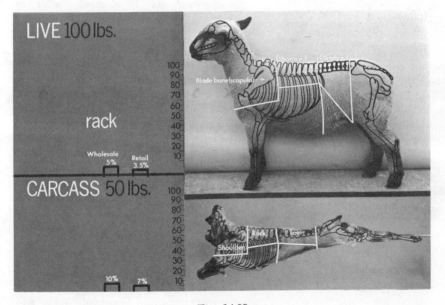

Fig. 14.39

Figure 14.39. The smallest wholesale and retail cut of lamb is the rib (rack), since on the average only 3.5% by weight of the live lamb is actually retail rib (rack) chops. The term *rib* is sometimes used synonymously with the term *rack* and is now the recommended ICMISC name. Note the blade bone (*scapula*). A small portion of the blade bone cartilage appears in rack chops from the cranial end of the rack.

Fig. 14.40

Figure 14.40. Normally, for a close trim, the breast is separated from the rib (rack) by cutting lateral to the eye, a distance equal to one-half the width of the rib eye. However, to make a crown roast, which is a rather prestigious cut, much longer rib ends must be left on the rack to form the crown.

The diaphragm is termed *the skirt* as it appears on the foresaddle. Remember on the hindsaddle it was called the hanging tenderloin. The rib eyes are large and symmetrical when viewed from this loin or caudal end.

Figure 14.41. The fabrication of a crown roast is not something that is done every day by a meat retailer, in fact, the consumer would undoubtedly have to make a special request for one. It does take valuable time to fabricate this roast and therefore the retail price will be quite high. However, it is truly *the* roast for a special occasion.

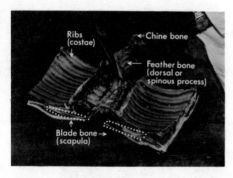

Fig. 14.41

Using the double rib (rack), the breast is removed leaving as much rib as possible on the rib (rack). After the ribs are sawed, the separation is completed with a knife.

The chine bones or bodies of the *thoracic* vertebrae are loosened by severing the rib connections with a saw and removed with the feather bones (*dorsal spinous* processes) attached. These feather bones are split in a beef carcass and the cartilaginous ends are examined closely in the evaluation of carcass maturity. The blade bone and its cartilage are prominent in this cranial (shoulder) end of the rib.

Frenching

Fig. 14.42

Figure 14.42. The fell and outside finish were not broken as the chine bones were removed. The rib bones are Frenched, that is, trimmed of most muscle and fat back from the rib ends a distance of 2½ to 3 inches.

The portion being trimmed away, which ordinarily belongs on the breast, is composed of thin layers of muscle interspersed with layers of fat, and therefore, lacks the high degree of palatability which the rib eye possesses. The muscles between the ribs, called rib fingers or *intercostal* muscles are removed so that the rib ends are completely bare, that is, Frenched. The blade-bone cartilage in the cranial end is removed.

Figure 14.43. Each end of the rib is tied together with heavy butcher's string by using a tying needle to penetrate the tissues. This finished crown roast shows the exposed rib-eye muscle from this caudal end. If the production of a crown roast is the major reason for fabricating a particular lamb carcass, regardless of the effect on other cuts, more ribs would be used in the crown roast. That is, if at least the last rib, now remaining on the loin, and the fifth rib, now remaining on the shoulder, had been included in the rack, the rack would have been longer and thus could have been shaped into a less oblong, more symmetrical crown roast with less rib-eye muscle exposed.

Lean ground lamb can be used to fill the center and provide a very desirable dressing for the roast. The

Crown roast

Fig. 14.43

Frenched rib ends can be decorated with small colorful paper or aluminum foil collars for serving. The properly prepared crown roast takes on a true "royal" appearance.

The roast is very easy to serve since all that needs to be done to obtain an individual serving is to cut between each rib with a knife, giving each person one rib and the accompanying tissues. (See Chapter 20.)

Fig. 14.44

Figure 14.44. The most popular widespread use of the rib is in fabricating individual rib chops in a similar manner to the way in which individual loin chops were fabricated. Thus, we must split a double rib (rack) into two single lamb ribs (racks). From the single rib (rack), the breast is removed in a close trim by cutting a distance equal to one-half the width of the rib eye away from the eye.

Figure 14.45. The wholesale primal rib differs in composition from end to end. Note the prominence of the blade-bone cartilage in the cranial end.

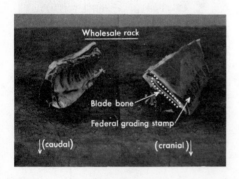

Fig. 14.45

The Federal grading stamp, when used, appears on every wholesale cut. Remember, grading refers to quality, and the quality grade is not required on every carcass that is sold. Inspection indicating wholesomeness, must by law be performed on every carcass. This quality stamp is applied by a roller, so theoretically, the stamp or a portion of the stamp should appear on each rack chop provided it has not been removed in fabricating the chops.

Figure 14.46. The fell and some fat are removed from the rack roast, since like the loin, its most popular use is as rib (rack) chops which are usually broiled. If the wholesale rack possesses more than ¼ inch of outside fat cover, it is trimmed to that thickness. When trimming overfat lambs, it may be necessary to remove the grade stamp, but usually care is taken to leave the stamp on the roast so that it can be seen on each chop in the self service meat case.

A rib chop is characterized by the presence of at least one rib. Due to the small size of rib and loin chops, they may be cut considerably thicker than pork chops or beef steaks; that is, approximately 1¼ to 1¾ inches thick so that two chops will make an acceptable cooked serving of 3½ ounces. Rack chops may be removed with a cleaver or with an electric band saw.

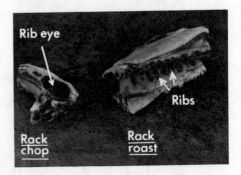

Fig. 14.46

Figure 14.47. Rib chops may be Frenched by exposing the end of the rib bone for at least 1½ inches. The retail cuts from the rib (rack) include the most popular rib chops, regular or Frenched; the crown roast, ideal for special occasions; and the rib roast. In any of these retail forms, the weight adds up to only 3.5% of the live weight of the lamb.

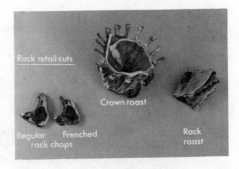

Fig. 14.47

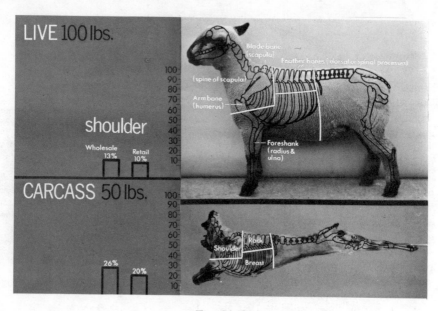

Fig. 14.48

Figure 14.48. The largest wholesale cut in the foresaddle, and second only in size to the leg in the whole lamb carcass, is the shoulder. Skeletal notations are especially helpful in shoulder-cut identification so note them carefully here on the carcass diagram. Shoulder cuts can be priced very economically and if fabricated and cooked correctly, can provide delightful dining.

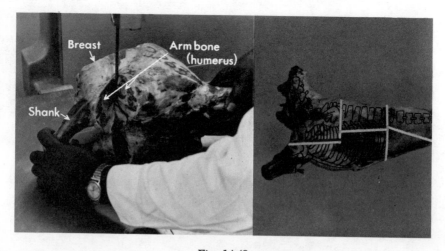

Fig. 14.49

Figure 14.49. While still in saddle form, breasts and shanks are separated from the shoulders by sawing across the arm bone or *humerus* at a point slightly above the knuckle, that is, the junction of the arm bone to the foreshank bone which is the fused *radius* and *ulna*. The heavy dark line in the carcass diagram to the right locates the cut.

Figure 14.50. The portion of the breast which was removed with the shank from the shoulder is that portion which would be called the brisket in beef. However, in lamb, the cuts known as the plate and brisket in beef are together called the breast.

The neck is removed from the shoulder by cutting in a straight line extending from the back.

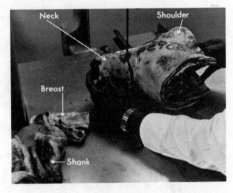

Fig. 14.50

Figure 14.51. The pair of shoulders can be separated exactly down the middle of the backbone with a band saw.

The wholesale primal shoulder is often called the square-cut shoulder because it usually fits the dimensions of a square. The arm face is so named because of the fact that the fore shank was removed, exposing a cross section of the arm bone (*humerus*). The blade face is adjacent to it.

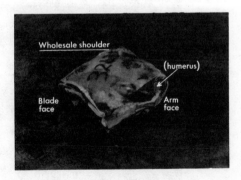

Fig. 14.51

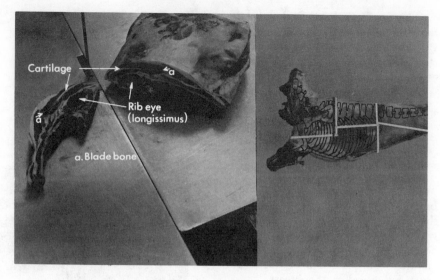

Fig. 14.52

Figure 14.52. If chops are removed from the shoulder, they are of two types. Those from the blade face are called blade chops because of the presence of the blade bone (*scapula*). The rib eye or *longissimus dorsi* extends through this area.

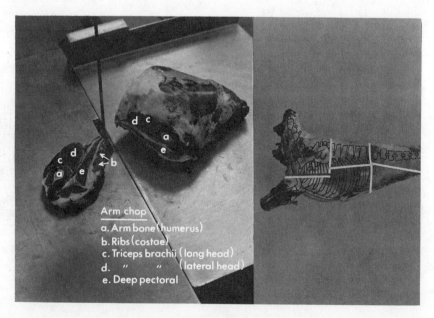

Fig. 14.53

Figure 14.53. At right angles to the blade face is the arm face. Thus, chops here are called arm chops. As in beef, the arm side of the shoulder is more muscular than the blade side, but less tender, since the *triceps brachii* and deep *pectoral* muscles do a considerable amount of work in providing locomotion for the live animal. Generally, the more use a muscle receives throughout life, the less palatable it will be after death.

Shoulder chops, be they blade or arm chops, just do not compare to rack or loin chops for overall palatability, because the shoulder does contain a considerable amount of connective tissue surrounding numerous small muscle systems.

Figure 14.54. There are several alternatives for shoulder fabrication which are preferred to making chops, because the resulting products are more likely to please the consumer. One alternative is the boneless blade (Saratoga) roll, which is an extension of the rib-eye muscle into the shoulder. The first step in its fabrication is the removal of the rib cage. Next, the eye and all muscles lying above the blade bone are removed, following the natural seam.

The eye is rolled tightly within the adjacent muscles and held in the tight Saratoga roll by the use of wooden skewers.

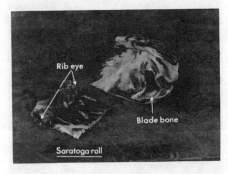

Fig. 14.54

Figure 14.55. The Saratoga roll is cut between each skewer to form boneless-blade (Saratoga) chops. The rib-eye muscle or *longissimus dorsi* begins here in the shoulder and extends all the way to the leg. It is the largest muscle in the lamb carcass but also one of the most palatable. Thus, boneless Saratoga chops composed largely of this eye muscle are very tender and juicy and the type of lamb cut that will encourage the consumer to repeat lamb purchases.

Fig. 14.55

Fig. 14.56

Figure 14.56. The remainder of the shoulder may be diced for lamb stew or kabobs (shish kabobs) after the blade and arm bones have been removed. Outdoor cookery is becoming ever more popular nowadays, since people have more leisure time. Shish kabobs rank high on the list of desirable meats for outdoor cookery.

Figure 14.57. A third alternative for shoulder fabrication is to completely bone out the square-cut shoulder and utilize it as a boneless roast.

In boning the shoulder, the muscle along the inside of the neckbone (*longus colli*) is removed, and any evidence of dried blood deposits remaining from slaughter are trimmed away. The rib cage is removed leaving as little muscle as possible on the bones. The neck leader is very unpalatable since it is composed of elastin which will not break down during cooking and must be removed.

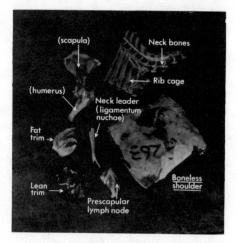

Fig. 14.57

The large, flat-blade bone (*scapula*) and the round-arm bone (*humerus*) are separated at their junction and the blade bone with its protruding spine is pulled free. The arm bone is then removed.

The *prescapular* lymph node is located in the shoulder in front of the scapula and is surrounded by a large fat deposit. It must be removed since it would detract from the desirability of the roast. Finally, outside fat cover is removed where it exceeds ¼ inch in thickness. The fell is left intact if possible.

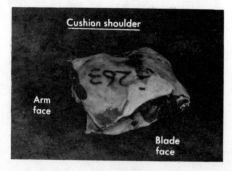

Fig. 14.58

Figure 14.58. The boneless shoulder maintains its original square shape quite well. It may be stuffed with dressing and sewn together at the blade and arm face seams to make a rather desirable cushion shoulder roast.

Figure 14.59. The jet-netted boneless shoulder roast may be the most preferred method of merchandising the shoulder. The roast is rolled around the extension of the rib eye before being placed in the netting. This netting remains in place throughout roasting. After the roast has reached the desired degree of doneness, the net is removed before serving.

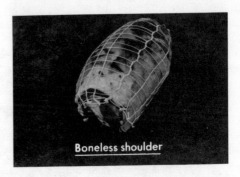

Fig. 14.59

Figure 14.60. By cutting through the center of this boneless shoulder, it becomes obvious that even after boning and trimming rather carefully, the boneless shoulder still contains some undesirable seam fat and connective tissues. Yet when properly roasted, this boneless roast will please far more consumers than would be pleased with improperly broiled arm or blade chops from the bone-in shoulder.

It is useful to compare the boneless leg and the boneless shoulder. Certainly the leg is more desirable since it has larger muscle systems with less seam fat and fewer connective tissues. However, if we put a price differential of 50¢ per pound between these two cuts, perhaps the shoulder would seem more desirable. The point is, the boneless shoulder can provide some very delicious and economical eating. Certainly the leg would be preferred for "special" occasions, but the shoulder in this form is special for "regular" occasions.

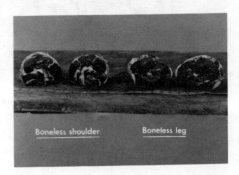

Fig. 14.60

Fig. 14.61

Figure 14.61. A wide variety of retail cuts originate in the lamb shoulder. The square-cut shoulder may be merchandised as a retail cut but usually arm chops and blade chops are removed from it. Alternately, the rib-eye muscle may be utilized as Saratoga chops and the remainder for kabobs. A third method is to bone and roll the shoulder and make a highly desirable boneless shoulder roast.

The neck, which was removed from the paired shoulders, may be sawed into neck slices, a retail cut that lacks wide consumer demand. These are probably consumed only by those people who really appreciate lamb and enjoy the economy of such a meal.

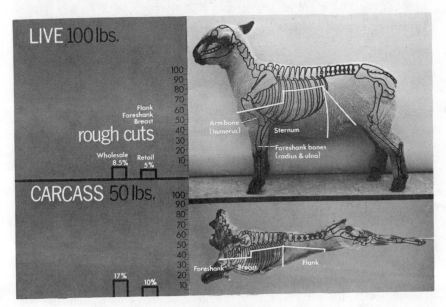

Fig. 14.62

Figure 14.62. The rough cuts of lamb are the flank of the hindsaddle and the fore shank and brisket of the foresaddle. All told, in retail form, they amount to 10% of the carcass weight.

The most proper use of lamb flanks is to trim away excess fat and grind the remainder for lamb patties.

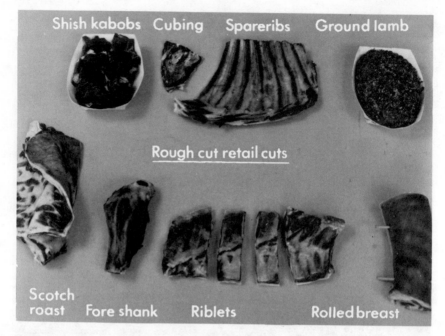

Fig. 14.63

Figure 14.63. The portion of the breast which corresponds to the plate in beef contains rib bones and the sternum. For the several alternate fabrication methods, the diaphragm or skirt is removed. For a breast for stuffing (Scotch roast), the meat portion of the breast is peeled away from the bone structure leaving a natural hinge along the full length of one side. This pocket then may be stuffed with ground lamb or lamb dressing and sewed, jet-netted, or tied for roasting. Alternately, the breast may be cut into riblets by merely cutting between each rib of the breast. A third alternative is to remove the sternum and rib cage leaving a boneless breast composed of layers of thin muscles separated by layers of intermuscular fat. The rib cage and sternum are called lamb spareribs and may be prepared by barbecuing much as pork spareribs are prepared. The boneless breast is usually rolled. Only thin muscles are included in the rolled breast, which may be confused with the boneless blade (Saratoga) roll. There is a vast difference in the value of a rolled breast and a boneless blade (Saratoga) roll since the Saratoga roll contains the very tender rib-eye muscle. By closely examining the two, one can quickly determine the presence of the rib eye in the Saratoga roll. The rolled breast is identified by the alternate layers of thin muscle and fat in the cross section of the roll.

That portion of the breast which corresponds to the brisket in beef does contain a rather thick muscle. This may be separated from the sternum and utilized for cubing much as the beef bottom-round steak was utilized. Lamb fore shanks may be utilized as mock duck or simply lamb shanks for braising. The rough cuts may be many and varied. Shish kabobs or lamb for stewing can originate from large thick pieces of rough cut lean.

Perhaps the most highly justified use for all of the rough cuts would be to process them into ground lamb. Ground lamb has very many delightful uses, while some of these variations of rough cut fabrication can only lead to consumer dissatisfaction due to improper cooking or simply unfulfilled expectations of good eating.

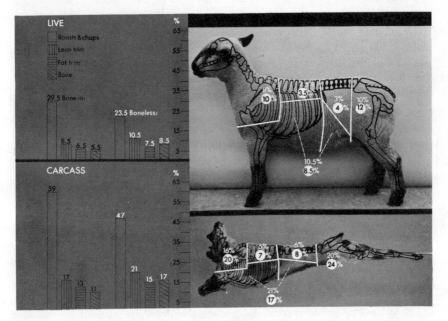

Fig. 14.64

Figure 14.64. By studying this figure, you will be able to answer the question: How much retail product does one lamb (or lamb carcass) produce?

First of all, solidify your thoughts concerning the relation between live and carcass weights. With lambs it is simple, since a lamb carcass weighs approximately 50% as much as the live lamb. Thus the bone-in retail leg represents 12% of the live lamb (shown in black figures in a white circle on the live lamb) while this same bone-in leg represents 24% of the carcass (shown in black on the carcass diagram). The carcass weighs one-half as much as the live animal so the percent of leg must be two times as great.

Bone-in figures (in black) and boneless figures (in white) are shown, since in this chapter, we have discussed bone-in and boneless fabrication for the two largest primal cuts, the leg and the shoulder. We have not shown the fabrication of a boneless loin or rack because it is so seldom done in industry. However, the boneless yield figures mean that *all* cuts are boneless, including the rough cuts.

Examine the bone-in figures first. The chart indicates that roasts and chops comprise 29.5% of the live animal. Check these percentages on the live animal by adding 12% from the leg, 4% from the loin, 3.5% from the rack and 10% from the shoulder to total 29.5%. This same system works for carcass and live, bone-in and boneless cuts. The figures placed on each cut indicate the percent that that particular *retail* cut represents of the carcass or live weight.

In the chart, lean trim represents the trimmed boneless rough cuts as well as lean trim produced when the wholesale primal cuts were fabricated into retail cuts. With the live lamb, lean trim from bone-in fabrication amounts to 8.5% of the live weight. Thus total bone-in *retail* yield amounts to 38% of the live lamb, i.e., 29.5% + 8.5%.

This same system works for bone-in and boneless retail yield based on live or carcass weights.

Check yourself:

What percent of the carcass is bone-in retail product?
   *Answer—*76% determined by adding 59% for roasts and chops to 17% for lean trim.

What percent of live weight is boneless retail product?
   *Answer—*34%; 23.5% + 10.5%.

What percent of the carcass weight is total boneless retail product?
   *Answer—*68% which is 2 × 34%, since the carcass = ½ the live weight, or is also 47% + 21% from the carcass chart.

All percentage figures used here are based on averages of the detailed carcass analysis of approximately 175 lambs evaluated in the University of Illinois Live Animal and Carcass Evaluation Course during the period from 1965 through 1974. This so-called average lamb possessed the following "vital statistics":

Leg conformation	High Choice
Loin-eye area	2.35 square inches
Fat over twelfth rib (top)	0.23 inch
Fat over lower twelfth rib	0.67 inch
Average fat cover	0.45 inch
Percent of kidney fat	3.8%
USDA Yield Grade	3.6

Since all percentage figures quoted here are averages, they can vary according to the methods of cutting and the fatness and muscling of the lambs.

New Developments in Lamb Handling and Distribution

Lamb slaughter is becoming concentrated in fewer packing plants and packing companies. The packers involved in slaughtering and processing lambs are streamlining their operations to bring lamb to the consumer more efficiently. The generally light weight of lambs and lamb carcasses compared to pork and beef, puts lambs at a competitive disadvantage in terms of product output per hour of fabrication labor. The anatomy of the species is similar, thus very similar techniques of boning and cutting can be used. However, when similar techniques are used, taking approximately equal time but with much less product produced from one species than another, the species producing less product has more labor per pound charged against it. Thus, the push for efficiency in lamb fabrication and marketing.

One of the largest lamb slaughterers in the United States presently is Monfort of Colorado located in Greeley. Approximately 5,000 to 6,000 of the 15,000 lambs slaughtered each week at Monfort Packing are broken by their lamb fabrication department.

Fig. 14.65—Mopac lamb in a box eliminates carcass handling. (Courtesy, Monfort of Colorado)

Fig. 14.66—Lamb fabrication line in action on hindsaddles. (Courtesy, Monfort of Colorado)

The lamb fabrication department processes both Mopac boxed lamb packed in CO_2 pellets and fully boned and vacuum packaged cuts.

Figure 14.65 shows the boxed Mopac lamb, which basically consists of a carcass in a box, trotters (hock bones) off. This box is lined with plastic, and five pounds of CO_2 pellets are added as a preservative. This method is an improvement over carcass shipping in handling, preservation, and sanitation. It virtually eliminates all handling of the product once it is placed in the box.

Some lamb carcasses are completely processed into the cuts illustrated in this chapter (Figure 14.66). Those fabricated lamb cuts are shipped primarily to restaurants and restaurant and hotel supply houses. Lambs utilized for in-plant fabrication generally weigh 64 pounds or more.

CHAPTER 15

The Veal Carcass and Its Cuts

Veal has very little protective fat covering, is high in moisture, and does not lend itself to aging or ripening. It is necessary, therefore, to move veal into retail channels without delay.

Beef and veal cuts, aside from their water, fat, and ash content, differ mainly in size and terminology. Veal is tender by nature, because of its age. Calf carcasses fall between the veal and beef stage and are usually considered inferior to both, grade for grade. This is due to the fact that the flesh of calf carcasses has developed beef characteristics without the accompanying fat covering and marbling that enhance beef qualities.

WHOLESALE CUTS

The size of the carcass will determine the method of cutting. The larger calf carcasses are generally halved and then quartered, whereas the smaller calf and practically all veal carcasses are cut into foresaddles and hindsaddles. A *foresaddle* is the part of the carcass anterior to the twelfth rib or the two unsplit forequarters. A *hindsaddle* consists of the two unsplit hindquarters posterior to the twelfth rib. Other wholesale cuts of veal are *long saddle*—two unsplit hindquarters with loin and nine ribs attached; *shoulders or veal chucks*—split or unsplit shoulders of four ribs with briskets and fore shanks attached; *legs*—single or unsplit, cut in front of the hips; *veal backs*—single or unsplit, and cut from the fourth rib to the hip bone (including loin and nine ribs); *rattles*—the unsplit shoulders with breast and shanks attached; and *rib backs*—the unsplit ribs (eight ribs on each side).

A veal carcass is generally sold with the liver and sweetbread (thymus) attached. The demand for veal liver is so great that retailers invariably demand it. The average liver in a 90-pound veal carcass weighs about 3½ pounds. At $1.00 per pound, it represents a value of $3.50, or approximately 4 cents a pound on the 90-pound carcass.

RETAIL CUTS

The method of cutting veal follows the same pattern that is employed in cutting beef (Chicago style), with a few exceptions. One of these exceptions is where the boned neck and brisket are rolled in with the shoulder of light veal carcasses in making the rolled shoulder. Another variation is where a style of cutting is followed similar to lamb, where the sirloin is left on the leg.

The Veal Shoulder

The term *veal* precedes the name of the cut to differentiate it from beef, lamb, and pork. The term *veal chuck* is just as appropriate as the term *veal shoulder*. Small veal shoulders are often boned and rolled, using the same method as was followed in boning a shoulder of lamb. The chucks of calf carcasses can be made into top and bottom shoulder rolls which are more nearly the size desired by the trade. In some sections, the shoulder is cut from the carcass between the third and fourth ribs to make a three-rib chuck, while in others it is cut as a four-rib chuck, while the standard is five ribs.

Slices that include the first through the fifth ribs cut parallel with the ribs are termed *blade veal steaks or veal chuck steaks*. Cut from the arm, they are called *arm veal steaks* (arm steak in beef). Unscrupulous dealers have been known to misrepresent *arm veal steak* as "veal round steak" (veal cutlets). Large quantities of veal shoulder are used in making "*veal stew*" and "*city chicken*." The latter generally consists of 1-inch squares of veal cut ½-inch thick and placed on a 5-inch skewer with alternate layers of pork.

Veal shanks and breasts usually are boned, and the meat is diced or ground. *Ground veal* is commonly used in combination with pork for veal loaf (20% pork), and for mock chicken. When used for the latter, the mixture should be seasoned by the retailer before it is molded and placed on skewers. The seasoning for veal loaf is added by the housewife. The same combination can also be molded into patties, each patty bound by a slice of cured bacon. A mixture of 80% pork and 20% veal makes an excellent sausage. Veal breasts are also boned and made into breast rolls which are boiled and used cold as a jelled cut, or sausage breast rolls—a layer of sausage rolled into the breast, or a pocket is made between the ribs and the meat to hold stuffing. A five-rib shoulder is 23% to 25% of the weight of the carcass. The neck, shank, and breast represent another 16% to 18%.

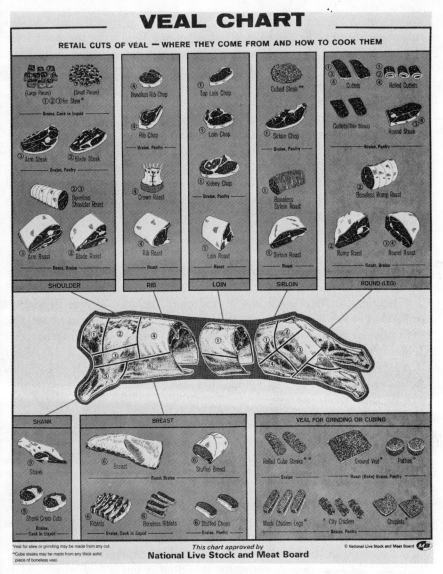

Fig. 15.1

Ribs

A cut which is the result of chopping with a cleaver is termed a *chop*. Only soft bones and the solid bones of young animals are adapted to the use of the cleaver. Round or hollow bones and the bones of older animals will splinter and should be sawed. The ribs of veal when cut into slices for braising are called *veal rib chops*. Removing the meat from the end of the rib for a distance of 1½ to 2 inches is called *Frenching*. When a loin or rib chop is cut from ¾ to 1 inch thick and a pocket is made in the eye muscle, the chop is called a *bird* or a *chop for stuffing*. This practice is followed in both veal and pork. If the opening for the pocket is made on the flank side of the eye muscle, the stuffing can be inserted and will remain so without pinning the opening. On a rib chop, the opening can be made from the inside of the rib.

Ribs from light veal carcasses can be made into veal crown roasts (see lamb for details). Ribs from heavy veal carcasses can be prepared for roasts either as standing ribs (bone in) or as rolled veal rib (boneless). A seven-rib saddle represents 6.5% to 7% of the weight of the carcass.

Loin

From the last rib to the hip bone (short loin in beef) is the region of the lumbar vertebrae from which loin veal chops (Porterhouse and T-bone steak in beef) are cut. If the chop includes a slice of kidney imbedded in the kidney fat, the cut is known as a *kidney veal chop*. The veal fillet or tenderloin which lies on the underside of the vertebrae is seldom removed as a separate cut. The loin is more suitable as a roast if it is boned and rolled, preferably taking the loin saddle which includes both sides. The loin of veal with kidney, suet, and flank represents about 17% of the carcass weight.

Leg or Round and Rump

As in lamb, the leg includes the sirloin roast and steaks. However, the greatest demand is for veal round steak or veal cutlet. Considering that the leg with the rump off represents 27% of the carcass weight and that only 50% to 60% of this can be cut into cutlets (round steak in beef), it must be evident that this cut is the most expensive in a veal carcass. The veal round is removed in the same manner as a leg of lamb. Cutlets may be made in thicknesses of ½ to 1½ inches, depending upon the use to which they are put. A cutlet for breading is cut ½ inch thick unless the customer specifies otherwise. The first three to four slices should be priced higher than the remainder of the cuts. Slicing ceases when the stifle joint (shank knuckle bone) is reached. The meaty part on the back of the shank can be cut for a small heel of veal round pot roast.

The rump is suitable as a roast with bone in or boned and rolled.

CHAPTER 16

Sausages

The subject headed by the above title is truely *vast* and can by no means be covered with any facsimile of completeness in this chapter. Complete books, old *and* new, have been written on the subject and perhaps then, only a fraction of the total knowledge, handed down by sight, practice and verbal communication throughout the years, has been recorded. The subject, which for many years developed as an art rather than a science, has in recent times "come of age" in terms of science and technology. Thus, this chapter is designed to help the reader comprehend the foundation of this colorful segment of the meat industry and yet understand the basic scientific principles on which it continues to flourish today.

The tonnage of sausage of many different types manufactured in more recent years has been phenomenal. About 250 varieties are sold in the United States. The consumption of frankfurters and soft drinks would have to be included in any mural drawn to depict the American way of life. Peruse the following facts: Today approximately 1 out of every 7½ pounds of meat produced in the United States is consumed as sausage. Ten years ago it was 1 out of every 10. Sausage production has become the most profitable segment of our meat packing industry. Sausage, which was once considered to be predominantly a product of pork, now contains more beef than pork in most of the formulas. Sausage has made possible a much greater variety in our meat diet. It has taken an important role in our hurried way of living by giving us quick meals of high nutritive value. It has made use of meats that might have otherwise been lost items for the meat packer. Ironically, the dairy industry, which clamored so long and loudly against margarine, is one of the largest suppliers of sausage beef besides furnishing the milk that is included in the margarine formula.

Approximately 3.8 billion pounds of sausage products are currently processed in Federally inspected plants, equivalent to 18.4 pounds per person annually. Ten years ago 2.5 billion pounds were processed, equal to 13.5 pounds per person then. Frankfurters, wieners, and bologna types accounted for the bulk of the noncanned items, and luncheon meat was the leading canned sausage product.

It is in the sausage business that the manufacturer has his largest field for individual effort in developing new products. Today, without too much effort or searching, one can probably find the edible parts of an entire hog reposing in the supermarket in either a skin, a plastic bag, or a tin.

Sausages have been variously catalogued but may be classified for our purpose as Domestic and Fancy.

DOMESTIC SAUSAGES

Small sausages—Wieners, Frankfurters—In skins or skinless—smoked and cooked. Fresh: Loose or cased. All-pork breakfast style, light, medium, or heavy sage. Pork and beef, coarse ground, country style, no sage. Smoked sausage.

Large sausages (2 inches or over in diameter)—Fine cut (emulsion), Fine cut with ground or chunk meat added, Coarse cut—long or short, round or square—smoked, cooked.

Bologna—beef and pork, smoked and cooked

Kosher all beef sausage—smoked and heat treated

Lebanon bologna—smoked, semi-dry, and uncooked

Summer sausage (regular)

Pork and beef (pork predominating) cooked, not smoked

Summer sausage (Wisconsin style)

Beef and pork (beef predominating) smoked and cooked

Braunschweiger

Liver and pork, cooked (is not smoked if some smoked meat was added)

Liver sausage

Liver and pork, cooked and can be smoked

Luncheon meats

Smoked and cooked or cooked and not smoked

Meat loaf

Cooked in water or oven baked—fine chopped (silent cutter); Fine chopped; ground meat or chunk meat added; course cut; meat chunks added; to facilitate chopping or mixing, water or ice may be used in an amount not to exceed 3% of the total ingredients used; cooked: boneless hams, pork shoulders, pork loins pressed in cooking mold; jellied type loaves: souse, head cheese, chicken loaf, jellied tongue, combination meat and cheese loaves, and diced loaves. The above loaves fall into the category of sausage, in which the amount of the extenders added is limited to 3.5%, either individually or collectively.

Pork Sausage

The term *pork sausage* is generally implied to mean the ground and seasoned fresh pork product. There are, however, several kinds of fresh pork sausage which differ in texture, seasoning, and meat content.

Country Style—This style usually contains from 10% to 20% of beef ground with the fresh pork; it is coarsely ground, using the 3/16-inch plate, and does not contain sage as a seasoning. It is stuffed into hog casings or regenerated collagen casings of different sizes and is unlinked. It is also sold loose (unstuffed).

Breakfast Style—This is an all-pork sausage that is finely ground and seasoned with sage, salt, and pepper. It is stuffed into medium and large sheep casings and the smaller size hog casings or regenerated collagen casings which are then linked to make the various-sized sausages.

Such terms as *farm* or *country* shall not be used on labels in connection with products unless such products are actually prepared on the farm or in the country. However, if the product is prepared in the same way as on the farm or in the country these terms, if qualified by the word *style* in the same size and style of lettering, may be used. Further, the term *farm* may be used as part of a brand designation when qualified by the word *brand* in the same size and style of lettering, and followed with a statement identifying the locality in which the product is prepared. Sausage containing cereal shall not be labeled "farm style" or "country style," and lard not rendered in an open kettle shall not be designated as "farm style" or "country style."

The requirement that the label shall contain the name and place of business of the manufacturer, packer, or distributor shall not relieve any establishment from the requirement that its label shall not be misleading in any particular.

A lean sausage (20% to 25% fat) with a mild seasoning of sage is probably the most popular but also the most expensive. The incorporation of pork fat cheapens the sausage and increases the cooking shrink. Sausages produced in Federally inspected plants cannot contain in excess of 50% trimmable fat. Several sausages such as Bratwurst, fresh Thuringer, and Bockwurst contain some beef and/or veal along with the pork and are not cooked or smoked.

Seasoning Pork Sausage

The farm practice of tasting raw sausage to determine the amount of seasoning is unsatisfactory in view of possible health hazards and in that it caters to only one person's desires. The most satisfactory way to get the seasoning nearly right for the greatest number of people is to weigh the sausage and add the following mixture for each 100 pounds of ground pork:

28 to 30 oz. table salt
6 oz. black pepper
2 oz. ground sage

This imparts an excellent flavor and the different batches of sausage will always be seasoned the same. Many prefer butcher's pepper (coarsely ground black pepper) instead of table pepper.

Those desiring a more highly seasoned sausage might try the following formula:

2 lbs. salt	⅞ oz. Jamaica ginger
6 oz. dextrose (corn sugar)	⅞ oz. ground mace
⅞ oz. red pepper	⅞ oz. thyme
3 oz. white pepper	2 oz. rubbed sage

Whole Hog Sausage (The Ground Hog)

"Whole Hog Sausage" is sausage prepared with fresh and/or frozen meat from swine in such proportions as are normal to a single animal and may be seasoned with condimental substances as permitted any sausage product. It shall not be made with any lot of product which, in the aggregate, contains more than 50% trimmable fat; that is, fat which can be removed by thorough practicable trimming and sorting. To facilitate chopping or mixing, water or ice may be used in an amount not to exceed 3% of the total ingredients used.

Modern whole hog sausage is made from 240- to 250-pound butcher hogs. Depending on the fatness (grade) of the hogs, leaf lard may be pulled out of the raw material for sausage or, conversely, certain lean muscles (ham, loin, tenderloin) may be pulled out if the hogs are too lean. Of course, the carcasses must be boned out before being ground into sausage. This is presently done with hand and mechanical knives, resulting generally in a 15% to 20% yield of bone based on carcass weight. Mechanical deboners, which force the meat and bones through a sieve which traps the bone and lets the meat pass through, are now used in the poultry industry, but are not approved for use in the meat industry because of a slightly higher than normal mineral content of the resulting meat. Such machines salvage an amazing amount of meat left on the bones by hand or mechanical knife boning. Further research may justify their use, which would surely aid the "whole hog sausage" segment of the industry.

Sausage Meats

Pork trimmings of two degrees of leanness are listed on the market and are (1) special 80% lean and (2) regular 50% lean. The better grades of all pork sausages are made from a combination of these pork trimmings.

Meats suitable for processed sausages (cooked or cooked and smoked) are bull meat (which has good binding and water absorbing qualities), plates, boneless chucks, cheeks, and hearts in the beef category; pork trimmings, trimmable fats, fat backs, and jowls in the pork line; and boneless veal shoulders and shanks of veal in the veal line. Such miscellaneous items as tongues, tips, snouts, tripe, weasands, brains, spleen, hog ears, pigskins, and pigs' feet are useful as binders or fillers.

In addition, Federal regulations permit the use of additives such as nitrate, nitrite, and ascorbic acid in prescribed amounts, also cereals, nonfat dry milk solids, and other nonmeat substances as set forth in the regulations.

Casings (Natural, Cellulose, and Collagen)

Natural casings are the middle wall of the small and large intestines of cattle, hogs, sheep, and goats. Some other organs such as the bung, bladder, and (in the case of hogs) the stomach are used as containers for special sausages. It is the opinion of discriminatory gourmets that natural casings are superior to synthetic casings for their form-fitting and flavor-sealing qualities.

Cellulose casings are made from cotton linters which are solubilized and regenerated into casings of any desired diameter. Fibrous casings are cellulose casings which have been reinforced with fibers to give added strength.

Collagen casings, made from a collagen source, such as the *corium* layer of beef hide, are completely edible, and are used in the dry state, thus eliminating stripping and preparation time.

Plastic nettings made of polyethylene threads that contract with the heat are particularly suited to boneless hams.

Processed Sausage

Certain equipment is essential in large-scale sausage production, the most important of which are the grinder, the silent cutter or chopper, the stuffer, the linker, the peeler, and the air-conditioned smoker and cooker. The purpose of the grinder is to reduce the pieces of meat to a conglomerate mass of uniform size according to the plate openings used.

The beef is ground separately from the pork. The ground beef is then placed in the silent cutter along with the salt, sodium nitrate, sodium nitrite, spices, and seasoning and is chopped fine. The ground pork is added and the mixture chopped to the desired fineness. Since heat is generated in the emulsion by the friction of the high-speed knives, it is necessary to add shaved ice to hold the temperature below 60° F. The amount of water added to get the proper consistency of the sausage is governed by law. The APHIS regulation states that the moisture in the finished cooked sausage must not exceed four times the meat protein (by analysis) plus 10%. In fresh sausage that is not processed, the moisture is limited to four times the protein plus 3%.

If the colloid mill is used, the emulsion is prepared by one passage through the machine or by using two mills in tandem. Where stuffing and

Fig. 16.1—A colloid mill. (A type of "Silent cutter.")

smoking are to be a continuous process without any holding period for curing, it is necessary to add ascorbic acid (¾ ounce per hundredweight) in solution a short time before the end of the chop, otherwise there will be an uncured core in the center of the sausage. Some manufacturers vacuumize their sausage mix before stuffing to remove the captured air since it gives better color stabilization to the product.

If ascorbic acid or any of its derivatives have been included in the emulsion for proper color development, the processing can be continuous (without curing period) and is done in three stages, the length of each period depending upon the nature of the product and its size. The first stage consists in drying and warming the product at a temperature set at 130° to 140° F, requiring about 15 to 20 minutes. No smoke is admitted during this warm-up. The next stage involves the application of smoke while the temperature is raised gradually to 165° F and held there until the internal temperature of the product reaches 145° to 155° F. The humidity should be maintained at 78° to 80° to avoid excessive drying which causes a tough shell to form on the product and interferes with proper peeling. The third stage consists of cooking the product by showering with hot water in the smoker or by removing it to a conventional type water cooker (Jordan cooker) and removing the product when the internal temperature reaches 155° F. It is then showered with cold water for three to five minutes and allowed to hang at room temperature to dry. When dry, it is placed in a cooler temperature of 45° to 55° F.

Coloring

The coloring of casings has become a standard practice. APHIS restricts the use of coloring matter to the coal tar dyes and the natural coloring substances alkanet, annatto, carotene, and cochineal. The law states that the dye shall not penetrate into the product. Those who do not use colored cellulose casings may add the dye by dipping or include the dye in the recirculating hot water shower.

Both natural and cellulose casings of different sizes and strengths are used, depending upon the product to be stuffed. Cellulose casings are used for the production of skinless sausages since they are easier to peel. The manufacture of skinless frankfurters without previous stuffing is in limited production. Hand linking has been largely replaced by mechanical linking machines which reduce labor costs.

Kolbassi

This sausage, as its name implies, is of European origin and consists of 80% pork and 20% beef. Pork shoulder meat is ground through a ⅜-inch plate; the beef (chuck, brisket, plate, or shank meat) is ground through a ⅛-inch plate (twice, if desired). The ground beef and pork are mixed and the following cure added (per 100 pounds of meat): 40 ounces salt, 8 ounces sugar, 2 ounces sodium nitrate, ¼ ounce sodium nitrite (dissolved in 2 quarts of water). The cure is mixed with the meat and refrigerated for 24 to 48 hours.

Seasoning per 100 pounds of meat (approximate):

    6 oz. butcher's black pepper
    2 oz. mustard seed
    1 oz. paprika
    1 oz. red pepper
    ½ oz. garlic powder (dissolved in water)

The seasoned sausage is stuffed into large hog casings in 12- to 14-inch lengths and smoked at 120° to 130° F until brown. The smoked sausage is placed in 170° F water for 30 minutes, drained and refrigerated. Kolbassi makes a good cold cut or can be served hot.

FRANKFURTERS AND/OR WIENERS

Although frankfurters (franks) and wieners (hot dogs) have merged their identity, let it be said for the record that wieners as originally formulated were a combination of veal and pork. Today's frankfurters are constituted of many variations of meats and seasoning but have one thing in common, viz.—processing. The following formulas illustrate one of many differences.

Frankfurters

50 lbs. reg. lean beef trimmings
15 lbs. fresh bull beef
25 lbs. fresh lean pork trimmings
20 lbs. shaved ice
5 lbs. dried skim milk
3 lbs. salt
8 oz. sucrose
2 oz. sodium nitrate

¼ oz. sodium nitrite
6 oz. white pepper
2 oz. ground coriander
1 oz. ground sage
1 oz. ground cinnamon
1 oz. fresh garlic
2 oz. mace

Wieners

35 lbs. reg. pork trimmings
10 lbs. pork cheeks
30 lbs. veal trimmings

2 oz. white pepper
2 oz. ginger
2 oz. coriander

18 lbs. ice
5 lbs. milk powder
12 oz. dextrose
2 lbs. salt

2 oz. mace
1 oz. sodium nitrate
¼ oz. sodium nitrite

See previous discussion (Processed Sausage) for processing steps. To make skinless franks, the franks should be sprayed with water and allowed to stand a day for easier peeling. Relative humidity is one very important factor in successful peelability. Ideally, the casing will slip off after being cut, leaving a smooth, eye-appealing surface on the frank.

A Modern Sausage Kitchen

The mechanization necessary for efficient sausage production is difficult for the layman to visualize, especially the majority of consumers who enjoy tasty hot dogs but are prone to complain if they seem to cost too much. Most of these consumers probably never take time to think about how the product became transformed from the living matter it once was into the delicious, nutritious, human food product they enjoy.

Americans do love hot dogs—to the tune of 14 billion in a recent year, or nearly 80 per person per year. Another way of looking at that consumption is on a per-second basis; 500 hot dogs are being eaten every second of every day all year.

Figures 16.2 through 16.6 depict a modern sausage kitchen that

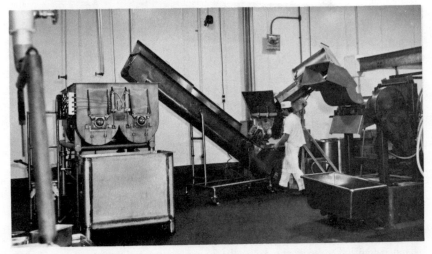

Fig. 16.2—Portable incline screw conveyor moves meats from a Weiler grinder (with add-on sides) to a Griffith blender. (Courtesy, *The National Provisioner*)

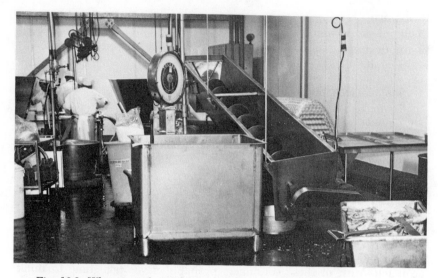

Fig. 16.3—When smooth emulsion products are made, the meats are moved to this high-wall batching screw conveyor mounted to a Toledo scale. This has ample space above the conveyor discs to accumulate a batch before unloading into the silent cutter (colloid mill). (Courtesy, *The National Provisioner*)

Fig. 16.4—At this linking station, natural casing products such as mettwurst are separated into link sizes of approximately the same weight with the aid of a Pratco clipper. (Courtesy, *The National Provisioner*)

Fig. 16.5—Frankfurters in cellulose casings have been stuffed and linked with this Townsend machine. (Courtesy, *The National Provisioner*)

Fig. 16.6—Six-station trolley cages are moved into position for cooking and smoking in fully automatic Alkar cook cabinets. (Courtesy, *The National Provisioner*)

occupies 35,000 square feet. This firm (Hummel Bros., New Haven, Connecticut) manufactures about 100,000 pounds of frankfurters in natural and cellulose casings per week in addition to a complete line of sausage items. It is a very modern set-up, but does not as yet utilize continuous processing (see next section), although space was provided in this plant for later incorporation of continuous processing.

Continuous Frankfurter Processing

Dr. Selwyn Simon[1] reported to the 1973 American Meat Institute Convention the recent developments in continuous processing systems. More than 55 meat packing plants in the United States have continuous frankfurter processing lines, capable of manufacturing in excess of 12,000 pounds of frankfurters per hour. Some plants also have continuous lines for processing large sausage and luncheon meats.

In a typical system, the frankfurter emulsion is stuffed into a cellulose casing and linked with a high speed mechanical linker. The links are then treated with either one or a combination of coagulants (natural smoke, vinegar, citric acid, or malic acid mixed with liquid smoke). The coagulants precipitate the meat proteins at the inner surface of the casing (to aid peelability) and also contribute to color and flavor.

After coagulation, franks are cooked in high velocity, high relative humidity cooking zones in a very large cooker. The cooked frankfurters are then chilled, peeled, and packaged. After the franks are stuffed and linked, the remaining processing time is usually 60 to 80 minutes. Chilling can be accomplished in about 10 minutes with a 6% brine solution refrigerated at about 28° F. Product is chilled to 38° to 40° F.

High-speed peeling machines can peel franks at a rate in excess of 5,000 pounds per hour with one operator. A knife edge slits the moistened casing as the strand of frankfurters is moved through the machine. An air jet assists in blowing the casing off the frankfurter.

To get the characteristic cured meat color in such a short processing time, ascorbate is essential, and the product must remain additional time in the oven *after* the internal meat temperature has reached 150° to 155° F. This extra heating to develop color takes about 20 minutes in a high velocity 200° F oven.

Country Style Bologna

80 lbs. lean beef chucks   2 oz. sodium nitrate

---

1. *The National Provisioner*, October 20, 1973. Dr. Selwyn Simon is manager, Food Science Institute, Union Carbide, Films Packaging Division, Chicago.

20 lbs. regular pork trimmings	¼ oz. sodium nitrite
10 lbs. shaved ice or water	2 oz. coriander
3 lbs. salt	6 oz. white pepper
8 oz. sugar	

Grind the beef and pork through the ¼-inch plate, season, mix, and regrind. Stuff into small casings in 15-inch lengths and tie the ends together. When dry, place in smokehouse and smoke to desired color and then cook at 170° F until the inside temperature of the bologna reaches 155° F.

Braunschweiger

Because braunschweiger and liver sausage are such an excellent outlet for pork livers or livers not needed in the retail trade, and because they provide a rather satisfactory profit item, let us see how they are made.

45 lbs. fresh pork livers	2 oz. white pepper
25 lbs. lean pork trimmings	2 oz. sugar
20 lbs. regular pork trimmings	8 oz. braunschweiger
10 lbs. cured & smkd. bacon ends	seasoning
3 lbs. dried skim milk	2 oz. sodium nitrate
2½ lbs. salt	¼ oz. sodium nitrite

The braunschweiger seasoning consists of toasted onion powder, cardamon, mace, and sweet marjoram in the proportion of 3 parts of the onion powder to one part each of the other spices.

The prepared livers (cut into sections and scalded) are placed in the silent cutter or colloid mill and chopped until the mixture becomes pasty and small bubbles appear. Add all the other ingredients with the exception of the pork and continue chopping until smooth. Grind all the pork items through the ⅜-inch plate and then through the ⅛-inch plate and add them to the liver emulsion, chopping just long enough to incorporate them with the emulsion. Stuff into special MP casings (developed by the Union Carbide Films Packaging Division) in opaque color designed to fit the color of the product. The casings are glossy and moisture-proof and may be printed in multicolored designs to give eye appeal to an otherwise drab looking piece of sausage. Use cooking water at a maximum temperature of 160° F until an inside temperature of 150° F is attained. After removing the sausage from the cook tank or hot shower, chill in ice water to an inside temperature of 90° to 100° F. Rinse with hot water and hold at room temperature for several hours before placing in cooler.

Liver Sausage (Puddin' Meat—Dutch Style)

25 lbs. pork trimmings
20 lbs. beef or veal
8 to 10 lbs. pork liver
4 loaves stale bread or 4 lbs. whole wheat flour

If beef or veal are not available, use pork only. The use of pork livers, hearts, tongues, brains, sweetbreads, and kidneys along with some pork shoulder meat combined with whole wheat flour as a binder makes a product that is very rich in minerals and vitamins and could properly be called "*Vitameat*." Cook the meat thoroughly and grind it through the fine knives along with the bread. To this mixture add 4 quarts of the broth and season to taste with salt and black pepper (chopped onions may be added if desired). Mace, celery seed, cardamon, and coriander are often used to add flavor. After seasoning, cook the mixture another 10 minutes and pour it into pans or crocks to cool and harden.

If liver sausage is stuffed into hog casings, the second cooking is done after stuffing. The sausages are then dipped into cold water to bleach, after which they are hung in a cool place to dry, or they may be placed in crocks without bleaching and covered with hot lard to preserve them for future use.

In rural districts, the above product is often referred to as "*Puddin'*" meat.

Lebanon Bologna

This is a semi-dry fermented sausage, smoked but uncooked. It originated among the Pennsylvania Germans in the vicinity of Lebanon, Pennsylvania. Since it contains no pork, it is safe to eat without being heat processed.

100 lbs. fresh lean beef	1 oz. ground mustard seed
1 lb. melted lard	1 oz. ground ginger
6 oz. white pepper	2 oz. sodium nitrate
3 lbs. salt	¼ oz. sodium nitrite
1 lb. brown sugar	2 oz. mace

Grind the beef through the ½-inch plate and mix with the curing ingredients (salt, sugar, nitrate, and nitrite). Spread in pans and set in cooler for 3 days to cure. Remove from cooler, remix, adding seasoning and the melted lard. Regrind through the 5/64-inch plate and stuff into fibrous casings 3¾ inches in diameter. It is customary to do the smoking in a wooden or wood-lined smokehouse using wet sawdust and a temperature between 70° to 100° F. The dampers are kept closed to enable the sausage to "sweat." After 24 hours the dampers are opened and the low temperature smoking continued for another six to seven days. At this time the sausages are sprayed with hot water to clean the outsides of the casings and allowed to hang at room temperature for an hour or so before being placed in the 40° to 50° F cooler.

Pig's-Foot Jell or Pig Souse

The pigs' feet should be clean, free from hair, and have the toes removed. Place the feet along with hearts and tongues and shoulder hocks in sufficient water to cover and cook until the meat separates easily from the bones. Cut the meat into chunks and replace it in the broth in which it was cooked and season to taste with salt, pepper, and vinegar. Pour into pans (2 to 3 inches deep) and set away to chill and jell.

Fagots

Fagots are composed of hog livers, hearts, fresh pork, onions, salt, pepper, sweet marjoram, and hog caul fat (fat surrounding the stomach and intestines). The pork is thoroughly cooked and then ground with the raw livers, hearts, and onions. The seasoning is added and the meat is mixed and molded into 6-ounce balls. The caul fat is cut into approximately 7-inch squares into which the meat balls are placed and encased. They are baked in an oven for 45 minutes.

Scrapple

This is distinctly a Pennsylvania Dutch product and a very popular one in the East. Use head meat, feet, hearts, tongues, shoulder spare ribs, fresh picnic shoulders, or any pork trimmings that contain some fat. Liver may be used if desired. Twenty percent of the meat used may be beef or veal, but all pork is preferable.

Cook the meat in sufficient water to keep it covered and drain off the liquor when the meat separates readily from the bones. Remove the bones and run the meat through the fine knives of a meat grinder. Place the ground meat and the liquor in which it was cooked together in a kettle and bring it to a boil.

The cereal to be added is best mixed with water or some of the meat juice, adding the juice slowly and working the cereal into a dough with the hand or a dough mixer and then thinning to avoid lumps. The diluted cereal is then poured into the cooked meat and cooked for another 30 minutes. This eliminates the slow process of stirring in the cereal and avoids the formation of lumps.

The cereals used and the amounts are as follows:

1 lb. fine cornmeal to 3 lbs. ground meat
1 lb. buckwheat or rye flour to 10 lbs. ground meat
½ lb. oatmeal to 10 lbs. ground meat

There should be twice as much broth as there is ground cooked meat. Before the scrapple becomes too thick, season it with salt, pepper, mace, thyme, and nutmeg to taste. The addition of sage is favored by some.

Formula for scrapple:
For 20 pounds of cooked, ground meat use:
2 lbs. buckwheat or rye flour
1 lb. oatmeal
7 lbs. finely ground, untoasted cornmeal
2 oz. black pepper
10 oz. salt
¼ oz. mace
¼ oz. nutmeg
¼ oz. sage or ¼ oz. thyme

The scrapple is ready to be dipped into pans when it has lost its raw cornmeal taste and is thick enough so that it piles up.

Pig Snouts

The ringed and much maligned pig's snout is used extensively in the manufacture of Philadelphia scrapple. The jell in the snout gives scrapple binding qualities. We most often think of a pig's snout as being an instrument of destruction, something for the hog to push into a hole in the fence and follow it through. However, in France we find that pigs are used to hunt truffles, the delicious, highly prized underground tuberous mushroom. A pig seems to be the only animal that can locate the truffles beneath the ground. Thus, the pig's snout gains in stature in that it can find us food as well as be used for food. We find that Puerto Rican fishermen, who go out of sight of land to fish, carry a pig along deck. He immediately points his snout in the direction of the nearest land and away they go. So pig snouts make compasses to save lives at sea.

Pan Haus (Pon Hos)

Some prefer to cook the skinned, split head (jaws and eyes removed), feet, kidney, heart, tongue, liver, and some shoulder meat together and thus use all the odd cuts in making a single product. After these cuts are thoroughly cooked, the bone removed, and the meat ground, the procedure is the same as if scrapple were being made. There is another form of pan haus which contains very little meat and a large amount of cornmeal that is made from the broth left over when making liver sausage. In this case the broth is thickened with cornmeal and buckwheat or wheat flour as in scrapple and seasoned with salt and pepper.

Head Cheese

Skin out the head and remove the jaw bones, eyes, and ears. The remainder of the head and jowl are cooked along with some hearts and tongues, if desired, and the cooked meat with the bone removed is ground and enough broth added to make a thick porridge. This is seasoned with salt, pepper, and marjoram to taste and placed in crocks where it takes on a covering of lard, due to the excessive amount of fat present in the jowl rising to the top. Head cheese usually is eaten cold.

Boiled Ham

This is made from a cured, unsmoked ham by trimming off most of the outside fat and removing the bone. The boning operation can be made simple by opening the ham from the stifle joint through the center of the ham to the aitch or pelvic bone. A boning knife or sharp vegetable paring knife is necessary for this operation. Begin boning at the shank end of the ham. By following the bone closely, even an amateur can do a fairly neat job. After the bone is removed, take butcher's cord and tie the ham firmly and securely by wrapping the cord around the ham, spacing the wraps one inch apart. Instead of tying the ham, pork packers place the boned hams in specially constructed ham boilers which compress and shape the ham.

Place the ham in a cooker with water temperature at 170° to 175° F and process it to an internal temperature of 155° to 160° F. The hams may be allowed to cool in the cooker but are more often chilled in cold water and then removed from the ham mold to be stuffed into a fibrous cellulose casing.

Summer Sausage (Farmer Style)

40 lbs. lean beef
60 lbs. lean pork
2½ lbs. salt
8 oz. sugar
6 oz. white or black pepper

2 oz. sage or 1 oz. ground mustard seed
3 oz. saltpeter (dissolved in 1 pt. water)

Run the beef and pork through the ¼-inch plate of a meat grinder, add the seasoning and the saltpeter, and mix thoroughly. Regrind through the 3/16-inch plate and spread the sausage on trays. Place in the refrigerator to cure for several days and then stuff into hog casings. Smoke, using wet sawdust, at a temperature of 100° to 110° F until the sausage is a rich to dark brown color. Discontinue the smoke but heat the sausage to an internal temperature of 142° F. Store in a dry, cool (40° to 45° F) place for several weeks before using.

Dutch Loaf

65 lbs. regular pork trimmings	4 lbs. fresh onions
(60% lean)	8 oz. white pepper
35 lbs. veal trimmings	2 oz. sage
10 lbs. dry skim milk	2 oz. sodium nitrate
25 lbs. shaved ice	¼ oz. sodium nitrite
3 lbs. salt	

Grind the veal and onions through the ⅛-inch plate and the pork through the ¼-inch plate. Place the ground veal and onions in the silent cutter or colloid mill, adding the ice, dried skim milk, seasoning, and cure. Chop for three to four minutes. Place the ground pork in a mixer and add the emulsion from chopper or mill and mix for four minutes. Place in pans and bake at 225° to 250° F for three hours or until the internal temperature of loaf reaches 160° F. When cool, stuff in cellulose casings to fit the loaf.

SPICES

The expression that "glue holds the world together" could be applied to spices in a slightly different sense by saying that "spices bring the world together." They come from all parts of the world to give flavor and essence to the foods of all peoples.

The spice manufacturer imports many of these spices in forms unsuitable for consumption until they are cleaned of foreign material and dust and graded on the basis of quality. They may be ground to different degrees of fineness or the manufacturer may extract the essential oils and oleoresins from the spices for soluble spice extract seasoning. These can be secured in the liquid form or coated on salt and sugar.

The soluble spice is favored where the inclusion of a natural spice would discolor the product, such as sage in pork sausage (use soluble sage). The flavor retention between natural spices and the soluble oil is no different if the product contains equivalent quantities of the active spice.

100 Pounds Natural Spice	Extract Equivalent in Pounds
Allspice	3.5
Black pepper	1.5
Black pepper (oleoresin)	6.0
Cardamon seed	5.0
Cinnamon	1.0
Coriander seed	0.5
Garlic (imitation flavor)	0.25
Mace	12.5
Nutmeg	12.5
Paprika (oleoresin)	8.0
Sage	2.0

The bacterial contamination of natural spices is of some concern even though the amount used in any product is less than 1% of the total. Sterilized natural spices are available. Tests have shown some antioxidant properties for sage, black pepper, mace, cloves, ginger, rosemary, and thyme in pork sausage. Cardamon, mustard, and coriander are aromatic spices commonly used in sausages, and celery seed is a popular seasoning in loaves.

HOME CANNING PORK, BEEF, OR VEAL

Cut the boneless pieces of loin, ham, or shoulder into convenient pieces to fit the jar. Remove excess fat from the meat, brown in a frying pan, being careful not to let the meat get dry and hard. The meat can be packed raw, but it will not have so good a flavor as when browned first. Arrange meat in clean jars. Press down to remove air but do not pack too tightly. Leave a half-inch head space. Add a teaspoon of salt to each quart of meat. Pour fat from the pan over the meat. A small amount of water may be added to the fat in the pan and the liquid poured over the meat. After processing, the meat shrinks and the jar is not full. This will not cause the meat to spoil.

When the jars are filled, carefully wipe off the necks of the jars with a clean cloth, place a tested rubber on each jar, partially seal, and process in a pressure cooker at 15 pounds pressure for 60 minutes for a pint and 70 minutes for a quart. Or meat may be processed in a water bath for 180 minutes for a pint and 200 minutes for a quart. If a water bath is used, the meat should be packed hot and the water should be nearly boiling when the jars are added. The water should be kept boiling during the entire processing time. Remove the jars from the processing container as soon as the time is up and complete the seal. Stand the jars in an upright position to cool.

Make sausage into cakes, brown, and can them in the same way.

Gas or electric ovens with heat controls may be used to "ovenize" canned meats. In this method, the meats are placed in cans or jars in the raw state, and salt and water are added as explained above. Tins are sealed, but glass jars are only partially sealed before placing them in the oven. Set the oven temperature at 300° F and allow two hours of processing for pints and three hours for quarts. If meats are browned before being placed in jars, the time for processing at 300° F may be reduced by one-half. The glass jars are sealed tight upon removal from the oven. Do not place cold glass jars in a hot oven as the glass is likely to crack.

Pickled Pigs' Feet

Remove the hoof section of each foot and make sure that the feet are clean and free from hair. Place them in a 75° F pickle solution for several weeks and then cook, chill, and remove the meat from the bone. Place the boned meat in clean jars, add a solution of equal parts of water and vinegar, with a pinch of pepper and a teaspoonful of salt per pint jar. The vinegar solution must be put on hot. Seal the jar and set in a cool place until used.

FANCY SAUSAGES (DRY AND SEMI-DRY)

Most of these sausages are of European origin and take their name from the town in which they originated. The peculiar wrapping and twining are old-world identification features. They are either dry or semi-dry and in most cases are ready to serve without any further cooking. The semi-dry sausages are fairly perishable and should be held under refrigeration or in a dry, well-ventilated, or air-conditioned room in which the temperature range is narrow and below 50° F.

Uneven temperatures cause sweating, and a moist sausage surface is, unfortunately, ideal for the development of molds. White molds are not serious as they can be wiped off with a damp cloth, but other molds may require the sausage to be soaked in cold water and scrubbed with a stiff brush. Molds are objectionable and should be avoided.

Summer Sausage or Cervelat originated in Germany and is considered to be the most popular of the semi-dry sausages.

Chorizos is a Spanish pork sausage that is coarsely ground and seasoned with Spanish pimento and sweet red pepper. It is stuffed into hog casings (4-inch links) and given a light smoke and then air-dried. The sausages weigh about 3 ounces each.

Capacola is made from boneless Cala butts and is the American substitute for Italian Coppa forte (forte meaning strong), referring to the red pepper pods used in seasoning.

Coppa Picante are Cala butts that have been cured and coated with black pepper. They are molded in a square shape and wrapped in cellophane in 2- to 3-pound weights.

Caserta Peperoni is an Italian product consisting of 75% pork and 25% beef, stuffed in hog casings and linked in pairs (12 ounces to each piece). Peperoni are red pepper pods and Caserta is a town in southern Italy.

Farmer Sausage originated with the farmers of northern Europe and is made of 65% beef and 35% pork. It is chopped medium fine, seasoned, stuffed in beef middles, and heavily smoked. Each piece weighs from 1 to 2 pounds.

Gothaer is a summer sausage reported to be impossible to manufacture in any but the winter months (believe it or not).

Goteborg sausage takes its name from Swedish town of Goteborg. It is composed of 60% beef and 40% pork that has been chopped coarse, seasoned, and stuffed in beef middles. Each smoked piece weighs about 1½ pounds.

Holsteiner is the same as Farmer sausage, except that the ends are tied together (sometimes called horseshoe sausage). Dried and smoked, it appears on the market in pieces weighing about 1 pound each.

Mett is a semi-dry, 100% pork sausage intended for cooking (it can be fried or boiled). It is a smoked product coming in half-pound pieces.

Mortadella sausage originated in the city of Bologna, Italy, from whence our common ring bologna received its name. It is 75% pork and 25% beef, and the seasoning contains some garlic. Placed in beef bladders, this sausage is not smoked but is pressure steamed for several hours and then dried. Pieces weigh from 5 to 7 pounds each.

Prosciutti (pronounced Proshooti) is a dry-cured (black pepper included) Italian ham.

Sopressata (a word used to designate any sausage stuffed in crinkly hog middles) consists mainly of pork that is coarsely chopped and has whole black peppers as one of its condiments.

Salami, of which there are a number of varieties, is characterized by its coarse chop and spicy flavor. Practically all contain garlic and have as their containers either sewed hog casings, beef middles, sewed beef casings, beef bungs (cooked salami), or, as in the case of Kosher Salami, kosher beef weasands. Pork is the main meat used, along with some beef. Salami is distinctly an Italian sausage with different variations of twining or cording. B. C. Salami, for example, has only a few vertical and horizontal cordings, whereas Genoa Salami has many wrappings of twine, both vertical and horizontal, in basket weave effect. Some of the Salami sausages on the market are as follows: B. C. Salami, H. C. Salami, Genoa, Savona Genoa, Milan, Arles, Nola, Sicilian or Sicani, Lola, Cooked Salami, Liguria Salami, Lombardia, Kosher Salami, Alessandria, Lazio, Novaro, Catania, Bobbio, Sorrento, Ancona, Capri, Corti, Cotto, De Lusso Genoa, Golden West Milano, Cotechino, Salamina Corti, D'Annunzio, La Triestina, Caruso Genoa, Fiume, Margherita Salami Cotto, Margherita Milano, Venezia, and others.

Thuringer is a summer sausage that originated in Germany in the acient province of Thuringia. It consists mainly of beef with a small amount of pork and generally comes in 6- to 8-pound pieces.

Use of Intestinal Tract

Pig stomachs are trimmed and cleaned, and they are either made into sausage containers or cooked as tripe for sausage manufacture. The inner linings of pig stomachs are used in the manufacture of pepsin.

Roasted Pig Stomach

A practice among the Pennsylvania Germans is to make an opening in the stomach about 3 inches long where the gullet makes its entry. The stomach is turned inside out and washed thoroughly. It is then immersed in hot water (150° to 160° F) to loosen the lining and facilitate its removal. Another method is to remove the lining without scalding, in which case it is necessary to wear canvas gloves in order to grip the membrane.

Several pounds of sausage mixed with sufficient bread and diced potatoes and seasoned with parsley, salt, and pepper constitute the filling. The roasting period is from 2 to 3 hours, depending upon the size of the roast. Large quantities of pig stomachs are used in the manufacture of sausage.

Tripe

The first and second (rumen and reticulum) stomachs of cattle make up the bulk of the tripe sold under that name. Pig, calf, and sheep stomachs are also made into tripe but are put to a different use. To clean the cattle stomachs, scald at 128° to 130° F for 15 to 20 minutes, using one pound of soda ash per 25 gallons of hot water. When the stomach lining is loose, scrape with a dull knife to remove the lining and give several washings. Tripe is considered to be clean when the water squeezed from it is as clean as the rinse water. The cleaned tripe can be cut into large or small pieces and pickled in a 60° F salt brine or cooked and pickled in a weak salt and vinegar brine. If it is preserved in dry salt and air-dried for future use, it should be stored in a cool, dry place.

Casings

The small intestines are cleaned and used for sausage casings. On the farm it is best to clean them while they are fresh. The only tools necessary for cleaning the intestines are a piece of flat, smooth-surfaced board and a straight-backed knife. Cut the casings into convenient lengths (6 to 10 feet) and start scraping with the back of the knife at a point midway between the ends. This eliminates having to push the contents the whole length of the 6- to 10-foot piece. With the casing on the smooth-surfaced board and the pressure exerted by the smooth straight back of the knife, nothing but the clean membranous walls of the intestine will remain, and the turning of the casing for further cleaning is not necessary. In large-scale operations, intestines intended for casings are soaked and slimed and then run through scrubbing machines. The cleansed casings are salted if they are not to be used for several days. Dry salted casings can be purchased from packers or casing houses in hanks or tierces at so much per pound. Salted casings must be soaked and rinsed free of salt before using.

Calcium Pectin

A pectinous material which can be made from citrus peel or apple pomace can be used as a soluble protective covering for sausage and other meat and food products. The meat or meat product is dipped into the warm calcium pectinous solution (gels a 104° F) for three seconds, removed, and the gel coating dried in a current of warm air for 30 minutes. A firm film coating of good strength is formed, and the treated product can be stored. Boiling the product dissolves the film, and in frying or roasting, the coating can be consumed with the meat as it is tender and edible.

Chitterlings

According to APHIS, the term *Chitterlings* shall apply to the large intestines of swine, or young bovine animals when preceded with the word *Calf* or *Veal*. Meat food products that contain chitterlings or calf or veal chitterlings shall be identified with product names that refer to such ingredients, as for instance, "Chitterling Loaf," "Chitterling Pie," or "Calf Chitterlings and Gravy," and shall be packed in containers having a capacity of 3 pounds or less and of a kind usually sold at retail intact and bearing such other information as is required by this part.

The small and large intestines of hogs are emptied and rinsed thoroughly but not scraped. When cooked in this form they are commonly known as "chittlins." They are relished by many people.

Fried Pigskins

Meat Inspector Division Memorandum No. 119 permits the use of names such as "Fried Pork Skins," "Fried Bacon Skins," or "Fried Bacon Rinds" to designate the finished product when fried pork skins are prepared from skin removed from smoked pork bellies.

Pronto Pups (Wieners Dun in a Bun)

A wiener or franfurter is impaled upon a wooden skewer and dipped into a quick-cooking bread coating. With ¼ to ⅜ inch of coating adhering to it, the wiener is placed in an oven and baked.

Spud-dog

Bore a ¾-inch hole lengthwise through the center of a potato, insert a skinless wiener and bake.

Smoked Sausage

Country style sausage is supposed to be better for smoking because the added beef makes it a leaner product that will not shrink and wrinkle in the smokehouse. This is true when the heat of the smokehouse is too high; however, a temperature between 90° and 100° F will not wrinkle an all-pork sausage, and a five- to seven-hour smoke is generally sufficient.

Added Water in Sausage

APHIS Meat and Poultry Inspection Regulation 319.140 was set up to control the water content of sausage. This regulation is based on the theory that meats contain water and protein in a proportion of less than 4 to 1. Moulton, Trowbridge, and Heigh at the Missouri Agricultural Experiment Station found that fat-free flesh of animals at different ages varied from 80% water and 17.5% protein in calves at birth (4.6 to 1 ratio) to an average of 76.5% water and 21.88% protein in fresh beef (3.5 to 1 ratio). Fresh pork fat ran 7.5% water and 1.5% protein (5 to 1 ratio), with fresh beef fat testing 20.5% water and 4.8% protein (4.2 to 1 ratio).

To facilitate chopping and mixing and to make a product of the texture and consistency desired by the trade it has been found necessary to add water to sausage formulas or recipes.

Since the meats are run through a chopper equipped with rapidly revolving knives that cause the mass to heat because of friction, the water is added in the form of ice to keep the mass cool. A great deal of cured beef and pork, which has lost moisture in curing, is used. Cooking and smoking result in further drying and unless water is added in the manufacturing process, the product will be too dry. The Government recognized this fact when it ruled that 3% to 10% water above that calculated by multiplying the protein content of the sausage meat by four might be added. On this basis, a batch of sausage analyzing 15% protein may contain four times 15% or 60% water, plus an additional 3% for non-cooked sausage and 10% for cooked.

The Use of Nitrate and Nitrite in the Curing of Sausage

Not more than 3 ounces of either potassium or sodium nitrate nor more than ¼ ounce of nitrite per 100 pounds of meat are permitted by Federal regulation (B. A. I. order dated October 19, 1925). This is now APHIS Regulation 318.7(c)(4). If both are used in a mixture, the nitrite must not exceed ¼ ounce and the additional nitrate must be such an amount so as not to give a total of the two in excess of 3 ounces.

Research has shown that only nitrite, not nitrate, reacts with the meat pigment to form the characteristic color and flavor of cured products. Nitrate was present only to be converted to nitrite by "friendly" bacteria during the time the meat was in cure. Now, with the rapid processing techniques in use, there is not sufficient time for the nitrate to be converted, so most processors are leaving it out of their formulations with no detrimental effects to the final product.

Nitrosamines

The chemical reactions which result in the formation of *nitrosamines* when secondary amines (products of protein breakdown) and nitrous acid (product of nitrite) combine have been known for some time. However, recently, nitrosamines have been shown to be carcinogenic, and thus concern has been raised in the meat industry. Results suggest that normally, the chemical reactions do *not* take place in cured meat causing nitrosamine formation but that nitrosamines have been found in isolated cases in cured meat. Research is presently underway to determine what conditions exist which prevent or encourage the reaction. As a result, within the past year, an FDA ruling was released which directed curing premix manufacturers to keep the nitrite and seasoning packaged separately in shipment, because laboratory tests have shown that seasonings promote the formation of nitrosamines after long exposure. Nitrosamines have not been found in curing mixes, so this action was purely a precautionary measure. Nitrosamines are a topic of immense current interest in the meat industry which is as yet unanswered.

Regulations Continually Updated

Recently, comments from more than 5,000 consumers and industry members helped change Federal meat-inspection regulations about the content of frankfurters and other cooked sausages and their package labels. Normal procedures for changing any part of the standards involve APHIS calling for comments on proposed changes. Thus the 5,000 replies and resulting changes.

The changes give consumers a choice of three types of frankfurters and cooked sausages, such as bologna and knockwurst. And it allows Federally inspected meat processors to use common nicknames on their labels such as "hot dog," "frank," and "furter," instead of only "frankfurter" and "wiener."

The first type of product many consumers wanted is made only from skeletal meat, which can include up to 15% poultry meat, and the normal ingredients needed for processing, such as water, sweeteners, and curing substances. It can't have more than 30% fat or 10% added water, and it can't be labeled "all meat." If it's made from the meat of only one species of livestock, that information must be on the label.

The second type is made the same as the first with the addition of animal by-products such as hearts, tongues, and tripe. These must be distinctly labeled "with by-products" or "with variety meats," and each by-product must be identified on the label statement.

The third type is made with either of the first two products plus up to 3.5% non-meat binders, such as non-fat dry milk, cereal, or dried whole milk, or 2% isolated soy protein. These products also will have to be clearly labeled—with names such as "franks with by-products, non-fat dry milk added," and their extra ingredients will have to be named in the ingredient statement on the label.

Miscellaneous Regulations

1. To treat dry sausage with potassium, a mold inhibitor, 2.5%
   solution of potassium sorbate may be applied to the dry sausage

after stuffing and prior to drying, or casings may be dipped into the water solution before stuffing. Sausage so treated must be branded or labeled, "Dipped to retard mold growth."

2. Isolated soy protein may be used as a binder in sausage and certain other meat products.

3. Glucono delta lactone, a sugar derivative that speeds up color fixation and reduces the smoking period, may be added to the mix using 8 ounces for each 100 pounds of meat.

Fat Is Monitored

Federally inspected cooked sausages, including frankfurters and bologna, can't contain more than 30% fat. To determine fat content, tests—based on moisture and protein content—are made on samples from all Federally inspected meat plants. If fat content is near 30% during screening, the samples also are subjected to specific analysis.

Official USDA, APHIS figures show the average fat content of 2,756 samples analyzed specifically for fat content during a recent three-month period to be 28.3%. Screening tests on the remaining 1,928 samples showed their fat content was 30% or less, although the exact percentages of fat weren't determined. Consistently, approximately 98% of all samples are in compliance. The samples specifically analyzed for fat generally average about 28.5% fat.

CHAPTER 17

The Preservation and
Storage of Meat

Various methods of preserving meat have been practiced through the ages, the most common of which are drying, smoking, salting, and freezing. The preservation of foods by the use of salt and sugar is accomplished by the simple process of dehydration, in which osmosis withdraws water from the protoplasm of the spoilage organisms, shriveling or inactivating the cells.

BACKGROUND INFORMATION

Jerked Beef (Jerky, Charqui, or Xarque)

The Spaniards who came to North America during the century following Columbus found dried meat in use by the Indians of what is now southwest United States, Mexico, and Central and South America. The native Indian word used by Chileans and Peruvians for meat cut into long strips and dried quickly in the sun and wind was "charqui" (pronounced sharkey). The Portuguese explorers of Brazil called it "xarque" and the English adventurers called it "jerkey" or "jerked beef."

With a plentiful supply of bison in the southwest, the practice frequently was to use only the eye muscle of the back, from the hump to the rump, and the tenderloin muscle. These muscles were cut into long, thin, flat strips and hung in trees, on poles, or in the tops of huts or tepees out of the reach of dogs. The dried strips, which were very hard and inflexible, were powdered by beating them with stones or wooden mallets and were mixed with dried fruits and vegetables to form "pemmican." In this form the dried meat was transported in skin sacks or bladders and was the principal food whenever the tribes were migrating.

The tongue of the bison was the most highly coveted part of the animal and was given to the man who killed the animal. The meat from the shoulders and hindquarters, which was usually tough, was left behind. The fat from the hump, which resembled bone marrow in flavor, was highly prized.

The intestines of fat bison were removed, turned inside out, and washed at a stream. When cooked crisp, these chitterlings were considered a real delicacy.

Smoking Meat

The preservation of meat in North and South America by smoking was undoubtedly a practice that originated where the meat was dried in the top of a tepee or over the camp fire. The advantage of this type of preservation lay in the fact that the smoke overcame other objectionable flavors that were certain to develop if the drying did not proceed at a rapid rate. The pyroligneous acid in the wood smoke had an added preservative effect on the dried meat. The favorite wood smoke was produced by hickory and oak, although the primitive Indians also used semi-dry grass, sage, and various aromatic seeds and plants.

The drying and smoking of meats was known to the Egyptians as well as to the ancient Sumerian civilization which preceded them.

Salting Meat

Dry salting and pickling meats have been practiced since the fifth century B.C. and possibly longer.

The following was written by the Roman scholar Cato,[1] who lived in the third century B. C.

> *Salting of hams and of the small pieces*
> *such as are put up at Puteoli*
>
> Hams should be salted in the large storage jars or in the smaller jars in this way: When you buy the hams cut off the feet; (take) for each ham a half-*modius*[2] of Roman salt ground in a mill, sprinkle the bottom of the large jar or of the smaller one with the salt, then put in a ham, skin side down, and cover completely with salt. (2) Then put a second on top, cover the same way, take care that meat does not touch meat. Cover them all the same way. When you have placed them all, cover above with salt so that the meat

---

1. *Cato the Censor on Farming*, Ernest Brehaut, Columbia University Press, 1933, pp. 145-146.
2. A unit of volume of Cato's time, approximately equal to ½ U.S. gallon.

will not show. Make the salt level. When they have been five days in the salt, take them all out, salt and all. Place on the bottom those that were on top, and cover and arrange in the same way. (3) After twelve days in all, take the hams out, wipe off all salt and hang them in the wind for two days. On the third day wipe them off well with a sponge, rub thoroughly with olive oil and vinegar mixed, and hang them up on the meat rack. Neither moths nor worms will touch them.

Just how dry salting originated is not definitely known. It is quite likely that the use of salt for preserving meat was entirely accidental. Since saltpeter was probably an impurity in the salt that was used, it remained for the chemist to develop this color-retaining agent in its pure state. The salted meats of the ancients were very unevenly cured, and objectionably dry and salty. The latter part of the eighteenth century marked the beginning of the salt curing of meat on a scientific basis.

Parma Ham (Italian)

A direct tie from present-day ham curing practices back to those used in Cato's day exists in the hand-massaged hams still prepared in the northern Italian city of Parma, located in the Po Valley. Parma hams are said to be among the most prized in the world. Production has almost quadrupled in the past 10 years. The value of Parma ham is estimated at $80 million a year, much of it in export earnings.

The trick of ham massaging, the cold winter, and the dry, hot summer climate of the Po Valley hills are credited with giving Parma's famous hams their light pink color and tender texture.

To preserve the fine quality and delicate flavor which poets back in Roman times described as divine, the Parma Chamber of Commerce has imposed these rigid rules:

—Every ham bearing the name of Parma must be from a one-year old pig of roughly 180 kilograms (400 pounds) of weight raised in the north Italian region around Parma. It must have been fed exclusively on maize—American corn—, oats, and rinds from Parma's equally famous Parmesan cheese. No slop-fed hogs qualify.

—After slaughter, processing of the hams starts with a 24-hour hardening period in deep freeze, then they are pared of outer fat into a drumstick shape, salted, seasoned, and frozen for eight days.

—On the ninth day, they come out to the kneading bench for the first of 30 or 40 massages to squeeze out the juice and tenderize the meat.

—They are salted again, put in deep freeze for 18 days, hauled out into fresh air for a day or two, then have a 30-day chill at exactly the freezing point, and three months in the drying chamber.

—Then they are scrubbed with warm water, sandpapered to an attractive outer finish and put into ventilated storage until time to sell.

—The total curing time lasts from 10 to 15 months.

Virginia Ham (Old Time)

The post Civil War period offers some interesting information on the production of Old Virginia Ham. The practice was to kill the pork in November when the points of the new moon were up. This was considered very important and was explained on the basis that if the points of the moon were down, a flat board placed on a plot of grass for a week would wither the grass and be full of worms and grubs, whereas, if placed there when the points of the moon were up, the grass would grow more luxuriantly and actually lift the board off the ground with no worms or grubs in sight. Therefore, if the hams were salted when the moon points were down, the hams would lose weight, wither, and be unfit to eat.

Fine table salt was rubbed into each ham in one long, thorough rubbing. Then the hock end was packed with salt, and an extra layer of salt was spread over the entire ham. They were packed in barrels and left to cure for seven weeks in a dry, cool place.

At the end of the seven weeks, the hams were rubbed with a mixture of New Orleans molasses, brown sugar, black pepper, cayenne pepper, and saltpeter. These ingredients were mixed in the following amounts to be rubbed on 100 pounds of ham: ½ pound black pepper, 1 quart of New Orleans molasses, 1 pound of brown sugar, 1 ounce of saltpeter, and 1 ounce of cayenne pepper. The hams to be rubbed were brushed of all visible salt and then rubbed with the mixture and left to lie in a cool room for another two weeks. At the end of this second period they were hung in the meat house with the hocks hanging downward because it was thought that a ham hung by the hock would lose flavor, toughen, and spoil. They were not smoked but were allowed to age for another 30 days.

Virginia Ham (Smithfield)

In 1925, the Virginia State Legislature passed an act wherein Smithfield hams must be processed in Smithfield and come from hogs grown in the peanut belt of Virginia and North Carolina. The hams are sprinkled with saltpeter, using 4 pounds per 1,000 pounds of ham, and are then given a rubbing of fine salt. Three to five days later they are given a second rubbing of salt and stacked in a curing room to cure for 1 day per pound of ham. After the cure, they are washed and given a cool smoke (80° to 85° F) for 7 to 10 days, using hickory wood and smothering the blaze with apple wood sawdust. After smoking, they are rubbed with pepper and hung in aging rooms for a period of 7 to 18 months. The shrinkage from green weight is around 25%. The dryness and saltiness of the hams require the consumer to soak them for 24 hours and simmer them for 4 to 6 hours.

Westphalian Hams (German)

This is a ham of distinctive flavor, produced by smoking with juniper twigs and berries over a beechwood fire. The juniper shrub is indigenous to Northwestern Germany and so plentiful, especially in Westphalia, that to its presence is due the growth, during the past several centuries, of two principal industries of this German province: the distillation of gin and the preparation of hams. According to the most authoritative information obtainable, Westphalian hams (to be sliced and eaten raw) are prepared as follows:

Rub the hams thoroughly with a mixture of 16 pounds of salt and 1 ounce of saltpeter per 100 pounds of pork. Place them on shelves or stack them on concrete floors and allow them to cure for two weeks, then place them in a 22% brine solution (90° pickle) and allow them to cure 18 more days. At the expiration of this period, remove them from the brine and pack them one upon another in a cool, dry cellar for four weeks, during which time they undergo a ripening process. Then clean them with a stiff brush in lukewarm water and allow them to soak in fresh water for 12 hours.

They are then ready for the smokehouse. Beechwood only is used except that juniper twigs and berries are constantly thrown on the fire. Beechwood sawdust is strewn over the fire in case it becomes too hot. The process continues for a period of seven to eight days.

Scotch Hams

Fresh hams are skinned and most of the fat removed, after which they are boned and given a mild cure according to a formula and practice followed in some parts of Scotland. The cured ham is then rolled and tied and placed in a cellulose casing but is not smoked.

Some Salty Statements

Prior to the advent of artificial refrigeration, salting and canning were the practices employed to preserve meats. Winter freezing freshly killed animals and game was popular.

Refrigeration and sub-zero storage are now in vogue and have replaced salt in large measure as a preservative. Yet, two-thirds of our pork products are consumed as cured and smoked products. The human palate has become more sensitive to salt than it has to nicotine or alcohol. Mildness and brightness (appearance) play a larger role in appetite and sales appeal. Yield is a factor that has become more critical to the processor than in bygone days when haste and waste were not so important. Speed has become a necessary part of our economy. Fast cures that are mild and light smokes have relegated long, heavy cures to the outskirts of civilization. Today, cured meats add variety and a distinctive flavor to products that must in turn be preserved by refrigeration.

WHY PRESERVATION?—MICROBIOLOGY

Animal tissues are sterile, or nearly so except for lymph nodes in the living and growing animal. But as soon as the process begins which converts that living tissue into human food, it becomes subject to degradation by chemical, physical, and biological reactions. If the knife used to sever the jugular vein and carotid arteries is not sterilized before use, an "infection" is inoculated into all of the animal tissues, edible and non-edible, via the circulatory system. Chapter 2 covered sanitation and stressed its extreme importance to the meat industry. Proper sanitation is the first big step for successful meat preservation.

A means of preservation should be practical and usable, should not make the produce unpalatable or worsen its appearance, and it must be safe, i.e., not harmful in any way, to those who consume the meat. Meat is preserved from microorganisms which thrive on its rich supply of nutrients just as humans thrive on meat.

A book about meat must have a section on meat microbiology, since it is indeed an integral part of the story of meat. Yet this book can only touch the very most important points in meat microbiology. There are very excellent whole books published on the subject.

Meat is an ideal culture medium for microbes, i.e., they like it and thrive on it because meat is:

1. High in moisture
2. Rich in nitrogenous foods of various degrees of complexity
3. Plentifully supplied with minerals and accessory growth factors

4. Usually has some fermentable carbohydrate.
5. At a fairly favorable pH (~ 5.6)

Factors Affecting Microorganism Growth on or in Meat

Temperature

Some microbes grow well at temperatures just above freezing and slightly higher (0° to 35° C; 32° to 95° F). They are known as *psychrophiles*. Examples are *pseudomonas* bacteria and some yeasts and molds. Others, called *mesophiles* grow well at temperatures between 15° and 40° C (32° to 95° F). Most bacteria belong to this group. A few microbes called *thermophiles* grow at higher temperatures between 40° and 65° C (104° to 109° F).

Moisture

Moisture level can be expressed as percent water, and when expressed that way, most bacteria require at least 18% water to grow. Molds grow in media (tissue) that can be as low as 13% water. A more definitive measure is water activity (a_w) which is defined as:

$$a_w = \frac{\text{vapor pressure of solution}}{\text{vapor pressure of pure solvent (H}_2\text{O)}}$$

Fresh meat has an a_w of 0.990 or above.
Salmonellae bacteria can grow at a_w of 0.94 or above.
Staphylocci bacteria can grow at a_w of 0.86 or above.
Molds can grow at a_w as low as 0.75.

Oxygen

Some microbes need oxygen in order to grow. These are called *aerobic* and include many bacteria and the yeasts and molds.

Those that cannot grow where oxygen is present are called *anaerobic*. Examples are *clostridium* and the putrifiers (those which degrade proteins and form very strong smelling gases).

A third group are called *facultative,* meaning that they grow in either aerobic or anaerobic conditions.

Physical Properties of Meat

If the meat is in a form that provides a greater surface area, the microbes have more room to grow. For example, a whole carcass has the minimum amount of surface area exposed. When it is cut into wholesale cuts, more area is exposed; when it is cut into retail cuts (steaks, etc.) still more area is exposed. When meat is ground, the maximum total surface area is exposed. Thus, the further meat is processed, the more vulnerable it is to microbial action.

Degree of Acidity or Alkalinity (pH)

Most microorganisms thrive on pH near neutrality (pH of 7.0) although there are exceptions (see later section in this chapter).

Meat processors or anyone who "handles" meat can control the factors that affect microbial growth and thus give meat longer "shelf life," meaning that the meat stays in top wholesome condition longer. For example, beef carcasses can hang in a 33° to 35° F cooler for perhaps 3 weeks to age (not a standard practice), and depending on the relative humidity of the cooler, perhaps only a few molds and some harmless bacteria such as pseudomonas would grow on limited areas of the carcass. But cut the carcass into its cuts, or grind it, or raise the temperature and/or relative humidity of the cooler, and the above factors are affected such that microbiological growth could flourish.

New processing techniques involving the use of vacuum packaging allows carcasses to be cut into primal, subprimal, or even retail cuts, after which each cut is placed in an airtight "envelope." In such a wrap, in the proper temperatures, cuts may be held for extended time periods during marketing without the occurrence of damaging microbial growth.

Organisms of Concern in Meat

Clostridium Botulinum

Botulism, a food borne intoxication (ingestion of a food which contains a microbial toxin) is caused by various strains of Cl. botulinum which produce toxins Type A, B, and E affecting the nervous system of man. The organism is identified as a gram-positive, anaerobic, spore-forming rod, able to grow under relatively thermophilic conditions. The toxin, which is destroyed by boiling for 15 to 20 minutes, is probably the most deadly poison known to man. One gram properly distributed (an impossibility) would be enough to kill up to 10 million people. Clostridia is fairly widely distributed in soil and will grow well on protein, low-acid, improperly canned foods. Canned vegetables, meat, and fish are most often incriminated. About 24 to 48 hours after consumption of the contaminated food, the symptoms begins to be noticeable, i.e., muscular weakness and loss of those functions dependent on nerve action. About two-thirds of the cases are fatal. The nitrite component of a curing mixture has been shown to control the growth of *Cl. botulinum* in cured meats (see later discussion).

Staphylococcus Aureus

Staphylococcal food poisoning (intoxication) is caused, in most cases, by *Staphylococcus aureus* which produces a very heat stable toxin capable of causing severe gastrointestinal upsets. These may occur 2 to 6 hours after ingestion of the toxin. *S. aureus* is a typical gram-positive staphylococcus or micrococcus, occurring in masses like clusters of grapes or in pairs and short chains. All enterotoxin-producing *S. aureus* cultures are beta-hemolytic and coagulase-positive (coagulating oxalated blood plasma) and are facultative in their oxygen requirements in a complex glucose medium, but not all coagulase-positive staphylococci are necessarily toxigenic. Some of the toxigenic cocci are tolerant and grow in salt concentrations approaching saturation and also tolerate nitrites fairly well. The cocci also can grow in lower pH solutions aerobically, below 5.0, than anaerobically. The microorganism itself is somewhat heat-resistant, sometimes being able to withstand pasteurization temperatures in milk, but the enterotoxin is *very* heat-resistant.

This organism most often causes a problem after a roast, perhaps cured and smoked or even fresh, has been properly cooked and served. If the leftover roast remains at room temperature for a period of time, before being refrigerated, the *S. aureus*, if present, has a good opportunity to grow at favorable temperature conditions. Also the previous cooking may have destroyed any competitive "friendly" microorganisms, thus giving *S. aureus*, with its slight temperature tolerance, a chance to grow. Even if the leftover roast is thoroughly re-cooked before being eaten, any toxin formed during the period at room temperature will not be destroyed.

Salmonella

A food-borne infection results from ingesting a high number of potential infection microorganisms or by allowing their growth and multiplication in the digestive tract. The bacteria must be living to cause infection.

Salmonella infection is caused by any one of a large number of species of that genus. The salmonellae are gram-negative, non-spore-forming rods that ferment glucose, usually with gas, but not lactose or sucrose. They grow best in nonacid foods at an optimum temperature of about 98.5° F (37° C) but will grow well at room temperatures. They are killed by pasteurization equivalent to that given milk (161° F for 15 seconds or 143° F for 30 minutes). After ingestion the incubation period will normally be 12 or 24 hours before digestive upsets occur.

Clostridium Perfringens

Little is known about the exact cause of perfringens food poisoning. Most incidents have been associated with processed, "made-up" or canned meats, or gravy stock. Symptoms are relatively mild abdominal pain and diarrhea which develop 8 to 22 hours after ingestion. Ordinary cooking will destroy many strains but processing at somewhat higher temperatures is necessary to destroy the heat-resistant spores. Most contamination occurs after cooking, so sanitation and refrigeration are important.

THE CURING INGREDIENTS

Salt

The most important of the curing ingredients is salt (NaCl). It makes up the bulk of the curing mixture because it is not only a good preservative but it provides the most desirable flavor. Its diffusion in meat is by the process of osmosis. Salt inhibits the growth of bacteria and in some products is more effective in conjunction with nitrite. There are some bacteria, yeasts, and molds that flourish in salt concentrations of various degrees, but salt as a preservative reduces the many to a few.

Sugar

Sugar, a secondary ingredient in the curing formula, counteracts the astringent quality of the salt, enhances the flavor of the product, and aids in lowering the pH of the cure. Its role in color development and color stability under present commercial curing practices has been found to be negligible. The sugars most frequently used are sucrose, cane sugar, dextrose, and invert sugar.

Nitrite and Nitrate

Other ingredients that are preservatives, but which are used in small amounts and were originally included as curing ingredients primarily to develop color in the cured products, are sodium nitrite ($NaNO_2$), sodium nitrate ($NaNO_3$), potassium nitrite (KNO_2), and potassium nitrate (KNO_3). Bacterial reduction of the nitrates in long cures results in the formation of nitrites. A common practice was to add some of the old pickle to fresh pickle to introduce the nitrate-reducing bacteria. The difficulty with this method was the lack of control that the processor had over the nitrite formed. Too much nitrite caused nitrite burn, and too little can result in under-cure. Since modern quick-cured meats have insufficient time for the reduction to take place, nitrate has little place in modern curing mixtures. It is, however, necessary to use some nitrite in the cure. Functions of nitrite as a curing ingredient in addition to fixing color are: (1) inhibits growth of certain microorganisms (*Clostridium botulinum*), (2) contributes to the characteristic flavor of cured meat, and (3) retards the development of rancidity.

The use of sodium nitrate, potassium nitrate (saltpeter), sodium nitrite, potassium nitrite, or a combination of nitrite and nitrate, should not result in the presence of more than 200 parts per million of nitrites in the finished product. The maximum amounts of nitrates and nitrites that may be used are:

Sodium or Potassium Nitrate

7 pounds in 100 gallons of pickle.
3½ ounces for each 100 pounds of meat in dry salt or dry cure.
2¾ ounces in 100 pounds of chopped meat and/or meat by-product.

Sodium or Potassium Nitrite

2 pounds in 100 gallons of pickle at 10% pump level.
1 ounce for each 100 pounds of meat in dry salt or dry cure.
¼ ounce in 100 pounds of chopped meat and/ or meat by-product.

Myoglobin is the pigment occurring in the muscle which acts as a vehicle for oxygen storage in the muscle. Hemoglobin is the pigment that acts as a carrier of oxygen in the blood. It is the reaction of nitric oxide (NO), a decomposition product of the nitrite, that combines with myoglobin to form nitrosomyoglobin. This is the red color that heat will change to the desired pink color (nitrosohemochromogen).

Ascorbic Acid and Sodium Ascorbate

The time element has posed some problems in color development and retention in cured meats and particularly in emulsion-type products that are heat processed immediately. It was found that ascorbic acid, iso-ascorbic acid, or their salts, hastened color production due to either a chemical reaction with the nitrite, producing more nitric oxide, or by reducing metmyoglobin to myoglobin.

Federal regulations permit the addition of 75 ounces of ascorbic acid or 87.5 ounces of sodium ascorbate to 100 gallons of pickle and ¾ ounce of ascorbic acid or ⅝ ounce of sodium ascorbate to each 100 pounds of sausage meat or emulsion.

Spraying the surface of cured cuts prior to packaging with 5% to 10% ascorbic acid or ascorbate solution, the use of which shall not result in a significant addition of water to the product, has been found to deter color fading caused by light. The ability of ascorbic treated cured meats to resist fading is ascribed to residual ascorbic acid maintaining reducing conditions on the exposed cured meat surface.

Ascorbate is commonly known as Vitamin C, and in addition to its beneficial effects on color, it has been shown to inhibit the formation of nitrosamines (Chapter 16) in cured meats.

Alkaline Phosphates

The primary purpose of alkaline phosphates is to decrease the shrinkage in smoked meat and meat products and the "cook-out" in canned meat products. The ability to increase the water binding quality of meat results in increased yields of up to 10%.

Approved phosphates are disodium phosphate, monosodium phosphate, sodium hexametaphosphate, sodium tripolyphosphate, sodium pyrophosphate, and sodium acid pyrophosphate and may be added to the pumping pickle for hams, bacon, pork shoulders, picnics, Boston butts, boneless butts, and pork loins. The pumping pickle shall not contain more than 5% of approved phosphate and the finished product shall contain no more than 0.5% of added phosphate.

The pH Factor

The symbol *pH* (the hydrogen-ion concentration) is an expression of the degree of acidity or alkalinity of a substance. The neutral point is 7 (using chemically pure H_2O as a basis) and a pH below 7 indicates the degree of acidity whereas a pH above 7 indicates the degree of alkalinity.

The pH of fresh meat ranges between 5.3 and 6.0 and will vary, depending upon the glycogen content of the muscle at the time of slaughter (see Chapter 19). Meat of more alkaline character (6.0 to 6.5) will spoil bacteriologically at a faster rate than meat in the lower acid range (5.3 to 5.7). In pickle cures the pH range should be between 5 and 6. This means that some acid such as acetic, citric, or lactic may have to be added if the sugar in the pickle will not furnish sufficient acid through bacterial fermentation. Whatever the means, an acid medium is necessary for the proper curing and manufacture of meat and meat products.

The claim is made that salt tenderizes meat at the 2% level. It is well known that acid will tenderize, so with an acid pickle, the two together should result in some tenderness.

CURING METHODS

Prolonged exposure of meat to salt action results in excessive shrinkage and high salt content. It is therefore important in any of these methods that quantitative measurements and time schedules be observed.

Dry Salt Cure

The dry salt cure was the original method employed by our ancestors who practically had to pick the salt out of their teeth. It involved the rubbing and packing of meat in salt for considerable periods of time. The only use made of this method today is in the production of salt pork where fat backs, heavy jowls, and occasionally heavy sow bellies are packed or rubbed with dry salt. Salt pork finds favor in the south where it is used as "seasoning meat" with greens. It is well to add 10 ounces of saltpeter to each 100 pounds of salt and use 10 pounds of cure per 100 pounds of pork as it is layered. Allow it to cure for two to eight weeks.

Dry Sugar Cure

The dry sugar cane has proven to be the safest method for farmers and operators who do not have refrigerated curing rooms or the equipment for injection curing. Its chief advantages are that (1) the rate of cure is more rapid than the immersion cure because the curing ingredients are applied directly to the meat surface in their full concentration; (2) the curing can be conducted safely at higher and wider temperature variations than is possible in immersion curing; (3) the time schedule is not exacting; and (4) there is less spoilage in the hands of the novice or under unfavorable curing conditions. A simple and time-tested formula consists of mixing 8 pounds of table or curing salt, 3 pounds of cane sugar, 3 ounces of saltpeter, and ½ ounce of sodium or potassium nitrite or a total of 4 ounces of the nitrate (saltpeter) if the nitrite is not available.

Use one ounce of the cure for each pound of pork. This will require three separate rubbings for hams at 3- to 5-day intervals; two rubbings for picnics and butts; and one thorough rubbing for bacon, with a light sprinkling over the flesh side of each bacon after it is rubbed. For heavy hams (over 20 pounds), use 1½ ounces of cure per pound of ham, or four rubbings. Place the rubbed meats in boxes, on shelves, or on wooden tables to cure but do not place them in tight boxes or barrels where they will rest in their own brine.

The length of the curing period is seven days per inch of thickness. Since most hams weighing 12 to 15 pounds measure five inches through the cushion, they will cure in 35 days; a bacon two inches thick will cure in 14 days. If the cured cuts remain in cure for a longer period of time, they cannot become any saltier and that makes it possible to smoke them all at the same time.

If some salt is forced into the aitchbone joint to guard against bone souring, the curing can be done at higher temperatures and in a shorter time. This is because salt absorption is more rapid at the higher temperatures.

Box Curing (Pressure)

The pressure method of box curing was popular method before curing became so highly mechanized and is applicable only to bacon. It is practiced by packers who produce a mild cured product. The amount of cure used is about ¾ ounce to each pound of bacon. Tight boxes and in many cases ordinary curing vats are used. The size of the box should be such that the bacon will fit in snugly without overlapping regardless of the number of rows. A lid fits loosely inside the box or vat, upon which considerable pressure can be exerted either by a dead weight or a screw jack on a crossbar attached to the sides of the container.

The pressure on the bacon causes the brine that is formed to rise to the top and cover the meat, thereby sealing it from the air. With just the right amount of curing having been added, the length of time to cure the bacon is of minor concern because it cannot become too salty. Packers have used this method of curing bacon as a means of storage, allowing it to remain in cure as long as 90 days.

The Hot Salt Cure

A practice followed in some communities and tested at the Pennsylvania Experiment Station with success is as follows:

Rub the cushion side and butt of the ham with saltpeter (1 ounce). Follow immediately with a rubbing of granulated or brown sugar over the entire ham. Allow the ham to absorb these ingredients for several hours before applying the hot salt. Heat sufficient salt so it is uncomfortable to the hands (wear cotton gloves). Place the ham in the hot salt and cover for five minutes to get the ham in a soft condition. Take a clean, round, pencil-size stick and force the hot salt into the aitchbone joint. Give the ham a thorough rubbing with the hot salt. An accurate measure would be an increase in weight of ¼ of an ounce per pound of ham.

Allow the hams to absorb the cure for five to seven days; rub with black pepper and smoke.

The Sweet Pickle Cure

A combination of salt and water is called a brine or pickle. A brine that has preservative qualities, such as sodium chloride (common salt) and water, is used for curing meat. The addition of sugar to a sodium chloride brine is called a sweet pickle. The proportion of salt to water determines the strength or salinity of brine or pickle. In the meat industry, two different types of brine are common—the pickling brines and the refrigerating brines. The latter are a combination of calcium chloride and water and are used to carry cold to refrigerated boxes operating under the indirect expansion system. In no instance is calcium chloride brine used as a pickle.

Sweet pickle with a salimeter reading of 75° to 85° is recommended for farm curing. Table 17.1 gives the amounts of the different ingredients and the water necessary to make such pickles. If the nitrite is available, reduce the amount of saltpeter (nitrate) to 3 ounces and add ½ ounce of

Table 17.1—Sweet Pickle Formulations

Salt	Sugar	Saltpeter	Cold Water		Degree of Pickle by Salimeter 40° F
- - - -(lbs.)- - - -		(oz.)	(gal.)	(lbs.)	
10	3	4	4	33 1/3	95
9	3	4	4	33 1/3	90
10	3	4	5	41 2/3	85
8	3	4	4	33 1/3	85
8	3	4	5	41 2/3	75
6	3	4	4	33 1/3	70
7	3	4	5	41 2/3	65
6	3	4	5	41 2/3	60

Cold water weighs 8.33 pounds per gallon, hot water 8 pounds per gallon.
Seven pints of salt weigh 8 pounds.
One quart of syrup weighs 3 pounds.
If salimeter is calibrated for reading at 60° F, subtract .116 per degree below 60°.

sodium or potassium nitrite. A good practice to follow is to heat the water to the boiling point and dissolve the ingredients in it. Allow the the pickle to chill before pouring it over the meat. A salimeter is a necessary piece of equipment when making up curing solutions of different salinities.

Containers

Cypress curing vats, clean molasses or vinegar barrels, or large stone crocks or stainless steel containers make suitable curing receptacles. A clean lid and a stone for a weight are necessary. Barrels in which any sort of spray material has been mixed must never be used. Metal containers that will corrode are unthinkable.

Temperature

The best temperature for the curing room is from 35° to 40° F. Unless curing vessels have been previously contaminated with ham souring bacteria, very little spoilage is experienced at these temperatures. Successful sweet pickle curing can be done at temperatures ranging from 40° to 50° F, which is the usual cellar temperature on farms during the winter. Temperatures of 50° F and over are too high for safe pickle curing. The brine will sour and become ropy and the hams will develop an off-flavor or will sour around the bone.

Length of Cure

Hams should be measured through the cushion back of the aitchbone to determine their thickness. All hams measuring the greatest thickness should be placed in the bottom of the vat with the lighter hams placed on top. A record of the thickness of each layer should be recorded on a card or in a book so that the date when they are to be taken out can be determined. The following is the curing schedule for the different strengths of sweet pickle:

85° pickle cure............ 9 days per inch
75° pickle cure............11 days per inch
60° pickle cure...........13 days per inch

Procedure on the Farm

Pack the chilled hams, shoulders, and bacon in the barrel or vat in the order named and pour sufficient cold pickle over the pack so it will be covered when the lid is weighted down. Four gallons of pickle will cover 100 pounds of closely packed meat, but 4½ to 5 gallons are necessary if the meat is loosely packed. Overhauling meat once or twice during the curing period is desirable to permit the pickle to reach all parts of the meat.

It is necessary to follow rather closely the length of cure prescribed for the different strengths of pickle. As an example, consider a barrel of pork consisting of hams 5½ inches thick, on top of which are shoulders 3½ inches thick, over which are bacons 2 inches thick, curing in an 85° pickle. According to the schedule of 9 days per inch in cure the bacons must come out in 18 days, the shoulders in 30 days, and the hams in 50 days. If 5 gallons of water are used to dissolve the 8-3-3 formula, making a 75° pickle, it will be necessary to cure at the rate of 11 days per inch. A 75° pickle is preferable if the curing room temperature does not rise above 45° F.

A large part of the pork spoilage occurring on the farm could be eliminated if from 4 to 8 ounces of pickle were pumped into the center of the ham and around the hip joint soon after slaughter. A good syringe-type pickle pump will cost from $17 to $20.

Shrinkage

There is very little difference in the shrinkage of pork cured by the dry and sweet pickle methods at the end of a 60-day aging period. Sweet pickle cured hams will gain an average of 5% in cure as compared to a loss of 5% to 7% for hams in dry cure. Sweet pickle hams lose about 5% during smoking as compared to 2% for dry cured hams. Bacon will show about 5% higher shrink than hams because of the large surface area.

Soaking

All farm cured pork, whether dry or sweet pickle cured, should be rinsed or soaked in cold water before it is placed in smoke. The soaking removes the excess salt on the outside and eliminates the formation of salt streaks on the meat when exposed to the heat of the smokehouse. Quick cured meats are rinsed but not soaked.

Soaking pickled bacon and shoulders one hour and ham about two hours is sufficient for farm purposes. Dry sugar cured meats cured with 1 ounce of the cure per pound of meat need not be soaked. Rinsing is sufficient.

Curing Terms Defined

Pumping.—The forcible introduction of pickle into a ham by means of a ham pump.

Stitch or Gun.–A single insertion of the needle in the pump method. The number of stitches or guns given each ham varies with the size of the ham and the strength of the pump pickle. They range from 2 to 6 per ham, running from 2 to 4 ounces of cure per stitch.

Cover Pickle.–The pickle in which hams cure.

Salimeter (salometer or salinometer).–A ballasted glass vacuum tube graduated in degrees and used for testing the strength or salinity of pickle.

Overhaul.–The rehandling or repacking of ham during the pickling period to permit a more uniform distribution of pickle.

Quick cure.–A term applied to a pickle containing sodium nitrite or a combination of nitrite and nitrate.

Immersion cure.–Curing in a cover pickle.

Injection cure.–Stitch pumping or needling.

Artery cure.–Injection of cure into femoral artery of ham and artery in the shoulder.

The Combination Cure

A successful method of curing hams on the farm is the use of the dry cure and the sweet pickle cure in combination. The quicker the salt gets to the center of the ham, the less danger there is of loss from spoilage. Experiments show that where 1½ to 2 pounds of salt per 100 pounds of pork is rubbed into hams 24 to 48 hours before they are placed in a 75° pickle, they will cure in 9 days per inch. This one rubbing of salt is all absorbed overnight and has more rapid penetrating qualities because it is not mixed with other ingredients or dissolved in water.

Pump Pickling (Stitch or Spray Pumping)

To hasten the introduction of the cure to the center of the ham, processors can use the practice known as pumping. This consists of forcing the curing pickle into the center of the ham through a needle attached to a plunger-type syringe or by means of mechanically operated pumps. Pumping pickle may be the same strength as the cover pickle although a 5° to 10° stronger pickle is generally used. The curing of a ham is hastened considerably under this method as it takes place from the inside as well as from the outside. Hams should not be stitch pumped with more than 8% of their weight of 85° pickle. That would mean that 1½ pounds of 85° pickle is pumped into a 20-pound ham and the ham is then cured in a 75° pickle 7 days per inch, or 2½ days per pound of ham. (This shortens the cure 4 days per inch.)

When using a 70° to 75° pickle, stitch pump the ham with 10% and cure in 75° pickle 9 days per inch of thickness.

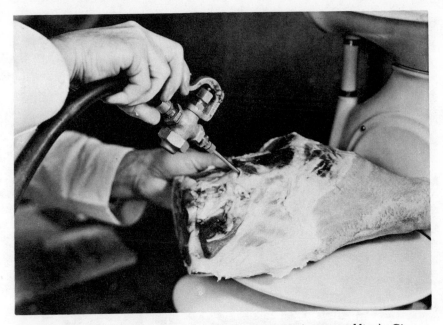

Fig. 17.1—Giving the ham a stitch at the hip joint (pump pickling). Give remaining stitches in cushion, stifle joint, hock end, and butt end.

Hams have been cured very successfully, experimentally, by using a combination of pumping and dry curing. The procedure is to use an 85° pickle at the rate of 8% of the weight of the ham and then rub with one-half its usual application or ½ ounce of the recommended formula per pound of ham and cure it 2½ days per pound.

Advantages of Pump Pickling

1. The salt is introduced to the center of the ham before spoilage has a chance to take place.
2. The curing period is shortened almost one-third.
3. A quicker turnover is effected.

The Artery Cure

Artery curing cosists of forcing a pickle into the femoral artery on the inside butt end of the ham by means of a small needle attached to a hose and connected to a pump that exerts a pressure of 40 to 50 pounds. The artery-pumped hams are either rubbed with the dry mix or placed in a pickle of similar strength for five to seven days to com-

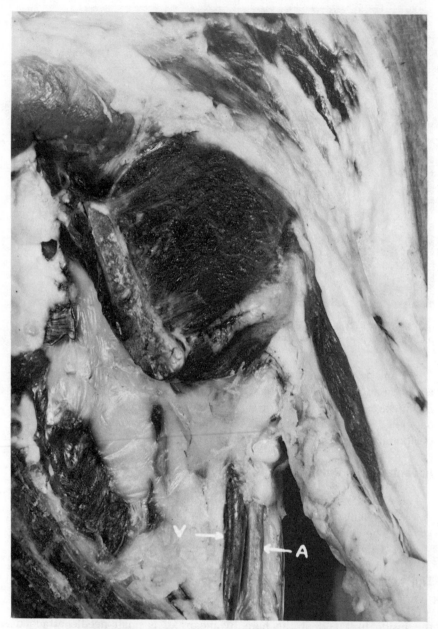

Fig. 17.2—Loosen the leaf fat over the inside of the ham butt and separate the artery "A" from the fat. Cut the artery long. It differs from the vein "V" in that it is strong and elastic.

plete the curing. The salinity of the pickle to use will depend upon how long and under what conditions the ham is to be stored. A pickle strength of 60° to 65° on the salimeter is acceptable where hams are to be tenderized and held under refrigeration.

Repeated tests, using the formula recommended in this text, produced higher flavor and better keeping quality where hams were artery-pumped with 10% of their weight using a 75° pickle. These artery-pumped hams were given a light rubbing of the dry cure mixture and left to shelf cure for several days before being smoked. These hams had longer storage life and their flavor was more acceptable to the trade than were the hams cured with 60° or 65° pickle. For farm curing, the use of the 85° pickle (10% by weight) and one thorough rubbing of the dry cure produced a ham of high flavor and good holding quality.

The advantages of artery-curing are speed and uniform flavor. It is particularly adapted to pork processors and those doing custom curing. These hams cannot be tenderized if they are to be summer stored but must be smoked at the conventional temperature of 110° to 125° F.

To be labeled as "ham" under Federal requirements, the meat, while in the smokehouse, must be shrunk back to its original fresh weight before the curing solution was injected. If they do not come down to

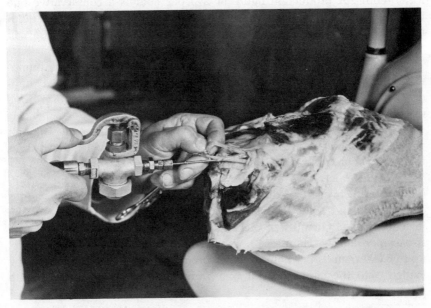

Fig. 17.3—Pump pickle into main artery ahead of the branch. If artery is too short, pump each branch separately.

their fresh weight, the hams are returned for further heating and shrinking or must be labeled "Ham, Water Added" or "Imitation Ham."

Products labeled as "Ham, Water Added" may contain up to 10% added moisture, while those labeled as "Imitation Ham" contain anything over 10%. Such labeling insures that the consumer will know what she is buying when she purchases these hams.

Mechanized Pumping

Both artery pumping and stitch or spray pumping have been mechanized to a high degree in industry. Figure 17.4 shows the Comcure[3], a machine designed to eliminate problems of control, yield, and production in ham processing. Each of the four stations is independent and may be turned off without affecting the others. The desired percentage is dialed on the front of each station and reads down to tenths of a percent for splitting numbers. The operator has no decisions to make regarding the correct amount of pickle. He merely places the ham on the platform, clamps the gun onto the artery, pushes the programming start button, and proceeds to the next station.

Should a ham be an extremely bad leaker and not hold the correct percentage, it will sit on the platform, and the red fill light on the panel will flash on and off indicating that the ham should be removed for stitching. A production figure of 240 per hour is a conservative one to allow for situations involving heavy hams at high percentages. Pumping hams in the 12- to 16-pound range at percentages of 10% to 15% will exceed the 240/hour figure easily.

Figure 17.5 shows an InjectoMat®,[4] a machine using the spray pumping principle with the exception that the needles inject the brine at hundreds of points. The pressure of the brine forces relatively uniform brine distribution throughout the meat.

InjectoMat is fully automatic. The operator loads the conveyor belt with the product—bone-in, semi-boned, or boneless—which discharges into a barrel or truck after injection.

Needles operate in unison until they strike an obstruction; *spring-loading* protects each needle when it strikes a bone. A control bar aligns each needle and holds the product in position during the instant of the injection stroke. Quantity of pickle is adjusted by belt speed *volume* and *strokes-per-minute*. Hams are pumped at the rate of 6 to 12 per minute, up to 6,000 pounds per hour. Smaller product units, like briskets, may be loaded onto the conveyor belt two wide for more than 12-per-minute production speed.

---

3. Vogt, Inc., Clawson, Michigan 48017.
4. Koch Supplies, Inc., Kansas City, Missouri 64108.

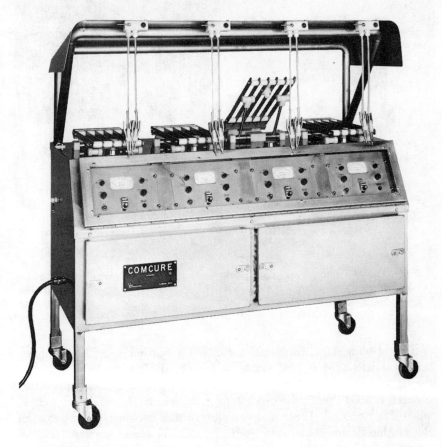

Fig. 17.4—An automatic artery pumping machine which is electronically controlled. (Courtesy, Vogt, Inc.)

Tenderized Hams

Hams of several degrees of tenderness are produced for the market, many of which require further preparation in the home. The tenderizing occurs in the smokehouse that is thermostatically heat controlled. The cured hams are first soaked in tap water to remove excess outside salt and are then placed in a smokehouse. It takes about 24 hours to tenderize hams, and it is usually accomplished in three stages. During the first eight hours or the drying stage, the gas burners or steam (if steam coils are used) heat the house to 125° F. All drafts are opened to carry off excess moisture and there is no smoking during this period. During the

Fig. 17.5—An automatic bone-in pickle injector. (Left) An overall view showing volume and stroke adjustment controls. (Right) A close-up of InjectoMat® injecting a ham.

next eight-hour stage, the drafts are closed about half way, the temperature raised to 135° F, and smoke is generated. The smoking continues throughout the third stage with all drafts closed, and the temperature is raised to 165° F until the inside temperature of the ham reaches 142° F, when it is removed. These hams require further cooking in the home for full tenderization. Hams sold as "fully cooked" are those that have received extra heat processing to bring the internal temperature of the ham to 150° F or higher. But unlike sausages, in which the meat is very finely ground, a ham processed to an internal temperature of 150° F will not eat like a sausage and therefore, must have further preparation. An internal temperature of 160° F makes it ready to eat.

APHIS requires that cured and smoked hams be heated to at least 137° F as a safeguard against trichinosis (see Chapter 3).

Curing Frozen Meat

Sharp frozen hams or hams frozen in freezer lockers at 0° F and held in storage for one to eight weeks were immersion cured experimentally in three days less time per inch of thickness or one-half day less per pound than unfrozen hams.

It was found unnecessary to thaw hams before placing them in cure.

Allowing frozen hams to thaw in pickle kept down the temperature of the pickle for a longer period, which was an advantage where there was no means of control in the curing cellar temperature.

A curing period of six days per inch of thickness when frozen hams were placed in an 85° pickle, and five days per inch if previously thawed and covered with an 85° pickle, gave the most desirable salt content. This was the equivalent of two days per pound of ham.

Hams that were locker frozen and then cured were sound and very palatable after being held for three months in summer storage under farm conditions at 80° F.

Curing on the Basis of Days per Pound

In a study of the weight of hams versus their thickness, it was found that the following curing schedule is somewhat analogous:

> 60° pickle cure.........4 days per pound of ham
> 75° pickle cure.........3 days per pound of ham
> 85° pickle cure.........2½ days per pound of ham
> 90° pickle cure.........2 days per pound of ham

The dry sugar cure requires two days per pound minimum (using 1 ounce of dry formula per pound).

Bacon must be cured on the basis of thickness.

Aging Hams

Repeated experiments have shown that the salt concentration in the outside inch of hams is 10 to 20 times as great as in the center at the time that they are removed from cure. The longer the curing period in a weak pickle, the greater the salt equalization. Hams cured under 60 days should be aged at least an additional 30 days to permit the salt to equalize.

Hunt, at the Maryland Station, found that hams aged in incubators at 108° F for 10 to 12 weeks were comparable in quality and chemical composition to hams stored a year or longer at ordinary ham room temperature. He reported that hams aged in incubators shrank less for the same degree of aging than those aged in a ham room. The combined shrink of curing, smoking, and aging for nine weeks in a standard incubator was the same for both sweet pickle and dry cured hams, 23.2% in each case.

Canadian Bacon

The pork loin muscle (*longissimus*) or sirloin (*gluteus medius*) stripped from heavy pork loins is used to make this product. It is given a mild cure and a light smoking. The two methods of cure are as follows:

Dry Cured Formula

| 2¾ lbs. salt | 3 oz. sodium nitrate |
| 1¼ lbs. sugar | ¼ oz. sodium nitrite |

This is sufficient to cure 100 pounds of pork loin. Rub it on and place the rubbed loins in a tight box. Put sufficient pressure on the meat so it will be covered with brine within several days. Cure for 10 to 14 days (depending upon size) in a temperature of 36° to 38° F and then wash in hot water and drain for half a day. Place each loin in an artificial casing, tie one end of the casing, and force out the air pockets before trying the other end. Smoke for 12 to 15 hours at 125° to 130° F, and after it has chilled to room temperature, dip it in water of 180° F for a minute and wipe dry to remove the grease. Place the meat in room temperature to dry. The yield of boned and fatted loins will average 45% to 48% with ham butt removed.

Pickle Cured

Make up a 65° salimeter strength salt solution and to each gallon of pickle add ½ pound of sugar and ½ oz. of cure (3 oz. of nitrate, ¼ oz. of nitrite). Overhaul the meat on the third and seventh days and cure for two weeks at 36° to 38° F. Soak the loins in tap water for several hours and drain. Smoke for 10 to 12 hours at 125° F. If they are to be tenderized, smoke them at 125° to 135° F for eight hours and at 155° to 165° F for four hours.

Dried Beef

Both the dry cure and the sweet pickle cure methods are employed. In either case, the formula is the same: 8 pounds of salt, 3 pounds of sugar, 3 oz. of sodium nitrate, and ¼ oz. of sodium nitrite. When dissolved in 4 gallons of water this formula makes sufficient pickle to cover 100 pounds of meat. When used as a dry cure, apply 1 to 1½ ounces to each pound of meat. To do the latter will require two rubbings at three- to five-day intervals. Frequent overhauls are necessary where the self-formed brine collects in a tight vessel; otherwise, pieces resting in this brine will become too salty. Pickle curing requires less labor.

The length of time required to cure beef depends upon the size of the cuts, but three days per pound for the 85° sweet pickle cure and two days per pound for the dry cure are sufficient. The rounds of thin or inferior animals are used for this product. The muscles of the round are taken out in three pieces called the *beef ham* or dried *beef set*. They consist of the top round, the bottom round and eye muscle (together), and the knuckle piece (sirloin tip). In case of large rounds, one or two extra pieces are made by splitting the top round. The shoulder clod muscle in the forequarter is also used.

After the beef is cured, it is rinsed with cold water, allowed to hang for 24 hours to dry, and then given a light or heavy smoke as desired. It is stored in a dry, well ventilated room for further drying.

Corning

The preservation of beef by the use of salt is termed *corning*. Lexicographers explain the origin of the word by referring back to the sixteenth century when the word *corn* was synonymous with the word *grain*. At that time manufacturers of gunpowder used the word *corning* to indicate that their product had been spread out and allowed to dry in single grains. The term *corned* was later applied to the process of curing beef by sprinkling it with grains of salt.

The method used in making "corned beef" today entails more than the mere application of salt. A formula that is rather popular consists of dissolving 8 pounds of salt, 3 pounds of sugar, 4 ounces of baking soda, 3 ounces of sodium nitrate, and ¼ ounce of sodium nitrite in 4 gallons of water. This is sufficient to cure 100 pounds of beef. Some sections of the country, such as the New England district, prefer a gray color to the cured beef, in which case the saltpeter is omitted. A very good color is secured by using 4 ounces of cream of tartar instead of the saltpeter. Boneless cuts of brisket, plate, chuck, and round usually are used for corning. Pack the cuts in a stone crock or wooden tub or barrel, cover them with the chilled pickle, and weight the meat with a board upon which a non-metal weight can be placed. If the brisket is not rolled and other cuts do not have more than 3 inches of thickness, they will cure (corn) and be ready to use in 12 to 14 days.

If more flavor is desired, a slight amount of garlic or pickling spices can be added.

Souring

Most bacterial contamination comes from outside sources which can be controlled in part by rigid sanitation.

Various scientists (Bunyea, McBryde, Rerth, Boyer, Lewis, Moulton, and others) have worked on this problem and found that the organism that causes souring of beef around the deep-seated hip joint is *Bacillus megatherium* (Bunyea) while *Clostridium sporogenis, Cl. putrefaciens,* and *Cl. putrificum* cause souring in pork. These organisms are proteolytic (which means that they break down proteins into amino acids and ammonia) and flourish best at room temperatures or higher.

The results of considerable experimental work on beef and ham souring proved rather conclusively that quick chilling of the carcasses to 36° to 38° F, and similar holding and curing temperature, will practically eliminate the difficulty. From 3% to 5% salt concentration in the center of the ham, and small amounts of saltpeter and sodium nitrite, had inhibitory action on the ham souring organism. Moulton reports that the nitrite was 10 times as effective in this respect as the nitrate.

Although curing ingredients inhibit the development of these anaerobic organisms, they do not entirely destroy them. In very mildly cured products, proteolysis may continue to the point where the product is unfit for food. The remedy in this case is to hold the product under refrigeration. Presently, some packers inject dry ice (CO_2) snow deeply into the pelvic joint before the carcass leaves the slaughter floor to guarantee a quick chilling of this internal area.

Flavor

Probably the greatest objection of consumers to quick cured, tenderized ham has been its apparent lack of flavor in comparison with long cured ham. The curing process entails more than simply the introduction of sufficient salt to preserve the meat. In the prolonged curing process there is an enzymatic action and a bacterial action by the clostridia which produces a distinctive flavor that is not as pronounced in "quickies" (quick cured hams). This action in combination with just the right amount of salt, enough sugar, and a good pink color makes for quality in a ham.

THE SMOKING PROCESS

Cured meats are soaked or washed before being placed in the smokehouse. They should be allowed to drain and dry before a fire is started. Care should be taken to avoid one piece of meat touching another. Wire hangers are preferred to string for supporting the different cuts. These can be made out of No. 9 gauge galvanized wire or they may be purchased from a butchers' supply house. Net ham bags are used by packers.

Where wood is subjected to destructive distillation it yields inflammable gases, a strongly acid aqueous distillate and a quantity of tar. The residue is wood charcoal. The aqueous distillate contains methyl (wood) alcohol mixed with acetic acid and acetone and a little methyl acetate and is known as pyroligneous acid (liquid smoke).

The wood used to generate the smoke should be of a species in no way related to the pine or resinous tree. Hickory is the most popular, but apple, plum, peach, oak, maple, beech, ash, or any non-resinous wood will give satisfactory results. Dry corn cobs are excellent for starting logs to smoldering; in fact, meats can be smoked successfully by the use of corn cobs alone. Where a cool smoke is desired, hardwood sawdust is the most satisfactory. Hardwood sawdust is used in the smoke generators that are a part of the equipment in producing tenderized hams. Smoke generated by friction (revolving the surface of a log against a spinning steel plate) is used to some extent.

Liquid Smoke

Smoke is probably composed of as many as 200 different compounds, which can be grouped into four major categories: acidic compounds, phenolic compounds, carbonyl compounds, and the hydrocarbons. The first three contribute to smoke flavor. Hydrocarbons, on the other hand, are present only in trace amounts, if at all, but are undesirable, since they have been shown to be carcinogenic.

Liquid smoke can be prepared as a concentrate by burning wood (pyrolysis) and condensation or by making mixtures of pure chemical compounds to produce a synthetic smoke. In so doing, the desirable compounds are included while the undesirable hydrocarbons are eliminated. These liquid smoke manufacturing procedures take place completely separate from meat processing itself. Liquid smoke in bottles or barrels is transported to the processing area and applied to the product either by spraying (vaporizing) or painting or may be mixed directly in the emulsion as in the case of sausages.

The advantages of liquid smoke are uniformity of smoke, simplicity of application, ease of clean up, possible solution to smoke emission environmental problems, and elimination of a *possible* carcinogen from the food supply.

If smoke flavoring is added in the emulsion of a sausage product or painted or sprayed on the outside of a product, the words "Smoke Flavoring Added" or "Artificial Smoke Flavoring Added" as the case may be, must appear on the label.

Temperature in the Smokehouse

The absorption of smoke and the change in color of the outside surface of smoked meat is hastened by high temperatures. The nature of the smokehouse and the outside temperatures are governing factors in the length of time required to smoke meat. It requires about 30 to 40 hours to smoke meat to a chestnut brown in one continuous smoking period with a smokehouse temperature of 90° to 100° F. The same results are secured in 18 hours with a smokehouse temperature of 125° to 135° F, but it will require three to four days to get the same color with a cool smoke of 80° to 90° F. There is no particular advantage in a prolonged smoking period.

The colder the weather, the drier the wood should be to get the required heat. In warm weather a semi-green wood is preferable. Meats that have been subjected to four to six days of smoke or until they become dark brown in color have some added keeping qualities, but unless the outside surface is trimmed off before cooking, the meat is likely to cause digestive disorders. This is due to the poisonous effect of too large quantities of the pyroligneous acid.

Shrinkage

Shrinkage in weight is not as great during the smoking process as it is in the subsequent holding of the smoked meat. Sweet pickled meats will lose only the 2% to 5% that they gained in cure. If they are sold as soon as they are smoked there is practically no shrink from the green weight. The real shrinkage takes place during the first month of storage and this averages about 7% for hams and 10% for bacon.

Dry cured meats shrink from 5% to 7% during the curing period and thus do not lose as much weight in smoke or in the subsequent holding period. Dry cured meat shrinks about 2% in smoke as compared to 4% for the sweet pickled meats. Smoked hams held for 3 months will shrink about 20% from green weights.

The Smokehouse

The most satisfactory type of home smokehouse, that will serve also as a storage place for the cured and smoked meat, is one that is constructed of tile or cement blocks with a fireproof, insulated ceiling. The floor should be made of concrete, and the entire building must be rodent and vermin proof and have well-screened ventilators. One intake ventilator near the floor and an outlet near the roof are necessary. The dead air spaces provided by a tile or concrete block building make for a more even temperature for storing meat in winter and summer.

The size of the building is dependent upon the amount of smoked products to be run through it. On the average farm a house 6 by 8 feet with walls 9 feet high is entirely adequate. The metal rods to support the meat should be about 8 feet from the floor. If the fire is built in the smokehouse itself, it will be necessary to hang the meat so that it will

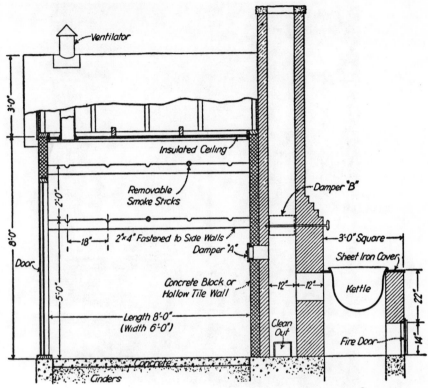

A 6'×6'×8' COMBINATION SMOKE AND STORAGE HOUSE AND COOKER

Fig. 17.6—Plan for a combination smokehouse and cooker. There are two tiers of removable smoke poles made from 2-inch pipe, drilled and pegged every 18 inches, the metal pegs extending through either side of the pipe for hangers. The oven with a 28-inch (50-gallon) cast-iron, open fire kettle built in, is used for rendering and cooking as well as being the firebox for generating smoke. This firebox is made of brick and can be erected at the end of any building that is to be used as a smokehouse. When the kettle is to be used for cooking purposes, close damper A and open damper B. When smoking meat, keep water in the kettle, close damper B after the fire is started and open damper A. Two inches of concrete laid over 6 to 9 inches of rock and cinders will make a satisfactory floor.

not be directly over the fire. Another method is to weld a piece of heavy sheet metal about 3 feet square to four metal legs about 3 feet long and place it over the fire so it will diffuse the heat.

Where a cool smoke is desired it will be necessary to construct a fire pit outside the smokehouse and conduct the smoke into the house through terra-cotta pipes.

The modern smokehouse units now in use are a far cry from the chimney type that once was so common. Today's smoke units are con-

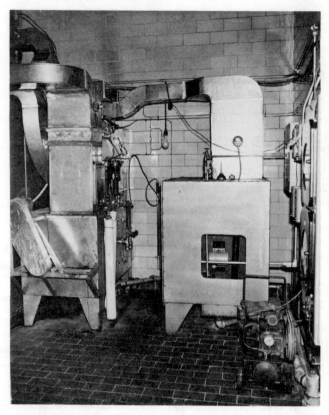

Fig. 17.7—The smoke generator and controls. Sawdust produces the smoke.

structed of shiny, noncorrosive metal, well insulated and electronically controlled. They are designed so the volume of smoke and the temperature can be set automatically. The smoke vents are distributed around the ceiling and the smoke circulated downward to eliminate dead spots. Some units also do the cooking by showering the products with hot water and then chilling them with cold water. It requires skill to operate these units, and even more to repair them, but the improvements in the quality of the product, the speed of production, and the control of the processing are indisputable (note also Chapter 16).

Cleaning the Smokehouse

The deposit of the wood distillate on the walls and hangers of smokehouses that are in regular use develops a scale that falls on the meat, making it necessary to remove the scale periodically.

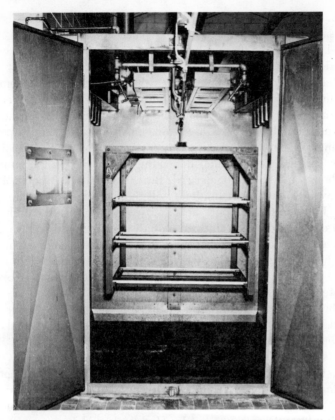

Fig. 17.8—The vented smokehouse with water showering equipment.

Since the tarry material is combustible, a torch must never be used. A detergent should be sprayed on the walls to soak the tar; follow this with a forceful spray (25 to 50 pounds per square inch) of hot water. Special detergents for this purpose are made by many excellent firms in the food equipment cleaning and sanitation phase of the meat industry.

Smoked Turkey

The process of curing turkey, which also has been successfully applied to chickens, is very similar to that used for curing pork. The make-up of the curing formula differs from the pork curing formula mainly in the spices used.

The following formula gave excellent results at the Pennsylvania station: 6 pounds of salt, 2 pounds of cane sugar, 2 ounces of saltpeter, 1 ounce of bay leaves, 1 ounce of parsley leaves, and 1 ounce of black pepper. Dissolve in 4½ gallons of hot water and let cool. This constitutes a 65° salimeter pickle. The birds are placed in a clean barrel, vat, tub, or crock with rumps up and back to the vessel. This puts the breasts on the inside. The next row would be placed breast to breast. Place a weighted board over the birds and cover with pickle. Cure them 1½ days per pound of bird. A quicker cure is to make a 75° pickle and cure 1 day per pound. Both tests gave about the same results in flavor and salinity.

When cured, the birds are rinsed in cool water and suspended by the wings to dry. This will require several hours. The smoking will require from 4 to 36 hours, depending upon the temperature of the smokehouse and the color desired. Birds smoked for 8 hours at 110° F will have a bright amber shade as will those smoked for 24 hours at 80° to 90° F. Four to six hours at 135° to 140° F is faster and produces a good color. Birds to be shipped long distances should receive a heavier smoke and be dark chestnut in color. Tenderized turkeys can be produced by subjecting the carcass to a smokehouse temperature of 170° F for 8 to 12 hours (depending upon size) and applying the smoke during the latter part of the period.

The flavor of smoked turkey has very little resemblance to fresh roasted bird and has little to recommend it unless the smoked flavor is further supplemented with spices. By the proper blending of certain spices, some brands of smoked turkey have become popular. Needless to say, these formulas are trade secrets. Some formulas do not contain saltpeter since it causes a slight reddening of the meat. To illustrate the elaborate degree of seasoning and spicing that can be employed, the following formula as suggested by Highlands and Burns in *Food Industries* is given:

Water 5 gals.   Salt 4 lbs.   Sugar 30 oz.

Oil of celery............8 c.c.	Oil of Marjoram..........5 c.c.	
Oil of black pepper.......8 c.c.	Oil of bay leaves..........6 c.c.	
Oil of parsley leaves.......8 c.c.	Oil of sweet basil.........6 c.c.	
Oil of sage...............5 c.c.	Oil of coriander..........5 c.c.	
Oil of thyme.............5 c.c.	Oil of cardamon..........5 c.c.	

Oils are dissolved in 200 c.c. of alcohol and 1 gr. of gum tragacanth.

The dissolved oils are added to the brine and the birds cured for 1.5 days per pound of dressed weight.

Cured and smoked turkey do not have the keeping qualities of cured pork and should be used as soon as possible. They are unsuited to storage because they have insufficient salt content to keep down bacterial action; They mold easily and dry out rapidly.

Retarding Molds on Stored Meat

Mold spores are prevalent in the air and require only the proper moisture conditions for their development. They flourish in a rather wide range of temperatures and under varying degrees of light intensity. The most effective way of preventing molds on untreated smoked meats is to store them in a dry, well ventilated room ranging in temperature between 45° to 55° F. Suspend the unwrapped meat in such a manner that it does not touch other meat. The disadvantage of this method of holding meat is the larger loss in weight due to dehydration, but loss in weight is preferable to moldy flavored meat.

Storage of Smoked Meats

Various methods of holding and storing cured and smoked meats have been tested with varying degrees of success. Hams and bacon sides that have been given the long cure are the only farm-cured products that can be stored without being refrigerated. Suspending them, unwrapped, in a dark, well ventilated, well screened room, gave the best results. Use the finest mesh screening available and inspect the meats daily. Figure 17.9 illustrates some common pests of non-refrigerated country-cured meats.

PRESERVING BY REFRIGERATION

Natural or artificial refrigeration retards the development of molds and bacteria for a limited period only. The most effective refrigerator temperature outside of subfreezing temperatures is between 30° and 32° F. Commercial meat coolers are usually held at 29° to 38° F.

How Cold Is Produced

The formation of heat for the production of cold is the thermodynamic principle involved in artificial refrigeration. A gas that will turn to a liquid when compressed by mechanical means, and that will again revert to a gas when the pressure is released, will accomplish this, and when it is so used is known as a refrigerant. One of the most common refrigerants used to chill the coolers of meat packers and cold storage houses is ammonia (NH_3). It is seldom used in household refrigerators because of the noticeable odor in case of a leak. When ammonia gas or any gas is compressed, heat is generated. If the heat is removed by passing the compressed gas through water-jacketed coils (condensers) or a fan-cooled condenser, the gas turns to a liquid. Permit this liquid to

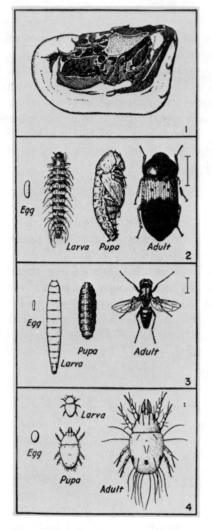

Pests of Nonrefrigerated
Stored Meat

(1) Cross section of ham showing damage by insects and mites.

(2) The larder beetle is typical of several species of small beetles and their woolly larvae that feed on meat and cheese. The beetles are strong fliers.

(3) The ham or cheese skipper gets its name from the jumping habit of the larvae. The flies are smaller than houseflies. They lay their eggs on meat and cheese and multiply very rapidly.

(4) Cheese mites are not insects, but cause damage to meat and cheese similar to that caused by insects. Though they cannot fly, they are carried by various insects.

Fig. 17.9—(From Pamphlet A15-52, U.S. Dept. of Agriculture, Washington, D.C.)

escape slowly through an aperture in a valve (expansion valve) into expansion coils located in a refrigerator, and the first element that is required by the refrigerant is the heat which had been taken from it by the condensers.

The only available heat supply is in the air that lies in direct contact with the expansion coils and the refrigerant absorbs this heat as it passes through the coils on the return trip to the compressor to which it is drawn by the suction of the pistons. The cycle continues as long as the compressor is in operation. In the household type refrigerator, the heat taken out of the refrigerator helps to keep the kitchen warm. In the case of water-cooled condensers, it disappears down the drain. To save on the water bill, large establishments chill the water after it leaves the condenser and reuse it until it becomes too rusty. Some of the common refrigerants are carbon dioxide (CO_2), sulfur dioxide (SO_2), ethane (C_2H_6), propane (C_3H_8), butane (C_4H_{10}), isobutane ($CH_3)_3CH$, methyl chloride (CH_3Cl), ethyl chloride (C_2H_5Cl), and the freons. Virtually all of these refrigerants are noncorrosive in the absence of moisture. SO_2, CO_2, and Freon are nonexplosive. Freon-12 is the most widely used refrigerant (see later discussion in this chapter).

History and Development of Commercial Locker Storage

The purpose of the cold storage locker is to freeze and store properly prepared meats, fruits, and vegetables for future consumption. The particular kind of service rendered by a locker plant is reported to have started on the Pacific Coast about 1903. The Chico Ice and Cold Storage Company of Chico, California, is credited with being one of the first plants to rent cold storage space to local merchants for storing eggs, apples, and other produce. They extended this service to farmers for the storage of meat in boxes in 1908. The demand for this type of storage increased to such an extent that in 1917 it became necessary to construct another room in which wooden lockers of different sizes were built to operate as drawers in a frame.

A similar cold storage business was started at Centralia, Washington, in 1917. About 1920, soon after the beginning of the dry era, a former brewery at Sioux City, Iowa, was converted into a dairy plant which provided freezer locker service for former patrons. In 1927, at Walla Walla, Washington, the local dairyman's association provided room for the members of the association to use to freeze and store rabbits and other game. A number of creameries, ice plants, and milk plants installed freezer lockers throughout the Middle West in the ensuing eight years, but it was the period following 1935 that witnessed a phenomenal increase in this type of service. The increase in locker plants during 1940 to 1945 was insufficient to meet the demands of clamoring patrons who were growing their wartime food suppiles. The limiting factor was wartime priorities.

The popularity of the freezer locker plant was at its highest in the late 1940's and the early 1950's. Since 1952 there has been a declining trend in the number of locker plants and an increase in the number of freezer provisioning plants. The latter have been meeting the needs of the increasing number of cabinet freezer owners among the urbanites. The rapid development of the home freezer cabinet, and particularly the standard refrigerator with a freezer compartment, was a hard blow to the locker operator. However, no one could say that the patrons enjoyed making trips to the locker plant to get their frozen meats. It is far more convenient to have their freezers in their homes. Quantity buying of meat is not for the average consumers who are limited in funds and experience. Daily or weekly buying is their forte.

Now with the freezer in her own kitchen and the wide selection of pre-cut meats available, the homemaker has a new sense of freedom. She is a great follower of specials. Specials on fresh meats, frozen vegetables, detergents, etc., keep her in fighting trim. Aluminum foil is her handyman. With zero temperature and her handyman, she has it made, as they say.

For those who wish to buy quarters or whole carcasses or have animals of their own raising to be processed, the complete service locker plant is still a useful institution.

The Present Status of Frozen Meat

In an extensive study conducted by Kansas State University,[5] the distribution costs, acceptance, cooking, and eating qualities of frozen meat were investigated. Processing steps which met with the most success included fabricating retail cuts at least 48 hours post mortem in a room no warmer than 55° F; allowing a 30-minute period for bloom to develop before freezing or packaging; initial freezing at −70° F, initial storage in the dark at −15° F or lower, and display at case temperatures of −20° F or lower; packaging in a film with moderate to high oxygen permeability to maintain color; and using a 5- to 6-second water dip at 90° to 95° F to remove color bleaching.

The least costly method of distribution was to ship the carcass to a central processor to be cut into retail cuts and then shipped to retail stores. The most costly was to ship the carcass through a central distributor and then to a retail store to be cut and wrapped.

Results of comparative cooking tests of frozen versus unfrozen steaks and chops showed that freezing did not impair the palatability of beef steaks, but that fresh, unfrozen pork chops were preferred to frozen chops, even though the frozen chops were acceptable. Frozen chops and beef steaks generally had higher cooking losses than their fresh counterparts. In the retail market, most of the customers who purchased the frozen meat liked its palatability, but not all; 23% were dissatisfied

---

5. *Research Publication 166*, September, 1973.

with either tenderness, juiciness, or texture. More than 85% of the non-purchasers indicated that the frozen meat was unappealing, unappetizing, or appeared artificial.

A supermarket survey conducted by Seth T. Shaw[6] in mid-1973 indicated that 93% of the beef sales were fresh and 7% were frozen in 1972. Frozen beef sales are expected to rise to 15% by 1977, according to this survey.

A rise in frozen meat sales has been predicted since the 1950's, but it has been slow to come. Consumers are still suspicious of frozen meat at the retail level. Unfortunately, they would rather buy fresh retail cuts and freeze them at home many times in an inadequate freezer and in an inadequate wrap.

The Effect of Freezing on Meats

Freezing is the modern means employed to preserve food products in a condition that most closely resembles the fresh product. This is accomplished by the almost complete inactivation of enzymes and bacteria through the use of low temperatures. The lower the temperature, the greater the inhibitory action and the longer the period of satisfactory storage. To secure and maintain very low temperatures requires expensive construction and entails high operating costs. The industry has been utilizing temperatures ranging from 0° to −32° F.

Lean meat averages from 60% to 65% water, a liquid which expands at both high and low temperatures. The actual point at which meat juices will freeze solid is not 32° F but 28° to 29° F. The rate of crystallization and the size of the crystals formed are dependent upon the temperature. Slow freezing causes the water to separate from the tissue into pools that form large crystals. These stretch and rupture some of the surrounding tissue. Rapid freezing results in very little water separation and the crystals are therefore small and less expansive. Because there is practically no pool crystallization in very low temperature freezing, the drip is considerably less than on meats frozen at higher temperatures.

To prevent the growth of spoilage-producing bacteria deep in carcass tissues or in the center of containers of warm meat, meat temperatures must be brought down to 40° F within a 16-hour period. If hot meat goes directly to the freezer, it must reach 0° F within 72 hours to prevent the growth of putrefactive bacteria. For large packs of hot meat, a freezer temperature of −5° F with air velocities of 500 to 1,000 feet per minute is recommended. For some freezers, the amount of meat frozen at one time should not exceed two pounds per cubic foot of

---

6. *The National Provisioner,* November 3, 1973.

freezer space. More than this amount raises the freezer temperature and slows down the freezing process. The key rule is "fast to 0° or below."

Low temperatures do not destroy vitamins. Most of the vitamin loss is caused by heat or light or is lost in the juices that escape.

Experimental work to date for the purpose of freezing meat has indicated that for best results:

1. An animal must be physically sound (in good health).
2. An animal must be properly bled (fiery carcasses do not keep well).
3. The animal heat must be removed as rapidly as possible (chill room temperature of 29° to 36° F).
4. The aging period must be restricted.
5. The wrapping material must be of good quality.
6. The holding temperature should be 0° F or lower.

This is predicated on the assumption that proper sanitary precautions have been observed.

Oxidative Rancidity

The development of rancidity in animal fats depends upon their ability to absorb oxygen from the air. This weakness for oxygen varies with the basic chemical structure of the fat involved. Any fat that has one or more double bonds in the carbon chain will be vulnerable to a cleavage caused by the oxygen taking the place of the double bond and forming aldehydes and fatty acids. These products, so formed, generally are no longer pleasing in taste or odor. As a result, they affect the palatibility of the fat and the adjoining lean.

Since pork fat is fairly high in fats (oleic acid—one double bond; linoleic acid—two double bonds; linolenic acid—three double bonds) having the ability to absorb oxygen, it follows that its storage life is lessened considerably. Beef and lamb, on the other hand, are higher in stearic acid, a fat with no double bonds in its structure, and therefore less susceptible to oxygen absorption and oxidative rancidity, with a subsequently longer storage life.

The obvious ways to combat oxidative rancidity are to eliminate the air or to use anti-oxidants. The elimination of air can be done in several ways, the most practical of which is to use a wrapping material that is airtight and moisture-proof and properly appiled. The loss of moisture from meat or any other food is usually termed *shrink* or *dehydration*. The loss of moisture from the frozen surface of meat has been dubbed *freezer burn*. A good wrapping material will serve to reduce both oxidative rancidity and freezer burn.

Australian workers have shown that freezer burn is less when meat is frozen at −4° F compared to 14° F. This is of practical use for the storage of large cuts and carcasses which are too unwieldy to wrap properly.

Factors Which Stimulate Oxygen Absorption

Increased temperatures accelerate absorption, as has been mentioned previously. Nitrites used in curing meat products make for more rapid oxidation. Ultra-violet light used in the sterile lamps that are part of the equipment of some coolers accelerates oxidation. The minerals copper, iron, manganese, cobalt, and lead are also guilty. Salt (NaCl) increases the susceptibility of fats to oxidation.

Aging

Experiments show that the length of the holding (aging or ripening) period has a direct bearing on storage life because it permits oxygen absorption by the exposed fat. This raises the question whether meat that is to be frozen should be aged. It was found that the aged meat showed higher peroxide values and shorter storage life than the 48-hour chilled meat. It also showed that although the ripened meat was slightly more tender during the first month of storage, this advantage disappeared in the subsequent months, the fresh and aged meats being on a par for tenderness. These things being true, aging meat for the development of flavor, aside from its tenderizing effect, becomes a questionable practice for meat that is to be held in zero storage for more than six months.

It may be of interest, at this point, to give the results of a test run at the Pennsylvania station on the effect of different freezing temperatures on the tenderness of meat:

> We had read where a scientist predicted that in the not so distant future there need not be such a thing as tough meat. When subjected to temperatures approaching the absolute, all meat would be made tender. We felt encouraged and slaughtered an eleven-year-old Angus cow. The carcass was chilled for 48 hours and steaks were cut from the top round. Three of these steaks were frozen at −110° F., the lowest temperature we had available and some 300 degrees from the absolute (−461° F.). The other three were frozen at 0° F. All six steaks were stored at zero. At the end of one month, the test showed the steak frozen at −110° F. to be the more tender but it was far from being so tender that it could be cut with a fork. At the end of six months of zero storage, the −110° F. and zero frozen steaks were of the same tenderness but the low temperature steak was

not as juicy. The same was true at the end of ten months when both steaks were beginning to show a slight degree of rancidity.

It is now well known that the 48-hour chilling period saved the cow from being unbearably tough; for if her muscle had been frozen at −110° F within 24 hours post mortem, cold-shortening would have resulted; i.e., an intense shortening of the muscle fibers as in *rigor mortis*. The scientist's prediction evidently came before our knowledge of this phenomenon.

Trimming Fat

What about the fat on meat? Again the results indicate that it is advisable to trim closely before freezing. The fat probably won't be eaten even if it is palatable; it will taint the lean if it oxidizes; and it takes up that much more storage space. In the case of pork, the nature of the fat makes it more vulnerable to oxidation and therefore lowers its storage life below that of beef, veal, and lamb. It is very important, therefore, to trim closely or to freeze only those cuts that are quite lean. For example, tests on sausage of different degrees of fatness showed that the lean sausages had longer storage life than those containing more fat. It has also been demonstrated that pork that was frozen after 48 hours of chill had longer storage life than pork that was chilled for 7 to 14 days before it was frozen. The same was true of the sausage made from such pork.

Cutting Method for Frozen Storage Meats

Tests conducted at Kansas and Michigan experiment stations show that boning meat has no effect on the flavor or juiciness of the cooked meat and that packaging boneless meat is easier, causes less damage to wrappers, and saves up to 35% of frozen storage space. The expense of boning adds to the labor charge over the usual manual bone-in method which is absorbed in part by less necessary rental space, smaller amount of paper required, and the ease and satisfaction in cooking and carving.

Probably one of the best methods for breaking down a carcass of beef for subsequent boning is the method explained in this text. Regardless of the method used, the cuts should be made ready for the oven and in such sizes as will best meet the needs of the family. Some cuts other than the standard ones, such as the top round muscle sliced into chipped steak (about No. 7 on the slicing machine) make for variety and aid in menu making. Giving the top round a slight freeze (not solid) will make it slice evenly.

Wrapping Materials

Wrapping materials suitable for meats come under five general groups:

1. Wax or paraffin treated kraft papers.
2. Cellophane (of lessening importance).
3. Aluminum foil.
4. Laminates.
5. The films (polyethylene and pure or mixed polymers or co-polymers of vinyl chloride, vinyl acetate, or vinylidine chloride).

The characteristics of these wrapping materials differ, and their suitability for packaging meats, vegetables, and fruits depends upon how closely they come to meeting the following requirements:

1. Low moisture vapor transmission.
2. Good tensile strength.
3. Pliable.
4. Maintain pliability and tensile strength at subzero temperatures.
5. Non-toxic.
6. Odorless.
7. Ease of marking for identification.
8. Stripping qualities (will peel from meat when frozen).
9. Grease- and stain-proof.
10. Differing oxygen permeability, depending on use.

The moisture loss or shrinkage of any food during freezer storage must be held to a minimum. An excess of 8% shrink in meats and 3% in fowl is considered to make them unacceptable as fresh meat. This loss in weight is easily measured and the change in color, aroma, flavor, and texture are in about the same proportion as the loss in weight. To hold dehydration to a minimum necessitates the use of a paper that has a low moisture-vapor transmission at low temperatures.

The manufacturers of packaging materials have made rapid strides in producing superior grades in the five groups mentioned. The materials in Group 1 are basically wood pulp papers. Kraft (German meaning strong) is the most widely used wrapping material. The waxed and the laminated kraft papers are popular for wrapping foods to be frozen. They come in many forms having different qualities that give protection against oil, grease, chemicals, molds, moisture-vapor and oxygen transmission, and water.

Another wood pulp paper that is used extensively is vegetable parchment, which has many uses, depending upon its treatment. Some grades are impervious to oxygen, carbon dioxide, and nitrogen. The coated parchment is used for freezer-wrapped meats. The newest type is the silicone-treated vegetable parchment which has anti-sticking properties that make it useful as dividers for frozen meat cuts and hamburger, sausage, and lamb patties in particular.

Still another non-porous, very dense pulp pare is known by the name *Greaseproof*. The more highly refined greaseproof paper is Glassine. The laminated, coated, and waxed varieties are not only greaseproof but also moistureproof and vaporproof, keeping odors from penetrating from the outside.

Cellophane, the original transparent film, which has lost the retail packaging market to the polyvinyl chloride copolymer films, comes in many forms. The one most prominent for packaging fresh meats is coated on one side with a nitrocellulose coating which is moistureproof but allows oxygen to enter. The meat is placed on the uncoated or wettable side. The increase of the water content absorbed from the meat increases the film's rate of oxygen permeability. This was the recommended cellophane for wrapping fresh meat displays that must have bright color and maintain it for 24 to 48 hours. It is the oxygen that is allowed passage to the meat that is necessary to combine with the pigment myoglobin to form oxymyoglobin, which gives the desirable bright red color.

Regarding the polyvinyl chlorides, Dr. D. O. Westerburg[7] states,

> For fresh retail packages, the film has good sparkle, is very clear and is relatively elastic so that finger marks and punches will mostly disappear and give good package appearance even after excessive handling. This, of course, is desirable for retail packages. The soft vinyl is heat sealable to form relatively strong packages. This film has taken the retail packaging market from cellophane during the last five years and is the most widely used material today at the retail level.

To maintain this bright red color and increase oxygen solubility, it is necessary to maintain a low temperature. The time that meat will maintain this bright color is also dependent upon sanitary conditions and the method of handling. The darkening of the meat, which is the further oxidation of the oxymyoglobin to metmyoglobin (brown pigment), is hastened by bacteria and increasing temperature.

Since the maintenance of cured meat color depends upon the absence of oxygen, a paper impervious to oxygen must be used. Cured meat color changes to gray and shades of brown when displayed under lights, dependent upon light intensity.

Aluminum foil has become a standard kitchen accessory in the

7. Union Carbide, Films Packaging Division, Chicago.

American home because it serves so many uses. It is tasteless, odorless, non-toxic, waterproof, greaseproof, non-absorptive, non-shrinking, non-swelling, non-softening, has an extremely low gas transmission rate, is pliable and shapeable, making close contact with the product it encloses, heats and cools quickly, and is non-inflammable—making it a cooking utensil in itself. Its weakness is its lack of strength. Laminated foil makes an excellent wrap for frozen meats.

Laminates are made by combining two or more layers of different materials into a single sheet to eliminate weaknesses that occur in one and not in the other. They are strong and will withstand rough handling.

The plastic films, made in most part from synthetic resins or synthetic or natural polymers, have certain advantages over the packing materials just discussed. These advantages are flexibility, toughness, durability, and sealability. Probably the most suitable of the plastic films for frozen food packaging is polyethylene. It is moistureproof, has a low vapor transmission rate but a high transmission rate to other gases is tough and flexible at low temperatres, and can be heat sealed. Several shrink-on, breathing polyethylene films are adapted to contour packaging of fresh meats and poultry.

Polyvinylidene chloride films have low vapor and gas permeabilities which make them well suited for vacuum and gas packaging. They are either opaque or transparent, strong, tough, heat sealable, and can stand temperatures as high as 300° F for short periods. This makes them suitable as casings for products that are to be heat processed. Saran of DOW, CryOvac of W. R. Grace, and Perflex of Union Carbide are examples of this type of film, the latter being particularly adapted for articles of irregular shape about which they can be heat shrunk by dipping the vacuumized package in hot water to form a skin-tight covering. This type of bag is used to vacuum package primal and subprimal beef cuts for distribution to retail stores. In 1972, 43% of these cuts arrived in vacuum packages; this is expected to rise to 65% by 1977.

Another type of film, having a rubber base, is known by the trade name of Pliofilm (rubber-hydrochloride). Many types are made for special uses but it has not been employed to any appreciable extent as a wrap for frozen meats. The films have gained wide consumer acceptance as a preservative cover for fresh vegetables, particularly in the bag form. They lack the qualities sought as a cover for frozen foods in that they are difficult to handle and hard to mark for identification.

Manner of Wrapping

The most desirable method from the standpoint of maximum air seal is the apothecary or drug store wrap, although work at Kansas showed as good results with the use of the butchers' wrap, a quicker and more rugged method, which gives the package a double thickness of paper. With a little practice most people, and particularly the gentle sex, become quite proficient and speedy with the drug store wrap. It does not pay to economize on paper, either in quality or quantity.

It is highly important that cuts of meat be compact and as nearly square or rectangular in shape as possible. There should not be sharp edges of bone protruding to puncture the paper. Press the paper tightly to the meat to exclude all the air possible and make the entire job practically airtight. Place waxed paper between cuts if several are wrapped in the same package. An adhesive tape made especially for low temperatures is used in securing the package. It has the added advantage that the mark of identification can be placed on it. Heat sealing gives another advantage in that it excludes the air and does the binding at the same time. Ground meat should be compacted to exclude as much of the captured air as possible before wrapping. Waxed cartons or containers with inner bags or lining make suitable receptacles for diced and ground meats.

Temperature, Length of Storage, and Thawing

The lower the temperature, the longer the period of successful storage. Recommendations are definitely for zero or lower, the limiting factor being the cost of the equipment and the cost of maintaining the lower temperatures.

The length of the storage period should not be over 12 months, for economic reasons if for no other. With a proper wrap in good quality paper and a zero temperature, practically all "lean" meat will keep well for six to eight months with some exceptions. These exceptions have to do with products that contain salt, such as seasoned sausage, liver pudding, scrapple, sliced ham, and bacon slices. Table 17.2 summarizes the recommended storage times for red meat.

W. L. Sulzbacher, former bacteriologist for the USDA, reports: "There is no indication that frozen meat becomes more perishable after thawing than fresh meat."

Repeated tests made at the Pennsylvania station showed:

1. That meat which was thawed in the unopened package exceeded the keeping quality of unwrapped fresh meat.
2. That meat which was alternately thawed and refrozen as many as three times before being unwrapped was the equal of the meat used after one thawing.
3. That meat which was unwrapped and thawed and then rewrapped and refrozen was not materially changed in palatability

other than that it was slightly drier because of the juices it had lost.

There is no reason to hesitate to refreeze meat when occasion demands, but it should be done within the day. If it is to be used the following day, place it in the rear of the refrigerator rather than refreeze it for that short period. Thawing may be accomplished in various ways to suit the conditions, or the meat may be cooked in the frozen state, in which case it will require a slightly longer cooking period.

Table 17.2—Storage Time Chart[1]

(Maximum Storage Time Recommendations for Fresh,

Cooked, and Processed Meats[2])

Meat	Refrigerator (38° to 40° F)	Freezer (at 0° F or lower)
Beef (fresh)	2 to 4 days	6 to 12 months
Veal (fresh)	2 to 4 days	6 to 9 months
Pork (fresh)	2 to 4 days	3 to 6 months
Lamb (fresh)	2 to 4 days	6 to 9 months
Ground beef, veal, and lamb	1 to 2 days	3 to 4 months
Ground pork	1 to 2 days	1 to 3 months
Variety meats	1 to 2 days	3 to 4 months
Luncheon meats	1 week	not recommended
Sausage, fresh pork	1 week	60 days
Sausage, smoked	3 to 7 days	
Sausage, dry and semi-dry (unsliced)	2 to 3 weeks	
Frankfurters	4 to 5 days	
Bacon	5 to 7 days	
Smoked ham, whole	1 week	60 days
Smoked ham, slices	3 to 4 days	
Beef, corned	1 week	2 weeks
Leftover cooked meat	4 to 5 days	2 to 3 months
Frozen combination foods		
Meat pies (cooked)	—	3 months
Swiss steak (cooked)	—	3 months
Stews (cooked)	—	3 to 4 months
Prepared meat dinners	—	2 to 6 months

1. Lessons on Meat, National Live Stock and Meat Board.

2. The range in time reflects recommendations for maximum storage time from several authorities. For top quality, fresh meats should be used in two or three days, ground meat and variety meats should be used in 24 hours.

Freezer Storage of Seasoned Meats

Salt affects the rate of fat oxidation, causing cured meats or meat products seasoned with salt to acquire a flat, rancid taste in a shorter time than the unseasoned product. Whole hams, picnics, or butts properly wrapped in a good grade of locker paper will maintain the original flavor for two months or possibly more. However, half hams or sliced bacon will lose flavor within the month.

The freezer storage life of fresh sausage can be lengthened by omitting the seasoning, adding the seasoning after the sausage is thawed. The addition of an antioxidant such as BHA, BHT, or propyl gallate (see Chapter 6) inhibits oxidation and may be added to the sausage at the second grinding. Pork trimmings can be frozen for future sausage making, but the holding period should not exceed one month. Smoked sausage has longer storage life than fresh sausage.

Liver pudding, pon haus, and scrapple can be frozen, but the frozen product is inferior to the fresh. It is preferable to cover the pans or crocks containing the products with a half inch of hot lard and place them under refrigeration.

Preparing and Freezing Poultry

Broilers and fryers are cut into halves or quarters, and fowl can be left whole for roasting, cut into stewing joints, or boned. Cut up fowl is popular because second joints, drum sticks, and white meat can be packed separate from the less desirable wings, backs, and necks. It has the added advantage of compactness, eliminating the large body cavity which traps considerable air, thus requiring less storage space. Roasters frozen whole should have the excess internal fat removed as it will oxidize and become rancid far more rapidly than the rest of the fowl. Wrap the giblets in cellophane or foil and place inside the bird.

In large scale operations, poultry, turkey, ducks, geese, and other fowl are usually vacuum packed by placing the fowl in a CryOvac bag and exhausting the air by the use of a vacuum pump. The end of the bag is then made air-tight by placing a metal clamp around the opening. It is then immersed in hot water to give it a skin tight shrink. Zero storage will keep properly wrapped fowl edible for four to six months.

Freezing Eggs

Eggs may be frozen whole or as separate whites and yolks but they must be stirred enough to break the membranes but not enough to cause foaming. Freeze only strictly fresh eggs. Break each egg individually into a cup and, if sound, put it into a container with the good eggs. It requires eight broken eggs to fill a pint cup and they will weigh about a pound. Add one tablespoonful of corn syrup, honey, or sugar, or one teaspoonful of salt (depending upon how the eggs are to be used) to each two cups of broken whole eggs or broken egg yolks, stirring it in gently. This is necessary to prevent the eggs from becoming gummy. Use the best container available, one that is liquid-tight. They can be held at 0° F for one year. Thaw them in the container before using. Do not freeze cooked eggs, as they become tough and rubbery.

Freezing Fish

Fish, including shell fish, can be divided into two main groups based on the oil content of the flesh. The non-oily fish (less than 3% oil) store their oil in the liver rather than in the flesh and are represented by the cod, haddock, halibut, and swordfish, to mention a few. The

Table 17.3—Storage Period for Frozen Fish

Species	Round or Headed and Gutted	Wrapped, Packaged
Croaker	6–8 mo.	8–10 mo.
Grouper	6–8 mo.	8–10 mo.
Lake Herring	6–8 mo.	8–10 mo.
Ling Cod	6–8 mo.	8–10 mo.
Mackerel (Spanish and Boston)	6–8 mo.	8–10 mo.
Mullet	6–8 mo.	8–10 mo.
Red Snapper	6–8 mo.	8–10 mo.
Rockfish	6–8 mo.	8–10 mo.
Rosefish (Ocean Perch)	6–8 mo.	8–10 mo.
Sablefish	6–8 mo.	8–10 mo.
Salmon	6–8 mo.	8–10 mo.
Sea Trout	6–8 mo.	8–10 mo.
Shrimp	6–8 mo.	8–10 mo.
Cod	8–10 mo.	10–12 mo.
Flounder (Sole)	8–10 mo.	10–12 mo.
Haddock	8–10 mo.	10–12 mo.
Halibut	8–10 mo.	10–12 mo.
Pike (All Species)	8–10 mo.	10–12 mo.
Pollock	8–10 mo.	10–12 mo.
Porgie (Scup)	8–10 mo.	10–12 mo.
Sole	8–10 mo.	10–12 mo.
Whiting	8–10 mo.	10–12 mo.
Smelt	8–10 mo.	8–10 mo.
Whitefish	8–10 mo.	8–10 mo.

fatty group (over 3% oil) have the oil distributed throughout the flesh. Some representatives of this group are herring, mackerel, and salmon.

The chief type of spoilage in frozen fish, as in warm blooded animals, is caused by the oxidation of the fats resulting in rancidity. The action of bacteria and enzymes is inhibited by low temperatures, but air must be excluded if oxidation is to be held to a minimum. It is necessary, therefore, to wrap the eviscerated fish, either in the round (unsplit) or the fillet, in plastic film, excluding as much air as possible and freezing it at 0° F or below. Fish that are too large to be wrapped should be quick-frozen and dipped in cold water several times to cover them with a glaze of ice. The ice glaze will evaporate within several months unless the humidity of the holding room is very high. Reglazing or wrapping in moisture-vapor-proof material is then necessary. Frozen fish that has been well wrapped can be stored with other foods without imparting or transferring any odor or flavor to them.

Home Freezer Storage Units

Home freezer units are made in three popular styles referred to as:

1. The vertical, upright, or side door type.
2. The horizontal, top door, or cabinet type.
3. The refrigerator with built-in zero compartment.

The latter far outnumber the other two types, having been universally adopted by manufacturers of all the popular makes of household refrigerators.

The side door type has the outward appearance of the regular household refrigerator but the freezing element circulates through pipes between the walls, and in some models the pipes are in the shelves, making the shelf a freezer plate. The shelves are at a convenient height for easy access and visibility; the depth of the shelves does not require long arms or the use of tongs, and the space can be utilized efficiently. This model has been criticized by some for door leakage and spilling of cold air whenever the door is opened.

The top door (dunk-in) type has the advantage of less door leakage and practically no spillage of cold air but has the disadvantage of requiring reaching and stooping, and the food is rather inaccessible without considerable rearrangement. It also utilizes more floor space than the side door type. Most of them are designed with a −10° F sharp freeze compartment and a zero storage compartment. Both side and top door types are made in popular sizes ranging from 10 to 50 cubic feet capacity at prices varying from $25 to $60 per cubic foot.

Walk-in Storage Units

Manufactured units of this type usually are prefabricated at the plant and assembled on the owner's premises. The more popular practice is to buy the refrigerating unit and have local labor construct the refrigerator. This permits the owner a wider choice in capacity, and generally it is cheaper. The plan is to have a 35° room with either 4 inches of cork, 2 to 3 inches of spun glass, or 12 inches of planer shavings for insulation, and a zero room with 6 to 8 inches of cork, 4 inches of spun glass, or 18 inches of planer shavings for insulation. Another type consists of a 35° room in which a cabinet freezer is built. Single refrigerating machinery operated by a ½ to ¾ h.p. motor is proving satisfactory but it is advisable, whenever possible, to have a separate machine for each box. This will save closing down the plant in case one unit goes bad. Freon-12 gas is probably the most satisfactory refrigerant to use and forced air cooling units that are self-defrosting are in equal favor with gravity units. Sizes of 400 to 1,200 cubic feet capacity best suit the needs of farm familes.

Cryogenic Freezing

Methods of rapidly freezing meat are termed *cryogenic*. Various systems of producing cold are utilized.

The freezing system most closely resembling a conventional refrigerator or freezer employs a brine of −40° F circulating in a tank below and through plate fin coils above a stainless steel belt which carries the meat product through a chamber. Moist product (normally steaks, chops or patties) freezes instantly to the belt as it makes contact and later pops off at the end where the belt turns under to begin to return. Freezing capacities up to 3,600 pounds of 0° F product per hour are available.

Liquid nitrogen is used as the refrigerant in similar conveyor—tunnel—chamber arrangements and also is more widely used. Liquid nitrogen itself has a temperature of −320° F (−195° C), but very seldom is meat immersed directly into the liquid, rather, the liquid is placed under pressure of 15 to 22 psi and sprayed through nozzles over the product. The closer the product is to the nozzle, the nearer to −320° F is the temperature. Normally, freezing temperatures range from −100° F to −320° F.

Several modifications of this system are in use, from the tunnel food freezer described above to storage and transportation systems whereby containers, each equipped with a liquid nitrogen source, can be moved as units aboard ship, truck, or trailer throughout the marketing process. Such a transportation system, called the *Polarstream,* was developed by

Union Carbide Corporation, Linde Division and is illustrated in figure 17.10.

There are presently 8,000 cryogenic systems of this nature being used in the United States, accounting for only 2% of the total refrigeration in use. Compared with mechanical refrigeration systems, liquid nitrogen cryogenic freezing requires a lower initial investment in equipment (by a factor of 4), and requires less maintenance, operation, and power cost. Yet if the conventional system is used consistently at 80% capacity, the overall cost will be one-half as much as the cyrogenic system due to the cost of the liquid nitrogen. Further advantages of the cryogenic system, however, tend to balance the cost ledger. With the rapid freezing, product shrink (evaporation) is less than .5% versus 2% to 8% in the conventional system. A higher quality product results because of the finer ice crystals fromed within the cells meaning less drip, more desirable color, and truer flavor. Shelf life is increased because handling by people is cut down, thus microbial growth is lessened. The cryogenic system is more flexible, especially for shrimp, hamburger, chicken, and specialty gourmet items. Thus it appears as if its use will expand.

Fig. 17.10—The Polarstream "Sea Haul" system. Approximately 1,200 of these systems are being used to transport meat from Australia and New Zealand to the United States and Canada. The intact unit shown here was transferred from the ship to this truck. (Courtesy, Union Carbide Corporation, Linde Division)

Another refrigerant becoming more widely used is dry ice (CO_2), which has a sublimation temperature (temperature at which it changes from solid to gas) of $-108°$ F ($-78°$ C). Pellets of dry ice and dry ice snow are used in the new "boxed" beef and lamp shipments and in edible offal shipments. The CO_2 is either sprinkled in the box with the product or included in the box separately in a perforated bag which slows evaporation of the pellets. Dry ice is also used in cooling coarse ground meat during chopping. Mention was made earlier in this chapter of the injection of CO_2 snow into the deep pelvic joint to prevent bone souring in heavy carcasses. The above uses of CO_2 are all taking place at Monfort of Colorado's large beef and lamb processing plant in Greeley and in many other plants across the nation.

CHAPTER 18

Meat Merchandising

THE SOURCE OF SUPPLY

During 1972, the meat produced in the United States was 94.5% of the total red meat handled—the other 5.5% being imported. Beef imports were largely from Australia, New Zealand, Argentina, Mexico, Canada, Brazil, and Ireland; pork largely from the Netherlands, Denmark, Canada, and Poland; lamb from Australia and New Zealand. The present trend is to require by law that all imported meat and meat products be labeled with the country of their origin and to require retailers to display signs indicating that such meat is imported. Ever since the inception of meat inspection, all imported meats have to be passed by APHIS before they can be sold or used in the United States (see Chapter 3).

Marketing practices have changed considerably from the days of John Pynchon who is reputed to be the first meat packer in the United States (Springfield, Massachusetts, 1641). The packing industry moved westward with the railroads. Cities such as Cincinnati, Chicago, and Kansas City became large packing centers. Herds of cattle were driven on foot for long distances to railroad loading points to be shipped to market. Much of the glamorized history of our West centers around railroads, Indians, settlers, gold, cowboys, and cattle drives.

As livestock production moved westward from eastern population centers, distribution became a problem that was solved in 1880 by the invention of the refrigerator car. Unlike the mechanically refrigerated car of today, these cars were cooled from ice bunkers (ice and salt) built into each end of the car. These bunkers had to be refilled at different points along the route. A number of cars were derailed because the suspended quarters of beef began to sway. Efficient insulation had not yet been devised. But problems are made to be solved and they were. Today the modern refrigerator car has been supplemented and partially displaced by mechanically refrigerated trucks which can deliver the maximum load prescribed by the states through which they travel.

Large stockyards were constructed to receive live shipments. Commission houses and banking facilities were necessary adjuncts for the buying and selling operation. Meat packers had their buyers at the large centers or operated through brokers. It was to govern illegal practices in the buying and selling of livestock that the Packers and Stockyards Act was passed. Contract buying became popular, under which livestock came direct to the packer holding pens, eliminating the middleman. As trucking livestock took over, buyers went directly to the farmer or feeder or to the auction which had become popular in livestock communities the country over. In recent years the practice of dealing in futures has taken hold.

Packing houses which originally stood on the outskirts of towns found themselves practically in the centers of cities. Many plants had become obsolete, traffic conditions were slow, taxes increased with land values, and to keep the business profitable, a movement of dismantling old plants and erecting modern ones closer to the areas of production got started. This had an added advantage in that it cut down transportation costs. That is the story to now.

THE MEAT PACKER AND PROCESSOR

A *packer* is defined as a wholesale provisioner who packs for retail distribution. In the broadest sense, a meat packer starts with a live animal and performs the necessary steps to make it edible and usable by man. These consist of slaughtering, chilling, and processing. Not all packers are processors. Only the plants with a large kill do most of their own processing.

A processor is generally a specialist who manufactures strictly pork products or beef products or a combination of both. The products are varied and numerous and lend themselves to specialization even if it is only in the seasoning alone. The curing of hams by a special formula is an example of a one-item business.

Large-scale meat packers doing interstate business have branch houses for distribution purposes. The independent packer operates on a smaller scale and does business in a much smaller territory—not very often interstate. Packers doing slaughtering sell carcasses, primal or subprimal wholesale cuts, to wholesalers, retailers, processors, boners, breakers, and hotel supply houses. The chain stores (supermarkets) are large buyers of beef, veal, and lamb carcasses, since most do their own fabricating.

HOTEL-RESTAURANT INSTITUTIONAL (HRI) INDUSTRY

HRI is a rapidly expanding industry. Today, one out of every four meals is eaten away from home.[1] Based on 1970 figures, 10.7% of these meals were breakfasts, 45.8% lunches, 21.2% dinners, and 22.1% snacks. Distribution of the industry by establishment shows: restaurants, 58.3%; hotels/motels, 4.2%; hospitals/nursing homes, 6.3%; colleges and universities 5.0%; school systems, 13.6%; commercial/industrial, 4.9%; clubs, 1.0%; and specialized and other military, 6.8%.

Total food and non-alcoholic purchases and sales for the present and projected future appear in Table 18.1. As can be seen, the phenomenal growth pattern of the past few years is expected to continue.

Table 18.1—The Market for Food Away from Home[1]

Annual Gross Sales Volume and Annual Food and Non-Alcoholic Beverage Purchases (in Millions)

Year	Purchases	Sales[2]
1971	$17,546	$43,865
1975	24,746	61,866
1980	32,470	81,175

1. Representatives of Devro, Inc., Somerville, New Jersey, at 1973 Independent Meat Packers Association and American Meat Institute Annual Meetings.

2. Non-Commercial establishment "Sales" computed at retail sales equivalent.

A USDA study has shown that meat accounts for almost 32% of the dollar value of the HRI purchases (those listed in table 18.1). Beef equals 69.2% of the total meat, and the most popular beef products are: ground meat, 30.8%; roasts, 13.7%; and steak, 35%. Other meats equal 30.8% of the total meat, the most demanded being hams, 17%; weiners, 12%; sausage, 10%; and bacon, 10%.

---

1. Representatives of Devro, Inc., Somerville, New Jersey at 1973 Independent Meat Packers Association and American Meat Institute Annual Meetings.

The well established brokers and the distributors still provide the major channels of distribution, but there are two exceptions:

1. There is a growing trend for direct sales of packers to chains, multiple unit group and food service management firms, currently representing around 16% of food purchases.
2. A great deal of restaurant food is still purchased at the retail level. For example, 20% of the 39,000 restaurants doing between $1,000 and $2,000 per week, and 40% of the 46,000 counter-type restaurants buy their meat at retail.

Thus HRI is a significant part of the meat industry.

THE MEAT RETAILER

There are comparatively few retail meat markets where meat and meat products, poultry, eggs, butter, cheese, and milk are practically the sole items. The owners and operators of the successful ones are men who sell quality and dependability, spiced with personal attention and community banter. They are the men in white who call their customers by name, inquire about the family, make purchase suggestions, and are able to give competent information as to the preparation of the various cuts of meat. They are "The Vanishing Meat Merchandisers."

Specialty Shops

These shops may not handle fresh meats but specialize in various brands of sausage (dry and semi-dry), cured smoked meats, domestic and foreign varieties of cheese, meat supplements, meat sauces, tenderizers, condiments, and various items that are relevant but different. Most specialty shops bear names indicative of the products handled; examples are "Smoke House," "Sausage Shop," "Gourmet Cave," etc. The profit potential of these shops is excellent. Spoilage is low and labor costs are normal. These shops are selective in their buying and are in search for the unusual. They experience some difficulty in getting some items because they do not buy in large quantities unless they are a chain. Some of these shops furnish their own recipes to a processor who makes the product for them.

Combination Meat and Grocery Store

This type comprises a lessening percentage of the food stores in the nation. It is generally family owned and operated. It carries most of the needs of the community, is generally crowded for space, and usually lacks coordination in spacing and arrangement. Green goods are not its specialty. Standard brands of shelf goods prevail. Meats are usually limited to one grade. Because the volume of meat handled in many instances is low, a lower grade of meat will have to be marketed to meet competitive chain store prices.

Chain Stores or Supermarkets

The present-day supermarket is the hub of a shopping center. It is a woman's joy but an enigma to man, even though man devised it. Regardless of all the signs giving locations of various items, unless you are a regular customer and know from experience where everything is, it is sheer gambling to locate jar rubbers. Of course, you can sometimes tail a supply clerk for a fifth of a mile, but if your wife can find them, surely you can without the pursuit. Speed and time are no longer factors after the second lap. It has come to castigation and stigmatism, or surrender. Along the last aisle on the third lap you hear a voice: "May I help you, sir?" With considerable effort at self-control, you turn slowly toward the voice and hiss: "Could you direct me to the nearest store that sells jar rubbers?"

"Right in front of you, sir," says the voice pointing to the very spot at which you had been staring. You mumble in your beard and swear that—or just swear.

Meat Section (Supermarket)

The open refrigerated cases present a sea of appetizing meat and meat products. The wonder to children is why it is cold when they insert their hands in the case. You inform them that cold air is heavier than warm air and cannot escape. The surface of the cold air is in contact with the warm air and by diffusion absorbs some heat, but the refrigerated coils in the side of the case keep an even temperature to the air that is below the level of the top of the case.

Meats are displayed wrapped in PVC film that is sealed to a backboard. The cut of meat is placed on a suitable sized backboard and covered with a square of film of the proper size. This is then deposited on a conveyor which moves through a folding and sealing machine. The conveyor drops the sealed package onto an automatic scale that stamps the net weight and total price on an adhesive-backed stamp used for the particular cut that is being weighed. The name of the cut and the price per pound had been previously placed on the tag.

The arrangement of meats follows a pattern that is more or less standard. They are segregated as to kind (pork, beef, veal, lamb, poultry) and type of cut (steak, roast, ground beef, etc.). Smoked meats have separate display space as do fish, liver, and specialty items. Supermarkets account for 90% of grocery store sales of fresh beef.

The manager of the meats department directs and inspects the placement of the product into the self-service cases. The meat must be fresh in appearance, identifiable, and properly arranged. Hidden fat and excessive, partially visible bone is not conducive to a resale. A clerk behind the display cases adds a personal touch and furnishes a source of information for timid and uninformed customers.

The store manager should receive better sales promotion ideas. The meat department might suggest that it put on a meal-a-week sale. Example: Use one end of the refrigerated meat case nearest incoming patron traffic. The meal of the week, in a size that can be easily read from a distance of 30 feet, is placed at eye level as a backwall for the menu ingredients.

T & Z Meal of the Week		
Spare ribs	Sauerkraut	Mashed Potatoes
Jello Salad		Hot Rolls
Half Grapefruit		Coffee

Refrigerated	Shelves
Case	Bins

All the articles necessary to make the suggested meal are in the immediate area of the menu. Think of the possibilities this might present in moving different food items. This display could be supplemented with information on the preparation of the meal.

Important factors, other than low temperatures, in maintaining color and freshness in meats are cleanliness and proper sanitation. Contaminated meats have a short life. The washing and steam sterilizing of all the equipment each working day are a must. All workers coming on the job must make it a habit to wash their hands with the proper soap provided in the lavatory. Shop hand towels should be changed daily. Women workers should be required to have their nails short and free of nail polish. Meat cutters should have clean nails and wear white sanitary hair covers, with all who need them wearing hair nets.

PURCHASING (WHOLESALE)

Large chains generally have a central procurement office. The tie-in of the various stores to the main office is through district managers under whom the individual store managers operate. The procurement staff must be men of integrity who have had a vast and knowledgable experience in their particular field.

Although much of the business is done by telephone where standard packaged goods are concerned, the perishable goods present some problems that make it necessary for the buyers to be at the market. This is often the case with the meat buyer who will find it necessary under abnormal marketing conditions to be on hand to consummate deals that are advantageous to the company. Chains have selective privileges because of the large tonnage they are able to buy; and with this is the strong bargaining power they can wield because of quantity buying.

Their fresh meats are bought on a grade basis, mainly the U.S. Choice quality grade, and a yield grade specification of 2 or 3 is often made. Good grade beef may be purchased which they fabricate and sell under their own brand names. Chains and independents also are buyers of prize beef at fairs and particularly of "4-H Club" steers. These cattle are custom slaughtered in the immediate area or trucked to a packer having Federal inspection if the meat is to be shipped interstate.

Less than one-half of the beef, veal, and lamb carcasses are fabricated at the individual stores. Central fabrication and packaging of primal and subprimal cuts is becoming the major distribution channel (see chapters 13 and 17).

MEAT PRICING

The cost of the product, the cost of operating the business, and the desired net profit are the factors that enter into meat pricing. This is based on the assumption that the customer potential and parking facilities are adequate and the quality of the meat is in line with consumer demand. If you don't have customers, you don't need prices.

Whether sales prices are figured on a percentage basis or cents-per-pound markup, it is necessary to have available figures on cutting tests of the various wholesale cuts of the respective grades made according to the style of cutting used in the shop. More than one test is necessary to strike an average. In time these tests will become more meaningful and will not have to be continued other than to make occasional check tests.

Excellent aids in pricing relationships and cutting test examples can be secured from the National Live Stock and Meat Board, attention Ken Johnson, Merchandising Director.

A valuable lesson in the dangers of price cutting appears in Table 18.2.

Table 18.2.—Dangers of Price Cutting

Sometimes it is difficult to convince price cutters of the troubles that follow adventures in this field of commercial enterprise. The disease is likened to a creeping paralysis which suddenly catches the victim unaware and without warning.

A simple break-even chart, such as the one below, conveys the message very clearly that for the few that make any gain from price cutting a tremendous number completely fail.

If you cut your price by: (%)		Present gross profit is:								
		5	10	15	20	25	30	35	40	45
						--(%)--				
1	You will	25.0	11.1	7.1	5.3	4.2	3.4	2.9	2.6	2.3
2	need to	66.6	25.0	15.5	11.1	8.7	7.1	6.1	5.3	4.6
3	increase	150.0	42.8	25.0	17.6	13.6	11.1	9.4	8.1	7.1
4	unit	400.0	66.6	36.4	25.0	19.0	15.4	12.9	11.1	9.7
5	sales by:	—	100.0	50.0	33.3	25.0	20.0	16.7	14.3	12.5
6		—	150.0	66.7	42.9	31.6	25.0	20.7	17.6	15.4
7		—	233.3	87.5	53.8	38.9	30.4	25.0	21.2	18.4
8		—	400.0	114.3	66.7	47.1	36.4	29.6	25.0	21.6
9		—	1,000.0	150.0	81.8	56.3	42.9	34.6	29.0	25.0
10		—	—	200.0	100.0	66.7	50.0	40.0	33.3	28.6
11		—	—	275.0	122.2	78.6	57.9	45.8	37.9	32.3
12		—	—	400.0	150.0	92.3	66.7	52.2	42.9	36.4
13		—	—	650.0	185.7	108.3	76.5	59.1	48.1	40.6
14		—	—	1,400.0	233.3	127.3	87.5	66.7	53.8	45.2
15		—	—	—	300.0	150.0	100.0	75.0	60.0	50.0
16		—	—	—	400.0	177.8	114.3	84.2	66.7	55.2

(Continued)

Table 18.2 (Continued)

If you cut your price by:	Present gross profit is:	5	10	15	20	25	30	35	40	45
(%)						(%)				
17	You will need to increase unit sales by:	—	—	—	566.7	212.5	130.8	94.4	73.9	60.7
18		—	—	—	900.0	257.1	150.0	105.9	81.8	66.6
19		—	—	—	1,900.0	316.7	172.7	118.8	90.5	73.1
20		—	—	—	—	400.0	200.0	133.3	100.0	80.0

An example of the use of the chart is as follows:

QUESTION: If your present gross profit is 35% and you cut your selling prices by 10%, by how much do you have to increase your sales so that the same amount of gross profit is obtained?

ANSWER: On the chart, follow along the line from 10% on the left side of the chart to the figures in column under 35%. Read off the figure 40%. This means that you will have to increase your sales by 40% in order to continue to make your original gross profit.

Cutting Test

Table 18.3 shows a cutting test made on a Choice grade beef fore-quarter as explained in the text. All the cuts are boneless with the exception of the ribs and shortribs. Boneless beef has increased in popularity, but with the increase in beef prices, bone-in cuts move more readily because they bear a lower price tag.

Table 18.3—Cutting Test

Material: Forequarter   Grade: Y.G. 3, Choice
Cutting Wt.:   159 Lbs.   Billed Wt.:   160 Lbs.
Cost per Lb.:   49¢   Total Cost: $78.40

Cut	Pounds	Percent	Retail Price per Lb.	Sales Value
			- - - -($)- - - -	
Boneless				
Shoulder pot roast (outside or arm)	14.1	9	1.10	15.51
Chuck eye (inside or roll)	17.3	11	1.25	21.63
Brisket	8.0	5	.85	6.80
Ground meat	41.2	26	.80	32.96
Fat	33.6	21	.02	.67
Bone	23.8	15	.01	.24
Bone-in				
Short cut standing rib	15.9	10	1.37	21.78
Short ribs	4.8	3	.87	4.18
Total	158.7	100		103.77

Percentages are determined by dividing the weight of each retail cut by the weight of the wholesale cut. Eliminate fractions of a percent.

Gross sales $103.77 minus total cost $78.40 gives a gross margin of $25.37 which is 24% of the gross sales or 32% of the cost. The gross margin must cover all the prorated operating expenses including the owner's salary and net profit, if any. The money left over after covering all meat invoices and expenses is what the business earns, or net profit.

When a retailer says that he is just making a living at the business he means that he is meeting operating expenses and making a varying salary for himself with no net profit.

In the above cutting test, the retail price per pound was determined on the basis of the demand for, the intrinsic value of, and the general price trend in the competitive market. They are also the juggle figures. Slow-moving items or a buildup in some inventories may require specials which will require a price load shift to other fast-moving items.

Three Methods of Pricing

1. Markup on the basis of percentage of *gross sales*.
2. Markup on the basis of percentage of *cost*.
3. Markup on the basis of *cents per pound*.

The necessary materials to do the job are the figures from the cutting tests, the invoices, the cash sales records, and the record of operating expenditures.

To illustrate what is involved, let us use an actual case of one-month's business in a retail market where the meat department expenses were prorated with the food and miscellaneous section.

Reduced to round numbers:

```
Total meat sales...................................$7,800
Total cost of meat sold...........................$6,000
Gross margin .....................................$1,800
Total operating expenses..........................$1,750
Percent of gross sales ($7,800 divided into $1,800)........23.7
Percent of cost ($6,000 divided into $1,800)..............30.0
Percent operating cost ($7,800 divided into $1,750).......22.5
Tonnage 10,900 lbs. (averaging 55¢ per lb.)...........$6,000
Markup per lb.—16½ cts. (10,900 lbs. x 16½ cts.)........$1,800
```

It is interesting to note how closely the percentage markup on gross sales and on cost coincides with those of the cutting test. The bug in the ointment is the cents-per-pound when applied to invoice weight. In the cutting test it will be noted that 21% was fat and 15% was bone, a waste item of 57.4 pounds or 36% for that method of cutting. Deduct (in round figures) this 57 pounds from the 159 pounds, resulting in 102 pounds of salable meat which divided into the invoiced cost $78.40 changes the cost price per pound from 49 cents to 77 cents per pound. It is quite evident that on fabricated meats, a markup on the basis of cents per pound on the wholesale cost is meaningless. It must be based on the cost per pound of salable meat.

The percent of operating cost to gross sales varies with the management and the volume. It has practically doubled in the past quarter-century and now averages about 24% of gross sales and is still climbing.

CHAPTER 19

Meat as a Food

The word *meat,* when used as a general food term, has a rather broad implication. In this text its meaning is limited to the edible and inedible parts of the carcass of mammals and their organs and glands.

STRUCTURE OF MEAT

The edible meat of carcasses is composed primarily of striated or voluntary muscles which are for the most part connected directly or indirectly with the skeleton and referred to as skeletal muscles. A special variety of striated muscle that is involuntary in action is the cardiac muscle of the heart. A type common to the organs of the intestinal tract are the involuntary, non-striated, or smooth muscles, commonly referred to as the visceral muscles. Fat, nerves, veins, arteries, ligaments, and tendons are an integral part of a combination of muscles and must be considered as meat.

The edible organs and glands are designated as glandular meats or variety meats to contrast them with the muscle meats of the voluntary muscles. They consist of the heart, tongue, liver, pancreas (sweetbread), thymus (veal sweetbread), kidney, spleen, brain, and the walls of the stomach (tripe).

Muscles are made up of cylindrical, multinucleate muscle fibers of varying lengths, composed of sarcoplasm and enclosed in a sheath of sarcolemma. Bundles of these muscle fibers or fasciculi are enclosed in a tissue called perimysium and the entire muscle is in turn covered by a sheath of more or less compact connective tissue called the epimysium (Note Figure 19.1). It becomes increasingly evident from this brief histological description that the smaller and more numerous the muscles, the greater the amount of connective tissue. Since connective tissues are far less tender than the cell contents, it follows that their presence in large quantities characterizes the less tender cuts.

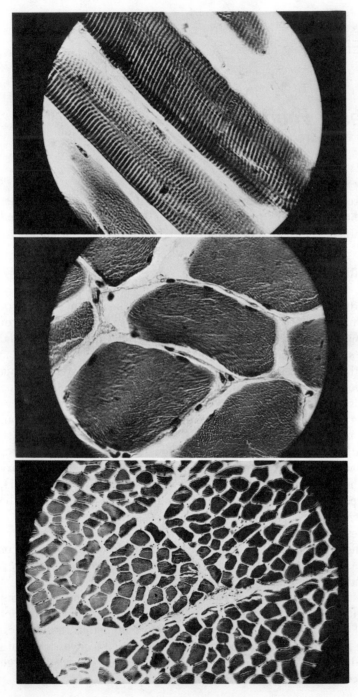

Fig. 19.1.—(Left) A cross section of the "bottom round" (*biceps femoris*) muscle showing four bundles of muscle cells separated by the connective tissue, perimysium, x 40. (Center) A section of the picture to the left showing several muscle cells surrounded by the connective tissue, sarcolemma. The black dots on the very edge of the muscle cells are the cell nuclei, x 200. (Right) A longitudinal section of the "top round" muscle, showing the striation of the cells which is characteristic of a skeletal muscle, x 100.

COMPOSITION OF MEAT

Table 19.1 gives nutrient values of the edible portion of meat, poultry, and fish products. A recent publication by Murphy, Watt, and Rizek[1] describes concisely the present state of nutrient tables and how they can be best utilized. It is recommended for the student interested in the complete detail of food composition. As indicated in previous chapters, the composition of our meat animals, and thus their carcasses and the meat we eat, has changed and continues to change toward a leaner, higher protein product. When utilizing a nutrient table, be sure that it is not outdated.

Proteins

Lean muscle consists of approximately 20% protein, 70% water, 9% fat, and 1% ash. These proportions change as the animal is fattened, resulting in a lessening in the percentage of protein and water and a proportionate increase in fat.

The major protein in muscle is actomyosin, a globulin that consists of two proteins, actin and myosin, combined in a ratio of 1 to 3. It is the structural component that gives muscle the power of movement. Muscle is also made up of collagen (connective tissue) that is the basis of structure and the most widely distributed protein in the animal body. Two lesser connective tissue proteins are elastin and reticulin. Muscle also contains pigments that give color to meat, such as the more prominent *myoglobin, nucleoproteins* which control heritable characteristics of the cell, and the many *enzymes* that perform a catalytic function for almost every reaction in the living cell. In addition there are many other functional proteins.

Another group of proteins that are really end-products of protein metabolism are the water soluble proteins or *nitrogenous extractives*. They have little nutritive value in themselves but are physical and chemical stimulants in that they excite the flow of gastric juice. Along with fat, they provide a great deal of the aroma and flavor of meat. Because of this stimulating effect, broths are served as the first course to prepare the stomach for the heavier food to follow. Examples of this group of proteins are creatine, creatinine, and the purines. More of these proteins are present in older animals, and they are particularly abundant in the much exercised or less tender cuts. They impart to game animals that so-called "gamey flavor."

---

1. Tables of Food Composition: Availability, Uses and Limitations, *Food Technology*, 27:40-51, 1973.

Table 19.1.—Nutritive Values of the Edible Part of Meat and Poultry[1]

(Dashes in the columns for nutrients show that no suitable value could be found although there is reason to believe that a measurable amount of the nutrient may be present)

Food, Approximate Measure, and Weight (in Grams)	Water	Food Energy	Protein	Fat (Total)	Fatty Acids Saturated (Total)	Unsaturated Oleic	Unsaturated Linoleic	Carbohydrate	Calcium	Iron	Vitamin A Value	Thiamin	Riboflavin	Niacin	Ascorbic Acid
(gm)	(%)	(cal)	(gm)	(gm)	(gm)	(gm)	(gm)	(gm)	(mg)	(mg)	(IU)	(mg)	(mg)	(mg)	(mg)
Bacon (20 slices per lb. 2 slices raw), broiled or fried crisp - - - - - - - 15	8	90	5	8	3	4	1	1	2	.5	0	.08	.05	.8	—
Beef,[2] cooked:															
Cuts braised, simmered, or pot roasted:															
Lean and fat - - - 3 ounces - - - - 85	53	245	23	16	8	7	Trace	0	10	2.9	30	.04	.18	3.5	—
Lean only - - - - 2.5 ounces - - - - 72	62	140	22	5	2	2	Trace	0	10	2.7	10	.04	.16	3.3	—
Hamburger (ground beef), broiled:															
Lean - - - - - 3 ounces - - - - - 85	60	185	23	10	5	4	Trace	0	10	3.0	20	.08	.20	5.1	—
Regular - - - - - 3 ounces - - - - - 85	54	245	21	17	8	8	Trace	0	9	2.7	30	.07	.18	4.6	—
Roast, oven-cooked, no liquid added:															
Relatively fat, such as rib:															
Lean and fat - - - 3 ounces - - - - 85	40	375	17	34	16	15	1	0	8	2.2	70	.05	.13	3.1	—
Lean only - - - - 1.8 ounces - - - - 51	57	125	14	7	3	3	Trace	0	6	1.8	10	.04	.11	2.6	—
Relatively lean, such as heel of round:															
Lean and fat - - - 3 ounces - - - - 85	62	165	25	7	3	3	Trace	0	11	3.2	10	.06	.19	4.5	—
Lean only - - - - 2.7 ounces - - - - 78	65	125	24	3	1	1	Trace	0	10	3.0	Trace	.06	.18	4.3	—
Steak, broiled:															
Relatively fat, such as sirloin:															
Lean and fat - - - 3 ounces - - - - 85	44	330	20	27	13	12	1	0	9	2.5	50	.05	.16	4.0	—
Lean only - - - - 2.0 ounces - - - - 56	59	115	18	4	2	2	Trace	0	7	2.2	10	.05	.14	3.6	—
Relatively lean, such as round:															
Lean and fat - - - 3 ounces - - - - 85	55	220	24	13	6	6	Trace	0	10	3.0	20	.07	.19	4.8	—
Lean only - - - - 2.4 ounces - - - - 68	61	130	21	4	2	2	Trace	0	9	2.5	10	.06	.16	4.1	—

(Continued)

Table 19.1 (Continued)

Food, Approximate Measure, and Weight (in Grams)	Weight (gm)	Water (%)	Food Energy (cal)	Pro-tein (gm)	Fat (gm)	Satu-rated (Total) (gm)	Unsaturated Oleic (gm)	Unsaturated Lin-oleic (gm)	Carbo-hy-drate (gm)	Cal-cium (mg)	Iron (mg)	Vita-min A Value (IU)	Thia-min (mg)	Ribo-flavin (mg)	Niacin (mg)	Ascor-bic Acid (mg)
Beef, canned:																
Corned beef - - - - - - - 3 ounces - - -	85	59	185	22	10	5	4	Trace	0	17	3.7	20	.01	.20	2.9	—
Chicken, cooked:																
Flesh only, broiled - - - - 3 ounces - - -	85	71	115	20	3	1	1	1	0	8	1.4	80	.05	.16	7.4	—
Breast, fried, 1/2 breast:																
With bone - - - - - 3.3 ounces - -	94	58	155	25	5	1	2	1	1	9	1.3	70	.04	.17	11.2	—
Flesh and skin only - 2.7 ounces - -	76	58	155	25	5	1	2	1	1	9	1.3	70	.04	.17	11.2	—
Drumstick, fried:																
With bone - - - - - 2.1 ounces - -	59	55	90	12	4	1	2	1	Trace	6	.9	50	.03	.15	2.7	—
Flesh and skin only - - 1.3 ounces - -	38	55	90	12	4	1	2	1	Trace	6	.9	50	.03	.15	2.7	—
Chicken, canned, boneless - 3 ounces - -	85	65	170	18	10	3	4	2	0	18	1.3	200	.03	.11	3.7	3
Heart, beef, lean, braised - 3 ounces - -	85	61	160	27	5	—	—	—	1	5	5.0	20	.21	1.04	6.5	1
Lamb, cooked:																
Chop, thick, with bone,																
1 chop, broiled - - - - 4.8 ounces - -	137	47	400	25	33	18	12	1	0	10	1.5	—	.14	.25	5.6	—
Lean and fat - - - - 4.0 ounces - -	112	47	400	25	33	18	12	1	0	10	1.5	—	.14	.25	5.6	—
Lean only - - - - 2.6 ounces - -	74	62	140	21	6	3	2	Trace	0	9	1.5	—	.11	.20	4.5	—
Leg, roasted:																
Lean and fat - - - - 3 ounces - -	85	54	235	22	16	9	6	Trace	0	9	1.4	—	.13	.23	4.7	—
Lean only - - - - 2.5 ounces - -	71	62	130	20	5	3	2	Trace	0	9	1.4	—	.12	.21	4.4	—
Shoulder, roasted:																
Lean and fat - - - - 3 ounces - -	85	50	285	18	23	13	8	1	0	9	1.0	—	.11	.20	4.0	—
Lean only - - - - - 2.3 ounces - -	64	61	130	17	6	3	2	Trace	0	8	1.0	—	.10	.18	3.7	—
Liver, beef, fried - - - 2 ounces - -	57	57	130	15	6	—	—	—	3	6	5.0	30,280	.15	2.37	9.4	15
Pork, cured, cooked:																
Ham, light cure,																
lean and fat, roasted - - 3 ounces - -	85	54	245	18	19	7	8	2	0	8	2.2	0	.40	.16	3.1	—

(Continued)

Table 19.1 (Continued)

Food, Approximate Measure, and Weight (in Grams)	(gm)	Water (%)	Food Energy (cal)	Protein (gm)	Fat (gm)	Fatty Acids Saturated (Total) (gm)	Unsaturated Oleic (gm)	Linoleic (gm)	Carbohydrate (gm)	Calcium (mg)	Iron (mg)	Vitamin A Value (IU)	Thiamin (mg)	Riboflavin (mg)	Niacin (mg)	Ascorbic Acid (mg)
Luncheon meat:																
Boiled ham, sliced - - - 2 ounces - - -	57	59	135	11	10	4	4	1	0	6	1.6	0	.25	.09	1.5	—
Canned, spiced or unspiced - - - 2 ounces - - -	57	55	165	8	14	5	6	1	1	5	1.2	0	.18	.12	1.6	—
Pork, fresh,2 cooked:																
Chop, thick, with bone,																
1 chop, broiled - - - - 3.5 ounces - -	98	42	260	16	21	8	9	2	0	8	2.2	0	.63	.18	3.8	—
Lean and fat - - - - 2.3 ounces - -	66	42	260	16	21	8	9	2	0	8	2.2	0	.63	.18	3.8	—
Lean only - - - - - 1.7 ounces - -	48	53	130	15	7	2	3	1	0	7	1.9	0	.54	.16	3.3	—
Roast, oven-cooked, no liquid added:																
Lean and fat - - - - 3 ounces - -	85	46	310	21	24	9	10	2	0	9	2.7	0	.78	.22	4.7	—
Lean only - - - - 2.4 ounces - -	68	55	175	20	10	3	4	1	0	9	2.6	0	.73	.21	4.4	—
Cuts, simmered:																
Lean and fat - - - - 3 ounces - -	85	46	320	20	26	9	11	2	0	8	2.5	0	.46	.21	4.1	—
Lean only - - - - 2.2 ounces - -	63	60	135	18	6	2	3	1	0	8	2.3	0	.42	.19	3.7	—
Sausage:																
Bologna, slice, 3-in. diam. by 1/8 inch - 2 slices - - -	26	56	80	3	7	—	!	—	Trace	2	.5	—	.04	.06	.7	—
Braunschweiger, slice, 2-in. diam. by 1/4 inch - 2 slices - -	20	53	65	3	5	—	—	—	Trace	2	1.2	1,310	.03	.29	1.6	—
Deviled ham, canned - - - - 1 tbsp - - -	13	51	45	2	4	2	2	Trace	0	1	.3	—	.02	.01	.2	—
Frankfurter, heated (8 per lb. purchased pkg.) - - - 1 frank	56	57	170	7	15	—	—	—	1	3	.8	—	.08	.11	1.4	—
Pork links, cooked (16 links per lb. raw) - - 2 links	26	35	125	5	11	4	5	1	Trace	2	.6	0	.21	.09	1.0	—
Salami, dry type - - - - 1 ounce - - -	28	30	130	7	11	—	—	—	Trace	4	1.0	—	.10	.07	1.5	—

(Continued)

Table 19.1 (Continued)

Food, Approximate Measure, and Weight (in Grams)		Water	Food Energy	Protein	Fat	Fatty Acids			Carbohydrate	Calcium	Iron	Vitamin A Value	Thiamin	Riboflavin	Niacin	Ascorbic Acid
						Saturated (Total)	Unsaturated Oleic	Unsaturated Linoleic								
	(gm)	(%)	(cal)	(gm)	(gm)	(gm)	(gm)	(gm)	(gm)	(mg)	(mg)	(IU)	(mg)	(mg)	(mg)	(mg)
Salami, cooked - - - - - - 1 ounce - - - -	28	51	90	5	7	—	—	—	Trace	3	.7	—	.07	.07	1.2	—
Vienna, canned (7 sausages per 5-ounce can) - - - - 1 sausage - -	16	63	40	2	3	—	—	—	Trace	1	.3	—	.01	.02	.4	—
Veal, medium fat, cooked, bone removed:																
Cutlet - - - - - - - - - 3 ounces - -	85	60	185	23	9	5	4	Trace	—	9	2.7	—	.06	.21	4.6	—
Roast - - - - - - - - - 3 ounces - -	85	55	230	23	14	7	6	Trace	0	10	2.9	—	.11	.26	6.6	—

1. USDA Home and Garden Bulletin No. 72 (Revised, 1970).

2. Outer layer of fat on the cut was removed to within approximately 1/2 inch of the lean. Deposits of fat within the cut were not removed.

Proteins are changed by the digestive juices into amino acids in which form they are readily absorbed into the blood stream. To date there are 23 recognized amino acids, 10 of which are considered essential to life. In the following list, the letter (E) designates those considered essential: Glycine, alanine, serine, valine (E), leucine (E), isoleucine (E), norleucine, threonine (E), aspartic acid, glutamic acid, hydroxy glutamic acid, arginine (E), lysine (E), cystine, methionine (E), phenyl-alanine (E), tyrosine, iodgorgoic acid, thyroxine, histidine (E), proline, hydroxy proline, and tryptophane (E).

It is noteworthy that all of the essential amino acids have been found prevalent in the heart, liver, kidney, and muscle tissue.

The ability of the human body to resist disease is dependent upon its ability to produce antibodies—substances which attack specific foreign bodies. Using new analytical methods, scientists discovered that the anti-body molecule is actually a molecule of globulin (a class of proteins). Since the blood globulin, as well as the albumins, is built up from the amino acids in food, it suggests to the scientist that the same conditions must apply for the proper synthesis of antibody globulin. Work completed at this writing has given proof that supplying sufficient amino acids in the diet to maintain the protein reserves of the body is an important factor in acquiring immunity to a disease.

The protein content of meat varies from around 16% to 20% in beef, veal, lamb, and pork.

Fats

Considerable energy in the average diet is supplied by animal fats which are highly digestible. Aside from its high caloric value, fat plays a most important role in adding palatability to the lean in meat because of the flavor and aroma contained in its oils. The firm, white, saturated fats are associated with quality meats. Highly unsaturated fats are soft and oily, and may lower the grade of pork carcasses.

The chemical difference between the two fats just mentioned lies in the number of double bonds existing between the carbon atoms. When the carbon valence is satisfied with hydrogen, the fat is saturated, where-as if it lacks this hydrogen, it is an unsaturated fat. Since iodine will unite with the carbon on the free hydrogen link, its addition to fat will denote the degree of unsaturation which is designated as the iodine number. Another method of determining unsaturation is to run polarized light through a prepared piece of fat and read its refractive ability. More recent methods use gas liquid chromatography.

Fats may be hardened by a process in which the missing hydrogen is forced to combine with the carbon by the use of a catalyst (sodium methoxide) which breaks the double carbon bond. This is known as the hydrogenation process and is now in general use for the hardening of vegetable oils and lard.

The melting points of fat vary with the class of the domestic animal and the kind of feed it received.

The following shows the range of melting points from the different classes of animals:

Pork
  Back fat .... 86°-104° F
  Leaf fat ....110°-118° F

Beef
  External fat .... 89°-110° F
  Kidney fat ....104°-122° F

Lamb
  External fat .... 90°-115° F
  Kidney fat ....110°-124° F

Carbohydrates

The liver is the carbohydrate reservoir of the animal body, containing about one-half of all the carbohydrates found in the body. The remaining half is distributed through the muscles and in the blood stream. It is stored in the liver in the form of glycogen and distributed to the muscles by the blood stream. The exact changes that take place in energy metabolism by the conversion of glycogen to glucose to lactic acid are somewhat complex and are controlled and mediated by enzymes and hormones. Glycogen changes to lactic acid and the process is reversible in the live animal but not in the dressed meat (see chapters 3, 17, and later discussion in this chapter). Because of this, the lactic acid content of a carcass increases during aging or ripening (letting meat hang for two to six weeks to become more tender).

Water and Minerals

Fat is low in moisture; therefore, the higher the finish, the lower the total water content of a carcass or cut. Mature fat beef may contain as little as 45% moisture, while veal may run as high as 72%. An important point to remember is that the leaner the meat demanded by the consumer, the more water he buys at meat prices.

Muscle itself is a poor source of calcium since the calcium content of the body is centered in the bone. It seems logical that the use of mechanical boning machines (Chapter 12), which results in the obtaining of boneless muscle which contains up to 1% calcium, would be permitted by APHIS, but as yet these machines have not been approved for use with red meat. However, muscle meats, and more particularly glandular meats, are exceptionally rich in iron and phosphorus. Iron is an essential ingredient in the formation of red corpuscles, a lack of which causes anemia, while phosphorus is an essential constituent of body cell tissue and is necessary for the assimilation of calcium from other sources. Liver is an excellent source of easily assimilated iron and is prescribed in the diet of anemia sufferers. Muscle contains less than half as much iron as liver.

It has been found that the animal body also requires copper, flourine, manganese, zinc, cobalt, mangnesium, and iodine for normal functioning. Only a trace of manganese has been found in muscle, with liver showing considerably more. A trace of magnesium is found in muscle and liver. Muscle contains a small amount of aluminum, liver a slightly higher content.

The presence of zinc in the pancreas led to further research which showed that it is a necessary mineral in the diet. Liver was found to be about four times as rich in this element as muscle. Copper, which is thought to increase iron utilization, is found in small quantities in muscle and in slightly larger quantities in liver. Sodium and potassium chloride salts abound in meat.

Vitamins

It was not until the latter part of the nineteenth century that scientists discovered that dietary factors other than the proteins, carbohydrates, and fats were vital for health maintenance. In 1912, Casimir Funk, a Polish bio-chemist, coined the word *vitamine* to cover this group of dietary essentials because he wished to designate a particular one which he believed at the time to be an amine. Since that time, new factors have been discovered, many of which have been isolated, identified, and chemically synthesized.

Vitamin A (Anti-xerophthalmia)

Vitamin A is an alcohol of high molecular weight which is soluble in oils and fats but nearly insoluble in water. It is stable to heat, acids, and alkalis but is destroyed by light and by oxidation. It occurs in animal tissues chiefly in the form of fatty acid esters. Alpha, beta, and gamma carotene ($C_{40}H_{56}$) and cryptoxanthin, the yellow coloring matter in many vegetables and fruits, are called precursors or "provitamin A," and the animal body is able to convert them into vitamin A. The beta carotene should yield two molecules of vitamin A, whereas the alpha and gamma should yield but one.

This vitamin received early recognition but was never given a chemical name. It is considered an essential factor in keeping the epithelial tissues and the mucous membranes of the respiratory and genito-urinary tracts and the cornea and conjunctiva of the eye in healthy condition. It promotes growth, aids in the resistance to infection, tones the nervous system, and is essential for successful reproduction. Sheep and calf liver are particularly rich in vitamin A, followed by beef, lamb, hog, and pig liver, kidney, and chicken liver in the order named. Cod liver oil, butter, cheese, eggs, and fish roe are also excellent sources, followed by beef fat, cream, ice cream, and whole milk. Apricots, broccoli, carrots, kale, spinach, pumpkins, yellow squash, sweet potatoes, and turnip greens, along with certain fruits, are excellent sources of carotenoid pigments which can be transformed into vitamin A in the animal body.

It is estimated that ¼ pound of calf liver or ½ pound of beef liver will supply the daily requirement of this vitamin.

Vitamin B₁—Thiamine (Antineuritic)

Vitamin B₁ is a thiazol-pyrimidine compound called thiamine and is soluble in water but insoluble in oils and fats. It exists in pyrophosphate ester form in animal tissue and is an important coenzyme which plays an important role in carbohydrate metabolism. Vitamin B₁ or thiamine was isolated in 1926, was chemically synthesized in 1936, and is sold as the salt, thiamine hydrochloride.

A deficiency of this vitamin is the cause of a nervous disease, known as beri-beri. Symptoms include loss in weight, loss of appetite, slowing of the heart beat, impaired intestinal functioning, impaired reproductivity functioning, and failure of lactation. Thiamine promotes growth, stimulates appetite, aids digestion and assimilation, and is essential for normal functioning of nerve tissue.

Pork is an excellent source of thiamine. One center cut pork chop contains 118 milligrams of thiamine, the equal of the entire daily requirement for women and children. From 12% to 50% of this vitamin may be lost during the cooking process, and some of the thiamine is extracted from the meat by the water in which the meat is cooked. In this case, the meat juice or broth contains the dissolved thiamine and should not be discarded. Fried meat shows a smaller loss of the vitamin. Yeast, bran, cereal grains, and legume seeds are rich vegetable sources. Liver, meat, bacon, fish, eggs, milk, and oysters are also considered good sources of thiamine, as are fruits and vegetables.

A half-pound serving of round steak or two hamburger patties will furnish 30 milligrams of vitamin B_1.

Vitamin B_2 (G) Riboflavin

A yellowish-green, fluorescent, water soluble pigment, a compound of flavin and the pentose sugar ribose, riboflavin is another of the growth promoting factors of the B complex. It was isolated in 1933 and chemically synthesized in 1935. Riboflavin is stable to heat, mineral acids, and oxidizing agents, but is rather sensitive to light. A deficiency of this factor causes stunted growth, premature aging, unwholesomeness of the skin, and a general lowering of the tone of the body. Riboflavin is now known to take part in a number of enzyme systems in the animal body, all of which play important roles in tissue oxidation. It has been found to be a valuable agent in addition to nicotinic acid and thiamine in the treatment of certain cases of pellagra.

Veal and beef liver, followed by beef kidney, lamb liver, pork liver, and pork kidney, are rich sources of vitamin B_2. Beef heart, milk, oysters, eggs, sardines, yeast, whey (dried), crabs, legumes, prunes, and strawberries are also excellent sources. Ham, bacon, chicken, fish, lamb, beef, cereals, and certain fruits and vegetables are good sources. Very little loss of the vitamin occurs in cooking. It is estimated that the meat in the ordinary diet furnishes about 20% of the necessary daily vitamin B_2 requirement. Farmers are reported to obtain 50% of their vitamin B_2 requirement from milk and about 17% from meat, poultry, and fish. Reports show that where 25% of the budget goes for meats, those products furnish about 30% of the vitamin B_2 requirement.

Nicotinic Acid (Niacin)

This is a simple compound, occurring as a white powder or in needle crystal form, soluble in water and alcohol. Its biological importance was discovered in 1937, and it is made synthetically. It is also called the anti-black tongue factor since it is a cure for black tongue in dogs. In the form of nicontinamide, niacin also plays an important part in oxidative enzyme systems in body tissues. A deficiency of nicotinic acid over an extended period will cause pellagra, dermatitis, glossitis, and insanity in humans.

Nicotinic acid is heat stable and is found abundantly in pork, beef, veal, and lamb liver. Pork and beef kidney rank next, followed by pork and beef heart, pork meat, veal, chicken, beef, and lamb. Salmon, wheat germ, whey (dried), and yeast are also excellent sources. Other sources considered good are buttermilk, eggs, haddock, milk, kale, peas, potatoes, tomatoes, and turnip greens.

One-fourth pound of liver or ½ pound of veal, pork, or beef per day is reported to furnish the daily human nicotinic acid requirement.

Vitamin B₆ (Pyridoxine)

Pyridoxine has been called the rat acrodynia factor, having been found to be essential for the maintenance of a healthy skin in rats and for the utilization of unsaturated fatty acids. It was isolated in the crystalline state in 1938 and is available commercially. It is water soluble, stable to heat, acids, and alkali, but is destroyed by light and ultraviolet irradiation. Pyridoxine ($C_8H_{11}NO_3$) has been used successfully with thiamine and nicotinic acid in treating beri-beri.

Pyridoxine deficiency symptoms in the human have been restricted primarily to infants and young children subsisting on certain prepared dietary formulas. It has been established that pyridoxine derivatives function in certain enzyme systems which have to do with the transfer of amino (NH_2) groups in metabolism of nitrogen compounds. Lean meat and kidney are reported to be slightly more potent sources of vitamin B_6 than liver, with heart and brains furnishing lesser amounts. Egg yolk, wheat germ, and yeast are also excellent sources. Fish, milk, legumes, and wheat are good sources. It is estimated that meat furnishes a large share of the daily requirement of this vitamin.

Folic Acid

Names formerly used for folic acid were vitamin M, vitamin Bc, and L. casei factor. It has been found to be essential for the development of red and white blood cells. Pure folic acid crystals are used medicinally for the treatment of pernicious anemia. It was synthesized in 1945, is only moderately heat stable, and is present in green leaves. Pteroylglutamic acid is the name of the folic acid molecule in the form in which it occurs in liver. At one end of the formula is the double ring of the pterin group, a previously known yellow compound. The central grouping in the formula is the para-amino-benzoic acid ring formerly thought to be protective against graying hair. The third component in the folic molecule is glutamic acid, a normal constituent of most proteins.

Liver, kidney, beef, veal, yeast, green leafy vegetables, and wheat are good sources of folic acid.

Vitamin B₁₂ (Anti-pernicious Anemia Factor)

The animal protein factor (APF) has turned out to be vitamin B_{12}, the only vitamin which contains an inorganic base; namely, cobalt. "Variety meats" contribute the most vitamin B_{12}. Muscle meats and fish are good sources, with eggs contributing to a lesser extent. Gastric juice in the stomach is an important factor since it releases vitamin B_{12} and improves its absorption. Folic acid may affect the storage of the vitamin. Both vitamin B_{12} and folic acid are effective in the prevention and treatment of human macrocytic anemia (enlarged red blood cells), a condition found in pernicious anemia, sprue, and the anemia of pregnancy.

Pantothenic Acid

This B vitamin plays an important role in the metabolism of fats and other fat compounds such as cholesterol. It is available as a synthetic preparation in the form of dextrorotatory calcium pantothenate. Experiments with rats, dogs, and pigs indicate that requirements of this vitamin are from 5 to 10 times those of thiamine or riboflavin. Clinical evidence indicates that humans on poor diets show increased retention of pantothenic acid.

Kidney, liver, and beef heart were found to be potent sources, followed by beef spleen, beef pancreas, and beef tongue, with beef, lamb, pork, and veal having 1/10 the potency of liver or kidney. Pantothenic acid is fairly heat-stable.

Vitamin C (Antiscorbutic)

This factor is a product of hexose sugar and is also known as ascorbic acid. It is water soluble and has been isolated and chemically synthesized. A deficiency of vitamin C causes scurvy. Sprouting plants are rich in this vitamin, as are citrus fruits and vegetables. Meats are only a fair source of vitamin C. The greatest concentration in animal tissue exists in the adrenals, corpus luteum, and the thymus. Open kettle cooking and wilting destroy considerable vitamin C. Ascorbic acid is used to hasten cure development; it also retards or prevents nitrosamine formation in cured meats (see Chapter 17).

Vitamin D (Antirachitic)

Vitamin D is formed following irradiation of ergosterol forming calciferol or vitamin D_2. Other forms of this sterol group are now well known, such as vitamins D_3, D_4, and D_5. Vitamin D is formed in human and animal bodies when the skin is exposed to direct sunlight or ultraviolet light. It is insoluble in water, soluble in oils and fats, and heat-stable. A synthetic form of vitamin D called Delsterol is now available.

The function of vitamin D is to regulate calcium and phosphorus metabolism and it is, therefore, essential to normal bone growth and tooth development. It prevents rickets in infants and children and softening of the bones in adults. Rich sources of vitamin D are cod liver oil, fish, egg yolk, irradiated foods, and milk. Pork and beef liver are considered good sources; calf liver and other meat products contain only fair amounts.

Vitamin E (Antisterility)

This vitamin is made synthetically and is available commercially as alpha-tocopherol. It is insoluble in water but is soluble in oils and fats and is heat-stable. A deficiency of this factor is the cause of resorption of the young in the female during gestation and the loss of fertilizing power in the male. The *tocopherols* are good antioxidants and retard development of rancidity in fats.

Cottonseed oil, corn oil, peanut oil, wheat germ oil, and green lettuce are rich sources of this vitamin, nearly all green leafy vegetables, whole grains, meat, milk, and eggs being considered good sources.

Vitamin K (Antihemorrhagic)

Vitamin K was discovered in 1935 and is made synthetically. Only two forms designated as vitamins K_1 and K_2 have been isolated from natural sources. It is fat-soluble and heat-and light-stable. It is essential for the production of prothrombin, a blood coagulant, and aids in the prevention of hemorrhage in newborn infants and in cases of obstructive jaundice. A form in vitamin K that can be injected into the blood stream in surgical operations has been developed.

The K vitamins were first isolated from alfalfa leaf meal and from putrefying fish, the principal commercial sources. Hog liver is also a rich source. Cabbage, carrot greens, spinach, soybean oil, tomatoes, hempseed, cauliflower, rice, bran, kale, and egg yolk are considered good sources. The principal commercial source is a synthetic product known as menadione.

Choline

This is the sixth crystalline member of the B complex and functions in normal fat metabolism, prevents slipped tendons in turkeys, and is one of the substances to which perosis responds. Liver, pancreas, and meat are considered rich sources of choline.

COLOR

Dark Cutting Beef

The color of beef muscle will vary with the age of the animal, ranging from the bright cherry red in yearlings and two-year-olds to the deeper shades of red characteristic of older animals. Occasionally the meat from one of these younger, well finished animals that would ordinarily have a bright red color, will have a very dark red color—in fact so dark that it appears somewhat black. This dark cutting beef had been a rather vexing problem to the producer and processor of meat and it was not until 1940 that some light was shed on the probable causes.

In the fall of 1938, the National Live Stock and Meat Board initiated the study of the factors responsible for dark cutting beef. The technical committee appointed was made up of members of the research staffs of the National Live Stock and Meat Board, the American Meat Institute, Armour & Co., Swift & Co., and Wilson & Co. Numerous cooperating agencies made the facilities for this work rather impressive.

The first record made on 308 4-H Club calves shown at the 1938 International Livestock Exposition showed that 2.6% were black, 5.8% dark, and 9.4% shady. The greatest number of dark cutting cattle came from the packinghouse that held the calves in outdoor pens (exposed to the cold.) Studies made on the rib-eye muscle of these cattle revealed a correlation between the color of the muscle and its water extractable sugar content. Dark cutting muscle contained .03% sugar, shady muscle .11%, and light colored muscle .18%. The pH of dark muscle was found to be 6.53, shady muscle 5.68, and light muscle 5.58.

Studies made on 228 cattle during the summer of 1941 indicated that the incidence of dark cutting beef was not increased by fasting the steers as long as three days. Where experiments were repeated on cattle exposed to severe weather conditions with insufficient food, the percentage of dark cutters increased. An experiment in which insulin was administered to the cattle showed that it was possible to produce dark cutting beef by depleting the muscles of their extractable reducing sugars.

It was found that the oxygen uptake capacities of dark muscles were greater than the light colored muscles, demonstrating a correlation between the water extractable reducing sugars and the color of the muscle.

A test made on 122 4-H Club steers from the 1941 International Livestock Exposition was designed to determine the effect of chilling and withholding feed as against warm housing and adequate feeding. When the cattle were chilled and fed, no dark cutters were produced, while those from which the feed was withheld in addition to the chilling produced some dark cutting beef.

A test on commercially fed cattle to check further the effect of chilling and withholding feed on the color of beef substantiated the former results, indicating that dark cutters are produced in direct relationship to the severity of the treatment given the cattle prior to slaughter.

More recent work at Illinois[2] showed that only four of eight Hereford and Angus steers cut dark after having been fasted for two days and heavily exercised the final 10 hours of fasting at temperatures near freezing. Thus some animals react to stress differently than others.

Another Illinois study with heifers indicated that those slaughtered while in estrus (heat) showed a tendency toward muscle darkness when color was measured with a reflectance meter. However, other research has shown under packing house conditions, that muscle darkness could not be detected by eyesight in heifers slaughtered while in estrus.

Dark cutting beef is related physiologically to pale, soft exudative pork (Chapter 3). The occurrence of either muscle condition depends on the rate of muscle glycogen (starch) breakdown. Muscle has only about 0.5% to 1.0% glycogen. When this glycogen breaks down in muscle, it forms acid. The acid condition in muscle alters the muscle protein structure and color in such a way that a very acid condition (low pH) produces pale, soft, watery muscle, while an alkaline condition (high pH) produces dark, firm, and dry muscle. When animals (pork or beef) are stressed, certain ones, not all, will begin to break down glycogen and form acid in the muscle. If they are slaughtered when the muscle is very acid, the meat will be pale, soft and exudative (watery) (PSE). If, on the other hand, they are not slaughtered during the time the muscle is acid, but sometime later, after the lactic acid has been removed from the muscle by the living animal's processes but before more glycogen is restored in muscle, the muscle will be dark, firm, and dry.

Dark cutting beef has been shown to be equal in palatability to normal beef, although it is more susceptible to microbial action. Thus discrimination against it in the market place is unfounded. Yet consumers remain suspicious of any abnormality in muscle color, especially that which is darker than normal.

Pigment

Myoglobin is the color pigment in muscle; *hemoglobin* is the pigment in blood. Very little hemoglobin occurs in the muscle of carcasses that were well bled, therefore the amount of myoglobin present will determine the color of the meat. Older animals have a higher myoglobin content, which causes their meat to be darker. The instances of dark

---

2. *Journal of Animal Science*, 38:38, 1974.

cutting or isolated dark muscles in young beef, discussed above, are caused by a depletion of muscle sugar or glycogen. Light colored beef has a pH in the range of 5.3 to 5.9, whereas the pH of dark colored meat ranges from 6 to 6.6. It is the glycogen that is converted to lactic acid that lowers the pH of the muscle.

Beef is always darker when first cut, but upon exposure to the air for 30 minutes the hemoglobin and myoglobin become oxygenated (a loose association of the pigment with oxygen), changing to oxyhemoglobin and oxymyoglobin, which are a brighter shade of red. After a period of time, depending upon favorable or unfavorable temperature and moisture conditions, the meat will again turn dark when the pigment becomes chemically oxidized (the Fe^{++} atom in the pigment molecule changes to Fe^{+++}). In other words, dark beef (1) may occur in certain animals or muscles regardless of age, (2) is a characteristic of the flesh of older animals, and (3) is also the color of meat after it has been cut for some time. This latter condition occurs mainly on the first quarter-inch of cut surface. Beef that has been aged from four to eight weeks will show a very dark, even a moldy or slimy cut surface, but a thin slice will remove this discoloration and the newly cut surface will be bright and fresh.

Vacuum packaged primal and subprimal beef cuts retain their dark color, characteristic of fresh cut beef, if put in the bag soon after cutting. Beef in a vacuum bag can thus be stored (aged) for a week or two or longer, if desired, at temperatures just above freezing. No mold growth or bacterial slime will occur, and at the end of aging, the bag can be opened and the bright cherry red color will return within minutes.

Pork muscle contains less myoglobin than beef or lamb muscle, which partly explains its greyish pink normal color. Abnormal pork color, either dark or pale, is a result of the same chemical chain reaction that affects beef color, but the end result (dark or pale) is dependent on time of slaughter.

The iridescent sheen sometimes seen on meat is caused by the breaking up of white light by the highly fibrous character of the meat surface and the film of fat on these fibers.

The blood remaining in animal carcasses varies—6% to 20% in muscle, 2% to 8½% in bone, and 1% to 2% in kidney.

TENDERIZING

Aging Meat

Fresh meat is usually rather tough. The resistance of warm, freshly killed meat to the shear test (using the Warner-Bratzler shear machine) is less than the same muscle tissue after 24 hours of chill. After the 24- to 35-hour chill, the meat becomes progressively more tender.

The action of proteolytic enzymes (called *cathepsins*) on the connective tissue in meat, reducing them to a gelatinous consistency, is the tenderizing action that transpires during the ripening process (holding or aging for 1 to 4 weeks).

"Rigor mortis results indirectly from the increased acidity due to lactic acid formation. The essential step in the phenomenon is the removal of phosphate from adenosine triphosphate (ATP), an enzymatically-catalyzed reaction. The enzyme responsible is inactive at acidities less than pH 6.5, but when the pH of the tissue after slaughter drops to this point as a result of lactic acid formation, rigor begins and is essentially complete in normal tissues by the time the pH reaches 6.3"[3] There is a slight rise in temperature in the first stages of rigor mortis ascribed to the glycogen-lactic acid reaction which changes the pH of the muscle.

The amount of connective tissue (collagen and elastin) is greatest in those areas where there are the greatest number of small muscles, such as the neck, heel of round, and shank. Since the eye muscle of the rib, the strip muscle of the loin, and the inside muscle of the round (top round) receive a minimum of exercise and are in themselves large muscles containing but little tissue, they are the recognized tender cuts of beef. The most tender muscle in the entire carcass is the tenderloin (tender or fillet) which is located in the loin directly under the region of the lumbar vertebrae. This muscle receives practically no exercise and is tender in animals of all ages regardless of finish but less desirable from the older animals.

Beef may be aged from one to four weeks but only a small percent of the total beef is now aged in carcass form. Rather, that which is aged is fabricated into primals so the loins and ribs, the high quality primals, can be vacuum packaged and aged while the chuck and rounds, rough cuts and trim, can move immediately into market channels. Cooler space is generally at a premium in an industry which depends greatly on turnover and volume to make ends meet. Thus, even these primals usually move out within a week and long-time aging, as such, is not widely practiced. Work at South Dakota[4] showed that 10 days aging of primal ribs improved tenderness compared to 5-day aging, but that tenderness did not improve significantly from 10 to 15 days post-mortem. Thus the present-day systems of marketing, which consume about seven days from

---

3. D. M. Doty, formerly of the American Meat Institute Foundation, University of Chicago, later the Fats and Proteins Research Foundation, Inc., and now retired.

4. *Journal of Animal Science*, 23:1204, 1964 (Abstr.).

slaughter to retail without a specified aging time, are probably allowing nearly the full expression of tenderness to develop.

Lamb carcasses are definitely not aged but are shipped or fabricated within 12 to 24 hours of slaughter in the United States.

Acetic Acid

The acetic acid in vinegar and lemon juice can serve in the same capacity as the sarcolactic acid formed in the muscle cells themselves. The juice of a lemon mixed with several tablespoonfuls of olive oil and a slight seasoning of salt is called a *marinade,* and acts as a tenderizer when applied to both surfaces of a steak two or three days previous to the time it is to be broiled. Because of the effect of the acid on metal, the treated steak must be placed in an earthenware dish. The object of the olive oil is to seal the surfaces from the air and thus cause the meat to keep fresh and bright in color for a longer period of time.

Venison and bear meat are much improved if placed in a diluted solution of vinegar (an equal amount of water and vinegar) for several days before cooking. Acetic acid also acts as a preservative.

Vegetable Enzymes and Proten Beef

Three enzymes of vegetable origin which dissolve or degradate collagen and elastin are (1) *papain,* secured from the tropical American tree Carica papaya (2) *bromelin,* secured from the juice of the pineapple, and (3) *ficin,* secured from figs (Latin: Ficus-fig tree). Elastin, unlike collagen, is not degraded by aging or cooking but is dissolved by these enzymes. They have made very effective tenderizers and have had good consumer acceptance. The most readily available commercial preparations contain papain.

Their use on steaks and small cuts is more effective than on large roasts due to the inability of the enzyme to penetrate the meat. This makes it necessary to fork the tenderizer into the meat. On roasts, it is necessary to make several punctures with a butcher's steel or a sharp knife, and then use the steel or knife to shove some tenderizer into the puncture. This is in addition to a surface application. Apply to steak ½ hour previous to cooking and to roasts about 2 hours before roasting.

A commercial tenderizer, known as a Controlled Meat Tenderizer, consists of hydrolized vegetable proteins, vegetable proteolytic enzymes (papain, bromelin, and ficin), salt, monosodium glutamate, dextrose, propylene, glycol, and other spices in a solution of purified water. The claim is made that one of the enzymes works on muscle fiber, another on elastin fiber, and another on connective tissue. It has been approved for use in government inspected plants.

A patented process of tenderizing meat, approved by APHIS, consists of the injection of a clarified, concentrated, standardized proteolytic enzyme (papain) into the animal's jugular vein minutes before slaughter. The size of the injection is dependent upon the weight and grade of the animal. The tenderizing enzyme is carried to all parts of the body through the blood stream and results in a significant increase in tenderness. The process was developed in the Swift and Co. laboratories, and the company was awarded the 1961 Food Technology Industrial Achievement Award, which is presented by the Institute of Food Technologists in recognition of an outstanding food process and/or product which represents a significant advance in the application of food technology to food production and which has been successfully applied in actual commercial operation at least six months but not over four years.

Proten beef is still widely used and accepted. Meat so treated is sold as Proten meats. The principle is also applicable to veal, lamb, mutton, and fowl.

High Temperature Aging

The Mellon Institute, in 1936, established the fact that native enzymes (cathepsins) are not very active at lower temperatures (32° to 36° F) but their activity increases as temperature rises. It was also known that high humidity lowers shrinkage. The problem was to hold down bacterial spoilage at the higher ambient temperature and humidity. It was discovered by Drs. M. D. Coulter and G. D. Beal, under a fellowship sponsored by the Kroger Food Foundation and the Westinghouse Electric Company, that ultraviolet light wave lengths in the region of 2,600 Angstrom units (250 million angstroms equal one inch) have the unique quality of being fatal to microscopic organisms coming within their range. It was later proposed that a supplementary germicidal effect existed due to the formation of ozone (O_3) at the meat surface.

The Sterilamp (Tenderay process) was thus developed incorporating (1) a cooler temperature of 60° F, (2) 85° to 90° relative humidity, (3) a three-day time period, and (4) the UV lamp to control surface bacteria.

This process was adopted and was widely used for 20 or more years. It had, however, several weaknesses. The major weakness was its inability to penetrate the meat, leaving the internal area, such as the deep-seated hip joint, unprotected to the ravages of anaerobic bacteria. This made it necessary to thoroughly chill the carcass before aging it at the higher ambient temperatures. Another objection to the process was the effect of the rays upon the human eye, necessitating the wearing of goggles or eye glasses for those working under the lights. The Sterilamp is lethal to bacteria, but only to those coming into contact with its rays, or the ozone.

The Tenderay process is practically if not totally nonexistent today, although there are still UV lamps hanging in coolers around the country.

Testender Beef

The development and use of the tenderometer, a portable instrument that non-destructively tests a raw carcass to predict its tenderness after cooking, has earned the 1973 Food Techonology Industrial Achievement Award (the same award Swift and Co. was awarded in 1961 for Proten beef) for Armour and Company. The tenderometer measures the natural tenderness of beef by measuring the resistance to the penetration of a multiple-needle probe into the eye of a carcass. A reading is given in pounds, the lower reading indicating more tender beef.

Testender beef, guaranteed tender, has been in national distribution since 1970. Sales have increased five-fold since that time and are now in the multi-million range. Use of the Tenderometer can reduce customer dissatisfaction, first by selling only tender beef as *tender* and second, by allowing less tender beef to age longer in order to improve in tenderness.

SELECTING MEAT FOR QUALITY

The word quality infers superiority. To determine the degree of superiority requires a knowledge of the visible elements in a piece of meat that give it quality. Since the consumer has very little if any opportunity to see any of the physical characters that indicate the age of the animal from which the meat was obtained, he or she must make a choice by looking for the following conditions (see Chapter 11, Federal Grading, also).

Color of Lean, Fat, and Bone

Color of the lean is important for the purpose of identification. For example, beef ranges in color from a bright cherry red to dark red; veal is a pinkish brown; pork is gray-pink to gray-red; lamb is light pink; and mutton is bright red in color.

Color of the lean is important in suggesting the age of the animal because as an animal grows older, the meat turns a darker shade. For example—young beef is light red, beef from old animals is dark red; lamb is bright pink, mutton is brick red; young pork is gray-pink, older hogs gray-red; and veal is a pinkish brown, and calf (older veal) is a reddish brown.

Color of the lean is important in that it may indicate how long a cut of meat has been held. The exposure of a cut surface to air, whether it is cold or warm air, will cause that surface area to lose moisture (dehydrate) and turn dark in a period of two or three days.

Color of the lean is *not* particularly important as an index of quality, since numerous cooking tests have shown that an otherwise prime or choice grade of meat from carcasses of similar age and finish eat as well regardless of whether the meat is a bright cherry red or a dark shade of red.

Color of the fat is *not* a true index of quality, but a white or cream white fat is characteristic of young, grain-fattened cattle. A yellow fat is prevalent in animals with more maturity, since they have, in their more extended life span, been able to store up more carotene from the large amounts of roughage and cottonseed meal they may have consumed in that time. Several of our prominent breeds of dairy cattle that are noted for the high fat content and rich color of their milk have a very yellow fat, and transmit this characteristic to their offspring in a proportionate degree when crossed with other breeds that have a light colored fat. This does not mean that the carcass from a young animal that carries a yellow fat is lacking in quality of fat if that fat is firm and dry. In fact a yellow fat will furnish more vitamin A to the consumer's diet, it will have just as rich a flavor, and be as acceptable as a white fat.

But—one must remember that if the yellow fat is there because of the age of the animal, the meat will be tough and stringy; if the fat is there because it is inherited from these dairy breeds, then the cut of meat will probably lack muscling and marbling by our present standards, because these cattle were originally developed for their milk-producing ability.

Research has shown that conformation (the shape that young dairy steers lack) is not reflected in significantly lower yields of edible meat, and that moderate to high levels of marbling are not essential to palatability of young beef, be it of dairy or beef breeding. Thus young dairy beef should not be considered second rate, and as evidenced by the increased dairy steer feeding, there is little danger of that happening.

Color of the bone is important to the purchaser of carcass meat and the meat grader because the color and texture of the bone indicate the age of the animal. The spinal column or backbone and the aitch or pelvic bone offer the most visible sign posts for determining age. Since the consumer wants as little bone as possible, it follows that these sign posts of age have been taken down as far as he is concerned. The backbone consists of interlocking vertebrae which vary in shape according to their location. Those in the region of the forequarter or thoracic region have rather long, thin, flat processes that extend upward and are known as the superior spinus processes, more commonly referred to as feather or fin bones. In young animals these feather bones have not hardened into bone at the tip but are still cartilaginous or white and are called buttons. The color of the ossified portion of the bone in a young animal is red and the physical appearance is porous.

As the animal increases in age, the buttons ossify or harden into bone, and the bone itself becomes more dense, loses its red color (becoming whiter), and increases in hardness. When the animal is four years of age, the buttons are hard and bony. The visible portion of the pelvic bone located in the rump will show a smooth surface with a white cartilaginous lining where the separation was made with a knife. In older animals (four years and up), the pelvic bone will lack this cartilage separation and will show a hard bone that was sawed. The bones in the sacrum (the backbone area of the loin end) will become very hard and fuse into one bone in advanced age. The signposts for age now read: Young (red, porous bone; button on the feather bones; smooth, glossy pelvic bone). Old (white, dense, flinty bone; no buttons; sawed pelvis; ossified sacrum).

Firmness

A soft, soggy, watery meat is not a quality meat. It may have a fine texture and be rather tender if it is from young beef, but this does not elevate it from the category of a "gravy" cut. A soft, greasy, or oily fat is a low quality fat. It should be dry, hard, and flaky.

Texture

The grain or texture of meat is seldom given any thought by the consumer. It will vary more with the age of the animal than it will between animals of the same species. A fine texture gives meat a smooth, velvety appearance, whereas a coarse texture appears globular, the difference being caused by the thicker cell walls in the latter. Since cell walls, made up of collagen, are the least tender part of a cell, it follows that any abnormal amount would affect the textural structure and appearance of the meat and make it less tender.

Marbling

Marbling is considered by present USDA grading standards to be the most important factor in giving quality to meat. Marbling is the intermingling of fat among the muscle fibers appearing either (1) as a fine webbing resembling a spider web (fine marbling), (2) as flashes of fat that are heavier and resemble streaks of lightning, referred to as coarse marbling, or (3) as flecks of fat giving meat a combination mottled and webbed appearance. A moderate amount of any one of these types is welcome in meat, and cooking tests have shown no preference in their effect on the flavor and juiciness of meat.

Marbling is found most abundant in the flesh of highly finished animals that are approaching or have reached maturity. Its development is slower than is the laying on of internal and external fat. For that reason higher marbling levels are normally found in carcasses of heavier, older cattle that have been fed longer and thus have more waste fat over the outside and internally. Oftentimes young animals will not have sufficient marbling to reach the U.S. Choice grade, but research has shown that due to youth, they will be nearly as tender as a carcass from an older animal with more marbling and probably have acceptable tenderness. Furthermore, the younger animal will most likely have a leaner carcass and will have gained weight more efficiently in reaching his more moderate market weight. Ideally, we would prefer a young animal with a lean, well muscled carcass and enough marbling to qualify for average Choice quality. We can breed these, but they are in a distinct minority in the market place, even today. Although research has shown that marbling accounts for only 5% of the total variation in tenderness, no *one single factor* has been shown to be the major tenderness factor. State of muscle contraction (rigor) probably comes the closest. Meanwhile, marbling does contribute to flavor and juiciness, and thus deserves a role in the standards, but in this day when fat is a "dirty" word, we should not be overemphasizing marbling.

Some of the most highly marbled meat appearing in a market could be from an aged fat cow of one of the beef breeds or its cross. The way to determine age has already been discussed and to allay the fear that might arise in the mind of the consumer, let it be said that reputable meat retailers do not sell this type of meat as retail cuts because the meat is tough and a customer's account might be lost.

Practically everyone enjoys a highly flavored, juicy, tender piece of meat. Let us compare the pan frying of a Choice grade steak (moderately marbled) as against a low Standard grade steak (traces minus marbling). In the frying process (the same thing happens in broiling or in roasting), the marbling in the Choice steak melts and encapsulates the cells, thereby holding in the water-soluble proteins which are rich in aroma and flavor. The fat itself is high in aroma and flavor. It also adds juiciness to the meat because it takes the place of the water that is driven off by the heat. The result is a tender, juicy, highly flavored steak with fat drippings that contain very little of the water-soluble proteins for gravy making. The unmarbled steak has no protection. The water-soluble proteins escape into the skillet, the moisture evaporates, the steak begins to curl, shrivel ,and become dry, hard, and tasteless. The best part of this kind of steak is the gravy; thus the term often applied to cuts of low grade meats is "gravy cuts."

Knowing these things does not guarantee the eating, because there is the cook who can even ruin the gravy.

"MEATLESS" MEAT—MEAT EXTENDERS AND ANALOGS

The soybean has long been recognized by Asian cultures as an important food stuff where incorporation of the whole bean into human food products is yet commonplace. For years in the United States, the soybean has been recognized for its value in livestock feeds as the protein supplement, soybean meal.

Edible soy proteins have been produced in the United States since the late 1930's, but it was not until recent years when the economic situation caused consumers to begin to search for alternate protein sources to meat, that U.S. technology developed the capabilities to produce high quality food products from the soybean. Now, no less than 10 corporations are involved in the development and sale of a textured vegetable protein product resembling meat.

Processing the Bean

In processing the soybean for ultimate use as a food product under sanitary conditions, the beans are cracked, hulls removed, and cotyledons heated and flaked. The flaked beans are extracted with hexane to yield a fat-free flake, composed of 50% protein. This flake is further extracted with water, each extraction step yielding a more highly purified product.

The National Soybean Processors Association has established the following product definitions:

1. Soy grits and/or soy flour—40% to 60% protein.
2. Soy protein concentrate—not less than 70% protein.
3. Isolated soy protein—not less than 90% protein.

A textured protein resembling meat fibers can be formed by passing the isolated soy protein through an alkaline medium, a spinnerette, an acid bath, and into a stretcher to form the fibers which are held together with edible binders, treated with flavoring, color, or added nutrients. This type of product is used to simulate meat and poultry products and generally is not combined with meat.

In a second process, called thermoplastic extrusion, soy flour is forced through a die thus forming a texturized product more reasonable in price than the above product, since a less costly starting material (soy flour) is used. This second thermoplastic product is most often used in combination with meat.

Nutritive Value

Any of the soybean products alone is deficient in the essential amino acid methionine and is about equivalent nutritionally to 80% of the value of casein, meaning it has a Protein Efficiency Ratio (PER) of 80. By adding methionine or blending with meat proteins the PER can be improved to 100%.

In 1971, the USDA approved textured vegetable proteins as a partial meat replacement in the school lunch program.

A new research project, financed by the National Live Stock and Meat Board and conducted by Dr. Robert M. Kark at Rush–Presbyterian–St. Luke's Medical Center in Chicago, is designed to measure several of the human body's responses to meat and meat products compared with fabricated soy proteins and other vegetable fabricated proteins. The investigation will seek comparative information by means of analyses of blood and urine samples of healthy medical students after a meal of meat versus a soybean meat-type product. One reason for study is scientific recognition that *isolated soy* protein products (spinnerrette process) are very high in sodium (500 to 4,000 milligrams per 100 grams) versus fresh meat (40 to 80 milligrams per 100 grams). This is one of several studies currently being conducted investigating the nutritive values of vegetable proteins for humans.

Economic Considerations and Palatability

Costs of the thermoplastic textured vegetable proteins, which are most suitable for mixing with meat, are often less costly than meat, so an economic advantage can be realized by blending the soy product into the meat product. The major limiting factor on the amount to be blended with a fresh ground meat product is its effect on palatability. Legal requirements are that if only a trace is added, it must appear on a label, and the product cannot be called hamburger or ground beef. In a processed meat product, i.e., sausage, frankfurter, etc., the use of soy protein additive comes under the regulations of cereal and dry milk, etc., listed in Chapter 16, i.e., it must be on the label, and isolated soy cannot exceed 2%.

Presently the USDA is considering the whole labeling situation regarding the use of textured vegetable proteins in meat blends of all sorts, with emphasis being given to clarity of the label for the consumer in terms of nutritional value and practicality of the label requirements for the processor.

Many of the textured soy proteins are relatively bland in flavor, and when they are mixed with ground beef, they take on the flavor and color of ground beef, if not added in too high amounts. The soy proteins have a high ability to bind water, some capable of binding as high as five or six times their dry weight in water. When rehydrated for use in blended products, however, usually water weighing from two to four times the dry weight of the protein is added to reach a water protein ratio similar to meat. The blended soy-meat products may exhibit a firmer texture than an all meat product, and theoretically are juicier after cooking since more of the juices are held in the product during cooking because of this binding effect. Research has shown cooking losses to be lower in the blended products. However, there is a limit to adding the extender after which the resulting product no longer remotely resembles the flavor, texture, or juiciness of a meat product. Most blended fresh products offered in the retail market today contain about 25% rehydrated soy by weight.

The USDA Economic Research Service conducted a study of the sales of soy-ground-beef blends in the summer of 1973 when the composite retail price of cuts from a Choice carcass reached $1.36 per pound, compared to $1.12 a year earlier. Under such a price influence, the soy blend was readily accepted, and now is available in all sections of the country. Most of the blends in this survey contained 25% rehydrated soy by weight.

During a seven-month period, the blend product averaged between 20% and 25% of the ground beef market, hitting a high of 30% during a time of extremely high beef prices. In comparison with regular ground beef and lean ground beef, it appeared as if the soy protein was more a direct substitute for the regular than the lean ground beef. The blend products were priced 15 to 20 cents lower than regular hamburger, at absolute prices ranging from 69 cents to well over a $1 per pound. Their lower price was the major reason for the blended products' success When the blend sold less than 10 cents below the price of regular ground beef, sales dropped significantly.

Manufactured soy product utilizing the extruded fibrous material from isolated soy which are made to resemble meat cuts but contain no meat are known as meat analogs. The cost of these products is generally high and their palatability does not compare with all meat steaks, chops, and roasts. The use of these products is confined largely to those people and groups who for one reason or another do not care to consume *any* meat.

It has been estimated that in 1972, 1% of the United States total meat consumption was composed of soy products. USDA's Economic Research Service has predicted that this will increase to 8% by 1980. Others predict it will rise to nearly 20%. The chief executive of a firm producing vegetable protein meat analogs and extenders in 1971 stated that the $30 million annual market for those products (compared to the $30 billion market for real meat) could achieve sales of $1.5 to $2.0 billion by 1980.

Thus the vegetable meat analogs and extenders are and will continue to be an important segment of our meat industry.

CHAPTER 20

Preparing and Serving Meats

METHODS OF COOKING MEAT

A national committee of investigators has simplified and standardized the cooking of meat into two fundamental methods: (1) cooking with *dry heat* where the meat is surrounded by dry air in the oven or under the broiler, a method that is adaptable to the preparation of the more tender cuts of meat, and (2) cooking with *moist heat* where the meat is surrounded by hot liquid or steam, a method suitable to the preparation of the less tender cuts of meat.

Dry Heat Method

Broiling

This method is employed with the more tender steaks and chops and cured pork. It consists of a direct exposure of the meat to heat either from above or from below, as with outdoor charcoal broiling, or from both sides. In the latter case, the steak is supported in a vertical position by wire grills with heat on both sides, as in a charcoal broiler. The seasoning may be applied before or after (which is preferable) broiling. (See Table 20.1 for broiling times and temperatures.)

Panbroiling

This is a method suitable for the same cuts used for broiling, but it differs in that heat reaches the cuts indirectly. The meat is placed in a heavy iron skillet or on a heavy griddle iron and is browned on both sides. After browning, the temperature is lowered and the cuts may be turned occasionally until done. The fat is poured off as it accumulates.

Table 20.1—Timetable for Broiling[1,2]

Cut	Weight or Thickness	Approximate Total Cooking Time	
		Rare	Medium
		- - - -(<u>min.</u>)- - - -	
Beef			
Chuck steak (high quality)—1 in.	1-1/2 to 2-1/2 lbs.	24	30
1-1/2 in.	2 to 4 lbs.	40	45
Rib steak—1 in.	1 to 1-1/2 lbs.	15	20
1-1/2 in.	1-1/2 to 2 lbs.	25	30
2 in.	2 to 2-1/2 lbs.	35	45
Rib-eye steak—1 in.	8 to 10 oz.	15	20
1-1/2 in.	12 to 14 oz.	25	30
2 in.	16 to 20 oz.	35	45
Club steak—1 in.	1 to 1-1/2 lbs.	15	20
1-1/2 in.	1-1/2 to 2 lbs.	25	30
2 in.	2 to 2-1/2 lbs.	35	45
Sirloin steak—1 in.	1-1/2 to 3 lbs.	20	25
1-1/4 in.	2-1/4 to 4 lbs.	30	35
2 in.	3 to 5 lbs.	40	45
Porterhouse steak—			
1 in.	1-1/4 to 2 lbs.	20	25
1-1/2 in.	2 to 3 lbs.	30	35
2 in.	2-1/2 to 3-1/2 lbs.	40	45
Filet Mignon—1 in.	4 to 6 oz.	15	20
1-1/2 in.	6 to 8 oz.	18	22
Ground beef patties 1 in. thick by 3 in.	4 oz.	15	25
Pork (Smoked)			
Ham slice—tendered			
1/2 in.	3/4 to 1 lb.		10-12
1 in.	1-1/2 to 2 lbs.		16-20
Loin Chops—		Always	
3/4 to 1 in.		cooked	15-20
Canadian style bacon		well done	
1/4 in. slices			6-8
1/2 in. slices			8-10
Bacon			4-5
Pork (Fresh)		Always	
Rib or loin chops	3/4 to 1 in.	cooked	20-25
Shoulder steaks	1/2 to 3/4 in.	well done	20-22

(Continued)

Table 20.1 (Continued)

Cut	Weight or Thickness	Approximate Total Cooking Time	
		Rare	Medium
		– – – –(min.)– – – –	
Lamb			
Shoulder chops—			
1 in.	5 to 8 oz.	Lamb chops	12
1-1/2 in.	8 to 10 oz.	are not	18
2 in.	10 to 16 oz.	usually	22
Rib chops—1 in.	3 to 5 oz.	served rare	12
1-1/2 in.	4 to 7 oz.		18
2 in.	6 to 10 oz.		22
Loin chops—1 in.	4 to 7 oz.		12
1-1/2 in.	6 to 10 oz.		18
2 in.	8 to 14 oz.		22
Ground lamb patties			
1 in. by 3 in.	4 oz.		18

1. This timetable is based on broiling at a moderate temperature (350° F). Rare steaks are broiled to an internal temperature of 140° F; medium to 160° F; well done to 170° F. Lamb chops are broiled from 170° F to 175° F. Ham is cooked to 160° F. The time for broiling bacon is influenced by personal preference as to crispness.

2. National Live Stock and Meat Board.

Roasting

This method is adapted to the preparation of the more tender cuts such as beef ribs, beef sirloin, top round, sirloin tip, veal leg, veal rump, veal loin, veal shoulder, pork loin, pork shoulder, leg of lamb, sirloin lamb roll, loin lamb roll, rolled shoulder of lamb, and fresh or cured pork. It is accomplished by placing the cut (preferably not less than 2½ inches thick) in an open roasting pan with the fat side up so that it will be self-basting. No water is added; neither is a lid used to cover the roast. Smoked pork, fresh beef, veal, and lamb are roasted at an oven temperature of 300° to 325° F, whereas fresh pork is roasted at an oven temperature of 325° to 350° F. (See Table 20.2 for roasting times and temperatures.)

The use of the slow oven (using low temperatures) in roasting has been found to cut down considerably on the shrinkage incident to high oven temperatures. Basting is eliminated by placing the fat side up, or placing loose fat or bacon strips on the top of lean cuts. Searing does not assist materially in keeping the meat juices from escaping but it gives the meat color and aroma.

Table 20.2—Timetable for Roasting[1]

Cut	Approx-imate Weight	Oven Temperature Constant	Interior Temperature When Removed from Oven	Approx-imate Cooking Time
	(lbs.)	- - - - - -(^{O}F)- - - - - -		(min. per lb.)
Beef				
Standing rib[2]	6 to 8	300–325	140 (rare)	23 to 25
			160 (medium)	27 to 30
			170 (well)	32 to 35
	4 to 6	300–325	140 (rare)	26 to 32
			160 (medium)	34 to 38
			170 (well)	40 to 42
Rolled rib	5 to 7	300–325	140 (rare)	32
			160 (medium)	38
			170 (well)	48
Delmonico (rib eye)	4 to 6	350	140 (rare)	18 to 20
			160 (medium)	20 to 22
			170 (well)	22 to 24
Tenderloin, whole	4 to 6	425	140 (rare)	45 to 60 (total)
Tenderloin, half	2 to 3	425	140 (rare)	45 to 50 (total)
Rolled rump (high quality)	4 to 6	300–325	150–170	25 to 30
Sirloin tip	3-1/2 to 4	300–325	140–170	35 to 40
(high quality)	4 to 6	300–325	140–170	30 to 35
Veal				
Leg	5 to 8	300–325	170	25 to 35
Loin	4 to 6	300–325	170	30 to 35
Rib (rack)	3 to 5	300–325	170	35 to 40
Rolled shoulder	4 to 6	300–325	170	40 to 45
Pork (fresh)				
Loin				
Center	3 to 5	325–350	170	30 to 35
Half	5 to 7	325–350	170	35 to 40
Blade loin or sirloin	3 to 4	325–350	170	40 to 45
Rolled	3 to 5	325–350	170	35 to 45
Picnic shoulder	5 to 8	325–350	170	30 to 35
Rolled	3 to 5	325–350	170	35 to 40
Cushion style	3 to 5	325–350	170	30 to 35
Boston shoulder	4 to 6	325–350	170	40 to 45
Leg (fresh ham)				
Whole (bone-in)	12 to 16	325–350	170	22 to 26
Whole (rolled)	10 to 14	325–350	170	24 to 28
Half (bone-in)	5 to 8	325–350	170	35 to 40
Spareribs		325–350	well done	1-1/2 to 2-1/2 hrs. (total)

(Continued)

Table 20.2 (Continued)

Cut	Approx- imate Weight	Oven Temperature Constant	Interior Temperature When Removed from Oven	Approx- imate Cooking Time
	(lbs.)	- - - - - -(°F)- - - - - -		(min. per lb.)
Pork (Smoked)				
Ham (cook before eating)				
Whole	10 to 14	300–325	160	18 to 20
Half	5 to 7	300–325	160	22 to 25
Shank or butt portion	3 to 4	300–325	160	35 to 40
Ham (fully cooked)3				
Half	5 to 7	325	130	18 to 24
Picnic shoulder	5 to 8	300–325	170	35
Shoulder roll	2 to 3	300–325	170	35 to 40
Canadian style bacon	2 to 4	325	160	35 to 40
Lamb				
Leg	5 to 8	300–325	175–180	30 to 35
Shoulder	4 to 6	300–325	175–180	30 to 35
Rolled	3 to 5	300–325	175–180	40 to 45
Cushion	3 to 5	300–325	175–180	30 to 35
Rib	1-1/2 to 3	375	170–180	35 to 45

1. National Live Stock and Meat Board.

2. Ribs which measure 6 to 7 inches from chine bone to tip of rib.

3. Allow approximately 15 minutes per pound for heating whole ham to serve hot.

Moist Heat Method

Braising

Water, meat or vegetable stock, sour cream or milk may be used to furnish the moisture. This method is employed on the less tender cuts such as the blade and arm roast of beef or steak from the same cuts; the heel of the round of beef; round and flank steak of beef; the steaks of veal, such as round, sirloin, blade, and arm veal steak; veal loin and rib chops; pork chops (both loin and rib); blade and arm pork steak from the pork shoulder; breast of lamb; neck slices of lamb; and lamb trotters.

The meat to be braised is first seasoned, dredged with flour (if desired), and browned and the necessary liquid added. The kettle or cooking utensil is covered, and the cut is cooked either in the oven or on top of the range at a simmering temperature. This method is commonly called pot roasting. (See Table 20.3 for braising times.)

Cooking in Water

This method of preparing small or large pieces of meat is suitable for such cuts as beef shank (soup bones), beef plate and brisket, veal shank and breast, lamb shank and breast, pork sparerib, and fresh or smoked pork shoulder (butts and picnics).

In the case of meat that is cut into small pieces for stews, the seasoning is added, and the pieces are browned (this is optional) in their own or added fat and then covered with hot water; in some cases tomato juice is added. The kettle is covered, and the meat is allowed to cook at a simmering temperature. If vegetables are to be added, they should be added just long enough before the meat is tender so that they will not be overdone. The liquid is thickened so that it may be served separately or with the stew. (See Table 20.4 for cooking in liquid and Table 20.5 for variety meats cooking times.)

Microwave Cooking

A regular oven is heated by either gas or electricity, and the heated air inside the oven cooks the food. In an electronic (microwave) oven, a magnetron (think of a vacuum tube) produces microwaves which are absorbed by the food, causing the molecules within the food to vibrate against each other. (These microwaves are a low-level form of radiant energy, just as are radio waves, visible light, and infrared heat; they all have long wave lengths, and so their radiant energy is nonionizing, meaning that it has no cumulative harmful effect on humans.) The

Table 20.3—Timetable for Braising[1]

Cut	Average Weight or Thickness	Approximate Total Cooking Time
Beef		
Pot Roast		
Arm or blade	3 to 4 lbs.	2-1/2 to 3-1/2 hrs.
Boneless	3 to 5 lbs.	3 to 4 hrs.
Swiss steak	1-1/2 to 2-1/2 in.	2 to 3 hrs.
Fricassee	2-in. cubes	1-1/2 to 2-1/2 hrs.
Beef birds	1/2 in. (x 2 in. x 4 in.)	1-1/2 to 2-1/2 hrs.
Short ribs	Pieces (2 in. x 2 in. x 4 in.)	1-1/2 to 2-1/2 hrs.
Round steak	3/4 in.	1 to 1-1/2 hrs.
Stuffed steak	1/2 to 3/4 in.	1-1/2 hrs.
Pork		
Chops	3/4 to 1-1/2 in.	45 to 60 min.
Spareribs	2 to 3 lbs.	1-1/2 hrs.
Tenderloin		
Whole	3/4 to 1 lb.	45 to 60 min.
Fillets	1/2 in.	30 min.
Shoulder steaks	3/4 in.	45 to 60 min.
Lamb		
Breast—stuffed	2 to 3 lbs.	1-1/2 to 2 hrs.
Breast—rolled	1-1/2 to 2 lbs.	1-1/2 to 2 hrs.
Riblets		1-1/2 to 2-1/2 hrs.
Neck slices	3/4 in.	1 hr.
Shanks	3/4 to 1 lb. each	1 to 1-1/2 hrs.
Shoulder chops	3/4 to 1 in.	45 to 60 min.
Veal		
Breast—stuffed	3 to 4 lbs.	1-1/2 to 2-1/2 hrs.
Breast—rolled	2 to 3 lbs.	1-1/2 to 2-1/2 hrs.
Veal riblets		2 to 3 hrs.
Veal birds	1/2 in. (x 2 in. x 4 in.)	45 to 60 min.
Chops	1/2 to 3/4 in.	45 to 60 min.
Steaks or cutlets	1/2 to 3/4 in.	45 to 60 min.
Shoulder chops	1/2 to 3/4 in.	45 to 60 min.
Shoulder cubes	1 to 2 in.	45 to 60 min.

1. National Live Stock and Meat Board.

Table 20.4—Timetable for Cooking in Liquid[1]

Cut	Average Weight	Approximate Time per Pound	Approximate Total Cooking Time
	(lbs.)	(min.)	(hrs.)
Smoked ham (old style and country cured)			
Large	12 to 16	20	
Small	10 to 12	25	
Half	5 to 8	30	
Smoked ham (tendered)			
Shank or butt half	5 to 8	20 to 25	
Smoked picnic shoulder	5 to 8	45	
Fresh or corned beef	4 to 6	40 to 50	
Beef for stew			2-1/2 to 3-1/2
Veal for stew			2 to 3
Lamb for stew			1-1/2 to 2

1. National Live Stock and Meat Board.

friction that is created causes heat penetration within the food itself, thus cooking it. Microwaves are reflected by metal (the oven walls), transmitted through glass, paper, pottery, and plastic (the materials the food is to be cooked in) and absorbed by the food. This explains why only the food gets hot, leaving oven walls and pan cool.

The primary advantage of electronic cooking is speed; cooking time is usually cut in half. (This includes the actual cooking time plus the "standing time" that most foods require for heat equalization after cooking—conventionally cooked food continues to cook for a while after it is removed from the oven.)

Because there is no heat in the oven itself, meat and other foods, which require the hot air of a conventional oven for browning and crisping, may not be as satisfactory—unless the speed factor is more important than a crisp, brown exterior. One alternative is to cook the meat electronically until it is halfway done, then use a regular oven or broiler for quick browning and crisping.

A microwave oven can be used to thaw frozen foods quickly, and later they can be cooked with a regular range. The electronic oven is especially good for large, slow-thawing roasts and poultry. Precooked frozen foods can be quickly thawed or reheated; this method has been

Table 20.5—Timetable for Cooking Variety Meats[1]

Kind	Broiled	Braised[2]	Cooked in Liquid
	(min.)		
Liver			
Beef			
3- to 4-pound piece		2 to 2-1/2 hrs.	
Sliced		20 to 25 min.	
Veal (Calf), sliced	8-10		
Pork			
Whole (3 to 3-1/2 pounds)		1-1/2 to 2 hrs.	
Sliced		20 to 25 min.	
Lamb, sliced	8-10		
Kidney			
Beef		1-1/2 to 2 hrs.	1 to 1-1/2 hrs.
Veal (Calf)	10-12	1 to 1-1/2 hrs.	3/4 to 1 hr.
Pork	10-12	1 to 1-1/2 hrs.	3/4 to 1 hr.
Lamb	10-12	3/4 to 1 hr.	3/4 to 1 hr.
Heart			
Beef			
Whole		3 to 4 hrs.	3 to 4 hrs.
Sliced		1-1/2 to 2 hrs.	
Veal (Calf)			
Whole		2-1/2 to 3 hrs.	2-1/3 to 3 hrs.
Pork		2-1/2 to 3 hrs.	2-1/2 to 3 hrs.
Lamb		2-1/2 to 3 hrs.	2-1/2 to 3 hrs.
Tongue			
Beef			3 to 4 hrs.
Veal (Calf)			2 to 3 hrs.
Pork ⎱ usually sold			
Lamb ⎰ ready-to-serve			
Tripe			
Beef	10-15[3]		1 to 1-1/2 hrs.
Sweetbreads	10-15[3]	20 to 25 min.	15 to 20 min.
Brains	10-15[3]	20 to 25 min.	15 to 20 min.

1. National Live Stock and Meat Board.

2. On top of range or in a 300° F to 325° F oven.

3. Time required after precooking in water.

used successfully for years in many restaurants.

Microwave cookery is not yet the panacea for the home or the institutional cook, but it does offer tremendous advantages. More research into its application to meat cookery is needed, and is planned.

COOKING LOSSES

It is common knowledge that the major loss in weight in cooked meat is due to the loss in moisture evaporated by the heat. This change in weight alters the percentage of protein, fat, and ash of the cooked meat as compared to the fresh meat. Another weight loss is that of the melted fat. This will be affected in large part by the degree of doneness.

The work of Leverton and Odell of Oklahoma in 1956-1958 showed that evaporation loss during cooking varied from 1.5% to 54.5% with an average range between 15% to 35%. The cooked lean meat without any marbling and with all separable fat removed contained from 5% to 10% fat and up to 35% protein.

The ratio of fat to lean is more important to people of moderate means than to those with higher incomes. It is easy to say, "You must have fat to have quality in meat," and "You don't have to eat the fat,"— but it is rather difficult to compromise on fat with a lean wallet.

REMINDERS

The guess work in determining the doneness of meat is eliminated by the use of the meat thermometer, a very much appreciated kitchen accessory. It is particularly useful in determining the doneness of roasts. Experiments conducted in commercial and college laboratories on the time required to prepare various meats are based on the use of the meat thermometer and automatically regulated oven and broiler temperatures. This does not mean that expert cooks—mothers, for example—with years of cooking experience have any need for these modern gadgets, but beginners must have specific answers and directions. Some of these are as follows:

Bacon is more desirable when pan broiled below its smoke point (290° to 300° F) in its own grease until crisp and a light golden brown in color. Draining off the grease as the bacon fries may cause scorching or burning. However, bacon broiled on a rack about 4 inches below the flame retains more of its original thiamine (vitamin B_1).

A temperature of 300° to 325° F is best for deep fat frying.

Do not boil meat, but use a simmering temperature of 185° to 205° F. This includes soup making.

A constant oven temperature of 300° F for roasts of beef, veal, and lamb, and 325° to 350° F for pork, produces more tender and palatable roasts than higher temperatures.

High oven temperatures affect the cost of the meat by increasing fuel consumption and shrinkage in meat poundage. It's very disheartening to open an oven and find the roast charred and about half its original size.

The shape being the same, the larger cut will require a longer total cooking period but fewer minutes per pound.

Meat cooked without undue shrinkage is juicier and more highly flavored. Burned meat results in damaged proteins.

Searing meat does not hold in the juices, but it is done by many cooks to brown the outside of a roast and develop aroma.

The water soluble B vitamins leak into the drippings. Low temperature cooking will result in more of these vitamins remaining in the meat. Gravy should never be discarded. It is the valuable by-product in meat cookery.

Maintaining a constant broiler temperature of 390° to 400° F gives the best broiling results.

Boneless or rolled cuts require from 5 to 10 minutes more time per pound to cook than unboned cuts.

Roasts with long bones require less time than thick, chunky cuts.

Retention of the B vitamins in properly roasted meat averages: thiamin—70%, riboflavin and niacin—90%.

Meat that is cooked without undue shrinkage has higher nutritional value.

The tenderness of steaks decreases with the decrease in carcass grade.

Cooking time can be decreased by the use of metal skewers and by unventilated ovens.

Small roasts, under 2 pounds and less than 2 inches thick are rather uneconomical. They also tax the patience of the retailer. Many fine dishes can be made from leftovers. And how about those handy cold cuts of roast beef, pork, lamb, and veal for sandwiches or midnight snacks?

Don't increase the cost of hamburger by buying expensive cuts such as steak for grinding. The cheapest cut, mixed with sufficient beef suet or fat back, will be as delicious and even more nutritious. This applies to personal marketing and not to telephone-order buying.

When buying meat for making a meat loaf, buy ¼ pound of fresh pork for each pound of beef and have them ground together. Pork shoulder and boneless beef shank, neck, or plate are good buys.

Meat should not be removed from its package upon delivery, but placed immediately under refrigeration. Aged meats left to lie in a warm kitchen for half a day may develop an odor that is offensive, indicating microbial growth and possible cause for food infection or intoxication (see Chapter 17).

A good kitchen scale makes an efficient short-weight detective.

Lard should be placed in a well-sealed fruit jar and stored under refrigeration.

A dark color in meat does not necessarily mean that it is spoiled or of poor quality (see Chapter 19).

Monosodium glutamate, the vegetable protein derivative, accentuates the natural flavor of food and has been considered as essential as table salt by the Chinese and Japanese.

Much of the fate of a cut of meat rests in the cooking.

HANDLING FROZEN MEAT IN THE HOME AND INSTITUTION

Below zero temperatures (the lower the better) are best for holding frozen meat.

Frozen meat that has been thawed under refrigeration need not be used immediately as is commonly recommended, because repeated tests have shown that such meat will keep as long as fresh meat properly refrigerated.

Refreezing meat does not materially affect its quality. Tests were made in which beef, properly wrapped in a good grade of locker paper, film, or aluminum foil, was thawed in the unopened package until it became warm, was refrozen, and later was rethawed and held in that condition at 38°F in a household refrigerator for an additional week, and was still in excellent condition when cooked. This does not mean that one should become careless, but it also suggests that one need not become panicky about using all the meat in a package that has been thawed if it is more than is needed for that meal. Rewrap it, refreeze it, and use it at another time.

Every time frozen meat is thawed it will lose some of the meat juices. If the position of the thawed meat package is reversed (turned over) when replaced in the zero compartment for refreezing, these juices will be reabsorbed to a large extent.

Zero temperatures materially depress the proteolytic enzyme action that breaks down connective tissue into gelatin during the aging process.

The so-called freezer burn on meats is caused by a considerable dehydration (moisture loss) of the meats or parts thereof, due to a poor grade of paper, improper wrapping, or holes in the paper. In badly dehydrated meat, water added in the cooking to replace that which was lost will help, but the meat will lose considerable flavor and tend to be tough and stringy.

Remember that it is not the lean meat that changes in flavor in zero storage nearly as much as the fat. The oxygen in air will combine with unsaturated fats and break them down into free fatty acids and aldehydes, giving them a stale, rancid flavor. This flavor is, in part, absorbed by the lean. That is the reason for using a good grade of wrapping paper, one that is moisture-vapor proof, and employing the drug store method of wrapping to exclude the air.

It is rather foolish to go to all this trouble, using expensive paper and tape and taking valuable time to do a good job, and then fling the package into a basket and rip it.

When roasting an unthawed cut, allow additional time equal to ¼ to ½ the recommended time for unfrozen cuts (see Table 20.2). If a meat thermometer is used, it should be inserted after the meat is partially cooked and the frost is out of the center.

If thawing meat before cooking is preferred, refer to Table 20.6 for a timetable for defrosting frozen meat.

Table 20.6—Timetable for Defrosting Frozen Meat[1]

Meat	In Refrigerator	Room Temperature
Large roast	4 to 7 hrs. per lb.	2 to 3 hrs. per lb.
Small roast	3 to 5 hrs. per lb.	1 to 2 hrs. per lb.
1-inch steak	12 to 14 hrs.	2 to 4 hrs.

1. National Live Stock and Meat Board.

In a study of cooking times, yields, and temperatures of frozen roasts, conducted at the University of Illinois[1] and cosponsored by the National Association of Meat Purveyors and the National Live Stock and Meat Board, the final conclusion was that "Roasts cooked from the frozen state yield as much as roasts partially or completely thawed prior to cooking." It was further observed after cooking 860 roasts weigh-

---

1. *Roasting Frozen Meat,* National Live Stock and Meat Board.

ing almost 4 tons, that roasting from a frozen state requires between 1.3 and 1.45 times as long to cook as from a chilled state.

PREPARATION OF FOOD FOR SPACE TRAVEL

No unusual diet, except for its preparation, needs to be prepared for your trip into space. Choose your favorite foods that have been pre-cooked and subjected to low temperature freezing under low pressure approaching a complete vacuum to remove the major portion of the moisture. This type of food requires no refrigeration, has very little weight, and will take up a minimum of storage space. The moisture content of this freeze-dried food must not exceed 3% and must be reconstituted (soaked in water) before serving. The reconstituted product resembles the fresh product in flavor and color and is of high quality. On your trip into space, pack each food item into a separate synthetic pouch type package so water can be added in a prescribed amount.

Freeze-dried foods are available on the market and will continue to increase as the food industry develops the potential for these products for widespread commercial use. One example is the freeze-dried soups in plastic packages that are available to the public. They have long shelf life and make delicious soups in ten minutes.

If irradiated (sterilized) foods are perfected, the refrigerator will have more space available for drinks and party specials.

COOKING POULTRY

Preparation

Frozen birds should be thawed to remove the giblets and internal fat. Sprinkle the inside of the bird with salt. Place a stuffing in the body cavity of the bird (avoid packing) and draw the ends of the drumsticks down against the opening, using a cord that laps over the back of the tail and the ends of the legs. Ducks, pheasants, and guinea fowl will require stitching to close the opening, but the legs of all fowl must be tied close to the body to avoid overcooking and drying. The loose skin at the base of the neck may be filled with the stuffing and the end tied with a cord. Birds may be stuffed the previous day only if bird *and* dressing are properly refrigerated, but the flesh will absorb the flavor of the stuffing, and this is considered objectionable by some.

Fold the wing tips back on the wings. Rub the breast and legs with butter or margarine and sprinkle with salt, preferably celery salt. Dust lightly with flour, if desired. Ducks and geese need no added fat.

Roasting

The procedure will vary with the age of the bird. Old birds should be steamed or braised for 1½ to 2 hours. This is done by placing the bird breast-up on the rack in the roaster. Cover the bottom of the roaster with hot water, place lid on roaster and braise in an oven temperature of 250° to 275° F. It may be necessary to add water several times during the braising process. Some prefer to braise the stuffed bird, and others add the stuffing after the braising period. After this steaming period, the lid and water are removed, and the oven temperature is adjusted to 325° to 350° F for the remainder of the roasting.

Young birds or those having a flexible tip on the rear end of the breast bone are placed on the roasting rack, with no lid and no water added. The position of the bird in the conventional method of roasting is with the breast up. The more recent practice is to place the bird on its side or squarely on its breast, depending upon the shape of the bird, and then turn in order from one side to the other every 45 minutes. Baste with pan drippings at each turning. Ducks and geese are self basting and the skin should be pricked with a fork during the roasting process to allow some of the fat to drain.

A bird cooked according to a time schedule may or may not be done because of various conditions such as age, weight, oven temperature, air circulation, etc. Some of the indications of doneness are a slightly shrunken flesh beneath the skin, a flexibility of the leg joint, and the absence of any pink juice when the flesh of the thigh is pricked with a fork or a skewer. Large birds with thick thighs had better have the drumsticks released from the cord that binds them to the body when the roasting period is about three-fourths completed. This permits the heat to circulate more readily around the thick, meaty highs.

The giblets are simmered to tenderness before adding them to the gravy. The neck may be cooked with the giblets. The liver needs only about 15 minutes of cooking and should be added during the last period. Allow one to one and one-half hours for chicken giblets and two to three hours for turkey giblets. If the giblets are to be incorporated with the stuffing, they should be cooked the previous day.

Stuffing

The ingredients that furnish the bulk to a stuffing are starchy in nature and consist of either bread crumbs, boiled rice, or mashed potatoes. To get added richness of flavor, melted butter or some melted fat taken from the body of the bird is added. The seasoning vegetables consist of celery, parsley, and onion. The spices or herbs that are in favor consist of thyme, sweet marjoram, pepper, and sage. Other ingredients that add variety to a stuffing are oysters, nuts, mushrooms, dried apricots or prunes, sausage, raisins, diced salt pork fried crisp, and sliced apple.

The dry stuffing is made of medium dry crumbs without milk or water added. The moist stuffing is made with crumbs, milk or water added, or with a base of boiled rice or potatoes.

A 4- to 5-pound bird will require about 4 cups of crumbs, and a 14- to 15-pound turkey will require from 10 to 12 cups of crumbs. An ordinary 1-pound loaf of bread (2 to 4 days old) will make approximately 4 to 5 cups of crumbs. Use 1 cup less of boiled rice than bread crumbs because the rice will swell.

Oyster Stuffing

(12-pound turkey)

1½ pints oysters	8-10 cups bread crumbs
¾ cup butter or other fat	½ teaspoon savory seasoning
⅛ cup chopped parsley	1 to 2 teaspoons celery salt
1 tablespoon chopped onion	

Heat the oysters for several minutes, then drain. Cook the parsley and onion for several minutes in the melted fat and add it and the drained oysters to the bread crumbs.

Sausage Bread Stuffing

(12-pound turkey)

1 pound sausage	2 tablespoons diced onion
2 eggs	1 teaspoon salt
1 cup milk	4 tablespoons chopped parsley
7 cups bread crumbs	1 cup diced celery

Pan fry the sausage until brown and drain off the fat. Beat the eggs slightly and add hot milk. Pour the egg mixture over the remaining ingredients.

Savory Stuffing

(12-pound turkey)

¾ cup butter or other fat	8-10 cups bread crumbs
1 pint chopped celery	1-2 teaspoons savory seasoning
½ cup chopped parsley	1-2 teaspoons salt
1 small onion chopped	Pepper to taste

Cook the celery, parsley, and onion in the melted fat for several minutes. Add to the bread crumbs and dry seasoning and mix. Add nuts, if desired. If chestnuts are used, boil them in water for 15 minutes, and remove the shell and brown skin while still hot.

Table 20.7—Roasting Timetable for Young Birds

Kind	Weight	Oven Temperature	Hours
	(lbs.)	(°F)	(hrs.)
Chicken	4 to 5	350	1-1/2 to 2
Duck	5 to 6	350	2 to 2-1/2
Goose	10 to 12	325	3 to 4
Guinea	2 to 2-1/2	350	1-1/2
Turkey	6 to 9	325	2-1/2 to 3
	10 to 13	325	3 to 4
	14 to 17	300	4 to 5
	18 to 25	275	6 to 8

Broiling

Young, plump birds split into halves are the only ones suitable for this purpose. The distance of the broiler rack from the flame will vary with different ovens, but a temperature of 375° to 400° F is desirable. This makes it necessary to have the broiler rack 3 inches from the flame in some ovens and from 4 to 7 inches away in others. The speed at which the bird browns will govern the distance to use. A 2-pound broiler should cook in 35 to 45 minutes.

Coat the bird with melted fat, season with salt and pepper, and sprinkle with flour if desired. Start with the skin side away from the broiler heat and turn several times as it browns. A good practice is to partly cook the bird in a 350° F oven and then broil. Small 3- to 5-pound turkeys, squab, guinea, and ducklings are broiled in the same manner.

Frying

Pan frying is more widely practiced than broiling. Various methods are used and all have enthusiastic supporters. One method consists of steaming the disjointed bird in a 300° F oven until practically tender and then dipping each joint in a beaten egg and rolling it in bread or cracker crumbs or in corn meal. Place in a thick skillet that contains melted butter or ½ inch of melted fat and brown quickly. Salt and pepper are added to the steamed bird.

Another method is to bread each joint, put the thickest pieces in the pan first, and have sufficient fat to come up around each piece. Cover the pan to avoid spattering, and cook at moderate or medium heat until brown, turning each piece as it browns. This requires from 20 to 25 minutes for chicken. It may be finished in a moderate oven (325° F).

Turkey Steak

The method of cutting the steak governs its preparation. The steaks, made by cutting crossways to the body, are dipped in egg, seasoned with celery salt, pepper, and a pinch of rubbed parsley and rolled in crumbs. Brown the steak in a skillet with ¼ to ½ inch of fat, and then steam in a roaster until tender (30 to 45 minutes).

If the boneless steaks have been tenderized by running them through a steak machine, they can be seasoned and broiled, or breaded, seasoned, and fried in deep fat. A short steaming period will make them more tender but it is not necessary. The secret in flavoring turkey steak lies in the use of celery salt and finely ground parsley.

Stewing

Stewing is employed because it produces a more tender and flavorous product. The flavor is due in large part to the type of bird used for stewing. The old bird is high in flavor. The same thing is true of all meat animals. High flavor depends upon the amount of water-soluble proteins and fat. These increase with the age of the animal or fowl. What is more delicious than a fat hen that has been stewed until she can no longer hold her beautiful form but simply disintegrates when speared with a fork! Or that tough old rooster whose morning crow announced the dawn and disrupted many a laggard's sleep—dismember him with strong hands and stony heart, place him in a kettle half filled with slightly salted water, cover and simmer and simmer. The old codger may need more water but stint him not—give him more. Subjected to 4 or 5 hours or maybe less of this treatment, served with a flour-thickened gravy, and his gastronomic appeal has such shocking import that it may bring remorse. Cooked any other way and he would be damned. And what a soup he makes—even his feet! He has uses no end. Chicken fricassee, chicken gumbo, chicken noodle soup, chicken consommé, cream of chicken soup, jellied chicken, chicken sandwich, chicken salad, chicken chop suey, chicken timbales, chicken risotto, chicken mousse, chicken soufflé, chicken croquettes, chicken à la king, chicken loaf, creamed chicken, curried chicken, and add your own.

CARVING POULTRY

The conventional method of carving pursued by most hosts is done with the bird on its back. The more recent method is to carve the bird as it rests on its side. With the bird on its back, the first step is to turn the platter with the legs of the bird pointing toward the carver. Grasp the end of the leg with the fingers of the left hand and cut between the leg and the body. Pull the point of the knife through the joint and sever the skin between the leg and back. Lift the leg to a second plate, if the platter space is limited, and separate the drumstick from the second joint or thigh. The dark meat is sliced from the second joint and also from the drumstick if it is too large for a single serving. Remove the wing by cutting around the area where it appears to join the body and force it toward the back.

If the bird is on its side, remove the wing between the first and second joint, leaving the second joint attached to the bird. Remove the

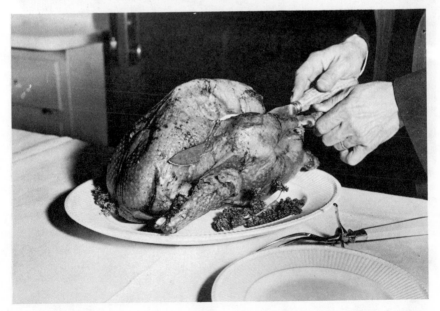

Fig. 20.1—Carving poultry (breast up). Removing the leg. (Photo by Peter Killian; courtesy, USDA)

drumstick, leaving the thigh attached to the body. This ends the most difficult part of the carving operation. Many a tragedy has occurred in disjointing a bird.

Slicing the breast meat by slicing down and away from the carver is the most comfortable method for a host who stands to carve a bird resting on its back. Most experts recommend placing the fork squarely across the breastbone toward the end of the keel. This places the left hand, which is steadying the bird with the fork, in a position that does not interfere with the right hand.

When the carver is in a sitting position, however, the breast of the bird must be next to him, in which case his right hand is working under his left arm. To avoid this unnatural position, point the front of the bird toward the carver, so he can place the fork into the opposite breast several inches below the keel, and slice as in the standing position. The slices of white breast meat can be arranged opposite the cuts of dark meat on a separate plate. When sufficient servings have been made or the one side of the bird is carved, shove the platter away from the carver

Fig. 20.2—Carving poultry (breast up). Slicing the breast meat. (Photo by Peter Killian; courtesy, USDA)

Fig. 20.3—Remove the wing portion. Grasp the wing tip firmly between thumb and fingers, lift up, and sever between the first and second joints. Drop the wing tip and first-joint portion to the side platter. The second joint is left attached to the bird.

Fig. 20.4—Remove the drumstick. Grasp the end of the drumstick and lift it up and away from the body, disjointing it at the thigh; then transfer the drumstick to the side platter for slicing the meat. The thigh is left attached to the bird.

Fig. 20.5–Slice the drumstick meat. Hold the drumstick upright and cut down, parallel with the bone, turning the leg to get uniform slices.

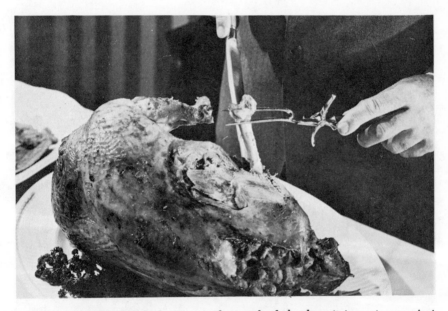

Fig. 20.6—Slice the thigh meat. Anchoring the fork where it is most convenient to steady the bird, cut slices parallel to the body until the bone is reached, and remove the slices to the side platter. Run the point of the knife around the thigh bone, lift up with the fork, and use either fork or fingers to remove the bone to the side platter. Then slice the remaining thigh meat.

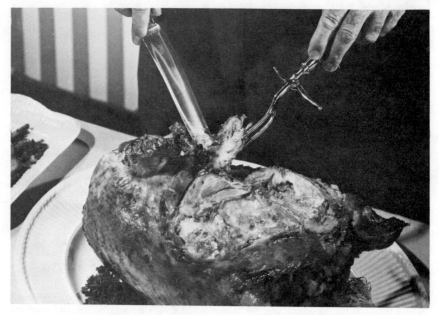

Fig. 20.7—Remove the "oyster," the choice dark meat above the thigh and adjoining backbone. Use the point of the knife to lift it out of its spoon-shaped cradle.

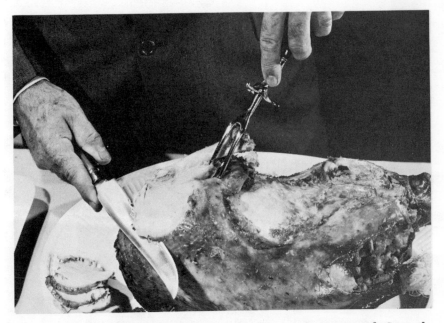

Fig. 20.8—Cut short breast slices until the wing socket is exposed. Sever the second joint of the wing and transfer it to the side platter. Slice the meat in the same manner as the drumstick meat.

Fig. 20.9—Continue slicing the breast meat. Steady the bird with a fork. Cut thin slices of breast meat until enough slices have been provided, or until the breast bone is reached.

Fig. 20.10—Remove the dressing. Slit the thin tissues of the thigh region with the tip of the knife and make an opening large enough for a serving spoon to enter. The dressing in the breast end may be served by laying the skin back onto the platter with the dressing uppermost. (Courtesy, Poultry and Egg National Board)

and have the plates put in its place. Put a spoonful of stuffing on the plate and a portion of white and dark meat on top or beside it. Some prefer to serve as they remove a slice of breast meat but this slows up the serving since it means extra handling of tools between each operation.

The illustrations on carving a bird on its side show that this method has the advantage of making the breast easier to carve, and eliminates handling the second wing joint and the thigh as separate pieces.

The breast of duck or goose is too shallow to be carved in the same manner as turkey, chicken, or guinea. Instead, cut long thin slices with the grain and parallel to the ridge or keel bone and then cut them into portions across the grain if they are too large. Another method consists of lifting the entire breast from the keel, loosening it with the point of the knife, and placing it on a separate plate. Portions for serving are made by cutting across the grain of the meat.

A napkin and not the tongue is used to wipe the fingers of the carver. Remember that the children are watching!

BARBECUING

This method of preparing meat has found great favor in roadside inns and is accomplished by several different processes.

Open Fire

The cut (generally ham or beef round) is attached to a metal rod that is mechanically rotated close to a layer of burning charcoal which glows through the grates. Steaks, chops, and kabobs are grilled on the grate.

Indirect Heat

The cut is coated with a half-inch layer of dough and placed in an oven (400° F) to roast. This is the least wasteful method since there is no charred meat and the product is very tasty and juicy.

Although entire hindquarters of beef are barbecued by the open-fire method, a more tasty product will be secured if prepared according to a method prescribed by the American Hereford Cattle Breeders' Association. It is known as the "Trench method."

The Open-Trench (Pit) Method

Barbecuing meat by this method has become one of the most popular means of preparing meat for large rural gatherings, particularly of the livestock interests. It gained considerable political stature when Governor J. A. Walton, of Oklahoma, used it to feed over 100,000 people at his inauguration.

To prepare the barbecued beef, pork, lamb, buffalo, deer, antelope, duck, goose, chicken, rabbit, squirrel, and opossum served on this occasion required one mile of trenches.

The cooking principle involved in this method of barbecuing is a combination of dry heat roasting and steaming. The steam is formed from the moisture in the meat and held in the sealed pit.

Building the Trench

The soil should not be sandy, but preferably a heavy soil containing plenty of clay. Sandy soil will require a brick lining to eliminate caving. Make the trench 3½ feet deep and 3 to 3½ feet wide. The length will depend upon the number of people to be served. A liberal serving is considered to be ½ pound (on a fresh meat basis) per person, or 50 pounds for 100 people. To barbecue 100 pounds of meat requires 3 feet of pit length; 200 pounds—5 feet; 400 pounds—10 feet; 600 pounds—15 feet; 800 pounds—20 feet; etc.

Provide covers for the pit. These may consist of pieces of corrugated sheet iron or rough boards. In case the latter are used, they should be covered with tarpaulins to keep the dirt from sifting through since the final seal will be made by using about a foot of dirt over the top. If steam leaks occur, they are plugged with more dirt.

Making the Bed of Hot Coals

Dry oak or hickory wood, measuring from 4 to 5 inches in diameter and cut in 2- to 3-foot lengths, is best in producing the 15- to 18-inch bed of hot coals. Apple wood is satisfactory but the soft and resinous woods are not. Any chunks of wood that are not burned to coals should be removed from the pit or moved to one end by the use of a long rod with a hooked end. Allow four or five hours for producing the bed of coals. It requires twice the volume of the pit in wood to make the desired bed of coals, or 1 cord (1 ton) per 7 feet of pit length. Inefficient cooking, to say the least!

The Sand Coating

The hot coals must have an over-coating of dry sand or fine gravel to the depth of 1 inch. If the sand or gravel is moist, place sheet iron over part of the pit, spread the sand on it, and stir occasionally to dry while the wood is burning. Wet sand will produce too much smoke.

The Meat

Any of the better grades of meat, poultry, or game are suitable for barbecuing, although beef is the most popular. The boneless cuts are a decided advantage for speed in carving, which is necessary when serving large groups. It is important to have each cut as nearly the same thickness as possible in order that all the cuts will cook uniformly.

The meat must be liberally seasoned with salt and pepper before being partially wrapped in aluminum foil. Use .0015 gauge foil with the drugstore lock wrap lengthwise, but leave the ends partly open to form a tube that will not scoop up sand. Place the tube-style wrapped meats on the hot sand by using a three-tined fork, the tines of which are bent into a right-angled curve to hold the roast. Place the creased fold part of the aluminum foil down on the fork and roll it off into position on the hot sand with the crease up. When all the meat is in position, place the cover over the pit and seal it with 8 to 12 inches of dirt. Be certain that the framework or sheet iron covering is strongly reinforced to prevent the top from falling into the pit.

Allow 12 hours for barbecuing and 4 to 5 hours for building the bed of coals. Do not open the pit until shortly before serving is to begin.

Barbecue Sauce

Regardless of what the authors may think of sauces or condiments other than salt and pepper for destroying the flavor of good meat, the majority rules and sauce it must be.

A sauce recommended by authorities with experience in its use is made as follows:

        6 bottles catsup (74 oz.)
        3 bottles Worcestershire sauce (18 oz.)
        ½ bottle prepared mustard (6 oz.)
        2 cups prepared barbecue sauce (on sale in stores)

Mix and heat. Serve hot. This is sufficient for 100 people. Dutchmen might prefer straight horseradish, so have some on hand.

Barbecue Menu for 100 People

The late Professor J. W. Cole, of the University of Tennessee, reported the following needs:

Meat—50 pounds (boned and rolled)

Buns—200 (sliced almost through and buttered)

Potatoes—6 pounds potato chips, or 30 pounds scalloped potatoes, or 100 pounds baked potatoes

Beans—30 pounds, baked

Salad—30 pounds potato salad, with pickles, eggs, etc., or
20 pounds cabbage salad, with dressing, or
15 to 20 pounds lettuce salad, with dressing

Pickles—1 gallon

Coffee—7 to 8 gallons (2 pounds of regular grind in a cloth bag, placed in a 10-gallon cream can with water, and boiled for three to five minutes)

Dessert—100 cups of ice cream, cup cakes, or fruit in season

Serving

Have separate tables for those doing the carving. The serving tables, size 3 feet x 10 feet, set on trestles, should be covered with clean wrapping paper, and the paper plates, paper napkins, and wooden or paper forks and spoons placed at the head end. Follow this by a systematic arrangement, such as buns, meat, potatoes, salad, relishes, dessert, and beverage. The serving may be run as self-service or attendants may fill each plate completely (excepting relish and beverage) before handing it to the guest.

Homemade Barbecue Grills

Use regular-size concrete building blocks for the walls, placing them end to end from two to three tiers high. The width of space between the lateral walls varies from 3 to 5 feet. The ends may be open or closed. Pressed charcoal briquettes are lodged in piles on the ground or gravel base and lighted with lighter fluid. Start the fire one to two hours before serving time. When the briquettes show gray areas (15-20 minutes), the piles can be leveled.

Metal reinforced grills are made with a frame of 1-inch pipe, with a grill surface 3 feet wide and 4 feet long, made of #9 gauge wire with 2-inch mesh. All sections of the grill have long handles. The cuts of steaks, chops, half chickens, burgers, kabobs, etc., are placed on the grill, and when it is time to turn the cuts (indicated by the appearance of moisture droplets on the upper surface of the patties, chops, or steaks) a second grill is placed over the meat. This permits two men, one on either side of the grill, to turn and baste the cuts. Hot butter containing some additional salt and some pepper is a good basting for practically all

Fig. 20.11—Grill walls made of concrete blocks.

Fig. 20.12—The double flip-over grill.

Fig. 20.13—A portable grill. (Courtesy, University of Illinois Hoof and Horn Club)

meats. It can be brushed on or sprayed on hot. In the case of chicken, the sauce consists of ½ pint of water, 1 pint of vinegar, ½ pound of butter, and 1 ounce of salt (sufficient for 10 chicken halves).

A similar type grill, but with the added advantage of portability obviously lacking in a concrete block grill, is shown in Figure 20.13. This trailer is made of heavy gauge steel and has held up well during two years of use and travel around Illinois.

An innovative arrangement for roasting whole hogs, beef rounds or any large cut on a rotisserie is shown in Figure 20.14. An old-fashioned hand cream separator is used for the power by reversing the direction of power flow from its initial design. In this case, rainy and windy weather forced the rig into the shelter of a stock trailer.

Fig. 20.14—Utilizing a discarded hand cream separator to power a roast pig rotisserie. (Courtesy, University of Illinois)

CARVING RED MEAT

Carving should not be an objectionable task but a proud accomplishment. Demonstrating carving dexterity will invariably provoke the commendations of guests, which is certainly not objectionable. There is a certain technique or way of carving different cuts that is best explained by drawings. In addition to knowing how to carve, one must remember:

1. That the carving knife must be sharp (it must not be sharpened at the table).
2. That whenever possible, carving should be done across the grain of the meat.
3. That the carving platter should be of ample size (it is embarrassing to serve cuts from the tablecloth or the lap).
4. That the purpose of the fork is to hold the cut and not to dull the knife.
5. That small, loose, striated pieces will make a fool of any instrument but a pair of molars or a meat grinder and should be ignored.

If a piece of meat will not hold together or desires to run a race around the platter, the carver should not attract the attention of the guests by condemning the meat, or the cook, or his own shortcomings as a carver, but should continue to work swiftly and quietly.

In order to do a commendable job, the carver must have elbow room and plenty of platter space. If it is more convenient to stand while carving, he should do so. Standing is particularly convenient for those sporting oversize waistlines. Figure 20.15 shows an arrangement of the carver's place with one tantalizing tumbler placed in the danger zone. The salad, sherbet, water, coffee, or whatever food is before each guest should be placed before the carver by the waitress when he has finished his task. If he is also required to serve the vegetables, the dishes containing them should be conveniently grouped to his right or left in some sensible pattern that has practicability for its theme rather than artistic effect.

Serving can be hastened and more carving space made available if the hostess will serve the vegetables. She will also earn his gratitude if she will divert the guests' attention from his carving by injecting them with a conversational hypo. (This will not "take" on commiserating husbands or those who came to learn how or how not to carve.)

A carver should always appear at ease, and this is not possible when the hand holding the fork is crossed over the hand doing the carving. In the case of pot roasts from the chuck, carving is simplified by cutting out solid chunks and turning them in position to make possible the

Fig. 20.15

carving of neat slices across the grain. It is not bad form to serve small slices, but it is rather embarrassing to serve large, straggly pieces with trailers.

Porterhouse steak is a cut that requires a little thought in carving because the tenderloin muscle is large enough for only a single serving. A good way to handle this situation is to remove the T-shaped bone and then carve across the tenderloin and loin muscle, giving a piece of each as a serving.

Carving a ham or leg of lamb is simplified by first slicing the meat from the front of the ham or leg (just above the stifle joint and anterior to the humerus.) This permits the cut to be placed on the flat carved surface with the back or meaty part of the cut on top. Now the carving should begin just above the hock and the slicing continued without the slices being removed until they are sufficient for completing the service. Then, a wedge-shaped piece next to the first slice at the hock should be removed. This makes room for flattening the knife so that all the slices can be cut and lifted from the bone with one final carving motion. For further carving, the roast can be placed on its side and sliced as before.

A familiarity with anatomy is of course of inestimable value in efficient carving. By efficient carving is meant the greatest number of neat slices. The housewife who takes pride in neatness and gastronomic appeal will not be satisfied with the arguments that meat is meat; it all goes to the same place; it has to be cut and mangled anyway; the small brown pieces are the best; and nothing goes to waste but all to the waist, so why be fussy.

The roast is placed on the platter with the larger cut surface down.

• Use the standard carving set or the slicer and carver's helper.

• With the guard up, push the fork firmly into the roast on the left side an inch or two from the top.

• Slice across the grain toward the fork from the far right side (first illustration). Uniform slices of ⅛ to ⅜ inch thick make desirable servings.

• As each slice is carved, lift it to the side of the platter or to another hot serving platter (second illustration).

• Remove each cord only as it is approached in making slices. Sever it with the tip of the blade, loosen it with the fork, and place it to one side.

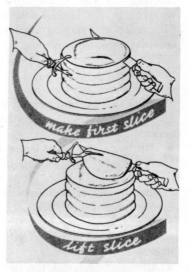

Fig. 20.16—Carving a rolled rib roast of beef.[1]

---

1. All prints on carving are by courtesy of the National Live Stock and Meat Board.

When a standing rib roast is purchased the meat retailer will, on request, remove the short ribs and separate the backbone from the ribs. The backbone can then be removed in the kitchen after roasting. This makes the carving much easier, as only the rib bones remain.

The roast is placed on the platter with the small cut surface up and the rib side to your left.

• Either the standard carving set or the roast meat slicer and carver's helper can be used on this roast.

• With the guard up, insert the fork firmly between the two top ribs. From the far outside edge slice across the grain toward the ribs (first illustration). Make the slices ⅛ to ⅜ inch thick.

• Release each slice by cutting closely along the rib with the knife tip (second illustration).

• After each cut, lift the slice on the blade of the knife to the side of the platter (third illustration). If the platter is not large enough, have another hot platter near to receive the slices.

• Make sufficient slices to serve all guests before transferring the servings to individual plates.

Fig. 20.17—Carving a standing rib roast of beef.

A lamb crown roast is made from the rack, or rib section, of the lamb. A pork crown is made from the rib sections of two or more loins of pork. Either cut is carved in a method similar to that of the pork loin roast.

• Use a standard carving set.

• Move to the side of the platter any garnish in the center which may interfere with carving. Dressing can be cut and served along with the slices.

• Steady the roast by placing the fork firmly between the ribs.

• Cut down between the ribs, allowing one rib to each slice (first illustration).

• Lift the slice on the knife blade, using the fork to steady it (second illustration).

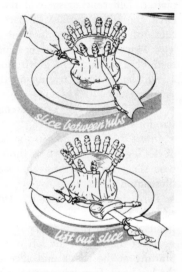

Fig. 20.18—Carving a crown roast of lamb.

The leg of lamb should be placed before the carver so that the shank bone is to his right, and the thick meaty section, or cushion, is on the far side of the platter. Different roasts will not always have the same surface uppermost because of the difference in right and left legs. However, this does not affect the method of carving. The illustrations show a right leg of lamb resting on the large smooth side.

- A standard carving set is a convenient size for this roast.
- Insert the fork firmly in the large end of the leg and carve two or three lengthwise slices from the near thin side (first illustration).
- Turn the roast so that it rests on the surface just cut. The shank bone now points up from the platter.
- Insert the fork in the left of the roast. Starting at the shank end slice down to the leg bone. Parallel slices may be made until the aitch bone is reached (second illustration). One-quarter to ⅜ inch is a desirable thickness.
- With the fork still in place, run the knife along the leg bone and release all the slices.

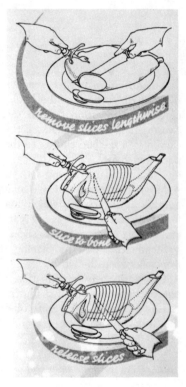

Fig. 20.19—Carving a leg of lamb.

It is much easier to carve a pork loin roast if the backbone is separated from the ribs. This is done at the market by sawing across the ribs close to the backbone. The backbone becomes loosened during roasting; note in the first illustration that it has fallen away from the ribs.

• The standard carving set is preferred for carving the pork loin, although a smaller size may be used.

• Before the roast is brought to the table remove the backbone by cutting between it and the rib ends (second illustration).

• The roast is placed on the platter so that the rib side faces you. This makes it easy to follow the rib bones, which are the guides for slicing. Make sure of the slant of the ribs before you carve, as all the ribs are not perpendicular to the platter.

• Insert the fork firmly in the top of the roast. Cut closely against both sides of each rib. You alternately make one slice with a bone and one without. Roast pork is more tempting when sliced fairly thin. In a small loin each slice may contain a rib; if the loin is large it is possible to cut two boneless slices between ribs.

• Two slices for each person is the usual serving.

Fig. 20.20—Carving a loin roast of pork.

SOME INSTITUTIONAL MANAGEMENT PROBLEMS

The operation of dining commons in many types of institutions presents many problems in dealing with grades of meat, the form in which they should be purchased, their cutting, and their preparation. Where economy, because of budget limitations, is the paramount issue, quantity and quality of meat purchases will naturally suffer. This does not mean that hash from cutter and canner stock must be the main dish. It is a challenge to a steward to make his kitchen a laboratory in which to discover:

1. What grades of meat best suit his special needs from the standpoint of complete utilization, consumer satisfaction, and cost per serving.
2. What advantages there may be in buying meat in the carcass as compared to wholesale and boneless cuts, fresh as compared to frozen, and from the packer as compared to the jobber.
3. What cuts furnish satisfactory roasts, steaks, etc., at the lowest cost per serving (for example—chucks as compared to rounds for roasts).
4. What method of cutting is best adapted to the utilization of all the meat.
5. What new and different ways the same cuts may be prepared and served so as to relieve the monotony so often prevalent.

The Cutting and Cooking Test

The most businesslike approach to the solution of these problems is to make cutting tests on carcasses and cuts of different grade and price levels, and thereby determine actual costs of servings. For example, if boneless beef is required for roasts and good grade chucks are quoted at 52 cents, good grade rounds at 75 cents, and 6- to 8-pound chuck rolls at 80 cents, which is the most satisfactory and economical buy for that purpose? Will a 52-cent chuck, when boned, furnish chuck rolls under 80 cents per pound, and can chuck or round be cut to better advantage? Also, what will servings cost and how do the two compare in palatability and ease in serving? The answers are found by cutting and preparing the meat for the oven and then dividing the usable weight into the total cost. The cooked product when served will give further information as to shrinkage and actual number of servings secured per pound of fresh meat. (Consult tables 20.8 and 20.9 for data on servings and cost per serving.)

The ham is placed on the platter with the fat or decorated side up. The shank end should always be to the carver's right. The thin side of the ham, from which the first slices are made, will be nearest or farthest from the carver, depending on whether the ham is from a right or a left side of pork. The illustration shows a left ham with the first slices cut nearest the carver. The diagram shows the bone structure and direction of the slices.

• Use a standard carving set or the slicer and carver's helper on the baked ham.

• Insert the fork and cut several slices parallel to the length of the ham on the nearest side (first illustration).

• Before the roast is brought to the table remove the backbone by cutting between it and the rib ends (second illustration).

• Turn the ham so that it rests on the surface just cut. Hold the ham firmly with the fork and cut a small wedge from the shank end (second illustration). By removing this wedge the succeeding slices are easier to cut and to release from the bone.

• Keep the fork in place to steady the ham and cut thin slices down to the leg bone (second illustration).

Fig. 20.21—Carving a roast ham.

• Release slices by cutting along bone at right angles to slices (third illustration).

• For more servings turn the ham back to its original position and slice at right angles to the bone (fourth illustration).

Table 20.8—Servings per Pound to Expect from a Specific Cut of Meat[1,2]

Beef

Cut	Serving	Cut	Serving
Steaks		Pot Roasts	
Chuck (Arm or Blade)	2	Arm (Chuck)	2
Club	2	Blade (Chuck)	2
"Cubed"	4	Chuck, Boneless	2-1/2
Filet Mignon	3	English (Boston) Cut	2-1/2
Flank	3	Other Cuts	
Porterhouse	2	Brisket	3
Rib	2	Cubes	4
Rib Eye (Delmonico)	3	Loaf	4
Round	3	Patties	4
Sirloin	2-1/2	Short Ribs	2
T-Bone	2		
Top Loin	3	Variety Meats	
		Brains	5
Roasts		Heart	5
Rib, Standing	2	Kidney	5
Rib Eye (Delmonico)	3	Liver	4
Rump, Rolled	3	Sweetbreads	5
Sirloin Tip	3	Tongue	5

Pork

Cut	Serving	Cut	Serving
Chops and Steaks		Picnic Shoulder (Bone-in) Fresh or Smoked	2
Blade Chops or Steaks	3		
Boneless Chops	4	Sirloin	2
Fresh Ham (Leg) Steaks	4	Smoked Shoulder Roll (Butt)	3
Loin Chops	4		
Rib Chops	4	Other Cuts	
Smoked (Rib or Loin) Chops	4	Back Ribs	1-1/2
Smoked Ham (Center Slice)		Bacon (Regular), Sliced	6
Steaks	5	Canadian-Style Bacon	5
		Country-Style Back Ribs	1-1/2
Roasts		Cubes (Fresh or Smoked)	4
Ham (Leg), Fresh, Bone-in	3	Hocks (Fresh or Smoked)	1-1/2
Ham (Leg), Fresh, Boneless	3-1/2	Pork Sausage	4
Ham, Smoked, Bone-in	3-1/2	Spareribs	1-1/2
Ham, Smoked, Boneless	5	Tenderloin (Whole)	4
Ham, Smoked, Canned	5	Tenderloin (Fillets)	4
Boston Shoulder (Rolled)			
Boneless	3	Variety Meats	
Loin Blade	2	Brains	5
Loin (Rolled), Boneless	3-1/2	Heart	5
Loin, Center	2-1/2	Kidney	5
Loin Smoked	3	Liver	4

(Continued)

Table 20.8 (Continued)

Lamb

Cut	Serving	Cut	Serving
Chops and Steaks		Shoulder (Boneless)	3
Leg Chops (Steaks)	4		
Loin Chops	3	Other Cuts	
Rib Chops	3	Breast	2
Shoulder Chops	3	Breast (Riblets)	2
Sirloin Chops	3	Cubes	4
		Shanks	2
Roasts			
Leg (Bone-in)	3	Variety Meats	
Leg (Boneless)	4	Heart	5
Shoulder (Bone-in)	2-1/2	Kidney	5

1. National Live Stock and Meat Board.

2. The servings per pound are only a guide to the average amount
to buy to provide 3 to 3-1/2 ounces of cooked lean meat. The cooking
method and cooking temperature, the degree of doneness, the difference
in the size of bone in the bone-in cuts, and amount of fat trim are some
of the factors that vary and will affect the yield of cooked lean meat.

What Grade of Meat Should I Purchase?

The answer depends upon whether you are serving paying or nonpaying clients. Choice and Good grades should be used for the former,
but tasty meals can be prepared more economically from Standard, Commercial, and Utility grades of meat. A good policy is to use the better
grades for chops, steaks, and roasts, and have some of the Utility grade
on hand to incorporate with the more wasty cuts, thereby enabling the
use of most of the excess fat. Whether hindquarters or forequarters
should be used for this fat-saving purpose will depend upon the difference in price between the two, hindquarters being preferred by many.
Hindquarters will usually average about 2% less bone than the forequarters. The tables on the retail cut yields of the beef carcass (Chapter
13) and of lamb (Chapter 14) should be helpful in estimating the yield
of edible meat from different grades of carcasses and cuts.

In the case of institutions having nonpaying clients or wards, it may
be necessary, because of limited appropriations, to use the Standard,
Commercial, and Utility grades of meat.

Table 20.9—Cost for a Serving of Meat at Various Price Levels[1]

Cost per Pound	Approximate Cost per Serving							
	1-1/2 Servings per Pound	2 Servings per Pound	2-1/2 Servings per Pound	3 Servings per Pound	3-1/2 Servings per Pound	4 Servings per Pound	5 Servings per Pound	6 Servings per Pound
				($)				
.39	.26	.20	.16	.13	.11	.10	.08	.07
.49	.33	.25	.20	.16	.14	.12	.10	.08
.59	.39	.30	.24	.20	.17	.15	.12	.10
.69	.46	.35	.28	.23	.20	.17	.14	.12
.79	.53	.40	.32	.26	.23	.20	.16	.13
.89	.59	.45	.36	.30	.25	.22	.18	.15
.99	.66	.50	.40	.33	.28	.25	.20	.17
1.09	.73	.55	.44	.36	.31	.27	.22	.18
1.19	.79	.60	.48	.40	.34	.30	.24	.20
1.29	.86	.65	.52	.43	.37	.32	.26	.22
1.39	.93	.70	.56	.46	.40	.35	.28	.23
1.49	.99	.75	.60	.50	.43	.37	.30	.25
1.59	1.06	.80	.64	.53	.45	.40	.32	.27
1.69	1.13	.85	.68	.56	.48	.42	.34	.28
1.79	1.19	.90	.72	.60	.51	.45	.36	.30
1.89	1.26	.95	.76	.63	.54	.47	.38	.32
1.99	1.33	1.00	.80	.66	.57	.50	.40	.33
2.09	1.39	1.05	.84	.70	.60	.52	.42	.35
2.19	1.46	1.10	.88	.73	.63	.55	.44	.37
2.29	1.53	1.15	.92	.76	.65	.57	.46	.38
2.39	1.59	1.20	.96	.80	.68	.60	.48	.40
2.49	1.66	1.25	1.00	.83	.71	.62	.50	.42
2.59	1.73	1.30	1.04	.86	.74	.65	.52	.43
2.69	1.79	1.35	1.08	.90	.77	.67	.54	.45

1. National Live Stock and Meat Board.

Contrary to most carving rules, a steak is carved with the grain. A steak need not be cut across the grain because the meat fibers are tender and already relatively short.

• Use the steak set with a knife-blade of 6 to 7 inches.

• Holding the steak with the fork inserted at the left, cut closely around the bone (first illustration). Then lift the bone to the side of the platter where it will not interfere with the carving.

• With the fork in position, cut across the full width of the steak (second illustration). Make wedge-shaped portions, widest at the far side. Each serving will be a piece of the tenderloin and a piece of the large muscle.

• Serve the flank end last if additional servings are needed (third illustration).

In order to protect the cutting edge of the knife, as well as the platter, a board cut to fit the center section of the steak is almost a necessity when carving a steak.

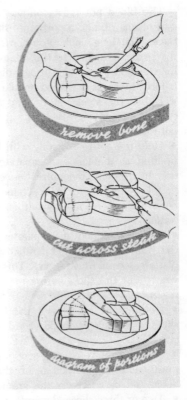

Fig. 20.22—Carving a porter-house steak.

The blade pot roast contains at least part of one rib and a portion of the blade bone. The long cooking process softens the tissues attached to the bones; therefor the bones can be slipped out easily before the roast is placed on the table.

• Either the steak set or the standard carving set may be used for carving the pot-roast.

• Hold the pot-roast firmly with the fork inserted at the left and separate a section by running the knife between two muscles, then close to the bone, if the bone has not been removed (first illustration).

• Turn the section just separated so that the grain of the meat is parallel with the platter (second illustration). This enables you to cut the slices across the grain of the meat.

• Holding the piece with the fork, cut slices ¼ to ⅜ inch thick (third illustration).

• Separate the remaining sections of the roast; note the direction of the meat fibers and carve across the grain.

• Two or three slices, depending on size, are served to each person.

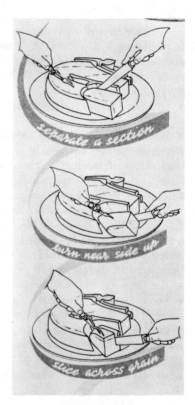

Fig. 20.23—Carving a chuck or blade roast.

Can Steak Be Cut from a Forequarter of Beef, and If So, How Much?

Steak can be cut from the forequarter, but it should be prepared as Swiss steak. Table 20.10 demonstrates a cutting test made on a Good grade forequarter, boned as illustrated in Chapter 13. The rib-eye and shoulder-clod muscles furnished the bulk of the steak. These steaks were cut into 4-ounce portions. The sort ribs were cut with the bone left in. If the brisket is cut into pieces slightly smaller but similar in shape to those from the short rib and included with them, this method produces about 21% steak, 21% short rib, and 27% stew (or hamburger).

The percentages in Table 20.11 were secured from Good to Choice loins (kidney out) weighing between 45 and 50 pounds.

Problem: What is the cost of these boneless cuts on the basis of current wholesale prices of trimmed loins? On the basis of a 7-ounce

Table 20.10—Cutting Test on a 169-Pound Forequarter (Good Grade)

Cut	Pounds	Percent
Steak	35	20.7
Short rib	25	14.8
Stew beef	45-1/2	27.0
Brisket roll (roast or stew)	11	6.5
Subtotal	116-1/2	69.0
Bone	29-1/2	17.4
Fat	23	13.6
Total	169	100.0

Table 20.11—Steak Yield from a Trimmed Beef Loin (Good Grade)

Cut	Percent	Cut	Percent
Strip loin	20	Stew meat	9
Boneless hip	33	Fat	20
Fillet	6	Bone	12

steak, how many servings can be secured from a 50-pound loin, and what is the cost per serving after crediting stew meat (or hamburger), fat, and bone? Figure the same problem if the fillet is not served but credited at current market price.

What Is the Meat Yield from Fresh Hams of Different Weights?

Table 20.12 demonstrates a ham cutting test made on 42 fresh hams of different weights.

Table 20.12—Ham Cutting Test

Number of Hams	Weight of Hams	Total Meat Yield	Roasts	Trimmings	Bone	Fat
	(lbs.)	- - - - - - - - - - (%) - - - - - - - - - - - -				
10	13-1/2	83	76	7	11	6
7	14-1/2	83	76	7	10.5	6.5
16	15-1/2	82	75	7	10	8
9	17	81	74	7	9.5	9.5

Problem: Roast pork is on the menu for 500 guests. How many 15-pound hams must be provided and what will be the cost per serving if 4 ounces of the roasted pork are served per plate? (Use current market prices and credit lean trimmings at sausage price, and skin and fat at waste fat price.)

What Percent of Edible Ham Steak Can Be Cut from a Smoked Ham?

Much depends upon the method of cutting and the amount of the less desirable ham steaks you wish to use. Table 20.13 shows the ham-composition yield of a 16-pound ham when cut as recommended in Chapter 12.

What Pork Cuts Make the Best Sausage, and Can I Save Money by Making My Own Sausage?

Fresh skinned pork shoulders of the better grades make an ideal

Table 20.13—Ham Composition

Cut	Pounds	Percent
Butt slices	2-1/2	15.63[1]
Center slices	8-1/2	53.12[1]
Heel slices	1/2	3.12[1]
Aitch bone and hock for boiling	3-1/2	21.88
Skin and fat	1	6.25
	16	100.00

1. This test shows a maximum slicing yield of 71.87%.

sausage since shoulder meat has about the right proportion of lean to fat. In the lower grades of unfinished pork it will be necessary to use additional pork fat. Heavy shoulders from gilts and sows can generally be bought at a lower figure than light shoulders. Sausage trimmings may be bought from packers for sausage making on which the following assumed prices are to be used in working this problem:

Regular pork trimmings, 50% lean.................34¢ per lb.
Special lean pork trimmings, 85%.................66¢ per lb.
Extra lean pork trimmings, 95%..................74¢ per lb.
Skinned pork shoulders..........................60¢ per lb.
Country style sausage, fresh in links...........94¢ per lb.
Country style sausage, fresh in bulk............84¢ per lb.

Tests show that fresh skinned pork shoulders will yield approximately 85% sausage meat.

Sausage Test on a 20-Pound Fresh Skinned Shoulder

17½ lbs. sausage meat
2 lbs. bone
½ lb. skin

Figuring 3 cents a pound for grinding and 1 cent per pound for seasoning, and considering that regular pork trimmings are generally too high in fat to be used alone (use with 50% of shoulder or special lean), determine the reply to the question.

What Percent Loss Can I Expect
in Slicing a Slab of Bacon?

The shape and trim of the bacon will have a large bearing on the waste. The rind (skin) on the bacon represents 4% to 6% of its weight, depending on whether it was removed by machine (4%) or by hand (6%). Slab trimmings amount to an additional 3%.

What Percent Loss Can I Expect
in Slicing a Beef Liver?

A beef liver in good sound condition and well chilled should not show more than 2% to 3% waste. This is of course dependent upon the manner of slicing and the skill of the man doing the slicing.

CHAPTER 21

Meat Judging and Evaluation

Intercollegiate meat judging contests were inaugurated and sponsored by the National Live Stock and Meat Board in the fall of 1926 when the first contest of its kind was held in connection with the International Livestock Exposition, Chicago, Illinois. This contest has since been moved to Madison, Wisconsin, but is still affiliated with the International show. The Meat Board now sponsors similar contests at Kansas City, Missouri; Dallas, Texas; Timberville, Virginia; and Portland, Oregon. These contests, in many instances, are concurrent with the livestock expositions held at those places.

The success of intercollegiate livestock judging contests, and the fact that more agricultural colleges were teaching meat courses, prompted Mr. R. C. Pollock, then general manager of the board, to get intercollegiate meat judging on its way. Ten teams competed that first year as compared to 26 teams in 1960 and 22 teams in 1973. It has accomplished what it set out to do, which is to give college students who meet the eligibility rules set up by a rules committee the opportunity to put to a test the meat knowledge they acquired in their respective institutions and to gain a wider knowledge of the meat industry. As was to be expected, it did more than that. Student met student, and they in turn met men in the industry. The meat industry (packers) became interested in these young men, with the result that many college trained men are now holding responsible positions with them.

Tables 21.1 through 21.5 list the participating schools and their ranking since each contest was started.

AK-SAR-BEN MEAT ANIMAL EVALUATION CONTEST

A contest designed to allow students to compete in an overall program was begun in 1964. The program includes (1) meat judging, (2)

Table 21.1—International—Rank of Meat Judging Teams—1926-1973

Institute	26	27	28	29	30	31	32	33	34	35	36	37	38	39	40	41	46	47	48	49	50	51	52	53	54	55	56	57	58	59	60	61	62	63	64	65	66	67	68	69	70	71	72	73
Brigham Young	–	–	–	–	–	–	–	–	–	–	–	–	–	–	–	–	–	–	–	–	–	–	–	–	–	–	–	–	–	–	–	–	–	–	–	–	18	–	–	–	–	–	–	–
Calif. Poly.	–	–	–	–	–	–	–	–	–	–	–	–	–	–	–	–	–	–	–	–	–	–	–	–	–	–	–	–	–	25	24*	13	23	20	20	–	–	–	–	–	–	–	–	–
Clemson	7	–	–	–	–	–	–	–	–	–	–	–	–	–	–	–	13	–	–	17	–	–	–	21	10	18	22	24	11	6	21	19	21	19	19	19	16	22	20	20	22	17	15	17
Colorado	–	–	–	–	–	–	–	–	–	–	–	–	–	–	–	–	–	–	–	–	–	–	–	9	16	21	6	18	25	22	26	–	24	19	16	10*	16	7*	13	2	19	–	18	10
Connecticut	–	–	–	–	–	–	–	–	–	–	–	–	–	–	–	–	–	–	–	–	–	–	–	–	13*	23	9	17	23	17*	13	20	10	–	–	13	14	15	7*	10	19	17	11	2
Cornell	10	6	4	8	7	5	–	–	–	12	–	5	7	11	2*	11	11	8	–	5	9	7	7	12	13*	–	10	6	12	16	20	3	4	6	3	9	14	15	7	10	2	8	11	2
Florida	–	–	–	–	–	1	3	2	7	10	9	12	14	15	–	–	2*	3	9	2	5	1	4	3	2	9	1	5	3	8	1	1	1	10	3	6	11	1	2	9	10	8	14	1
Idaho	2	1	5	2	8	2	3	6	1	10	3	3	5	2	10	5	4	12	4	10	2	11	4	15	2	1	1	2	16*	5	6	6	9	1	5	6	2	4	10	9	10	13	14	4
Illinois	3	–	2	4	6	1	4	1	–	9	9	10	5	14	5*	10	1	–	9	12	9	2	1	6	4	7	12	20	18	24	15	10	6	15	9	7*	15	10	21	19	17	5	19	5
Illinois State	–	–	–	–	–	–	–	–	–	–	–	–	–	–	–	–	–	10	11	18	4	17*	19	22	21	8	24	23	21	23	22	23	12	–	–	2	9*	16	13	11	14	15	6	7
Iowa	–	–	–	–	–	–	8	5	9	7	7	9	11	13	–	8	–	7	6	9	19	13	13	8	7	19	8	11	6	12	19	11	14	11	11*	17	17	12	8	14	18	11	20	18
Kansas	–	–	–	–	–	9	–	8	6	10	11	7	6	6*	13	7	10	16	12	15	20	12	13	10*	11	11	7	13	14	21	15	21	3	9	15	14	12	8	11	17	18	16	20	21
Kentucky	–	–	–	–	–	4	7	3	2	5	4	1	12	3	4	6	6	8	13	11	8	3*	6	6	12	14	17	4	5	11	17	6	3	11	11	11*	9*	12	8	14	16	3	7*	12
Maryland	–	–	–	–	–	4	1	2	–	1	5	1	1	8	2	2	2*	6	17*	21	11	15	11	17	15	17	12	21	15	9	17	16	8	1	15	14	9*	13	11	4*	8	4	7*	9
Massachusetts	–	–	3	6	4	8	–	–	–	–	–	6	4	10	2*	1	5	1	1	13	6	16	3	18	20	13	13	9	20	7	14	15	1	9	13	12	7*	13	17	13	21	16	12	9
Michigan	1	7	5	4	–	–	–	8	6	9	7	9	13	6*	–	8	10	10	11	18	4	17*	19	20	21	8	24	23	21	23	22	23	12	–	5	2	9*	6	1	3	9	15	6	7
Minnesota	–	–	–	1	–	–	–	6	–	10	11	7	6	6*	13	7	7	16	6	9	19	13	13	8	7	19	8	11	6	12	19	11	14	11	11*	17	17	14	18	11	14	11	13	18
Mississippi	9	–	–	9	9	9	–	8	6	1	1	7	12	3	1	–	16	16	12	15	20	12	13	10*	11	11	7	13	14	21	15	21	3	9	12	17	16	16	8	17	18	16	20	21
Missouri	4	7	7	5	2	9	1	2	1	5	1	1	2	8	4	6	6	8	13	11	8	3*	6	7	12	14	17	4	5	11	17	6	3	11	11	11*	12	6	11	14	16	3	7*	12
Nebraska	1	9	1	3	–	4	2	3	2	4	4	1	1	1	1	2	2*	6	17*	21	11	15	16	17	15	14	12	21	15	9	17	16	8	18	15	14	9*	13	9	4*	8	4	9	9
New Mexico	–	–	–	–	–	–	–	–	–	–	–	6	3	10	9	13	6	6	18	13	6	16	16	18	20	20	13	9	20	7	14	15	11	9	13	12	7*	13	17	13	21	16	12	9
North Carolina	–	12	3	6	–	8	1	9	8	11	8	8	4	5	2*	1	2*	8	17	16	7	2	3*	19	17	13	14	14	24	3	14	15	10	9	14	16	15	18	3	18	16	5	10*	14
North Dakota	–	5	8*	–	–	7	7	1	6	8	3	4	10	2	5*	–	3	2	5	13	17	3*	18	23	22	22	16	21	18	26	6	4*	5	1	15	14	5	1	5	1	5	12	4*	7
Ohio	3	5	–	–	4	–	–	–	–	6	2	4	–	3	–	1	5	3	1	20	15	15	3	18	20	20	13	9	20	7	14	15	11	–	13	12	19	19	17	13	21	16	–	–
Oklahoma	3	–	–	5	–	–	7	9	4	8	1	1	8	10	2*	–	2	1	2	13	6	2	9	1	17	13	16	14	8	4	6	1	5	5	14	16	5	8	9	1	–	18	–	–
Ontario	6	7	8*	–	5	9	7	1	4	6	5	11	8	4	9	12	3	2	3	16	17	3*	18	23	22	22	20	3	22	26	–	–	–	–	17	5	3	3	1	–	–	–	–	13
Panhandle	–	–	–	–	–	–	–	–	–	–	–	–	–	–	–	–	–	–	–	20	15	19	20	13	18	10	4	15	10	10	16	17	18	17	17	10*	4	20	18	8	13	18	17	13
Pennsylvania	6	7	6	1	9	3	9	7	5	4	6	11	8	4	7	4	8	4	10	14	16	5	10	10*	19	15	21	8	9	9	11	14	13	12*	10	7*	6	5	15	8	14	9	2	22
Purdue	5	2	1	6	1	7	1	4	3	7	6	2	13	9	1	4	7	7	16	6	10	17*	11*	14	5	5	18	12	13	14	4	2	20	11	6	3	10	21	15	4*	15	6	5	3
South Dakota	5	–	–	7	–	7	5	4	7	5	6	2	–	7	8	3	4	5	5	12	14	14	16	16	8	4	5	2	13	2	12*	18	13	1	2	1	10	5	4	12*	15	6	2	6
Tennessee	2	–	–	7	3	5	5	3	3	7	6	1	13	9	7	3	7	5	12	6	18	17*	15	16	6	8	18	12	3	1	4	2	20	11	6	3	10	21	15	12	4	1	5	1
Texas A & M	–	–	–	–	6	–	–	–	–	–	6*	–	–	6*	–	–	4	5	5	12	14	14	20	5	6	16	5	19	7	2	12	7	2	11*	2	4	1	19	19	7	7	6	3	19
Texas Tech.	–	–	–	–	1	–	–	–	–	–	–	1	–	8	8	3	7	7	10	7	18	20	15	1	8	1	23	16	15	1	24*	18	25	21	21	15	13	14	9	16	6	5	16	8
VPI & SU	–	–	–	–	–	6	1	–	–	–	–	1	6	–	12	12	6	14	14	8	1	8	8	17	12	–	19	16	7	13	23	–	15	14	18	–	1	19	14	6	6	2	–	–
Washington	10	1	5	9	3	1	6	1	–	11	8	3	9	1	12	14	12	5	14	4	7	1	17	24	1	1	19	16	1	15	7	12	17	8	8	15	–	3	9	6	6	2	16	8
West Virginia	11	1	2	9	6	6	6	6	4	9	3	9	9	1	14	9	12	14	14	8	3	6	17	4	3	2	2	1	4	20	7	7	2	3	7	11*	12	18	14	12	–	10	10	16
Wisconsin	8	8	–	–	–	–	1	–	–	6	2	–	–	5*	5*	9	9	7	3	3	17	6	15	4	3	2	2	1	4	–	4	–	–	1	8	8	7*	–	–	–	–	10	10	16
Wyoming	8	8	–	–	–	–	–	–	–	–	–	–	–	–	–	–	–	–	–	–	–	–	–	–	–	–	–	1	–	–	–	–	–	–	4	–	–	–	–	–	–	–	–	1

*Tie

Table 21.2—American Royal—Rank of Meat Judging Teams—1927-1973

Institute	27	28	29	30	31	32	33	34	35	36	37	38	39	40	41	46	47	48	49	50	51	52	53	54	55	56	57	58	59	60	61	62	63	64	65	66	67	68	69	70	71	72	73
Idaho	1	—	1	—	—	—	—	—	—	—	—	—	—	—	—	—	—	—	—	—	—	—	—	—	—	—	—	—	—	—	—	—	—	—	—	—	—	—	—	—	—	—	—
Illinois	—	2	1	5	3	—	—	—	—	—	8	11	8	6	9	—	7	14	4	5*	3	7	13	13	14	15	10	10	15	14	9*	2	4	7	11	12*	12	9	3	5	8*	8	4
Illinois State	—	—	1	1	2	2	1	1	1	1	5	10	8	10	6	10	8	8	6	1	7	8	6	5	6	4	9	5	5	4	4	5	8	2	12	8	10*	14	15	9	10	1	5
Iowa	3	3	3	1	2	2	2	2	6	6	5	—	6	10	6	8	10	4	5	4	6	13	15	9	8	9	5	3	1	1*	4	5	2	2	10	3	2	1	21	12	10	2	2
Kansas	4	4	2	2	1	1	2	3	4	5	3	—	6	9	7	8	8	4	14	14	6	14	3	8	10	9	8	7	12	12	1*	7	10	1	10	13	2	20	—	2	2	2	2
Kentucky	—	—	3	—	—	—	—	—	—	—	—	—	—	—	—	—	—	—	—	13	—	—	—	—	—	1	—	—	—	—	1*	—	11	3	—	13	1	2	1	1	1	2	—
Louisiana	—	—	—	—	—	—	—	—	—	—	—	—	—	—	—	—	9	2*	10	—	—	11	11	6	13	7	13	9	10	7	16	12	11	—	9	5	3	2	4	—	5	—	8
Michigan	1	1	3	—	—	—	—	—	3	—	1	9	7	7	2	5	1	11	14	9	8	4	2	2	7	12	17	16	11	7	17	13	11	—	13	18	10*	15	20	7	7	—	14
Minnesota	—	—	—	—	—	—	—	—	1	2	9	6	8	8	8	6	5	10	11	10	11	10	8	11	15	13	7	6	11	10	6	15	13	8	17	4	7	8	16	—	—	10	—
Mississippi	2	1	5	3	4	—	3	5	1	1	1	1	1	3	8	5	6	10	11	—	—	—	—	—	—	—	14	4	13	—	11	6	7	—	9	18	9	6	1	10	7	4	8
Missouri	5	—	4	4	—	—	—	—	—	1	—	—	4	—	3	6	—	—	—	—	8	4	8	—	2	13	12	18	11	—	6	15	13	—	17	17	7	8	—	11	6	7	—
Nebraska	5	4	—	—	—	—	—	—	—	—	—	—	—	—	—	—	—	—	—	—	—	—	—	11	—	—	—	8	—	—	3	—	—	—	2	7	14	4	—	13	15	—	9
New Mexico	—	—	—	—	—	—	—	—	—	—	—	—	—	—	—	—	—	5	3	8	10	5	5	10	12	11	12	18	16	15	11	9	7	10	15	7	14	8	18	16	14	7	15
North Dakota	—	—	—	—	—	—	—	—	—	—	—	—	—	—	—	4	3	2*	1	5*	1	1	4	4	11	6	6	12	8	2	12	14	9	—	2	10	17	7	13	15	13	9	9
Ohio	6	—	—	—	—	—	—	1	1	1	5	1	3	1	1	3	4	2*	1	5*	1	1	8	2	3	3	4	1	3	3	2	3	1	5	1	—	14	4	7	8	3	4	7
Oklahoma	6	6	—	—	—	—	5	4	5	6	2	5	3	—	1	—	—	13	12	11	—	15	14	15	11	1	11	17	14	17	13	11	12	1	16	15	16	16	7	16	14	14	13
Panhandle	6	6	—	5	5	—	—	—	1	7	7	7	9	2	5	3	3	—	—	—	—	—	—	—	2	8	16	14	—	8	—	—	14	—	3	3	6	12	13	15	13	6	18
Pennsylvania	—	—	6	—	4	4	—	—	—	1	2	2	5	5	4	2	1	6	7	2	5	9	12	14	16	8	16	14	6	6	8	8	—	9	11	11	6	12	11	2	12	13	3
Purdue	8	5	—	—	—	—	—	—	—	—	—	—	—	—	—	—	2	7	3	7	4	3	9	7	1	1	2	4	8	9*	9*	—	14	6	3	16	5	13	14	14	12	6	11
South Dakota	8	5	—	—	—	—	—	—	—	—	—	—	—	—	—	—	—	9	7	12	9	6	7	9	5	5	8	2	2	6	5	10	6	4	5	6	5	11	8	14	4	13	3
Tennessee	—	—	—	—	—	—	—	—	—	—	3	3	2	3	—	7	2	3	13	12	7	3	10	12	14	6	15	4	18	5	7	10	6	1	—	—	1	—	10	3	1	5	12
Texas A & M	—	—	—	—	—	—	—	—	—	—	—	—	—	—	—	—	—	9	3	—	4	12	—	4	4	—	2	—	—	—	—	—	—	—	—	—	8	5	8	4	—	1	—
Texas Tech.	—	—	—	—	—	—	—	—	—	—	—	—	—	—	—	—	—	12	9	2	9	9	9	7	—	1	15	4	18	13	7	10	6	—	14	6	5	21	3	3	2	—	12
U of Florida	—	—	—	—	—	—	—	—	—	—	1	6	1	1	—	—	—	13	13	12	—	12	10	12	9	—	—	15	—	—	—	16	—	1	—	—	8	18	10	—	—	—	17
VPI & SU	—	—	—	—	—	—	—	—	—	—	—	—	—	—	—	—	—	—	—	—	—	—	—	—	—	—	—	—	—	13	—	—	—	—	—	—	1	5	8	6	9	—	—
Washington	—	—	—	—	—	—	—	—	—	—	—	—	—	—	—	—	—	—	—	—	—	—	—	—	—	—	—	—	—	—	—	—	—	—	—	—	—	—	10	17	8*	15	17
West Virginia U	—	—	—	—	—	—	—	—	—	—	—	—	—	—	—	—	—	1	2	3	2	2	2	3	3	3	3	2	4	3	1*	3	5	1	7	9	—	12	6	—	—	—	—
Wisconsin	—	—	—	—	—	—	—	—	—	—	—	—	—	—	—	—	—	1	1	1	1	1	1	1	1	1	1	1	—	1	1*	—	1	1	1	9	—	—	—	—	—	—	—
Wyoming	7	—	—	—	—	—	—	—	—	—	—	—	—	4	—	4	—	2	1	3	1	2	1	—	—	—	—	—	—	—	—	—	—	—	—	12*	—	17	—	—	—	—	—

Table 21.3—Eastern—Rank of Meat Judging Teams—1950-1973

Institute	50	51	52	53	54	55	56	57	58	59	60	61	62	63	64	65	66	67	68	69	70	71	72	73
Clemson	—	—	—	—	—	—	—	—	12	9	10	3	12	10	10	—	6	—	10			10	—	—
Connecticut	—	—	—	5	7	5	7	12	9	10	6	11	11	9	11	11	7	—	9	N	N	—	11	10
Cornell	—	—	—	7	1	6	8	3	2	5	5	—	8	—	6	9	—	—	8	O	O	—	9	10
Florida	—	—	—	—	—	—	—	11	5	7	11	5	1	1	8	6	—	2	2			1	9	11
Illinois	—	—	—	—	—	—	—	—	—	—	—	—	4	1	9	7	—	1	—	O	O	1	1	7
Kentucky	5	6	6	4	8	9	10	7	13	13	13	9	—	—	—	—	—	—	—			—	—	—
Maryland	7	8	—	8	9	9	9	—	7	11	14	8	—	—	—	—	—	—	—			—	—	—
Massachusetts	—	4	7	—	3	—	4	—	3	3	2	—	2	2	4	—	1	—	—			—	2	3
Michigan	—	—	—	3	—	4	—	6	—	—	—	—	—	2	—	—	—	4	1	C	C	3	7	9
Mississippi	—	—	—	—	—	—	—	—	—	—	—	—	—	—	—	—	—	—	5			9	5	12
Missouri	2	3	5	9	4	7	3	1	8	—	8	—	5	—	—	—	—	—	—	O	O	7	—	—
North Carolina	1	2	2	2	5	3	5	5	10	—	—	7	6	8	1	3	—	—	—			6	3	4
Ohio	3	7	3	6	6	2	2	2	4	—	—	4	1	6	7	1	—	5	7	N	N	8	8	2
Pennsylvania	—	—	—	—	—	—	—	—	—	—	—	—	—	—	—	—	4	7	4	T	T	4	—	—
Purdue	—	—	—	—	—	—	—	—	—	—	—	—	—	—	—	—	—	—	—			—	—	—
Rutgers	6	5	—	—	—	8	—	9	6	—	—	—	—	7	5	4	5	6	3	E	E	5	6	6
Tennessee	—	—	—	—	—	—	9	—	—	—	—	—	10	5	—	—	5	6	—	S	S	—	6	1
Texas A & M	—	—	—	—	—	—	—	—	—	—	—	—	9	4	3	4	2	3	3	—	—	—	—	5
VPI & SU	4	1	4	10	—	—	—	4	11	—	10	10	7	3	2	10	3	3	6	T	T	2	10	—
West Virginia	—	—	—	—	—	—	—	—	—	—	—	—	—	—	2	8	3	6	—			—	—	—
Wisconsin	—	—	1	1	2	1	1	3	1	1	3	2	3	3	5	5	—	—	—			—	—	—

Table 21.4—Pacific International—Rank of Meat Judging Teams 1960—1973

Institute	1960	1961	1962	1963	1964	1965	1966	1967	1968	1969	1970	1971	1972	1973
Brigham Young	5	4	1	—	4	5	2	4	6	7	3	2	5	5
Calif. Poly. (Pomona)	—	—	—	—	—	7	—	1	2	3	—	1	3	1
Calif. Poly. (San Luis Obispo)	2	—	5	4	7	6	—	5	—	—	—	—	—	—
Chico State	—	—	—	—	8	8	5	—	—	—	—	—	—	—
Fresno State	3	2	2	3	9	1	3	2	4	4	—	3	4	7
Idaho	7	5	3	1	2	—	—	—	3	6	—	—	—	—
Montana	4	6	—	—	6	4	4	—	—	2	—	4	6	4
New Mexico	—	—	—	—	—	—	—	—	3	—	—	—	—	2
Oregon	6	3	—	—	3	3	1	3	1	1	2	—	7	1
Washington	1	1	4	2	1	2	1	—	—	5	1	5	2	6
Wyoming	—	—	—	—	5	—	—	—	—	—	—	1	1	3

Table 21.5—Southwestern Exposition—Rank of Meat Judging Teams 1938-1974

Institute	38	39	40	41	42	48	49	50	51	52	53	54	55	56	57	58	59	60	61	62	63	64	65	66	67	68	69	70	71	72	73	74
Abilene Christian	—	—	—	—	—	—	—	—	—	—	—	—	—	9	9	—	—	—	—	—	—	—	—	—	—	—	—	—	—	—	—	—
Arizona	—	—	—	—	—	—	—	—	—	—	—	—	—	—	—	—	14	13	—	—	—	—	—	—	—	—	11	—	—	—	—	—
Calif. Poly.	—	—	—	—	—	—	—	—	—	—	—	—	—	—	—	—	13	10	—	—	—	—	—	6	—	6	—	—	12	—	—	—
Clemson	—	—	—	—	—	—	—	—	—	—	—	—	—	—	—	—	—	—	—	—	—	—	—	—	—	—	—	—	12	—	—	—
Colorado State	—	—	—	—	—	—	—	—	—	—	—	—	—	—	—	—	—	—	—	—	—	8	—	6	7	8	6	—	—	7	8	7
Florida	—	—	—	—	—	—	—	—	—	—	—	—	—	—	2	3	9	5	2	1	7	1	1	1	1	1	2	1	1	1	3	2
Iowa	—	—	—	—	—	—	—	4	3	—	2	4	5	5	3	8	3	3	1	3	2	3	3	5	5	1	2	1	3	2	3	1
Kansas State	—	3	3	—	—	—	—	—	—	—	4	5	6	3	5	7	7	8	10*	10	—	1	6	7	8	8	8	—	1	9	1	2
Kentucky	3	3	—	—	—	—	—	—	—	—	—	—	—	—	—	—	11	12	10*	—	—	7	7	9	11	—	12	—	11	10	10	10
Louisiana	—	—	—	—	—	—	4	—	—	—	7	6	—	—	—	10*	4	7	8	9	10	—	1	1	1	3	3	8	4	8	5	4
Mississippi	—	—	—	—	—	—	—	—	—	—	7	7	—	—	—	10*	12	14	9	8	1	—	8	3	1	5	4	7	6	3	2	6
Missouri	2	2	—	2	3	2	1	1	1	1	1	1	2	1	6	1	3	1	5	1	1	1	1	1	2	2	1	2	2	6	4	3
Nebraska	—	—	—	2	3	1	1	1	1	4	6	6	8	8	9	6	6	9	4	6	5	4	5	2	6	9	10	3	3	4	6	11
New Mexico	—	—	—	3	—	—	5	5	4	2	—	—	3	4	7	9	8	6	3	5	4	2	2	4	3	7	4	11	7	4	7	5
North Dakota	—	—	—	5	—	—	2	—	5	—	—	—	4	6	4	2	2	4	7	2	6	1	1	1	10	7	1	1	1	1	1	1
Oklahoma State	2	2	—	—	—	2	1	1	1	1	1	1	1	1	1	7	3	2	7	7	9	1	1	1	1	11	10	2	8	6	1	9
Panhandle	—	—	—	—	—	—	—	—	—	—	—	—	2	—	—	—	—	—	—	—	—	—	—	—	—	4	10	10	2	—	—	—
Purdue	—	—	—	—	—	—	—	—	—	—	—	—	—	—	—	—	—	—	—	—	—	—	—	—	—	9	10	10	10	—	—	—
South Dakota	—	—	—	3	—	—	5	2	—	4	8	9	8	8	9	5	6	9	4	6	5	6	5	2	6	9	7	3	7	4	6	5
Tennessee	1	1	2	3	—	—	—	—	—	—	6	3	3	8	7	9	8	6	3	5	4	4	4	3	3	7	2	11	9	4	7	9
Texas A & M	4	4	5	5	—	3	2	5	5	2	6	8	4	6	4	2	2	4	7	2	6	2	1	4	3	7	7	1	1	1	7	1
Texas Tech.	4	4	—	—	—	—	2	3	2	3	5	10	7	7	8	7	10	11	1	7	9	1	1	1	10	11	5	9	8	1	1	9
VPI & SU	—	—	—	—	—	—	—	—	—	—	—	—	—	—	1	6	1	1	6	—	—	—	—	—	—	4	1	5	5	—	—	—
Wisconsin	—	—	—	—	—	—	3	3	2	1	3	2	1	2	1	1	5	1	—	4	3	6	—	—	9	10	9	5	—	—	—	—
Wyoming	—	—	—	—	—	—	—	—	—	—	1	—	—	—	1	1	—	—	—	1	—	9	—	8	—	10	9	6	—	—	—	—

*Tie

breeding animal judging, and (3) market animal evaluation. The following explanation of this contest was written by R. G. Kauffman, University of Wisconsin, one of the persons who was involved in this contest from the start and who has remained instrumental in the operation of the contest. (Kauffman has been trying unsuccessfully to remain anonymous, but he really deserves credit for the continued success of this contest.)

The coordinated approach to meat animal evaluation was initiated to assist and encourage students of animal science to be more aware of the relationships and limitations that exist when evaluating breeding and market animals, and to help them more fully appreciate the importance of carcass excellence as it related to production, as well as meat processing, merchandising and consumption. This program was specifically designed to stimulate college teaching and to motivate students to seek a more complete understanding of meat animal evaluation—from conception to consumption.

The basic idea took roots April 21, 1955, in Chicago, Illinois, when the National Live Stock and Meat Board, through encouragement by concerned educators, sponsored the first of several clinics to provide students an opportunity to evaluate market livestock, before and after slaughter. From this beginning, there has been a continued growth of interest, support and participation until now there are, in addition to the Ak-Sar-Ben MAEC, four similar regional activities: the Midwestern MAEC at Madison, Wisconsin; the Northwestern MAEC at Twin Falls, Idaho; the Southeastern MAEC at Baton Rouge, Louisiana; and the North Central MAEC for vocational-technical schools at Albert Lea, Minnesota. In addition some 40 universities and vocational schools have developed courses that are aimed at the concepts stated above.

The idea for the Ak-Sar-Ben MAEC developed when educators and businessmen of the livestock and meat industry designed an exercise that would emphasize all aspects of meat animal evaluation. It was decided that breeding livestock, market livestock and carcasses should be included and that such a program be educational, stimulating and competitive. They organized the first one through the cooperation of the Rath Packing Company, Waterloo, Iowa, in 1964. Forty students representing six universities competed through the cooperation of Farmbest, Inc. and Iowa Beef Processors, Denison, Iowa. In 1968, the contest was moved to Omaha, Nebraska, where 117 students from 11 universities competed under the sponsorship of the Knights of Ak-Sar-Ben, Safeway Stores, Inc., Union Stock Yards Co. and Wilson & Co. In the next five years the numbers continued to grow and this year, a record 173 students representing 21 universities were assembled to test and compare their knowledge.

Table 21.6 lists the winning schools in the AK-SAR-BEN Contest since its inception.

THE SET-UP

The rules and regulations governing intercollegiate meat judging contests are undergoing constant change. They are briefly as follows:

Any college or university having adequate instruction in meats is eligible to enter a team, which is composed of four members, men or women, either or both. The eligibility of each team member is determined by his institution. There is no entrance fee, and all blank forms, placing, and reason cards are provided by the management. The contestant must supply the pencil or pen and ink, whichever he chooses.

Each year the winning team is awarded the custody of a perpetual trophy which must be won three times for permanent possession. A plaque is awarded as the permanent property of the winning team, and place ribbons awarded to each of the 10 high teams.

An appropriate emblem is awarded annually to the highest ranking individual in total points and to the highest ranking individual in each of the major classes—Beef, Pork, and Lamb and Beef carcass grading and Lamb carcass grading (when lamb is included). There are ribbons for the 10 highest contestants in total points, and five ribbons for the highest contestants in grading.

Conduct of Contestants

The contestants must abide by the regulations and may be disqualified by the squad leader upon warning and continued violation. The rules forbid talking among contestants; the use of gimmicks such as grade guide cards, photographs, or measuring rulers; the handling of beef and pork cuts; or touching the rib eye in the carcass grading class. This has been made necessary by the large number of contestants working over the limited classes. Use the eye, not the hand.

Table 21.6—Past Winners AK-SAR-BEN Meat Animal Evaluation Contest

Year	No. Schools	Market Animal Division	Breeding Animal Division	Carcass Division	Overall
1964	6	Illinois	Illinois	Illinois	ILLINOIS
1965	7	Iowa State	Illinois	Michigan State	ILLINOIS
1966	8	So. Dakota State	Kansas State	So. Dakota State	SO. DAKOTA STATE
1967	11	Iowa State	Illinois	So. Dakota State	ILLINOIS
1968	11	Wisconsin	Iowa State	Michigan State	MICHIGAN STATE
1969	14	Michigan State	Kansas State	Kansas State	MICHIGAN STATE
1970	14	Minnesota	Illinois	So. Dakota State	(SO. DAKOTA STATE - WISCONSIN) Tie
1971	19	Iowa State	Illinois	Kansas State	ILLINOIS
1972	20	Texas A & M	So. Dakota State	So. Dakota State	ILLINOIS
1973	17	Wisconsin (Madison)	Illinois	Illinois	IOWA STATE
1974	21	So. Dakota State	Oklahoma State	Kansas State	SO. DAKOTA STATE

Table 21.7 lists the classes that will confront each contestant and which are to be placed on their merits, ignoring bruises or faulty trim or workmanship. Each class to be judged consists of four specimens.

Time

Fifteen minutes are allowed for note taking and placing each of the

Table 21.7—Classes for a Standard Contest

Class	Placing	Reasons
Beef carcasses	50	50
Beef carcasses	50	—
Beef cuts	50	50
Beef cuts	50	—
Pork carcasses	50	50
Pork carcasses	50	—
Fresh skinned hams	50	50
Lamb carcasses	50	50
Lamb carcasses	50	—
Beef carcass Quality grading (20)	200	
Score per carcass		
Correct 10 points		
1/3 grade off 8 points		
2/3 grade off 5 points		
Full grade off 0 points		
Beef carcass Yield grading (10)	100	
Score per carcass		
Correct 10 points		
Off 0.1 YG 9 points		
Off 0.2 YG 8 points		
Off 0.3 YG 7 points		
Off 0.4 YG 6 points		
Off 0.5 YG 5 points		
Off 0.6 YG 4 points		
Off 0.7 YG 3 points		
Off 0.8 YG 2 points		
Off 0.9 YG 1 point		
Off 1.0 YG 0 points		
	750	250
Lamb carcass Quality grading[1] (10)	100	

(10 points per carcass scoring, same as for beef carcasses)—Grand Total 1,000 points

1. Lamb carcass grading has not been included in any of the five contests since 1971 (see Chapter 11).

five reason classes. Contestants will stand back from all classes except grading classes, to observe general appearance. Ten minutes are allowed for judging each of the four nonreason classes. A two-minute warning is given before placing cards are collected.

MEAT JUDGING

For the serious student of meat judging, the *Meat Evaluation Handbook*, a 70-page manual containing more than 190 full color pictures, produced by the National Live Stock and Meat Board and edited by members of the American Meat Science Association, is highly recommended.

Judging carcasses differs from grading in several respects; the carcasses must be rated or placed in the order in which the one surpasses the other on the basis of muscling and conformation, finish, and quality. Since the four specimens may fall in the same grade, or with an assured spread of not more than two full grades, a more critical examination and evaluation of such factors as meatiness and trimmness as they affect yield may have to be emphasized. Remember, as far as quality goes, stage of maturity and quality come first. It takes a lot of conformation to compensate for a lack of marbling in the three top grades of beef, just as it takes a lot of marbling to compensate for maximum maturity. It is assumed that the previous chapters have been digested and assimilated, therefore no further explanation of conformation, finish, and quality, as they apply to carcass judging or judging of wholesale cuts, will be made.

Meat Judging in Three Easy Steps

1. Three *big* things are important in *meat*
   a. Muscling (conformation)
   b. Leanness or Fatness
   c. Quality→Palatability
2. What tells you
   a. Muscling?
      Rib-eye area
      Bulge and plumpness in round (ham) and chuck (shoulder) and through loin and rib; generally *width, thickness,* and *depth.*
   b. Leanness?
      Trimness over rib eye, lower rib, flank, brisket, round, chuck. If you see *blue,* you are seeing muscle in the round, not a thick covering of fat. *Penalize outside* fat and *intermuscular* (be-

tween the muscles), i.e., *seam* fat.

c. Quality?
   —Color—*beef:* bright cherry red
             pork: bright greyish pink
   —Firm texture
   —Smooth texture
   —Marbling—fine specks or strands *within* the muscle
   —Youth—cartilage between or on ends of bones
             blood in bones
             bright, light muscle color

3. Put 2a, 2b, and 2c together! The leanest carcass or cut with the most muscling and quality wins, and you place the others accordingly.

More emphasis on *muscle, leanness* (*quantity*):
   chucks, rounds, hams

More emphasis on *quality*:
   ribs, loins

The rest are about equal—balance them off.

Good luck.

Judging Routine

The first impression is more often right than wrong, so take a good look at the carcasses from a distance in the three minutes allotted. Don't stand there flexing your leg muscles for a jump toward the carcasses at the sound of the whistle to see how discourteous you can be to the opposition. The reason the first general impression is likely to be correct lies in the fact that it takes into consideration the outstanding points of excellence or inferiority as far as conformation and external finish are concerned.

Make note of this snap placing on these two factors. When the horn blows and the hunt is on, take a look at the rib-eye muscle of each carcass, and on the card below the snap placing put the numerical position of the way the carcasses rate in size, color, marbling, and firmness of the rib eye. Step back while the hounds bay and study the card which may look something like this:

no difference				maturity
1	3	2	4	conformation
3	1	4	2	external finish
1	3	2	4	size of rib eye

3	1	4	2		color
1	3	4	2		marbling
1	3	4	2	(W)	firmness
1	3	4	2		final

The (W) in this case means watery or soft. Remember, don't touch. Use the eyes—watery eye (not supposed to be a joke). Give the class a final inspection to check the placing and note whether stage of maturity is sufficient to cause a switch to be made. If so, it is because the committee made a slip; the carcasses are supposed to be of practically the same age.

It will be evident from what has been said that looking for the indications of quality on the inside of the carcass was unnecessary. All the factors of quality are evident in the rib-eye muscle, with the exception of coarseness of bone. This saves time that can be used for note taking in the reason classes.

JUDGING WHOLESALE (PRIMAL) BEEF CUTS

This is a closer approach to the retail cuts that a consumer must select.

Beef Chucks (Regular)

This primal cut is utilized primarily for pot roasts, Swiss and braised steak, boiling beef, stew beef, dried beef, and ground meat. The blade and arm ends of the chuck present a considerable cut area for judging quality.

Finish

Discount soft, oily fats. A tendency toward a heavy fat deposit over the clod muscle in the center of the shoulder is evident in highly finished chucks. It and large fat deposits between muscles (intermuscular fat) must be discounted.

Conformation (Muscling)

Uniformity of thickness is important. The arm end should be rounded and heavily muscled, and not fall away too rapidly into the English cut (arm end of the fourth and fifth chuck ribs, now called cross-rib pot roast). The blade end should be thick and give the appearance of plumpness as against flatness. A very good indication of meatiness and plumpness is the prominence of the shoulder joint.

The neck should be short and blend in with the rest of the chuck. Long, flat necks or long, thick necks are objectionable.

Quality

The first thing to do is to inspect the blade bone to see that it is still white and cartilaginous at the fifth rib. Then look at the chine bones to see if the ends (buttons) are still soft and white and the bone itself red and porous. It is always a good procedure in judging any wholesale cut to first determine the age of the animal because a hard bone, regardless of the excellence of conformation or the superiority of the marbling, will degrade a cut into the commercial grade. (Under present intercollegiate rules, handling is not permitted, but it will not be necessary to do so because cuts from only young animals are used.)

The color of the lean should be bright, cherry red. Degrade the darker colors of red. Marbling should be modest on the blade end. The same degree of marbling will not be in evidence on the arm end since the muscles are attached to the much exercised shank muscles. The surface of the meat should present a smooth, velvety appearance and be firm and not watery.

JUDGING BEEF RIBS

Beef ribs constitute the highest priced cut in the forequarter. It is suitable for dry-heat roasting, and the steaks cut from the top grades are becoming increasingly popular.

Finish and Conformation (Muscling)

The external finish should be firm and dry and evenly distributed over the entire cut. Excessive external fat covering is discounted.

The rib-eye muscle should be proportionally large in relation to the size of the cut and be oval in shape on the small end. A kidney-shaped eye muscle is undesirable. A large rib-eye muscle will make a meaty appearing rib. The blade end of the rib should be well fleshed, not flat nor too heavy. The contour of the external part of the rib down to the short rib section should be gradual and not dipped or dished. A combination of these desirable features of conformation result in a thick, well balanced cut that will yield a high proportion of the desirable rib eye (*longissimus dorsi*).

Quality

Inspect the bone to determine age, particularly the presence or absence of the buttons on the ends of the feather bones. Hard bone, flat ribs, a yellow cast to the fat, and a gummy feel to the lean spell "cow ribs."

Determine the degree of marbling, the firmness, the color, and the texture. Excessive intermuscular fat, particularly at the junction of the rib eye with the short-rib section, is objectionable.

JUDGING BEEF ROUNDS

Beef round, consisting of the rump and butcher's round, is the source of the very popular round steaks; popular because they contain so little bone and fat.

The external fat covering is generally rather sparsely distributed over the round but tends to be heavy or patchy over the rump in the more highly finished beef. Select for smoothness and less waste in this area.

The conformation is very important since it determines the poundage of round steak that can be cut from the area between the rump and the stifle joint. An ideal round is plump and thick, with good depth, and carries the muscling down well toward the hock (full at the heel). Flat, tapering, and dished rounds are heavily discounted.

Quality

The texture or grain of the muscles is easily determined and will be found to vary between top and bottom round. Use the top round in making this decision. Firmness, marbling, and acceptable color are top requisites for desirable rounds.

JUDGING BEEF LOINS

Quality is very important in this wholesale cut because from it are secured the most tender and most expensive steaks in the entire beef carcass. It represents 17% of the carcass weight.

Finish

Highly finished cattle have heavy external fat deposits in this area, and particularly over the region of the shortloin. Select for smoothness and a minimum amount of patchiness. In the trimmed loin (flank off, kidney and suet out) the remainder of the kidney fat should be hard and brittle. The external fat should have similar qualities. A lack of external and internal kidney fat is associated with excellent cutability.

Conformation

The thicker and heavier the muscling on a loin, the greater the yield of steak. Look for full, rounded, meaty loin·ends blending well into the shortloin. A dip or depression in front of the hip indicates trimness. The shortloin should show fullness with a large, oval eye muscle on the rib end. Degrade flat loin ends, prominent hips, and depressed and shallow shortloins.

Quality

Marbling is highly desirable in any cut of meat but it is doubly so in the loin cuts. When the choice is to be made between a fine web-like marbling or a coarse type of marbling, if the total amount appears to be the same, give preference to the former. Texture is also very important as it affects the tenderness of the steak. Color is probably more important in steak than in any other cut since the consumer sees such a large area of exposed meat, and is more apt to register a gripe if he does not like the color since it is a high-priced item.

The meat should be firm. Firmness increases as marbling increases, and moisture decreases as marbling increases. The reason, as stated elsewhere in this book but which can stand repetition, is that the moisture content of fat is 9% and of lean 60% to 70%. Another reason for desiring firmness in any wholesale cut, and particularly those that are cut into steaks, is that it is easier to cut a firm steak of even thickness without having it flop over the knife or ooze away from the knife edge.

Do not fail to inspect the chine bone to determine if it can qualify for the top grades for age, or whether a white, hard, fused bone in the sacral region will degrade it into the Commercial grade.

PORK CARCASS JUDGING

Finish

The reason that the authors consider finish before conformation in judging all classes of carcasses, with the exception of grading beef carcasses, is that the most obvious thing to the eye should come first. In pork, it definitely is the first thing considered because it is the basis of grading. Therefore, determine from the backfat thickness, the grade into which the carcass falls. To do this one must be familiar with the back-fat thickness that is associated with a certain length and muscling of carcass designated for the particular grade.

It becomes a matter of judgment as to the merits of one carcass over another carcass of the same or a near grade.

1. Look for an even distribution of backfat. Many hogs have a tendency to lay the fat on more heavily over the shoulder and the ham end of the loin.
2. Look for a firm, white fat that is not greasy to the touch. Soft pork must be discounted rather severely.
3. Look for the indications of marbling on the inside of the carcass. These are the fat covering over the rib, feathering between the ribs, and the evidence of marbling in the flank and exposed face of the ham. If the carcass is ribbed, look at the eye itself.

The final decision between two specimens may hinge on the general distribution of the external finish. A bulging or prominent shoulder on a fat hog does not necessarily indicate more muscling, but more often a heavy fat deposit in that area. A bulging ham, carried well down toward the hock—making it look meaty—is oftentimes a muscle mirage caused by heavy fat deposits. Try to detect these camouflages of conformation because they result in a higher fat yield.

Muscling

Note the form or shape of the carcass in respect to its length, depth, smoothness of side (freedom from wrinkles), plumpness of ham, shortness of shank, neatness of shoulder, thickness of the belly—particularly in the region of the ham pocket—, and trimness of the jowl. All of these characteristics give balance and uniformity to a carcass and are reflected in the yield of lean and fat cuts.

The length of the carcass is not too important provided it is in balance and conforms to standard measurements for the grade. Keep in mind, however, that the quality of the short carcass must be equal to that of the longer carcass and must have marketable cuts. It so happens that most of the carcasses that conform to the top grade specifications are between 29 and 31 inches long (from the first rib to the forward end of the aitchbone), and weigh between 140 and 185 pounds.

Discount heavy jowls, heavy shoulders, wrinkled sides, coarse skin, sloppy bellies (excessive mammary development), long ham hocks, tapering or banjo hams, flat hams, and carcasses that are too flat (those which lack loin development and spring of rib).

Quality

A carcass of quality is one that is bright in appearance, as evidenced by the bright pink color of the flesh on the inside of the belly and in the ham face and some feathering on the inside of the rib area. Dark muscle is associated with such things as maturity, underfinish, and softness, all of which are undesirable.

At present most pork has lower levels of marbling due to the young age at which hogs are marketed. Minus this quality factor, pork carcasses must be bright, firm, thick, and meaty and carry a backfat thickness that conforms to the standard set for the particular grade. They should show considerable feathering in the rib area to indicate marbling, even though it does not guarantee it.

Excessive backfat thickness is no guarantee that the lean is marbled. Actually, the only sure method of determining marbling in a pork carcass is to see a cross section of the rib-eye muscle. Since the size (area) of this muscle is very important, pork carcasses are ribbed down for most judging purposes as they have been ribbed for certified litter rating in developing breeding stock for meat type hogs.

JUDGING HAMS

Since hams are trimmed into skinned hams, thus removing the major part of the fat from about two-thirds the surface area of the ham, any mention of finish would be in reference to the amount of fat on the heel of the ham. Discount for a heavy layer of heel fat.

Conformation and Muscling

Basically, a ham may be considered in three parts: butt (rump), center cut, and shank. Individually they represent one-third of the weight of the ham. Price-wise, the center cut is the profit item, the butt is a 10% to 15% over-cost item, and the hock is a loss item.

This price picture sets up the pattern of what a ham should have as far as conformation is concerned. A short, slim hock, with a moderate fat bulge at the heel, means less weight in this loss item. A long (from aitch bone to 1 inch above stifle joint) center cut that is thick (the distance through the ham from inside to outside) and has a good proportionate depth will make for more profit. A ham butt that is full fleshed rather than pointed will throw more weight into this cut and more nearly cover the loss in the shank. The overall appearance of a ham of the desired conformation features meatiness, plumpness, thickness, and general trimness with as much weight as possible represented in the expensive center cut.

Quality

The quality of the lean is an important factor to consider in the judging of pork carcasses because it relates to acceptability of the fresh cuts and the successful curing of the cured cuts. In the case of the fresh, trimmed hams, quality is reflected in the firmness and color of the lean. Discount soft, oily, and off-color fat. Discount prominent amounts of intermuscular fat showing on the butt end.

The texture of the lean is very similar for hogs in the same age bracket. The grain and color of the lean change with the increased age of the animal. A desirable color for pork is considered to be bright pink but is more often a grayish pink tinged with red, and in many cases a muscle next to the bone (*psoas*) may be dark, giving what is termed a two-toned condition. Other things being equal, the brighter, more evenly colored meat is given preference. Unfinished pork may be referred to as being *vealy* in color, having a grayish red tinge to the meat.

Judging Lambs

The amount of finish necessary to make a choice quality lamb is very small. Consumers generally are not very tolerant of fats, particularly lamb and mutton fat. The great difficulty with highly finished lamb or mutton carcasses is that the deposition of intermuscular masses of fat outstrips intercellular marbling. This is particularly true of the shoulder.

Finish

Sufficient white, brittle fat to cover the back with ⅛ to ¼ inch of fat with a lighter covering over the leg and shoulder is adequate finish for a quality lamb carcass. A papery (no fat under the fell) back on a carcass shows lack of finish. A fiery color to the fat is slightly objectionable. Thin strips of lean under the fell over the back stand out quite prominently in well finished carcasses. This is referred to as the chevrons or the Christmas tree.

Conformation

Thickness and meatiness in lamb carcasses are important because the economic value of cuts from small carcasses is dependent in a large measure on the percentage of lean to bone. In Choice carcasses, the separable fat should not run over 30% (25% to 30%), and the lean should amount to 50% or 55% of the carcass as against 20% bone.

The carcass should be thick and uniformly wide. Carcasses that are slightly rangy are not objectionable provided they are uniformly wide and thick and not platy. Neat, smooth shoulders, well fleshed over the blades and covered with a thin layer of white fat, are preferred to narrow or heavy shoulders.

The legs should be short and plump. Long, tapering legs are not characteristic of a valuable lamb carcass. Only a light fat covering over the outside of the leg can be expected in even the most highly finished carcasses. A slight crease over the backbone is indicative of a well fleshed back, but a prominent backbone indicates a shallow muscling and a small rib eye. Flat lamb shoulders with prominent blades at the top of the shoulder are not characteristic of excellent conformation. The loin and rib rack should be broad, thick, full, and well turned in the rib to give the carcass a neat, trim appearance.

Pot-bellied carcasses are objectionable because they increase the amount of cheap flank and breast meat. The necks should be short and thick, rather than long and thin. The break joint must show four well defined red ridges.

Quality

The amount and character of the internal and external fat on a lamb are the visible conditions for determining quality unless the carcass is ribbed down, which is very desirable, since loin-eye size, fat cover, and marbling can all be readily and accurately observed. The fat should be firm, white, and waxy and be evenly distributed over the entire carcass. A papery condition over the backbone area is indicative of insufficient finish and lack of firmness. The fat covering on the legs is a good gauge of the amount of finish, because this region of the carcass is the last to be covered in the fattening process.

Feathering between the ribs in the chest cavity and fat streaks in the flank are indices of marbling. Firmness is associated with finish, and thin carcasses are naturally soft because the hard fat is absent. If, however, the fat is oily and soft, the carcass is lacking in firmness, even if it is well finished. The flank should be firm and dry, and the inside of the flank should show a few fat streaks (if the lamb is Prime) and have a bright pink color to the flesh.

It is the opinion of the authors that lambs should be ribbed down. This practice has been followed for years in the commercial carcass contests and is the only way to do the job right. It would make for more accurate student appraisal of quality in lamb carcasses, which is pretty much guesswork as it now stands. Contest lambs for FFA and 4-H should be ribbed.

REASONS

The ability to tell by oral or written word the reasons why one carcass or cut is superior to another depends upon (1) the contestant's training and experience, (2) his knowledge of meat terminology, and (3) his method of presenting the reasons.

Written reasons are unlike oral reasons in that the person who writes them has certain information before him that does not require repetition. The card upon which reasons are written is divided into four equal parts, headed respectively by First, Second, Third, and Fourth. If No. 2 carcass or cut is placed first by the contestant, it is suggested that the carcass placed under it be indicated as 2/1, meaning No. 2 over No. 1. This makes it easier for the person who is reading and grading his reasons.

As long as the contestant sticks to the facts and presents them clearly so the judge can follow the reasoning without glancing back to see how they were placed, he can be considered to be in good form. The amount of knowledge possessed by the contestant will show up in his use of meat terms and the applications of facts to economics. No two people express themselves alike.

Fifteen minutes are allotted to writing reasons, so don't waste time but write legibly. An intermission of three minutes will be given between writing reasons on each class to allow the contestant to review his notes on the next class.

It is no crime to find equal qualities in both carcasses or some of each in all four carcasses and admit it. The crime lies in improvising, or making a false statement, or referring to the wrong carcass. Tell the truth, as you see it, in a simple manner that can be easily followed by the committee who must grade the reasons.

A common fault of contestants is that of giving what is termed *sterotyped* reasons. This is generally true of those who have not had sufficient training, and who have acquired a vocabulary of meat terms that are more or less meaningless to them. As a result, they know how to say or describe certain things, and these are repeated verbatim for each carcass or cut.

Some are taught a *descriptive* method that simply describes the merits or faults without direct comparison. This method may be rather effective where judges are insistent that a contestant see certain points that they had in mind when they made the official placing. By following such a method, a contestant is less likely to miss these key points, but it weakens the effectiveness of a set of reason because it sidesteps argument.

The most convincing and effective reasons are those presented through *comparisons*, where a contestant presents the superior qualities of one carcass or cut over another.

Even though it is important to have the class placed correctly, a contestant can obtain a high reasons score on an incorrect placing if he has correctly analyzed the class and emphasized these points in his reasons in an eye-catching manner.

In most meats contests, the difference between first and fifth place is usually found in the reasons scores which makes reasons writing a very important aspect of meat judging. To write reasons exactly as you saw the class without any excess trivia requires much time, work, and dedication in practicing.

Reasons have to be graded rapidly so the contestant must present his thoughts in a well organized, clear, concise manner that is easily readable and understood.

It is important for you to develop your own style of reasons writing with these points in mind. Opening and closing statements must be strong since these are the first and last things a judge reads. Don't worry too much about different sets of your reasons looking quite similar since every set of reasons is corrected by a different judge. However, you must work on varying your comparisons within a class. Do not present all comparisons in the same manner or continually repeat the same terms. The point is to work on developing your own individual style, yet leave some room for variation within classes.

The most important part of writing reasons is accuracy. This means to double check your placing to make sure you are writing about the same cut or carcass you are thinking about. Don't shoot in the dark, or tell fibs just to have something to fill space. These practices will cut your score greatly.

Stress the more important factors first and make these factors the *primary* basis for placing one over another. Omit unimportant details if time and space don't permit. However, in a *close* placing small details may have their place in helping make the decision and should then be included.

Cover all the points under each category (conformation, finish, and quality) systematically. In order to be easily understood, it is not a good policy to mix conformation, finish, and quality statements in your reasons.

Judging usually involves placing one over another because the first had a greater balance or more desirable traits than the second. However, some classes of cuts and carcasses require more emphasis on either quality or quantity due to the way they are to be utilized.

Following is a classification of the classes according to areas you should place slightly more emphasis on. This does not mean that you should totally exclude the other factors.

Quality classes	Equal	Quantity classes
Beef ribs	Beef carcasses	Beef round
Beef loins	Lamb carcasses	Beef chucks
		Hams
		Pork carcasses

General Rules for Reason Writing

1. Use the past tense throughout reasons.
2. Use a variety of connecting words.
3. Use a variety of verbs.
4. Use a variety of words denoting *degrees of difference*.
5. In 2, 3, and 4 above, remember the meaning of the words you use. Don't plug in words indiscriminately.
6. As long as you are expending all this effort to write a full page of words, use a little more effort to write something worthwhile and meaningful.
7. Make opening and closing comparisons especially strong, because the opening comparison will influence the judge's thinking through the reasons, and the final comparison will be made immediately before the judge scores the reasons.

Penmanship and Grammar

Reason writing will give you training in neatness and good penmanship. Through the corrections made, spelling and good sentence structure will also be a part of the training. As oral reasons give you speech training, written reasons give you training in writing.

Grants

Many times *grants* are necessary in your thorough analysis of a class. Grants are admissions that an exhibit that has been placed below another has its merits, also. In an extremely close placing, the grants may take as much consideration in your reasons as the individual placed above it; however, in most cases, the grant is very brief and covers only one or two points.

Do not neglect grants if they are important in the comparison.

Terminology

Before reason writing can even be attempted, a knowledge of the terminology used for carcasses and cuts is essential. If you don't know the accepted carcass nomenclature, how can you accurately convey an idea to anyone else?

General and specific terms or statements may be used singly or several may be used in sequence. However, if you make a broad general statement, never forget to ask yourself where, how, or why to describe this statement more specifically.

Quality

	Specific	General

Specific

1. A higher degree
2. A greater amount of
3. More extensive
4. More abundant
5. More evenly dispersed
6. More evenly distributed
7. Redder rib bones
8. Lighter, brighter cherry-red beef color
   Lighter, brighter greyish-pink pork color
   Lighter, brighter reddish-pink lamb color
9. Smoother, finer textured
10. More finely dispersed marbling
11. More evenly dispersed feathering
12. Softer, more pearly white buttons (beef)
13. Whiter, flakier fat
14. More uniformly covered
15. Firmer, thicker flank
    Firmer, thicker side

General

1. More youthful
2. Higher quality
3. Firmer

Last Place Only

1. Underfinished
2. Lacked quality
3. Excessively finished
4. Wasty

5. Dark colored
6. Soft, oily
7. Hard-boned

Last Place

1. Ill-shaped
2. Small

3. Angular
4. Lacked meatiness

5. Long shanked, thin, tapering round

6. Long thin fleshed ham, leg
7. Poorly balanced

Conformation

Specific

1. Bulging
2. Thicker
3. Deeper
4. Fuller
5. Plumper
6. Wider
7. Shorter
8. Longer
9. Smoother
10. Heavier
11. Shorter shanked
12. Shorter necked
13. Larger
14. Deeper chined

General

1. More symmetrical
2. Straighter lined
3. Meatier
4. Heavier muscled
5. Blockier
6. Neater
7. Beefier
8. Thicker fleshed

Useful Terms

Comparative Verbs

1. As shown, showed
2. Displayed
3. Possessed
4. Exhibited
5. Indicated
6. Demonstrated
7. Lacked

Grants

1. Realize
2. Although
3. Grant
4. However
5. Recognize
6. Admit

Degrees of Comparison

1. Unsurpassed
2. Somewhat
3. Much
4. Great
5. Distinctly
6. Large
7. Extreme
8. Superior

9. Excessive
10. Higher degree
11. Little
12. Slightly
13. Small
14. Limited
15. Lesser
16. Lower

Connective

1. Furthermore
2. In addition
3. Also
4. Carrying into

5. Along with
6. Resulting in
7. As evidenced by
8. Blending into

9. Characterized by
10. For being
11. Contributing to

12. Coupled with
13. Shown by

Commonly Misspelled Words

1. Blade
2. Bulging
3. Carrying
4. Chine
5. Conformation
6. Desirably
7. Exudative
8. Feathering
9. Heel
10. Length

11. Loin
12. Meatier
13. Muscling
14. Quality
15. Quantity
16. Symmetrical
17. Thoracic
18. Trimmer
19. Value

Following is a list of the points to consider in judging classes of the different species.

Sample Note Cards

BEEF CARCASS AND CUT JUDGING

Quality

* marbling
  fineness
  dispersion
* firmness of cut surfaces
* maturity—chine bones
  ribs
  color of lean
  texture of lean
  color of fat
  texture of fat

Quantity

* conformation—balance
  percent high-priced cuts to low-priced cuts
* wastiness—kidney
  rib-eye cover
  cod
  pelvic
  neck and over chuck
  size of rib eye

LAMB CARCASS JUDGING

Quality

  sufficient outside fat cover
* feathering in ribs
* color of internal lean
* maturity—rib bones
  flank streaking
  firmness of flank
  color of fat
  texture of fat

Quantity

  conformation muscling—balance
  proportion of hindsaddle to foresaddle
* wastiness—kidney
  crotch
  overflow
  cover fat over rump and back
  spready ribs

---

* should receive more emphasis.

PORK CARCASS AND HAM JUDGING

Quality	Quantity
* firmness of side and outside fat	* loin-eye area if ribbed
* color of internal lean	* percent ham and loin
ham face	* average backfat thickness
feathering in ribs (use	balance
sparingly)	* length
Hams * seam fat *	uniformity of backfat, ham
* firmness of lean *	collar, and other fat
marbling	depth of chine
	lumbar lean area
	Hams * length and depth of center
	cut, size of butt face
	* amount of fat over cush-
	ion
	length of shank

---

* should receive more emphasis.

Notes

A good share of successful reason writing can be attributed to accurate and thorough note taking. Since reasons must be written in a limited time, the notes taken during judging need to be organized, clear and with enough phrase terms to be easily incorporated into the reasons. They should remind you of the class you are writing on.

Take notes *systematically* in a logical order; use abbreviations and short sentences to save time. Underline important facts and double underline to show more emphasis in both notes and reasons.

SAMPLE REASONS

The following reasons are copies from actual contests and the scores indicated were awarded in intercollegiate competition.

SAMPLE

Score 46

REPORT OF REASONS
Heavy Beef Carcasses

Placings: 1st 4   2nd 2   3rd 3   4th 1

FIRST 4/2—4 was an obvious top due to its superior muscling, trimness, and quality. 4 displayed greater width and length of round with more bulge of heel and cushion. 4 was wider in the loin and exhibited a larger rib eye. 4 excelled in trimness, having less finish over the round, rump, rib eye, and lower rib. 4 also showed less kidney, pelvic, and heart fat. 4 displayed higher quality in a brighter cherry-red color of the rib eye indicating youth and a finer dispersion of marbling. I grant 2 showed more abundant marbling.

SECOND 2/3—I placed 2 above 3 because of its much greater trimness indicating higher cutability. 2 displayed less finish over the round, loin rib eye, and lower rib. 2 showed heavier muscling in more length of round and a fuller turn of loin. I realize 3 possessed a slightly larger rib eye. 2 exhibited a finer dispersion of marbling, while I grant 3 had more marbling and a brighter cherry-red rib eye. However, due to 2's excelling in trimness, it would be of more value to the wholesaler.

THIRD 3/1—In this close pair of fatter carcasses, 3 over 1 due to its advantage in muscling, quality, and trimness. 3 displayed more width of round and bulge of cushion while also being fuller through the loin. 3 also possessed a more symmetrically shaped rib eye. 3 exhibited higher quality in more and finer marbling in a brighter cherry-red colored rib eye. Trimness was close with 3 being trimmer over the round and rump, while 1 was trimmer over the rib eye and has less kidney and pelvic fat.

FOURTH 1—1 placed last because of its inferior muscling. 1 displayed a smaller rib eye and was lighter muscled throughout. 1 lacked the quality of the others, but did possess acceptable marbling. However, as 3, it was overfinished.

S A M P L E

Score 46

REPORT OF REASONS

Beef Ribs

Placings: 1st 2   2nd 1   3rd 3   4th 4

FIRST 2/1—2 over 1 in an outstanding top as it exhibited a more desirable combination of quality and muscling. 2 displayed a more desirable cherry-red beef color, had a finer, more even dispersion of marbling, and was firmer textured. 2 was more muscular as evinced by a larger rib eye in the loin end, more width to the back, and exhibited more depth of blade. Granted 1 had a larger rib eye in the blade end. 2 was trimmer over the blade and rib ends, however, I realize 1 was trimmer over the rib eye and lower rib and displayed less seam fat. Due to its quality and muscling advantages, 2 would yield a higher percentage of more desirable steaks and roasts for dry heat cookery.

SECOND 1/3—1 over 3 in a close placing due to trimness. 1 was trimmer over the rib eye and lower rib, exhibited less finish in the rib ends, and displayed less seam fat. I realize 3 was trimmer over the blade. Granted 3 displayed a finer, more even dispersion of marbling and was brighter colored in the loin end, 1, however, was firmer textured and exhibited a brighter color in the blade end. 1 had a larger rib eye in the blade end and showed more depth to the blade, granting 3 displayed a larger eye in the loin end.

THIRD 3/4—3 over 4 due to its advantages in quality and trimness. 3 was trimmer over the blade, over the lower rib and over the rib ends. I grant 4 displayed less seam fat and was trimmer over the rib eye. 3 exhibited a distinct quality advantage as it showed a finer, more even dispersion of marbling and was firmer textured. 3 displayed a larger rib eye, however, I realize 4 showed more depth to the blade and width to the back. 3, due to its quality and trimness advantages, would yield steaks and roasts of higher consumer appeal.

FOURTH 4—4 last because it lacked quality and was wasty. 4 lacked marbling in both ends and was not firm textured. 4 was extremely wasty, especially over the lower rib, over the blade, and in the rib ends. 4 did have adequate muscling.

S A M P L E

Score 44

REPORT OF REASONS
Light Pork

Placings: 1st 4   2nd 1   3rd 3   4th 2

FIRST 4/1—4 over 1 in an easy placing by virtue of its advantages in muscling and trimness. 4 exhibited a larger loin eye, plumper shoulder, wider ham face and extended its muscling into a heavier muscled sirloin region. I grant 1 possessed more width through the center of the ham, a more bulging heel and less external finish over the collar. However, 4 displayed less finish over the eye, last lumbar and first rib. I grant 1 displayed a finer dispersion of marbling, however 4 exhibited a firmer belly. Due to 4's advantages in muscling and trimness it would possess a higher percent ham and loin than 1.

SECOND 1/3—In a close placing, 1 over 3, due to its advantages in trimness and quality. 1 exhibited less finish externally over the first and last ribs and last lumbar. 1 also exhibited less finish over the collar. I grant 3 displayed a larger eye, wider ham face and a firmer belly. However, 1 displayed a more desirable grayish pink pork color, finer dispersion of marbling and a finer texture. 1 displayed more width through the center of the ham and more bulge to the heel and cushion.

THIRD 3/2—3 over 2 in an easy placing by virtue of its advantage in cutability. 3 displayed an advantage in muscling as evinced by a more bulging heel and cushion, wider ham face and a heavier muscled sirloin region. 3 also exhibited a longer carcass with a larger loin eye. I grant 2 possessed a finer dispersion of marbling and a more desirable grayish pink pork color. However, 3 displayed less external finish over the first rib, loin eye, and last lumbar. 3 also possessed less fat trim over the collar and would yield a higher percent ham and loin than 2.

FOURTH 2—2 was last as it lacked muscling as evinced by a small loin eye, flat cushion and a narrow ham face. 2 possessed the most external finish over the first rib, loin eye and last lumbar, and displayed excessive finish over the collar.

S A M P L E

Score <u>48</u>

REPORT OF REASONS
Hams

Placings: 1st <u>2</u>   2nd <u>4</u>   3rd <u>1</u>   4th <u>3</u>

FIRST <u>2/4</u>—2 over 4 due to 2's superior quality. 2 displayed more marbling, a much firmer texture, and a more desirable greyish-pink color of lean. I grant 4 had more width of butt face, width of center section, and more area of muscle in the butt face. 2, though, was fuller in the forecushion, fuller in the heel, with more bulge to the cushion, and was shorter shanked. In addition 2 was trimmer over the collar, though 4 had less fat over the forecushion. Due to 2's quality advantage it would have much higher consumer appeal as a fresh ham.

SECOND <u>4/1</u>—In a close placing 4 over 1, because of 4's muscling and trimness advantages. 4 had more width and depth of butt face, greater width and length of center section, and was fuller in the forecushion. I grant 1 had more bulge of cushion, more depth of center section, and was fuller in the heel. I also concede 1 had higher quality with a firmer texture, more marbling, and more desirable greyish-pink color of lean. 4, however, had a definite trimness advantage with less collar fat, less seam fat in the butt face, and trimmer over forecushion and around the aitch bone.

THIRD <u>1/3</u>—1 over 3 due to 1's definite advantage in quality. 1 had a firmer texture, with more marbling and a more desirable greyish-pink color of lean. I grant 3 showed greater length and width of center section, but 1 had greater depth of butt face, more depth of center section, and much more bulge of cushion. 1 was also fuller in the heel though this was due partly to fat. I concede 3 was trimmer over the cushion and over the collar.

FOURTH <u>3</u>—3 last because it showed very undesirable quality. 3 was soft textured and displayed a pale, light color of lean which lacked marbling. 3 did have desirable width of center section but was a flat ham that was fat over the collar.

S A M P L E

Score <u>48</u>

REPORT OF REASONS
Heavy Lambs

Placings: 1st <u>4</u>   2nd <u>1</u>   3rd <u>3</u>   4th <u>2</u>

FIRST <u>4/1</u>—In an easy placing, 4 a wether placed over 1 a ewe because of muscling and trimness. 4 possessed more width and thickness to the leg which extended farther up onto the shank and fuller into the loin, rack, and shoulder. In addition 4 was bluer over the leg and shoulder while being trimmer in the crotch and over the dock. 4 also had less kidney and pelvic fat, however, 1 had less waste in the flank. Although 4 appeared to be slightly younger, 1 had more lacing, feathering, and flank fullness and firmness. Due to trimness and muscling 4 would have a higher % hindsaddle.

SECOND 1/3–1 placed over 3 because of muscling and quality. 1 exhibited more bulge and thickness of leg, a fuller sirloin, and muscling carried farther up onto the shank. 1 was also slightly fuller in the shoulder. In addition 1 was fuller and firmer in the flank with more lacing and feathering. Granted 3 was bluer over the leg with less fat in the kidney and pelvic region, breast, flank, and crotch. While 3 had less spread to the ribs, 1 was smoother in its external finish.

THIRD 3/2–In a close placing, 3 over 2, due to trimness. 3 was bluer over the leg and shoulder with less kidney and pelvic fat. 3 also exhibited less waste in the cod, crotch, and breast with less spread of the ribs. Granted 2 was slightly thicker through the center of the leg with more bulge to the loin and shoulder. Furthermore 2 possessed higher quality with more feathering, lacing, and flank fullness and firmness.

FOURTH 2–2 placed last as it was the wastiest carcass in the class being excessive in its external finish with a large amount of fat in the kidney knob. 2 did have adequate bulge and thickness to the leg with acceptable quality. However, it could not merit higher consideration because of fat.

HAM AND BACON SHOWS

The American Association of Meat Processors, at its annual convention, holds a National Ham and Bacon Show. Many states have a similar competition prior to the national show. Any meat processor who is a member of his state organization is eligible to enter a ham, bacon, or sausage product.

Although, as yet, intercollegiate competition does not include the judging of cured products, there is some talk of its inclusion in the future. Furthermore, knowledge of the criterion for judging hams and bacons complements the meat student's overall knowledge of meats. Thus the criterion for the National Ham and Bacon Show follows.

Basis for Judging Hams

1. General Appearance: 150 points. Hams are graded on eye appeal, conformation, trim, and cutability or yield. Scoring for general appearance will be done in two phases allowing up to 75 points for eye appeal, conformation, and trim before cutting—and 75 points for cutability and yield after cutting.
2. Aroma: 150 points. Off or foreign and sour or sharp odors will

downgrade the ham and the good mellow aroma that pleases the judge will upgrade it.

3. Texture of Cut Surface: 150 points. Excessive moisture is objectionable. The ham should not be too coarsely grained. There should not be an excess of fat marbled in the ham.

4. Inside Color: 150 points. The color should be uniform and appealing. It should not be too light or too red, and bruises would score quite heavily against color. If a ham should be noticeably cooler than the rest of the hams giving it an advantage in color and firmness, this will be considered and graded accordingly.

5. Flavor: 500 points. A full half slice of ham from the cushion side will be fried and two taste samples taken, one from the lower muscle and one from the top muscle, unless the ham is sour or has an off flavor in the first sample making it too inferior to be considered in the top places. The ham should not be too salty or too bland, should have the good mellow flavor expected in a good commercial ham.

Basis for Judging Bacon

1. General Appearance: 150 points. Eye appeal, conformation, and outside color will be the main points considered. Bacon may be skinned or unskinned.

2. Fat to Lean (After Cut): 150 points. Lean bacon is very desirable and will be scored accordingly unless it is so lean that it would indicate a poor quality hog.

3. Aroma: 100 points. Off or sour odors will downgrade the bacon and a good smooth aroma should upgrade it.

4. Texture: 100 points. Pumped bacon may be downgraded in texture, if it appears to have excess moisture. Temperature of the bacon should be considered in scoring texture since cooler bacon would be more firm.

5. Inside Color: 100 points. Lean should be light red, fat should be white, color should be uniform, and bruises will downgrade the bacon.

6. Flavor: 500 points. Flavor should be a full rich flavor that pleases the judge. Not too salty, not too bland, and off flavors would downgrade it heavily.

MEATS CONTESTS FOR VOCATIONAL STUDENTS

Competition is undoubtedly one of the greatest instruments for arousing interest among young people. It has proved so effective among the youth of the nation that it has actually become a so-called final examination for many courses offered in schools and colleges.

This method of fostering interest in the farm youth of the United States has been applied by the Future Farmers of America and the 4-H Club Congress to various phases of their work. Contests of national importance that have to do with meat are the Meat Judging Contest and the Meat Identification Contest held for Future Farmers of America at the American Royal Livestock Show at Kansas City, Missouri, and a similar contest held by the 4-H Club Congress at the North American Livestock Exposition at Louisville, Kentucky.

MEAT PLACING CARD

Class Name_____Class No._____

Contestant Name_____Contestant No._____

Placings: 1st_____ 2nd_____ 3rd_____ 4th_____

Tabulator's Score_____

Note: When placing carcasses and wholesale cuts of meat, consideration is to be given to conformation, finish, and quality. Perfect score is 50 points.

The FFA Meat Judging Contest requires the contestant to judge five classes of carcasses or wholesale cuts instead of the nine classes used in intecollegiate competition. These judging classes consist of one class each of the following: four beef carcasses, four wholesale cuts of beef, four pork carcasses, four wholesale cuts of pork, and four lamb carcasses. The contestant also grades 10 beef carcasses and 10 pork carcasses.

There are three contestants to a team, and each contestant is alalowed 10 minutes for making the placings and filling in the official placing card.

The FFA Meat Identification Contest is for the purpose of determining the contestant's knowledge of the various cuts of meat and the edible by-products of meat-producing animals.

Each contestant is given a meat identification card upon which are the names of 100 different retail cuts or edible meat by-products listed under the respective wholesale cuts from which they originate. A group of any 25 retail cuts constitute this class, the cuts being numbered from 1 to 25 consecutively. The contestant must write the number of the cut opposite the name of that cut on the score card in the column designated for that purpose.

Each contestant is allowed 20 minutes for identification. Three contestants compose a team, and the same team or a different team may be in each contest.

One point is given for each cut that is correctly identified as to its wholesale trade name, and three additional points are given if its retail trade name is correctly identified, making 100 points for a perfect score.

COACHING A TEAM FOR MEAT IDENTIFICATION

Charts, showing the location of the wholesale and retail cuts of a carcass, are of value in memorizing the location of the cuts in the carcass. The study of photographs alone for identification of cuts is of doubtful value. Whether purchaser or student, it is absolutely necessary that he comes in direct contact with the product, either through actual purchasing, by learning the cuts through meat displays, or by doing the actual cutting. It is rather useless for vocational schools to enter meat judging or meat identification teams in national contests with no coaching other than from photographs.

Suggested Coaching Methods

One of the most effective ways of securing the necessary training for each boy is to place him as a helper, for certain hours during the week, to a competent and interested meat retailer, with the understanding that the boy be given every opportunity to learn the names of the wholesale and retail cuts and to help make them whenever convenient. The boy works with or without pay according to agreement. Several weeks or a month of such training for each boy will teach him more than is possible by any other method.

Another method that is more convenient but not as fruitful is one in which arrangements are made with one or more meat retailers to give the pupils practice in identifying available cuts one evening a week.

Still another method that can be employed with some degree of satisfaction is one in which the coach makes frequent shopping tours with one or two members of the class to engage in identifying showcase display cuts. Under this method, it is of course a prerequisite that the instructor must know his meats. More than two pupils in a group is unwieldy and may crowd the otherwise already busy shop.

Under any system of coaching, a list of the cuts as published by the National Congress of Vocational Agricultural Students should be used so there will be no time lost in identifying cuts other than those indicated on the chart.

Where there are more trained contestants than the number required to constitute a team, an elimination contest can be arranged by the meat department of the state agricultural college.

Identification Features

The first task that confronts a contestant is that of determining whether the cut is beef, pork, veal, or lamb. These four kinds of meat are recognized by:

1. *Color of the lean.*
   Beef varies from bright to dark red.
   Lamb is light pink. Mutton is brick red.
   Pork is gray-pink to gray-red.
   Veal is pinkish brown. The older the veal, the more it borders on reddish brown.
2. *Size of the cut.*
   Beef cuts are large in size.
   Lamb cuts are small in size.
   Pork and veal cuts run similar in size.
3. *Type of fat.*
   Beef has a white or cream-white (yellow in the lower grades), firm, and rather dry fat.
   Lamb has a chalk-white, brittle, rather dense fat, usually covered with the "fell," a colorless connective tissue membrane.
   Pork has a characteristic white, greasy fat.
   Veal is readily recognized by the absence of fat.

Having identified the cut as to kind, the next task is to identify the cut, both as to name and as to the wholesale cut from which it is derived. This requires a familiarity with anatomy to determine location by the shape of the bone and the shape and contour of the muscles. The contestant must remember that the difference between a roast and a steak of the same name is one of thickness. Steaks are generally from ½ to 1½ inches thick, whereas roasts are over 2 inches thick.

Chapters 12, 13, 14, and 15 provide the basis for gaining a foundation in the knowledge of cut identification, and should be read before one attempts a great deal of direct contact. Variety meat pictures appear in Figure 21.1.

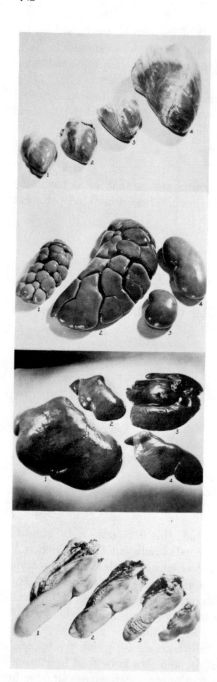

Fig. 21.1

Hearts

1. Lamb
2. Pork
3. Veal
4. Beef

Kidneys

1. Veal
2. Beef
3. Lamb
4. Pork

Livers

1. Beef
2. Lamb
3. Pork
4. Veal

Tongues

1. Beef
2. Veal
3. Pork
4. Lamb

MEAT IDENTIFICATION

BEEF

Wholesale Cuts	Retail Cuts	Number
Round	Round steak	
	Top round steak	
	Bottom round steak	
	Eye of round steak	
	Sirloin tip cap on	
	Sirloin tip cap off	
	Heel of round	
Rump	Standing rump	
	Rolled rump	
Sirloin (Loin end)	Sirloin steak	
	Top sirloin butt steak	
	Boneless sirloin steak	
Short loin	Porterhouse steak	
	T-Bone steak	
	Club steak	
	Top loin steak	
	Tenderloin steak	
Flank	Flank steak	
Rib	Standing rib	
	Rib steak	
	Rib eye steak	
	Rib eye roast	
Chuck	Arm pot roast	
	Arm steak	
	Blade pot roast	
	Blade steak	
	English (Boston) cut	
	Inside chuck pot roast	
	Shoulder clod pot roast	
Short plate	Plate (bone in)	
	Rolled plate	
	Short ribs	
Brisket	Brisket (bone in)	
	Boneless fresh brisket	
	Corned beef brisket	
Fore shank	Fore shank	
	Shank cross cuts	

MEAT IDENTIFICATION

PORK (Fresh)

Wholesale Cuts	Retail Cuts	Number
Ham	Fresh ham, butt half	
	Fresh ham, shank half	
	Fresh ham, boneless	
	Fresh ham, center slice	
Loin	Center loin roast	
	Sirloin roast	
	Blade loin roast	
	Rib chop	
	Loin chop	
	Tenderloin	
	Back ribs	
Fresh side (belly)	Fresh side	
Spareribs	Spareribs	
Fresh picnic shoulder	Fresh picnic shoulder	
	Arm roast	
	Arm steak	
Boston butt	Fresh Boston butt shoulder	
	Blade steak	

PORK (Cured and smoked)

Wholesale Cuts	Retail Cuts	Number
Smoked ham	Smoked ham, butt half	
	Smoked ham, shank half	
	Smoked ham, center slice	
Smoked loin	Smoked loin chops	
Smoked picnic shoulder	Smoked picnic shoulder	
Smoked shoulder butt	Smoked Boston shoulder roll	
Bacon	Slab bacon	
	Sliced bacon	
	Jowl bacon square	
	Canadian-style bacon	
Salt pork	Salt side	
	Salt fat back	

LAMB

Wholesale Cuts	Retail Cuts	Number
Leg	Frenched leg	
	American leg	
	Leg steak	
	Lamb leg, sirloin half	
	Sirloin chops	
Loin	Loin roast	
	Loin chop	
Rack	Rib roast	
	Rib chops	
Shoulder	Square cut shoulder	
	Rolled shoulder	
	Arm chop	
	Blade chop	
Breast	Breast	
	Riblets (breast)	
Fore shank	Fore shank	

VARIETY MEATS

	Kind	Number
Heart	Beef	
	Pork	
Tongue	Beef	
	Pork	
Liver	Beef	
	Lamb	
	Pork	
Kidney	Beef	
	Lamb	
	Pork	
Sweetbreads		
Brains		
Fresh pork sausage		
Fresh bulk sausage		
Beef for stew		
Ground beef		
Lamb patties		

APPENDIX

Organizations That Promote Meat

Per capita meat consumption in this country has varied considerably. Although the people of the United States were never heavy meat eaters when compared to some of their Latin American neighbors, they reached a new low of 117 pounds (exclusive of lard) per person in 1935. Previous to 1910 the annual per capita meat consumption was 152 pounds, not counting lard.

Dealing for years in a very popular though highly perishable food product, the producers and processors were satisfied to meet consumer demand without much fanfare or high pressure advertising until the 1920's. Then new food products and some meat substitutes began to find their way into homes, and suddenly the meat industry discovered that it was losing ground. These competitive food interests, along with a growing number of diet cranks and food faddists, were telling the public that meat was injurious to health; that it was the cause of certain diseases and ailments, among which high blood pressure, gout, rheumatism, hardening of the arteries, and Bright's disease. This condition made it necessary for the agencies interested in meat production and distribution to get together and work out a program to combat this propaganda, and not only to champion the cause of meat but to discover some of the nutritional possibilities of their product. As a result, the National Live Stock and Meat Board was organized in 1922.

THE NATIONAL LIVE STOCK AND MEAT BOARD

The board was unique in that every branch of the industry was given representation. Seventeen members were elected to the original board. The present board has 81 members representing livestock growers and feeders, livestock marketing agencies, the meat packing industry, the nation's meat retailers, and the restaurateurs. On the board are 12 state and 19 regional directors elected from the areas they serve.

It became apparent from the beginning that one of the real needs for combating anti-meat propaganda was more information on the food value of meat. Since this necessitated further research, the board, working through the National Research Council, made grants for research at leading universities. Dr. E. B. Forbes headed the committee which in 1924 selected and formulated the board's first research projects.

Research Program Highlights

Following are some of the results of this research program:

1. The findings of Dr. George H. Whipple at the University of Rochester which led to the discovery of the value of liver in the prevention and treatment of anemia.
2. The work of Dr. L. K. Campbell at Rush Medical College that established the importance of meat in weight-reducing and weight-gaining diets.
3. The evidence secured by Dr. R. S. Herzog at the University of Chicago that revealed the desirability of meat in the diet of children.
4. The discovery by Dr. George O. Burr at the University of Minnesota that lard is an important source of factors which promote growth and contains essential fatty acids valuable in proper nutrition.
5. The discovery by Dr. C. A. Elvehjem at the University of Wisconsin that meat is a rich source of thiamin, riboflavin, and nicotinic acid.

In 1924 the board was responsible for initiating a meat research project known as the National Cooperative Meat Investigations for the purpose of determining the factors which influence quality and palatability in meat. A committee of five selected to plan this project was headed by Dr. F. B. Mumford, then director of the Missouri Experiment Station. This project was very extensive, involving all the steps from the production of meat animals to the preparation of meat for the table. It was in progress at a score or more of state agricultural experiment stations and the United States Department of Agriculture, but was discontinued in 1942. Meat cookery was a very important phase of the work and through these studies many old cooking methods have been discarded and new ones adopted.

The meat board conducts a nationwide program of:

- Meat Research
- Education
- Information
- Promotion

Through a wide variety of services and facilities, the meat board disseminates correct, current information on meat identification, cookery, care, storage, selection, nutrition, and other factors related to the subject of meat.

In line with a tremendous increase in meat production accompanied by changes in the patterns of livestock production, the board has expanded its traditional program to include separate beef, pork, lamb, and sausage promotion programs. Membership on the board's 16-member beef industry council, 16-member pork committee, and 6-member lamb committee is comprised primarily of producers, but also represents market, packer, and consumer interests. On the sausage council of the board, advisory committee membership is mainly from firms involved in the various phases of processed meat production.

The Financial Set-up

The National Live Stock and Meat Board receives its revenue from voluntary contributions made by livestock growers and meat packers, collected at the time the livestock is sold. These contributions are made on the following basis: cattle and calves 3 cents per head; hogs, sheep, and lamb 1 cent per head; the packers in turn match these voluntary contributions. The program of the board has been endorsed by 87 leading livestock associations of the country. Its headquarters are at 36 South Wabash Avenue, Chicago, Illinois 60603, phone (312) 346-6465.

THE AMERICAN MEAT INSTITUTE

Organized as the American Meat Packers Association in 1906 to promote the interests of the meat packing industry, this group, representing the meat industry, was reorganized in 1919 under the name of the Institute of American Meat Packers. Added emphasis was then placed on research and informational effort, and cooperation with livestock producers, meat distributors, and governmental agencies. For the sake of brevity and to be more descriptive of the organization's wide activities, the name was changed again in 1940 to the American Meat Institute (AMI).

Its membership includes about 350 companies here and abroad, and its staff consists of 10 service departments made up as follows: Research,

Public Relations, Livestock, Packing House, Practice and Research, Waste Elimination, Marketing, Industrial Education, Advertising, Accounting, and Purchasing Practice. The program of the institute is administered under the supervision of committees of men in the meat packing industry who are specialists in their fields.

Outside Activities of the Institute

In 1923 the American Meat Institute (then the Institute of American Meat Packers) established an Institute of Meat Packing at the University of Chicago, designated to conduct research, develop publications, and give instruction in meat industry subjects. Conducted jointly by the university and the American Meat Institute, it offers home study courses for men engaged in or planning to enter the industry. Courses in Meat Merchandising and Managing Meat Markets, prepared by the Business Education Service of the United States Office of Education in cooperation with national retail meat and grocery trade associations and others, were inaugurated in 1941. These courses are offered by state and local boards of education in conjunction with the United States Office of Education under the provisions of the George-Deen Act. The courses were designed for the purpose of teaching the most approved practices of meat retailing, aiding in the development of trained salesmen, and assisting in the promotion of efficient meat market management.

Beginning in the autumn of 1940, a giant advertising campaign, sponsored by the institute, was launched in which each ad had the Seal of Acceptance of the Council on Foods and Nutrition of the American Medical Association. Its main purpose has been to educate the consumer by:

1. Telling the facts about proteins, vitamins, and minerals supplied by meat.
2. Showing housewives how to use the thrifty cuts.
3. Suggesting new ways of serving various meats.

The institute has also made a special effort to help the retailer carry meat's nutrition message to his customers more effectively.

The American Meat Institute Foundation was incorporated in 1944, and began operations on a moderate scale in 1947. In 1949, the foundation moved into a new laboratory building on the campus of the University of Chicago. This structure was designed to meet the specific needs of the foundation and, with equipment, represented an investment of about three-quarters of a million dollars. The funds for construction and equipment of the building were contributed by several hundred meat packing companies—ranging from the smallest to the largest—and by companies in allied industries. The foundation discontinued its experimental work at the university in January, 1964, but a committee of the American Meat Institute now allocates funds to colleges equipped to work on problems of the meat industry.

The American Meat Institute opened its new headquarters offices in the Washington, D. C. area in April, 1974. The new mailing address for AMI is: P. O. Box 3556, Washington, D. C. 20007. The new street address is 1600 North Wilson Boulevard, Arlington, Virginia, 22209. The new telephone number is: (703) 841-1030.

Both the Chicago offices and the former Washington office of the AMI have been closed.

The move to Washington, D. C., was approved by the AMI board of directors to bring the institute closer to Congress and the government agencies that regulate the meat packing and processing industry.

"In our new location, we will be better able to serve the needs of the membership," said Richard Lyng, AMI president. "In recent years, new federal agencies have been formed that have great impact on the operation of our business. In addition to the USDA and the Food and Drug Administration, we must also work closely with the Occupational Safety and Health Administration, the Environmental Protection Agency, the Federal Energy Office, the Department of Transportation and various consumer affairs agencies and consumer organizations. The American Meat Institute will continue to provide members with a full range of information services in all areas of industry concern."

OTHER INDUSTRY ORGANIZATIONS

Other industry organizations, formed in general to aid the development and maintain the viability of the entire meat industry, yet specifically interested in the welfare of the segment they represent are:

> American Association of Meat Processors
> National Association of Food Chains
> National Association of Meat Purveyors
> National Association of Retail Grocers
> National Independent Meat Packers Association (NIMPA)
> National Restaurant Association
> Supermarket Institute
> Western States Meat Packers Association (WSMPA)

THE RECIPROCAL MEAT CONFERENCE

In the autumn of 1947, Mr. R. C. Pollock, general manager of the

National Live Stock and Meat Board, addressed the coaches of the various meat teams in a meeting prior to the conclusion of the international contest. He proposed the formation of an organization of the coaches of all intercollegiate meat judging teams and those engaged in the teaching and research of meats in the institutions of higher learning. The purpose of the organization would be to meet annually for a two-day program devoted to the subject of meats in its many facets. This proposal was adopted.

The chairman for the first four meetings (1948-51) was Mr. W. H. Tomhave, who had served as head of the Animal Husbandry Department of the Pennsylvania State College from 1912 to 1925 and as Secretary of the Aberdeen Angus Breeders Association from 1925 to 1945. The organization was designated as the Reciprocal Meat Conference. It is wholly to the credit of Mr. Pollock and the National Live Stock and Meat Board that the conference came into being and its development sustained and implemented. The members of the conference have been appreciative of their sponsor and have helped to make it a conference of stature in the field of meats.

At the Seventeenth Annual Reciprocal Meat Conference held at the University of Wisconsin, at Madison, in June of 1964, the membership adopted the name of American Meat Science Association and a new constitution and bylaws. The proceedings, published through the courtesy of the National Live Stock and Meat Board, contain a wealth of material that is of value to its members and the meat industry as a whole.

The man chosen to be the association's first president was Dr. R. W. Bray, University of Wisconsin, who, incidentally, was the first elected chairman of the original Reciprocal Meat Conference (1952).

Past Officers of the American Meat Science Association

President

1965	R. W. Bray, University of Wisconsin
1966	L. E. Kunkle, Ohio State University
1967	J. W. Cole, University of Tennessee
1968	L. J. Bratzler, Michigan State University
1969	Z. L. Carpenter, Texas A & M University
1970	G. H. Wellington, Cornell University
1971	M. D. Judge, Purdue University
1972	A. M. Mullins, University of Idaho
1973	H. B. Hedrick, University of Missouri
1974	R. B. Sleeth, Armour & Company, Food Research Division
1975	J. D. Sink, The Pennsylvania State University

President-Elect

1965	L. E. Kunkle, Ohio State University
1966	J. W. Cole, University of Tennessee
1967	L. J. Bratzler, Michigan State University
1968	Z. L. Carpenter, Texas A & M University
1969	G. H. Wellington, Cornell University
1970	M. D. Judge, Purdue University
1971	A. M. Mullins, University of Idaho
1972	H. B. Hedrick, University of Missouri
1973	R. B. Sleeth, Armour & Company, Food Research Division
1974	J. D. Sink, The Pennsylvania State University
1975	J. D. Kemp, University of Kentucky

Secretary-Treasurer

1965-1975   W. C. Sherman, National Live Stock and Meat Board

American Meat Science Association Awards

Distinguished Teaching Award

Date	Recipient	Sponsor
1965	D. L. Mackintosh	Kern County Land Company
1966	L. E. Walters	NIMPA
1967	V. R. Cahill	Chicago Mercantile Exchange
1968	J. D. Kemp	Chicago Mercantile Exchange
1969	C. H. Adams	Safeway Stores, Inc.
1970	L. E. Kunkle	Armour Food Research Division
1971	L. J. Bratzler	Safeway Stores, Inc.
1972	R. G. Kauffman	Armour Food Research Division
1973	R. F. Kelly	Eckrich Foundation
1974	J. R. Stouffer	George A. Hormel & Company

Distinguished Extension Award

Date	Recipient	Sponsor
1965	R. E. Rust	WSMPA
1966	E. A. Pierce	Chicago Mercantile Exchange
1967	R. W. Snyder	Oscar Mayer & Company
1968	James A. Christian	Armour & Company
1969	John A. Christian	Swift & Company
1970	W. Y. Varney	Swift & Company
1971	C. O. Schoonover	Eckrich Foundation
1972	R. L. Reddish	George A. Hormel & Company
1973	B. D. Vanstavern	Armour Food Research Division
1974	W. C. Stringer	Eckrich Foundation

Distinguished Research Award

Date	Recipient	Sponsor
1965	A. M. Pearson	NIMPA
1966	E. J. Briskey	Kern County Land Company
1967	R. A. Lawrie	Kern County Land Company
1968	J. R. Bendall	Kern County Land Company
1969	R. W. Bray	Armour Food Research Division
1970	B. B. Marsh	Eckrich Foundation
1971	R. G. Cassens	Armour Food Research Division
1972	D. E. Goll	Eckrich Foundation
1973	R. E. Hamm	George A. Hormel & Company
1974	M. D. Judge	Armour Food Research Division

Past Chairmen of the Reciprocal Meat Conference

1948-1951	W. H. Tomhave
1952	R. W. Bray, University of Wisconsin
1953	J. W. Cole, University of Tennessee
1954	L. E. Walters, Oklahoma State University
1955	E. A. Kline, Iowa State University
1956	A. M. Pearson, Michigan State University
1957	T. N. Blumer, North Carolina State University
1958	V. R. Cahill, Ohio State University
1959	C. H. Adams, University of Nebraska
1960	G. H. Wellington, Cornell University
1961	L. E. Kunkle, Ohio State University
1962	J. C. Pierce, USDA
1963	J. D. Kemp, University of Kentucky
1964	E. J. Briskey, University of Wisconsin
1965	E. A. Pierce, Cornell University
1966	L. J. Bratzler, Michigan State University
1967	Z. L. Carpenter, Texas A & M University
1968	R. B. Sleeth, Armour & Company, Food Research Division
1969	M. D. Judge, Purdue University
1970	A. M. Mullins, University of Idaho
1971	H. B. Hedrick, University of Missouri
1972	C. E. Allen, University of Minnesota
1973	J. D. Sink, The Pennsylvania State University
1974	J. A. Christian, University of Georgia
1975	G. C. Smith, Texas A & M University

Past Chairmen of the Meat Industry Research Conference

1965	A. M. Mullins, Louisiana State University

1966   A. M. Pearson, Michigan State University
1967   R. B. Sleeth, Armour & Company, Food Research Division
1968   T. N. Blumer, North Carolina State University
1969   P. A. Goeser, Swift & Company
1970   M. E. Bailey, University of Missouri
1971   W. E. Kramlich, John Morrell and Company
1972   G. E. Brissey, Swift & Company
1973   R. A. Merkel, Michigan State University
1974   L. L. Borchert, Oscar Mayer & Company, Research Department

Recipients of the Reciprocal Meat Conference Awards for Signal Service in the Field of Meats

1956   Sleeter Bull, University of Illinois
1956   J. B. Francioni, Jr., Louisiana State University
1956   K. F. Warner, USDA
1956   P. T. Ziegler, The Pennsylvania State University
1957   P. A. Anderson, University of Minnesota
1957   J. L. Hall, Kansas State University
1957   R. C. Pollock, National Live Stock and Meat Board
1958   F. J. Beard, USDA
1958   E. C. Stillwell, Ontario Agricultural College
1958   W. J. Loeffel, University of Nebraska
1960   D. L. Mackintosh, Kansas State University
1960   R. B. Davis, National Live Stock and Meat Board
1961   L. E. Kunkle, Ohio State University
1962   L. J. Bratzler, Michigan State University
1962   R. W. Bray, University of Wisconsin
1962   R. W. Snyder, Texas A & M University
1963   D. M. Doty, American Meat Institute Foundation
1963   B. S. Schweigert, Michigan State University
1964   M. O. Cullen, National Live Stock and Meat Board
1964   A. M. Pearson, Michigan State University
1965   J. W. Cole, University of Tennessee
1966   G. H. Wellington, Cornell University
1967   C. H. Adams, University of Nebraska
1968   W. L. Sulzbacher, USDA
1969   T. N. Blumer, North Carolina State University
1969   P. A. Goeser, Swift & Company
1969   L. E. Walters, Oklahoma State University
1970   K. R. Franklin, National Live Stock and Meat Board
1971   D. E. Brady, Sun City Center, Florida
1971   O. D. Butler, Jr., Texas A & M University
1971   R. B. Sleeth, Armour & Company, Food Research Division
1972   G. E. Brissey, Swift & Company

1972   W. C. Sherman, National Live Stock and Meat Board
1973   R. L. Hiner, USDA, ASR
1973   M. C. Brockman, U. S. Natick Laboratories
1974   A. M. Mullins, University of Idaho
1974   Carl Neumann, National Live Stock and Meat Board, retired
1974   F. W. Tauber, Films Packaging Division, Union Carbide

Index

A

B